American Society of Interventional Pain Physicians

INTERVENTIONAL PAIN MEDICINE

DOCUMENTATION, CODING & BILLING

A Practical Guide for Physicians and ASCs

Laxmaiah Manchikanti, MD

INTERVENTIONAL PAIN MEDICINE DOCUMENTATION, BILLING AND CODING

Please address all correspondence to:

American Society of Interventional Pain Physicians
2831 Lone Oak Road
Paducah, Kentucky 42003

ISBN 0-9719951-0-9

DEDICATION

To the

Loving memory of my late grandmother: Gopamma - The Visionary

and

To my family

My Parents: Yadagiry and Laxmamma - my greatest supporters

My wife: Chandrakala - The Saint

My children: Anupama, Sunil, and Kavita - my greatest cheerleaders

CONTENTS

ABOUT THE EDITOR ix

ABOUT THE CONTRIBUTORS .... xi - xii

PREFACE .... xiii - xiv

I. BASIC CONSIDERATIONS

1. An Introduction to the Complex World of Documentation .... 3 - 12
Laxmaiah Manchikanti, MD

2. Fraud and Abuse in Interventional Pain Medicine .... 13 - 30
Laxmaiah Manchikanti, MD

3. Diagnostic Coding Systems .... 31 - 36
Laxmaiah Manchikanti, MD, Vijay Singh, MD, Bert Fellows, MA

4. Procedural Coding Systems .... 37 - 50
Laxmaiah Manchikanti, MD, Bert Fellows, MA

5. General Correct Coding Policies .... 51 - 56
Laxmaiah Manchikanti, MD

6. Compliance for Interventional Pain Medicine Coding .... 57 - 60
Laxmaiah Manchikanti, MD, Vijay Singh, MD

7. Local Medical Review Policy and Carrier Advisory Committee .... 61 - 66
Laxmaiah Manchikanti, MD

II. NON-INTERVENTIONAL SERVICES

8. Evaluation and Management Services in Interventional Pain Medicine .... 69 - 88
Laxmaiah Manchikanti, MD

9. Correct Coding Policies for Commonly Used Evaluation and Management, Physical Medicine, Psychological, Neurodiagnostic and Radiological Services .... 89 - 112
Laxmaiah Manchikanti, MD, Bert Fellows, MA, Trish Burks, LPT

10. Coding for Ancillary Services .... 113 - 116
Jo Anne E. Burkhardt

III. INTERVENTIONAL TECHNIQUES

11. Medical Record Documentation Guidelines for Ambulatory Surgical Services .... 119 - 122
Laxmaiah Manchikanti, MD, Vijay Singh, MD, Bert Fellows, MA

12. Coding for Interventional Procedures .... 123 - 144
Laxmaiah Manchikanti, MD

13. Correct Coding policies for Interventional Techniques .... 145 - 154
Laxmaiah Manchikanti, MD

14. Definitions of Interventional Procedures .... 155 - 168
Laxmaiah Manchikanti, MD

15. Interventional Pain Management Practice Policies .... 169 - 222
Laxmaiah Manchikanti, MD, Vijay Singh, MD, David Kloth, MD

16. Coding for the procedures and supplies in the office .... 223 - 238
Jo Anne E. Burkhardt, Amy G. Mowles

17. Facility Fees in Surgery Centers .... 239 - 240
Amy G. Mowles, Jo Anne E. Burkhardt

18. Coding for Minimally Invasive Procedures .... 241 - 244
Jo Anne E. Burkhardt

19. Coding for Radiological Services .... 245 - 246
Jo Anne E. Burkhardt

IV. COMPLIANCE

20. The Modern Age of Compliance .... 249 - 254
Ronald H. Clark, JD

21. Implications of Model Compliance Program for Interventional Pain Physicians .... 255 - 260
William A. Sarraille, JD

22. Physician Office Compliance Programs .... 261 - 262
Alan E. Reider, JD

23. The Value of Compliance Programs .... 263 - 264
Carson P. Porter, JD

24. Legal Audits for Compliance Programs .... 265 - 266
Ronald H. Clark, JD

25. Model Compliance Plan for Interventional Pain Medicine .... 267 - 302
William A. Sarraille, JD, Eileen Kahaner, JD

26. An Introduction to HIPAA .... 303 - 308
Laxmaiah Manchikanti, MD

27. HIPAA Privacy Regulations: Practical Information for Physicians .... 309 - 312
Erin Brisbay McMahon, JD, Tracy Lee-Huber, JD

28. HIPAA Privacy Guidance .... 313 - 316
William A. Sarraille, JD, Anna Spencer, JD

29. HIPAA Standards for Health Care Electronic Transactions .... 317 - 320
Erin Brisbay McMahon, JD

30. Implementation of the HIPAA Privacy Standards: Real Life Examples .... 321 - 326
William A. Sarraille, JD, Anna Spencer, JD, Jerome T. Levy, JD, Connie Raffa, JD, Eileen Kahaner, JD, Kathleen Cheney, JD

31. Stark II Rules and Interventional Pain Medicine .... 327 - *334*
To Modern Practice of Interventional Pain
William A. Sarraille, JD

32. Needlestick Safety and Prevention .... 335 - 338
Mark F. Tatelbaum, JD, William A. Sarraille, JD

33. Anti-Kickback Safe Harbors .... 339 - 344
William A. Sarraille, JD, Robert Wanerman, JD

34. Any Willing Provider Laws .... 345 - 354
Erin Brisbay McMahon, JD

V. APPENDICES

A. i. Patient Questionnaire .... 357 - 372

ii. Physician Assessment Form .... 373 - 396

B. Evaluation and Management Guidelines .... 397 - 428

C. i. Sample Initial Evaluation .... 429 - 518

ii. Sample Follow-up Evaluation .... 519 - 524

iii. Interventional Procedure Documentation in ASC and HOPD .... 525 - 540

ABOUT THE EDITOR

Laxmaiah Manchikanti, M.D., is the Medical Director of the Pain Management Center of Paducah and Ambulatory Surgery Center in Paducah, Kentucky, encompassing a multidisciplinary pain program.

He has been in private practice in Paducah, Kentucky, since completion of a fellowship in anesthesiology and critical care medicine in 1980. He graduated from Gandhi Medical College, Osmania University Hyderabad, India. He completed his internship, and residency in anesthesiology, at Gandhi Hospital, Youngstown Hospital Association, (North Eastern Ohio School of Medicine), Allegheny General Hospital, and fellowship in anesthesiology and critical care medicine at the University of Pittsburgh.

Dr. Manchikanti is certified by the American Board of Anesthesiology along with subspecialty certification in Pain Management, the American Board of Pain Medicine and American College of Anesthesiologists. Dr. Manchikanti is a member of numerous professional societies and associations. He is the founder and current president of the American Society of Interventional Pain Physicians.

Dr. Manchikanti has continued and expanded his academic interests, initially in anesthesiology followed by Interventional Pain Management, not only the scientific aspects, but also practice management aspects. He has published over 150 articles and book chapters in medical and scientific publications. He also serves on several editorial boards.

ABOUT THE CONTRIBUTORS

Jo Anne E. Burkhardt, CCS-P, CHC, CMM
CEO
Physician Management & Compliance Solutions, Inc.
7250 N. Cicero Ave., Suite 106
Lincolnwood, IL 60712

Trish Burks, LPT
Clinical Director
Pain Management Center of Paducah
2831, Lone Oak Road
Paducah, KY 42003

Kathleen Cheney, JD
Arent Fox Kintner Plotkin & Kahn, PLLC
1050 Connecticut Avenue, NW
Washington, DC 20036

Ronald H. Clark, JD
Arent Fox Kintner Plotkin & Kahn, PLLC
1050 Connecticut Avenue, NW
Washington, DC 20036

Bert Fellows, MA
Director of Psychological Services
Pain Management Center of Paducah
2831, Lone Oak Road
Paducah, KY 42003

Eileen Kahaner, JD
Arent Fox Kintner Plotkin & Kahn, PLLC
1050 Connecticut Avenue, NW
Washington, DC 20036

David S. Kloth, MD
Medical Director
Connecticut Pain Care, PC
69 Sand Pit Road, Suite 204
Danbury, CT 06810

Tracy Lee-Huber, JD
Wyatt Tarrant and combs,
250 W Main St # 1700
Lexington, KY 40507

Jerome T. Levy, JD
Arent Fox Kintner Plotkin & Kahn, PLLC
1050 Connecticut Avenue, NW
Washington, DC 20036

Laxmaiah Manchikanti, MD
Medical Director
Pain Management Center of Paducah
2831, Lone Oak Road,
Paducah, KY 42003

Erin Brisbay McMahon, JD
Wyatt Tarrant and combs,
250 W Main St # 1700
Lexington, KY 40507

Amy G. Mowles
CEO
Mowles Medical Practice Management, LLC
13425 Overbrook Lane
Bowie, MD 20715

Carson P. Porter, JD
Arent Fox Kintner Plotkin & Kahn, PLLC
1050 Connecticut Avenue, NW
Washington, DC 20036

Connie Raffa, JD
Arent Fox Kintner Plotkin & Kahn, PLLC
1050 Connecticut Avenue, NW
Washington, DC 20036

Alan E. Reider, JD
Arent Fox Kintner Plotkin & Kahn, PLLC
1050 Connecticut Avenue, NW
Washington, DC 20036

Anna Spencer, JD
Arent Fox Kintner Plotkin & Kahn, PLLC
1050 Connecticut Avenue, NW
Washington, DC 20036

William A. Sarraille, JD
Arent Fox Kintner Plotkin & Kahn, PLLC
1050 Connecticut Avenue, NW
Washington, DC 20036

Mark F. Tatelbaum, JD
Arent Fox Kintner Plotkin & Kahn, PLLC
1050 Connecticut Avenue, NW
Washington, DC 20036

Vijay Singh, MD
Medical Director
Pain Diagnostic Associates
1601 Roosevelt Road
Niagara WI 54151

Robert Wanerman, JD
Arent Fox Kintner Plotkin & Kahn, PLLC
1050 Connecticut Avenue, NW
Washington, DC 20036

PREFACE

Interventional pain medicine is an evolving specialty. The vast majority of interventional pain physicians are making an honest attempt to comply with highly complex laws and guidelines while at the same time attempting to provide quality medical care. The examples of fraudulent activities that make media headlines are usually so blatant that most physicians cannot envision themselves being involved in such outrageous legal schemes. However, the healthcare system in the United States is so complex that documentation, billing and coding errors can occur, even in well managed, well-intentioned practices, with well designed policy and procedures and compliance programs. Thus, interventional pain physicians should understand the issues of proper documentation, billing and coding as well as the necessity of keeping policy procedures and compliance up to date, thereby keeping the risks low.

The American Society of Interventional Pain Physicians believes that outcomes analysis for American medicine in its war against disease, should not be done by counting hospital beds or coronary artery bypass grafts, and certainly not by calculating the "medical loss ratio," but by evaluating the health and longevity of Americans. Specifically, in interventional pain medicine, outcome analysis should not be done by counting the number of interventional pain procedures, not by the "medical loss ratio," and certainly not by calculating errors in documentation, billing and coding, but by evaluating the improvement in quality of life and by evaluating cost effective pain management. The worth of interventional pain physicians is not measured by gross income, number of board certifications, or scores on a computerized quality-assurance scale, but rather, our true worth is determined by the immeasurable and incalculable "suffering and pain we have relieved or prevented."

Orient (1) described that in Attorney General Reno's Department of Justice, physicians had become the number two target. Some even believe that physicians are the worst enemies of society (1). In a Honolulu newspaper, it was reported that, "authorities say that healthcare fraud is far more damaging to the public than most violent crime because of its collateral effects, such as driving up the cost of medical care and stealing tax dollars from the government (1). However, many officials, as well as organized medicine, declare that most doctors are ethical and the huge new dragnet is just "out to catch a few bad apples (1)." The amount of healthcare fraud is declared to be over $100 billion. This number gains credibility by frequent repetition in authoritative sources, despite lack of any evidence that it is correct (1). Correct or not, these amounts are enormous. One hundred billion is one thousand million, thus, simply put, $100 billion is $100,000 million. Thus, if each thief can manage to steal only one million dollars in a year, it would take 100,000 thieves to steal $100 billion (1). Since there are only about 750,000 doctors in the United States about 450,000 of them in office-based practice, if 100,000 doctors are committing fraud and abuse, it will be either 1 in 7.5 or 1 in 4.5, ultimately guilty of massive fraud. Therefore, it does not seem feasible for doctors to be stealing all of this alleged $100 billion. Thus, one would reasonably suppose that most of the $100 billion is being taken in by large institutions or by outright scams. If we separate the fraud and abuse proportionately to the healthcare dollars spent and if 30% to 40% of these dollars are spent on physician services, massive fraud could constitute $30 billion to $40 billion attributable to practicing physicians. Considering the total number of physicians as 750,000, massive fraud would then calculate to be $133,333 per physician. If we consider only those 450,000 doctors practicing in office-based practice, the fraudulent activity would result in $222,222 per year, per physician. However, if physician fraud is considered as 30% or $30,000 million each physician would still be committing fraud of $40,000 to $70,000 which again is unimaginable. Calculated from this perspective, none of these figures appear to be realistic or credible.

Two of the major milestones in US Medicine are Medicare's passage in 1965 and passage of 1996 Healthcare Legislation. On August 1 and 2, 1996, Congress cleared for the President's signature, the Health Insurance Portability and Accountability Act of 1996 also known as Kennedy-Kassabaum Bill, which was signed into law on August 21, 1996 by President Bill Clinton (2). However, unknown to most Americans, the 1996 act contained major provisions of the Clinton Administration's previously rejected 1993 Health Security Act. After all, this bill came with makeup and was set to bring about health insurance "portability" and "accountability". The Office of Inspector General itself admits that the complexity of Medicare's rules results in multiple billing errors. The OIG's most recent report on Medicare fee-for-service error rates found that physician services accounted for the third largest category with the most common errors being related to the inadequacy of documentation and coding of services. Because of the increasing allegations of improper documentation, billing and coding, it is only prudent that interventional pain physicians learn as much as possible about proper documentation, billing and coding. Failure to understand specific documentation, billing and coding requirements could become "reckless disregard," exposing physicians to the Federal False Claims Act charges.

The patient's medical records are an assemblage of information gathered and recorded pertaining to appropriate patient care. A chart that is comprehensively documented enables the physician and other healthcare professionals to quickly access needed information. In the recent era of the practice of modern medicine under complex regulations with daily fear of being charged with fraud and abuse, interest in medical record documentation has acquired a new urgency. Appropriate medical record documentation also assists in proper billing, coding and compliance. Growth of regulatory compliance activity further mandates that documentation provided by the physician is not only accurate, but detailed and specific. Thus, documentation is facing ever increasing scrutiny.

This book was written to help physicians identify and avoid situations of inappropriate documentation, billing, coding and compliance. There are numerous misconceptions among interventional pain physicians about documentation of the services they provide and billing and coding for these services.

Documentation, Billing and Coding in Interventional Pain Medicine was written to assist physicians:

- To understand the importance of documentation, billing, coding and compliance
- To understand the implications of fraud and abuse laws in daily practices
- To understand and identify areas where inappropriate documentation, billing and coding could occur in their practices and lead to charges of fraudulent activities
- Finally, to assist in determining the steps that should be considered and taken to appropriately document, bill, code, be in compliance with rules and regulations, and minimize exposure to sanction.

Every interventional pain physician should know all the facets of appropriate documentation, billing and coding personally. Simply put, physicians should make sure that the information checked on billing forms is transferred properly to insurance forms. Practitioners also should know the compliance risks and prevention, as well as management of such risks. This book covers effective documentation, billing, coding and compliance actions that even a single practitioner or the smallest office practice can afford to follow and implement, while at the same time facilitating larger groups to address these issues as well.

Section I covers an introduction to the wide world of documentation and numerous concepts.

Section II covers a wide veriety of non-interventional services.

Section III covers all commonly used interventional techniques.

Section IV covers compliance related to interventional practices including billing, coding, and physician compliance. Stark laws; HIPAA compliance and a variety of other regulations. A model compliance program for Interventional Pain Practice(s) is also provided.

Section V provides wealth of information with sample patient questionnaire, physician assessment form; CMS's Guidelines of Evaluation and Management Services. Sample initial evaluation, follow up evaluation, and documentation of Interventional procedures in Ambulatory Surgery and Hospital patient settings.

The editor acknowledges his appreciation to the staff at Pain Management Center of Paducah, Kentucky, and the Ambulatory Surgery Center, also in Paducah, Kentucky, and the American Society of Interventional Pain Physicians who assisted in this project, and, specifically, Sunil Manchikanti, Vidyasagar Pampati, and Chandra Manohar Chepuri for setting up the text, and designing the book; Bert Fellows, MA, coordinator of ASIPP; Sonora Hudson for manuscript editing; and finally, Tonie Hatton and Denise Pratt for transcribing the manuscripts over and over again.

Because this book is designed and directed to the practicing physicians, your feedback and suggestions for future editions are encouraged and will be most welcome. Thank you very much for your dedication to Interventional Pain Medicine.

Laxmaiah Manchikanti, M.D.

REFERENCES

1. Orient JM. Can "health care fraud" be ended? *Medical Sentinel* 1998; 3:124-130.
2. Twight C. Medicare's progeny: The 1996 Health Care Legislation. In Feldmen RD (ed), *American Health Care*, The Independent Institute, New Brunswick, 2000; pp 87-118.

SECTION 1

BASIC CONSIDERATIONS

AN INTRODUCTION TO THE COMPLEX WORLD OF DOCUMENTATION

Laxmaiah Manchikanti, MD

Documentation is to provide evidence or information. For physicians documentation means providing information or evidence on multiple issues, including evaluation and management services, procedural services, billing and coding. If you want to get paid for what you do or stay out of fraud and abuse investigations, you have to document, document and document. Even though healthcare is not so different from other industries and services, documentation has become an inevitable and even desirable part of medical practice. The entire basis of documentation is control and the dominant role of the government. However, the question most commonly posed is, 'Is government's role and control desirable?' Roger D. Feldman (1), in his book American Health Care: Government, Market Processes, and the Public Interest addressed this issue and answered it with a qualified "no." Pauly (2) describes that public policy in health most frequently assumes that the social purposes people correctly ascribe to healthcare can only and obviously be solved by government, with the market possibly supplying services, but in very much a subsidiary role. Stigler (3) initiated a positive theory of regulation based on the plausible assumption that government regulators sometime pursue their own interest and those of the industries they regulate, rather than some vaguely defined public interest. However, these are not unthinking arguments against government. Quite the contrary, it is the recognition of the need for government, and of the power of its actions (2). Assurance of adequate care for those we care about, preventing monopoly pricing, and helping to encourage the flow of good information are topics that come up over and over, and represent tasks in which government has an inevitable role (2). Of these tasks, the assurance of adequate care is the one that most requires government, and which has proved the most stubbornly resistant to solution (2). The physician community believes that even though the public in general and the regulators believe that the provision of healthcare attracts more dedicated and selfless people than the typical commodity, there is always the possibility of providing inadequate care.

President Clinton's healthcare reform proposals of 1993 represented the most far-reaching program of social engineering to be attempted in the United States since the passage of Medicare and Medicaid in 1965 (4). Fortunately, this plan failed. Many people commented that the plan failed because too many people concluded that it wasn't credible. The fundamental fact is that the healthcare reform failed because people don't trust the government to manage their medical care – a business that accounts for one of every $7 spent in the United States, and a healing art that touches the lives of almost every citizen (4). However, the Clinton administration didn't stop assault on healthcare at that level. On August 1 and 2, 1996, congress cleared for the President's signature, the Health Insurance Portability and Accountability Act of 1996, known as the Kennedy-Kassabaum Bill (5). There was very little dissent even in the republican controlled congress. This bill came with a disguise and even the liberal press reaction was favorable. The bill included the sexy title: Portability and Accountability. President Clinton signed the bill into law on August 21, 1996 (5). Unknown until recently, this act contained major provisions of the Clinton Administration's previously rejected 1993 Health Security Act and many other issues regarding to privacy, administrative simplification, fraud and abuse leading to increased focus on documentation. Thus, in today's modern medicine, there has been such an emphasis on the description and definition of what the physician does for and to the patient, which has never been witnessed in the history of the United States. The Kennedy-Kassabaum Health Reform Bill of 1996 provided the Office of the Inspector General (OIG) and the Federal Bureau of Investigation with broad powers and directed them to identify and prosecute healthcare fraud an abuse.

HISTORY

The role played by documentation has always been a supportive one but a critical one. However, as the practice of medicine has become more sophisticated and complex, the need to record specific clinical data has grown in importance. What began as a simple written mechanism to remind the treating physician involved into a refined system to serve others assisting in patient care, which also has become a complex product. Until early 1970s, no clear standards existed for medical record documentation. In the olden days, medical documentation was not only seen and maintained but was used almost exclusively by physicians in medical staff. It was also considered as the property of the individual physician or provider organization. Thus, it was very unusual to submit patient care information to insurance companies. In contrast, in today's medicine specifically in interventional pain management, any claim submitted for reimbursement must be supported by clear and accurate documentation.

The developments in the mid 1970s, irrevocably affected the role of documentation in medicine. This was fueled by a dramatic nationwide increase in medical malpractice claims and awards, changes in the fledgeling Medicare program during the 70s, emergence of electronic review process in 1980s adding even a newer twist, Medicare Prospective Payment Systems, and finally, documentation for evaluation and management services in the early 1990s. Documentation is not all bad and it is not all cookbook practice of medicine. Subsequently, the requirements from Medicare spread to other private payors.

Medical records service a variety of purposes, all of which are important to the proper functioning of a physician practice or a facility.

IMPORTANCE OF DOCUMENTATION

Documentation reflects competency, character and caring of the pain management specialists (6). However, documentation is not limited only for the physician and provider practices, but also physicians are obligated to document incorrect or incomplete answers from third party payors, including Medicare and Medicaid programs. A general accounting office study submitted to Ways and Mean Health Subcommittee on September 25, 2001, showed that Medicare carriers were often wrong approximately 85% of the times and provided incorrect or incomplete answers. The Office of Inspector General reported overpayments of $23.3 billion in 1996, $20.3 billion in 1997, $12.6 billion in 1998, $13.5 in 1999, $11.9 billion in 2000, and $12.1 billion in 2001 in health fraud. As shown in Fig. 1, physician overpayments are significant. The government also has shown that increased efforts to prevent fraud and abuse have reduced the Medicare fee-for-service error rates significantly (Fig. 2). In fact, documentation errors were shown to be 70% and 79% in 1998 and 1999. The most important causes of the offensive on physician practices with heightened requirements for documentation or increasing healthcare costs, Clinton administration, HIPAA and

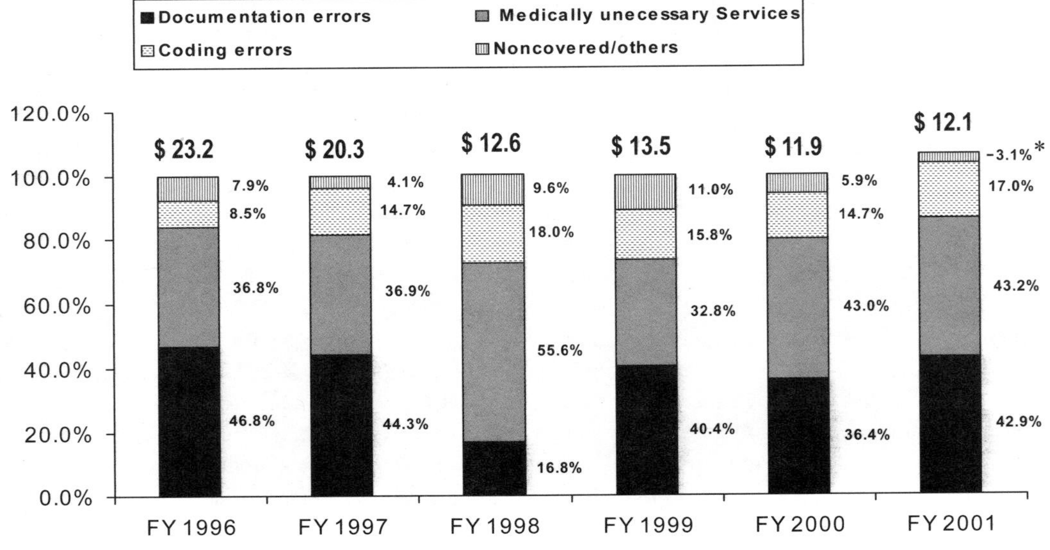

* - The –3.1% applied primarily to "other" errors. In these cases, medical reviewers determined that the amounts billed should have been higher or that amounts previously denied were correct.

Fig 1. *Improper Payments by Type of Error (in Billions)*

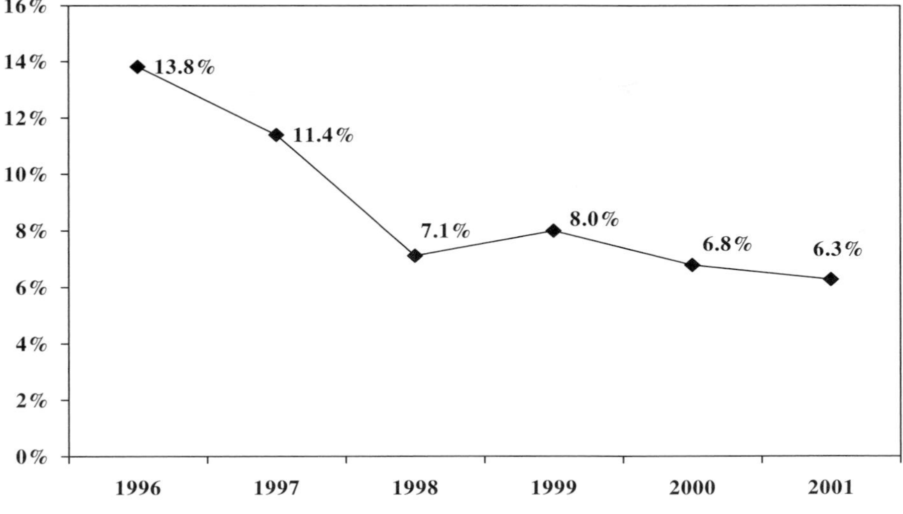

Fig 2. *Medicare fee-for-service (FFS) error rate*

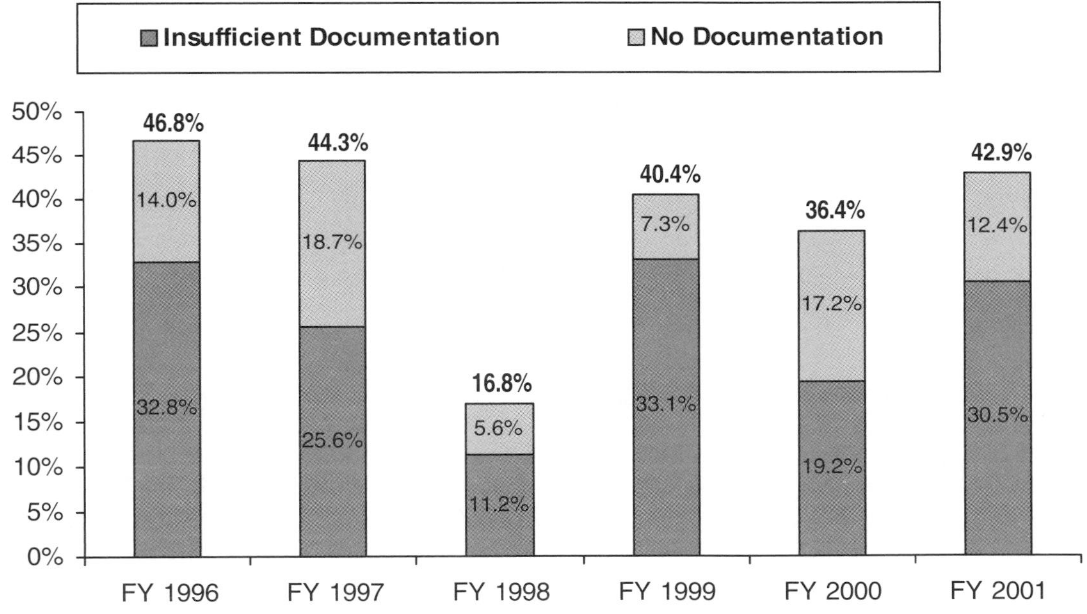

Fig 3. *Documentation errors as a percentage of total estimated improper payments*

Balanced Budget Act. Fig.3 shows documentation errors as a percentage of total estimated improper payments.

DEVELOPMENT OF MEDICARE

In June 1883, Bismarck, then chancellor of a newly united Germany, successfully gained the passage of a compulsory health insurance bill covering all factory and mine workers (7). In Great Britain, George, Chancellor of the Exchequer, from 1901 until 1914 introduced a national health insurance scheme on the part of the government in 1911, based on Bismarck's success (7). Thus, a compulsory system of health insurance became of subject of American presidential politics. On August 6, 1912, Theodore Roosevelt, as a presidential candidate, called on for a national compulsory healthcare scheme for all industrial workers (8). Following numerous tribulations, in spite of the opposition from AMA, with several presidents and congressional leaders changing their propositions, on July 30, 1965, President Johnson, signed the Medicare bill in the presence of former president, Truman into law in Independence, Missouri. The main provisions of the 1965 legislation were as follows (7):

1. Hospital insurance for all person's over the age of 65, otherwise entitled to benefits under the Social Security Railroad Retirement Acts, known as Medicare Part A.
2 Supplementary medical insurance for all persons over 65, eligible for participation in this program on a voluntary basis, without the requirement that they had earlier paid into the Social Security Program, known as Medicare Part B.
3. In addition, the 1965 legislation provided states a number of options regarding their level of participation in Medicaid, ranging from opting out of the program entirely to including all covered services for all eligible classes of persons.

In 1967, the Johnson Administration proposed amendments to the Social Security Program that included extending Medicare benefits to the disabled who were otherwise eligible for cash payments. Perhaps the most significant change to the Medicaid program contained in the 1972 amendments was the repeal of a provision contained in the 1965 legislation that made it mandatory that each state expand its Medicaid program each year until it offered comprehensive coverage for all the medically needy by 1977 (7). In addition, there was also a provision in 1972 legislation which established the Professional Standards Review Organizations, whose function was to assume responsibility for monitoring the costs, degree of utilization, and quality of care of medical services offered under Medicare and Medicaid. In 1974, a reimbursement cap was instituted that limited hospitals from charging more than 120% of the mean of routine costs in effect in similar facilities, a limit later reduced to 112%. In 1974, a new legislation was enacted whose goal was to reduce the construction of new hospitals. Thus, the National Health Planning and Resource Development Act mandated that Certificate-of-Need (CON) programs be instituted in each of the states to regulate the construction of new healthcare facilities. However, this program was of limited value despite its enormous cost, with little impact on new hospital construction.

In 1981, Omnibus Budget Reconciliation Act (OBRA) was enacted limiting reimbursements for a large number of inpatient and outpatient services. Subsequently, the Tax Equity and Fiscal Responsibility Act (TEFRA), was enacted in 1982, introducing a flat payment per hospital patient based on the historic average cost of care and instituted a ceiling on increases in hospital revenue. This act also permitted states to require copayments from most Medicaid recipients, altered the terms under which HMOs entered into risk-sharing contracts to make them more attractive and made Medicare the secondary, rather than the primary, insurer in the case of workers under the age of 70 covered by a company health insurance plan. The combined effect of OBRA and TEFRA reforms was to introduce hospital budget caps to Medicare patients. Subsequently, radical changes in payment systems appeared with a prospective payment system (PPS) introduced for hospitals in 1983, at which time hospital payments accounted for more than 68% of total Medicare expenditures. Subsequently, since physician payments were increasing out of proportion, a physician payment review commission was established in 1986. Prospective payment system for physicians also was implemented starting January 2, 1992 with reaching full implementation by 1996. Finally, the Outpatient Prospective Payment System was introduced in August 2000.

HEALTH CARE COSTS

Increasing healthcare costs has been a problem ever since Medicare was introduced. It was clear following the first full year of operation of the hospital insurance program that its costs significantly exceeded the estimates put forward by the programs proponents. By 1972, the costs associated with Medicare had increased at such a rate that even the

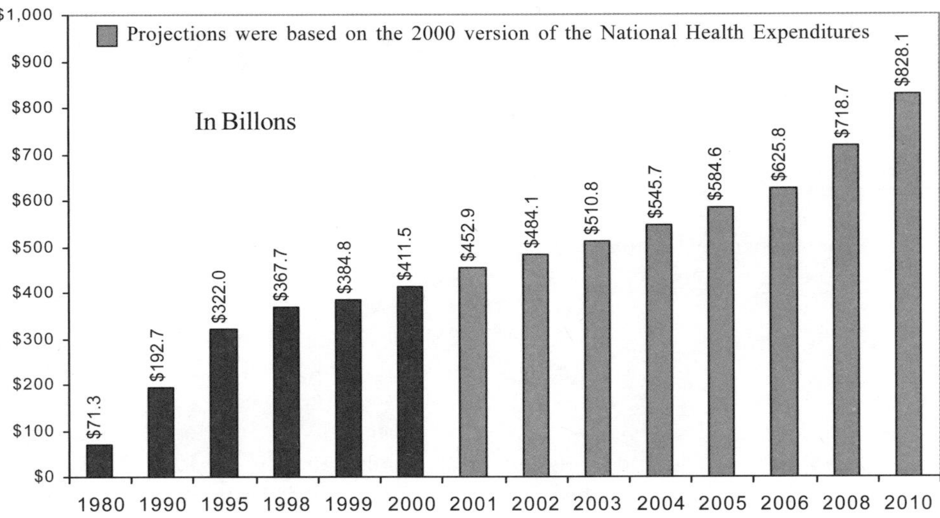

Fig 4. *Government sponsored Health care expenditure on health*

administration and Congress were expressing their concern. It was shown that hospital service charges rose much faster than the consumer price index and additionally faster than the medical care component of that index. Over the course of the first five years of Medicare that ended in 1971, physicians' charges rose 39%, compared with a 15% rise in the five years before the advent of Medicare. Further, healthcare expenditures of the elderly that originated in public sources rose more sharply than had been expected prior to Medicare's passage. In the fiscal year 1966, government programs provided 31% of the total expended on healthcare for the elderly. Just one year later, this proportion had increased to 59% and Medicare alone accounted for 35 cents of every dollar spent on health services by or for those over the age of 65. As shown in Fig. 4, Government sponsored Health care expenditures have increased substantially since its inception in 1965.

Along with Medicare expenditures, national healthcare expenditures also have been increasing. In fact, national health expenditures are projected to total $2.6 trillion and reach 16.8% of Gross Domestic Product (GDP) by 2010 after having declined from 13.4% in 1995 to 13.1% in 1999. Fig. 5 shows national health expenditures through 1980 to 2010 with actual numbers from 1980 to 2000 and projections (based on the 2000 version of the National Health Expenditures) from 2001 to 2010. Fig. 6 shows US population in millions with age less than 65 years

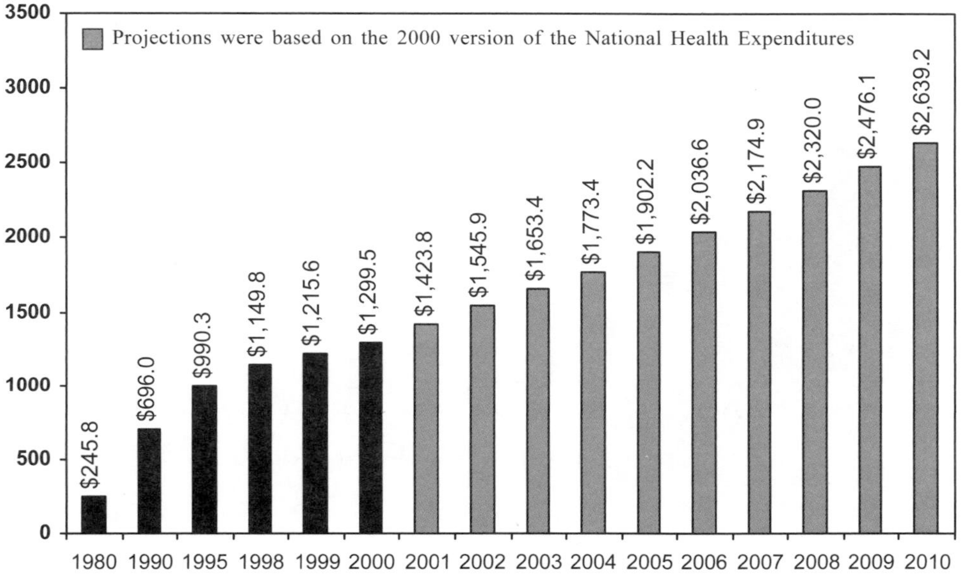

Fig 5. *National Health Expenditures (billions) for selected calendar years 1980-2010*

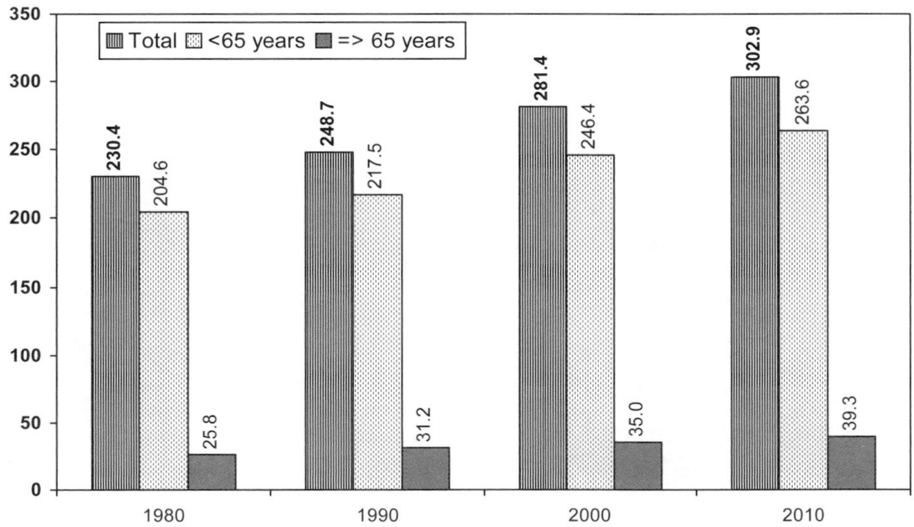

Fig 6. *Comparison of U.S. Population in millions (actual and projections) under and over 65 years of age from 1980 - 2010.*

and those 65 years and older. Fig. 7 shows national health expenditures as a percent of gross domestic product, which increased from 8.8% in 1980 to 13.2% in 2000 and is expected to increase to 16.8% in 2010. Fig. 8 shows growth of various sectors in healthcare with substantial increase for prescription drugs compared to all other sectors.

Thus, cost containment was initiated not only in the public sector, but also in the private sector. Managed healthcare took birth to cut the costs with increasing participation in managed care organizations from 1982 through 2000 (Fig. 9). Even though there has been increase in enrollment in managed care organization participation, trends in HMO premiums are increasing (Fig. 10). Now there is a slowly growing realization spreading across the country that the problem of rapidly rising costs has returned as the most significant

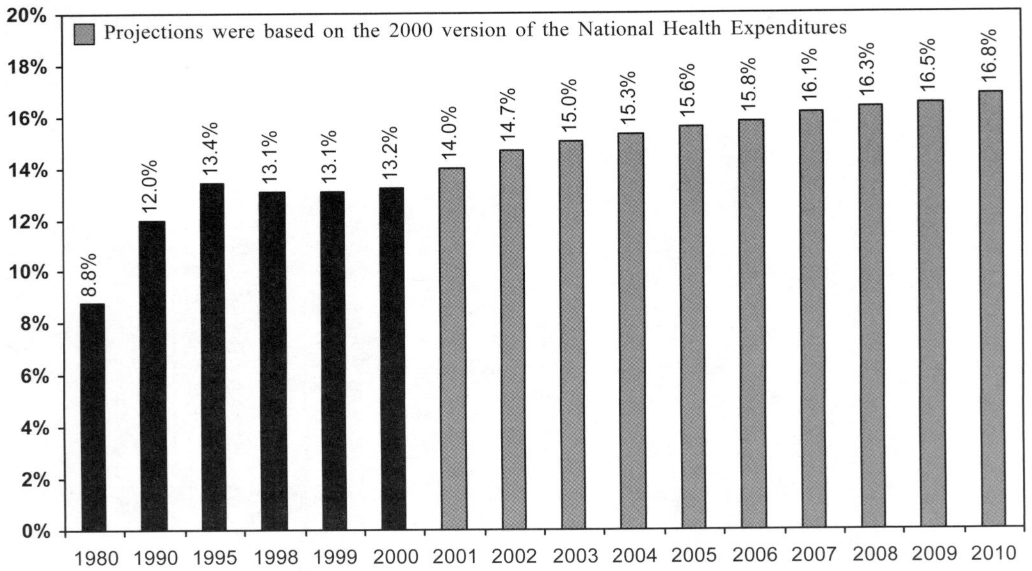

Fig 7. *National Health Expenditures as percent of Gross Domestic Product*

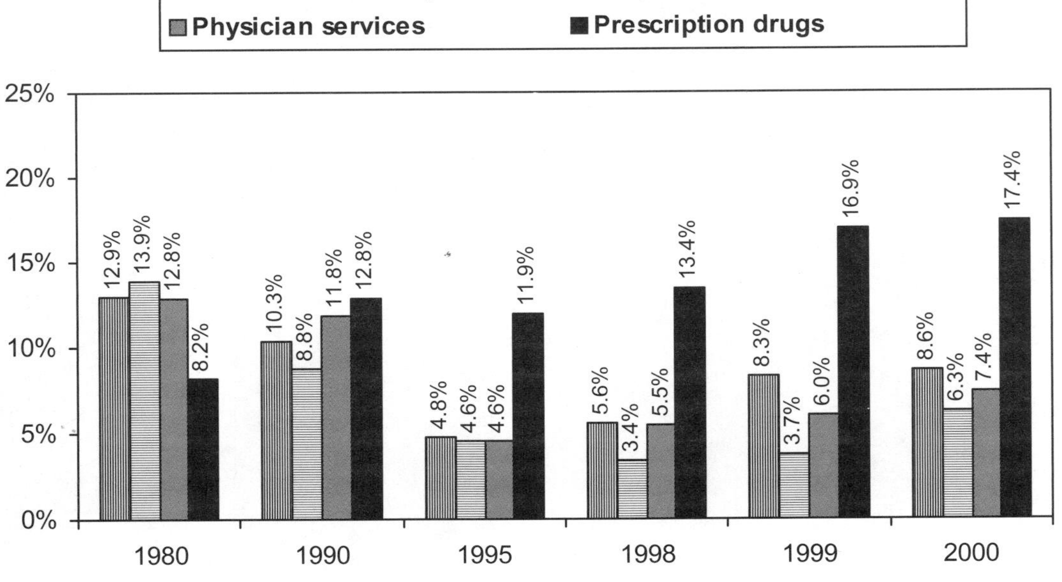

Fig 8. *National health expenditures - average percentage annual growth from prior year shown*

healthcare issue facing the nation (9). The trends in premiums suggest that we now are facing rates of increase that are equal to and soon to be greater than those of just a decade ago. In other words, we could say that we are right back where we used to be. Thus, it appears that we have lost the cost containment war, along with quality and access. There are several culprits and co-conspirators in the complicated world of healthcare for loss of cost containment.

ROLE OF DOCUMENTATION

Documentation is the cornerstone of the quality of patient care in medicine. While documentation is extremely important for billing and coding, its primary purpose is to assist healthcare professionals in providing appropriate services to patients. Thus, the documentation in each of the physician's office medical records, hospital settings, or am

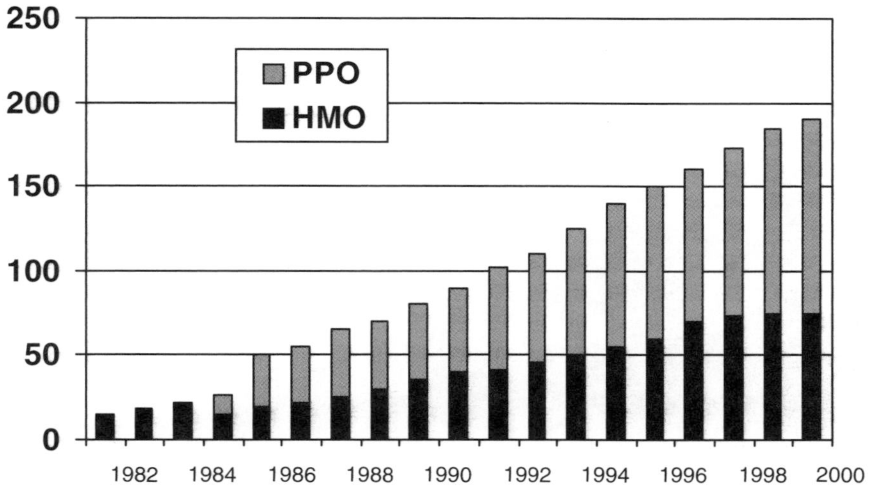

Fig 9. *Managed care organization (MCO) participation 1982-2000*

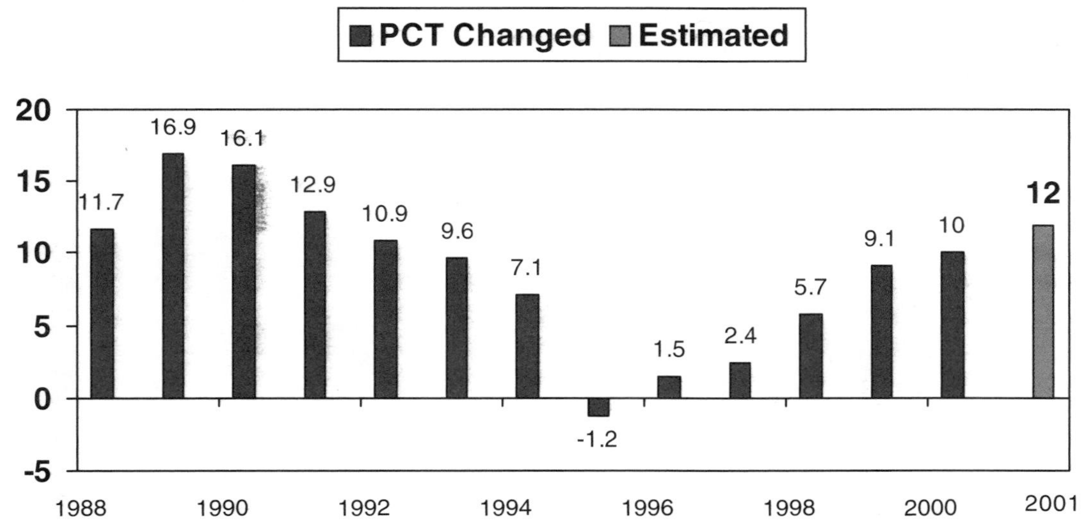

Fig 10. *Trends in HMO Premiums 1982-2001*

bulatory surgery centers, and rehabilitation centers and other settings must be accurate, complete, and reflect all of the services billed for each particular patient encounter. Accurate and complete documentation of the service is part and parcel of a solid compliance program and is certainly a necessity for delivery of quality care.

The medical record is the primary informational source for all services billed on behalf of the patient. Thus, the medical record must fully substantiate all types of services provided. The patient's medical record is an assemblage of information gathered and recorded pertaining to patient care. Appropriate documentation is fast becoming the only reliable assurance that providers can count on to provide appropriate patient care, to receive appropriate third party reimbursement, and finally, to retain a measure of protection against federal, state, and other payor auditors in their search for provider fraud and abuse. The accurate assignment and reporting of CPT and ICD-9-CM codes no longer guarantees payment, nor does the submission of "clean" claims. With the pre- and post-payment third party payor screens that edit services ranging from office visits to surgical procedures, almost all the claims submitted by the practitioner is potentially subject to meticulous scrutiny. In addition, in many of the cases, copies of the medical record entries must be sent to the carrier or for a final reimbursement determination when such information is requested. Thus, interest in medical record documentation has acquired a new urgency as it pertains to the correct coding and billing of services. Growth in regulatory and compliance activity further requires that documentation provided by the physician is not only accurate, but also detailed and specific. Documentation has never before been under such scrutiny by so many.

The physicians have not been historically taught and are required to be experts in documentation, billing and coding, and for many years they retained their independence over the medical records as their own territory. However, modern times are different and the medical record is a powerful weapon which can be used not only in protection of the physician or provider, but also against them.

Centers for Medicare and Medicaid Services (CMS) mandates the availability of provider medical records for Medicare beneficiaries for review of services billed to the Medicare program. The Provider Reimbursement Manual, Section 2304.1, states in part that "examination of such records and documents is necessary to ascertain information pertinent to the determination of the proper amount of program payments due the provider." In fact, federal, state, third party payor, and managed care plans rely heavily on provider documentation when accessing the claims for various parameters. These include:

- Was the billed service actually rendered or provided to the patient?
- Was the level of service or extent of the service accurately reported?
- Was the service or procedure medically necessary?
- Was the claim sent to the correct primary insurers for the service or procedure performed?

Documentation includes not only the physician handwritten or typed notes, nurses handwritten or typed notes, and the results of various tests and reports of consultation, etc., but also includes patient questionnaires, problem summary sheets, and finally, in-office or hospital notes as appropriate, to appropriately substantiate a particular claim for a particular service.

ELEMENTS OF DOCUMENTATION

Medical documentation may be of several types. Certain critical documentation, such as clinical notes and other medical records are always maintained in the patient's medical record. However, various other forms of documentation, such as patient waivers and financial data, insurance information, and patient hardship data may be maintained outside of the patient's chart. Under HIPAA Privacy Regulations, two charts will be mandatory.

The typical information for interventional pain medicine medical chart may include:

- Patient demographic data
- Medical insurance card copy
- Patient's drivers license copy
- Patient guarantee and authorization forms
- Initial evaluation
- Progress notes
- Summary sheet with problems and medication history
- Patient questionnaires
- Laboratory test results
- Radiographic evaluation results
- Results of various medical tests
- Medical records from other providers
- Facility notes
- Consultation reports
- Correspondence
- Advanced beneficiary notice
- Various other orders with prescriptions, etc.

Essentially the same information is maintained whether it is an electronic format or hard copy. Some forms such as medical information releases, third party payor requests, and insurance claim form copies may not be physically maintained in patient medical charts.

Documentation outside the patients' medical record in another format may include the following:

- Encounter forms or super bills or charge sheets
- Physician orders
- Prescription refill logs
- Records of laboratory tests orders
- Managed care referral forms
- Patient account records
- Copies of explanation of benefits
- Other records

However, in criminal investigation related to fraud and abuse, similar to a malpractice litigation, the definition of documentation is taken, at times out of context, and at times, much further than a patient's medical record and may include the following:

- Appointment schedules
- Surgery schedules
- Appointment calendars
- Work planners
- Travel logs and records
- Telephone message logs
- Various notes and internal memoranda, not intended for inclusion into the patient medical records and also not intended for external disclosure

DOCUMENTATION STANDARDS

The documentation of patient care in the medical records must be accurate, complete, and reflect all services that have been billed for the patient during each particular session. Each visit must meet medical necessity criteria and each claim should be stand-alone. The medical record is the primary source document for all services billed and not your super bill or charge sheet. Thus, we go to the old saying, "if you have not documented, you haven't performed the service" in the eyes of federal, state, third party payor and managed care organizations. Any medical service that is not properly documented in the medical record, was simply not provided. Even though the idiom, "if it is not documented, it is not done" has been said throughout the medical history and industry for centuries, its prominence and growth has been spectacular and it does not appear to disappear but also appears to grow even rapidly. Simple, yet extremely important standards of documentation are listed in Table 1.

GOVERNMENT'S PERSPECTIVE

CMS has published many, many guidelines, instructions for providers and answers to providers-submitted questions that pertained to the recording of the patient-related information, both inside and outside of the medical record. The federal government does consider the patient medical record the primary source or original document for all patient healthcare information, as well as for services provided, whether the record is retained by a physician, independent nurse practitioner, psychiatrist, psychologist, physical therapist, ambulatory surgery center, rehab facility, or a hospital, or any other recognized provider of healthcare services. Under HIPAA of 1996, the federal government has been charged to conduct investigations, audits, evaluations, and inspections relating to the delivery of and "payment for healthcare in the United States." However, this charge is not limited to federal programs, such as Medicare and/or healthcare programs that are wholly or partially subsidized by federal funds, such as Medicaid, but, this act covers all healthcare benefits programs in the United States, whether public or private.

Table 1. *Illustration of documentation standards*

1. Medical records must be legible
2. All entries must be dated with month, day, and year
3. Every page in the chart should be patient-identified
4. Medical records should always be documented in permanent ink (not with pencil)
5. Incorrect entries should be crossed out with a single line with rewriting of the correct entry
6. Corrections should be dated and signed
7. All additions are dated, signed, and are clear
8. The credibility of notes written more than 24 to 48 hours after the care was rendered are considered suspect
9. Always provide sufficient information with samples and prescriptions
10. Document all health risk factors, including allergies and adverse reactions to medications, foods or other substances
11. Summary sheet should have identifying information, height, weight, medication list, previous surgeries, and diagnosis
12. All telephone calls must be documented
13. Medical necessity for all diagnostic services or tests
14. Medical necessity for all procedures and interventions
15. Documentation of follow up treatment dates for coordination of services and services based on time, documentation of the time is crucial
16. All documents contained inside the chart should belong to that particular patient

DOCUMENTATION PROCESS

Who is responsible for documentation? It is an important question and frequently discussed issue in offices on a daily basis. A multitude of personnel associated with a practice or a facility are responsible; however, we believe that the buck stops with the physician or the provider. Thus, not only the physicians but also other treating providers such as physician assistants, nurse practitioners, and clinical nurse specialists must take responsibility in documentation for each and every patient encounter. Further, nurses and medical assistants who obtain patient histories and vital signs, administer injections and otherwise provide certain restricted services, must also likewise document and make clinical entries. Physical therapists, psychologists and other ancillary providers also need to complete specific medical treatment forms for the purpose of documentation of their services and findings are documented similar to physicians. Due to the fact that the patient medical record is considered not only a medical document, but also a legal document, authorization for making entries into the records should be limited by appropriate policy establishment. This will not only avoid entries by some personnel, which may go unnoticed by the provider, but also avoid unnecessary compromising, comments or situations.

There is tremendous variation in documentation standards among payors. Further, the variation is not just among the carriers but among individual carriers themselves with regional policies. Even Medicare carriers, which we believe must be consistent as they are all under Medicare administration, continued published varying documentation policies. This also applies to large health insurance companies such as Aetna, Blue Cross and Blue Shield, and United Health Care. To always meet the entire documentation criteria one should use a checklist and cover all aspects. Thus, a patient record:

- Support the medical necessity of the service performed,
- Provide clear description of the procedure or service including technique and end results,
- Should make it clear that the procedure was performed by the reporting or billing physician,
- Document appropriate and specific diagnosis code as, ICD-9 CM, diagnosis code,
- Provide documentation of indications and medical necessity, which may be reviewed by payors at any time,
- Must document specific regulations governing procedures performed in chronic pain management by many carriers, and
- Follow correct coding initiatives, and Local Medicare Review Policies with the limitations, which become part of documentation.

OTHER ISSUES OF DOCUMENTATION

Documentation is not only important for patient records, billing and coding, but also is extremely important in various other issues, such as employee training, employee warnings, contracts with various outside agencies, insurance correspondence, OSHA, billing and coding, as well as HIPAA complaints programs. Thus, documentation is the proof of each and every activity a practitioner performs in practice.

CONCLUSION

Medical documentation is created to establish and maintain an accurate and enduring record of patient encounters with healthcare professionals and services. Thus, medical documentation can range from the smallest note, to a detailed, comprehensive evaluation. Documentation is an important part of interventional pain medicine for appropriate coding and billing and to also prove medical necessity and protect against fraud and abuse investigations. Additional benefits include protection against liability and also assist in providing quality patient care. Thus, documentation of interventional pain procedures throughout patient encounters and subsequent billing and coding are of crucial importance, not only in complying with the regulations, but also for good patient care. All interventional pain providers should realize that there is heightened emphasis on the description and definition of what the physician does for and to the patient in the United States as never before. Compliance with laws and regulations encompassing documentation, medical records, coding, billing, collections, contracts, auditing, and other areas are also of crucial importance in today's interventional pain physician.

REFERENCES

1. Feldman RD (ed). *American Health Care*. The Independent Institute, Transaction Publishers, New Brunswick, 2000.
2. Pauly MV. Foreword. In Feldman RD (ed). *American Health Care*. The Independent Institute, Transaction Publishers, New Brunswick, 2000 pp ix-xi.
3. Stigler GJ. The theory of economic regulation. *Bell J Economics* 1971; 2:3-21.
4. Feldman RD. Introduction. In Feldman RD (ed). *American Health Care*. The Independent Institute, Transaction Publishers, New Brunswick, 2000, pp 1-12.
5. Twight C. Medicare's Progency: The 1996 Health Care Legislation. In Feldman RD (ed). *American Health Care*. The Independent Institute, Transaction Publishers, New Brunswick, 2000, pp 87-118.
6. RAJ PP, Johnston M. Organization and function of the nerve block facility. In RAJ PP, Abrams BM, Benzon HT. *Practical Management of Pain,* ed. 3, Mosby, St. Louis, 2001; pp 545-556.
7. Hamowy R. The Genesis and Development of Medicare. In Feldman RD (ed). *American Health Care*. The Independent Institute, Transaction Publishers, New Brunswick, 2000, pp 15-85.
8. Henry FP. Theodore Roosevelt, Harcourt Brace, New York, 1956, pp 396-397.
9. Hurley R, Rawlings RB. Who lost cost containment? A roster for recrimination. *Managed Care Quarterly* 2001; 9:23-32.

FRAUD AND ABUSE IN INTERVENTIONAL PAIN MEDICINE

Laxmaiah Manchikanti, MD

The Office of Inspector General's (OIGs)focus for 2002 includes reviews of:

- Procedure coding for outpatient services billed by a hospital and doctor,
- Use of Medicare advance beneficiary notices and their financial impact on physicians and beneficiaries,
- Coding for evaluation and management services in physician offices, and
- Conditions under which a doctor's bill is "incident to" services or supplies.

The U.S. Attorney's office in Philadelphia, described some of the "overnight files" – from the last week of January 2002.

- **Identity theft –** A non-licensed individual allegedly took a dead physician's medical license, whited out the old name, put his name in, photocopied it and presented the copy to a clinic for employment. The hiring clinic, needy for staff, failed to a thorough background check.
- **Unnecessary services.** A case alleges that lab personnel billed tests they knew were inaccurate. If a provider bills for tests he knows are inaccurate, false claims charges could result. Thus it's not enough to say you performed the test.
- **Gifts from suppliers.** Free VCRs, free equipment and unrestricted educational grants will be seen as potential bribes.
- **Diversion of prescription drugs.** Two physicians were indicted for illegal distribution of OxyContin.
- **Clinical research subject recruitment.** Providers trying to recruit patients for clinical trials must tell the patients all about he study, particularly about the provider's relationship with the sponsor of the study.

Federal Bureau of Investigation (FBI) for health care fraud opened a division on cybercrime, which includes improper billing over the Internet.

The FBI is looking into cases involving:

- Billing for unnecessary services,
- Home health agencies inflating the number of visits performed,
- Durable Medical Equipment (DME) companies billing used equipment as if it were new,
- Transportation companies billing basic service as if it were advanced life support, and,
- Mental health facilities for billing group therapy as if the therapist saw each patient individually.

Traits that help to recognize fraudulent providers are important. Provider background checks also should look for the following:

- Hire foreign-trained doctors, because they might be easier to manipulate,
- Have drinking, drug and gambling problems,
- Hire family members,
- Work in private companies (public companies have to disclose their practices),
- Avoid tax-exempt financing (too many questions asked), and
- "The money moves to places."

These are some of the issues affecting interventional pain medicine physicians in the practice of medicine today. The

OIG is one of the entities involved in fraud and abuse investigations. The OIG of the Department of Health and Human Services (HHS) performs audits and inspections of the Medicare program and other HHS programs, as well as pursuing investigations of suspected instances of fraud and abuse. The OIG investigates fraud, develops cases, and has the authority to take civil action in the form of civil monetary penalties and program exclusion, and to refer cases to the Department of Justice for further criminal or civil action (1).

In the past few years, not only the federal government has become far more aggressive in identifying and prosecuting healthcare professionals and entities suspected of what is commonly referred to as fraud and abuse, but private insurers are also becoming more active in prosecution of such cases. *Healthcare Fraud and Abuse, A Physician's Guide to Compliance* (1), published by the American Medical Association is a comprehensive resource for physicians to assist them in understanding various implications and statutes regarding fraud and abuse; entities involved in fraud and abuse investigations; Medicare review and audits and medical necessity denials; and, finally, ways to minimize risk of an audit, and fraud and abuse liability. Much of the information in this chapter is available extensively in this book.

Background

In a statement before House Budget Committee, OIG reported the following(2):

> ". . . . we would like to express our belief that the vast majority of health care providers are honest in their dealings with Medicare. When we talk about fraud, we are not talking about providers who make innocent billing errors, but rather those who intentionally set out to defraud the Medicare program or abuse Medicare beneficiaries. The importance of our ongoing work is not only to protect the taxpayers and ensure quality healthcare for Medicare beneficiaries but also to make the Medicare environment one in which honest providers can operate on a level playing field and do not find themselves in unfair competition with criminals.
>
> At the same time, we are concerned about all errors, even those that are totally innocent. The complexity of the Medicare program places an obligation on health care providers, beneficiaries, fiscal intermediaries, carriers, and the Health Care Financing Administration (HCFA) to take reasonable care to comply with its rules. Thus, our audits and studies are also intended to identify vulnerabilities to administrative errors and to the related dollar losses, which can be quite significant. "

The OIG also reported the following (2):

> "The HCFA is the single largest purchaser of health care in the world. With expenditures of approximately $316 billion, assets of $212 billion, and liabilities of $39 billion, HCFA is also the largest component of the Department. In 1999, Medicare and Medicaid outlays represented 33.7 cents of every dollar of health care spent in the United States. In view of Medicare's 39.5 million beneficiaries, 870 million claims processed and paid annually, complex reimbursement rules, and decentralized operations, the program is inherently at high risk for payment errors and fraudulent schemes.
>
> Like other insurers, Medicare makes payments based on a standard claim form. Providers typically bill Medicare using standard procedure codes without submitting detailed supporting medical records. However, regulations specifically require providers to retain supporting documentation and to make it available upon request.
>
> The OIG is statutorily charged with protecting the integrity of our Department's programs, as well as promoting their economy, efficiency, and effectiveness. The OIG meets this mandate through a comprehensive program of audits, program evaluations, and investigations designed to improve the management of the Depart; to detect and prevent waste, fraud and abuse; and to ensure that beneficiaries receive high-quality, necessary services at appropriate payment levels. As part of this effort, we conduct annual audits of the Department's and HCFA's financial statements, as required by the Chief Financial Officers Act, as amended by the Government Management Reform Act of 1994."

ABUSE

Abuse is defined in many ways. However, the key words in the definition of *abuse* are *knowingly* or *willfully*. A provider's intent is the most significant factor in determining whether noncompliance is considered abuse, rather than a fraudulent practice (1). Abuse may, directly or indirectly, result in unnecessary costs to a program such as Medicare or Medicaid, improper payment, or payment for services that fail to meet professionally recognized standards of care or that are medically unnecessary. Abuse also involves payment for items or services for which there is no legal entitlement to payment. Fundamentally, in abuse, the physician or healthcare professional has not knowingly and willfully misrepresented facts to obtain payment.

The most common examples of abuse include, but are not limited, to:

- Performance of services, that are not "medically necessary,"
- Inappropriate medical record documentation,

- Inappropriate billing practices,
- Violations of Medicare limiting charge, and/or
- Violation of the participation agreement.

To summarize, abuse involves actions that are inconsistent with sound medical, business or fiscal practices.

FRAUD

Fraud is much more serious than abuse and implies the intent to commit a crime. Fraud relates to intentional deception or misrepresentation to obtain some benefit, such as payment for medical services. Intent is an essential element in fraudulent billing.

Three types of fraud in healthcare services have been described. These include obvious fraud, incentives that promote overutilization, and matters of judgment or interpretation. Obvious fraud represents conduct that is indefensible and without controversy. Examples of obvious fraud include intentionally billing for services never provided, including "no shows;" misrepresenting the diagnosis to justify the services; applying for duplicate payment; and issuing certificates of medical necessity for patients unknown to the physician; and knowingly upcoding or unbundling (1).

The second category, the incentives that promote overutilization, is also troublesome under the antikickback statute, as well as Stark regulations. The third type of fraud involves matters of judgment or interpretation in which a large grey area of fraud can arise over the exercise of judgment. This involves selection of a level of service or the proper CPT code, unbundling and upcoding, etc. There is often a fine line between fraudulent conduct and legitimate disagreements over the interpretations of the clinical evidence. Inadvertent billing errors which occurred due to ignorance or misinterpretation of reimbursement policies also fall into this category. However, the Justice Department and the Centers for Medicare and Medicaid (CMS) maintain that there will be no prosecutions for billing errors. That only means that an occasional coding error is no reason for alarm and that the carrier will refer the matter to the OIG. However, practitioners should remember that repeated abuses can lead to fraud charges.

> According to *The Medicare Carrier's Manual for Fraud Unit Procedures*, Section 14011, Coordination with Carrier Medical Review unit's responsibilities includes looking for questionable billing patterns and practices. The term *abuse* describes incidents or practices of providers that are inconsistent with accepted sound medical practice. Abuse may, directly or indirectly, result in unnecessary costs to the program, improper payment, or payment for services that failed to meet professionally recognized standards of care, or that are medically unnecessary. Abuse involves payment for items or services when there is no legal entitlement to that payment and that provider has not knowingly and intentionally misrepresented facts to obtain payment.
>
> If the medical review unit finds, or suspects, such practices, it should consult with the fraud unit to determine whether the case should be referred to the fraud unit for further action.
>
> Medicare is most vulnerable to overutilization of medical and healthcare services. Abuse takes such forms as, but is not limited to, claims for services not medically necessary, or not medically necessary to the extent furnished.
>
> Although these types of practices may be considered abusive, under certain circumstances, they may constitute or evolve into fraud. If a provider appears to have knowingly and intentionally furnished medically unnecessary services or filed claims for services not furnished as stated on the claim form, or made any false statement on the claim form to receive payment, the case is discussed with the fraud unit. If the fraud unit agrees that there is potential fraud, the Medical Review unit then refers the cases to the fraud unit. When reviewing such situations, do not assume that the abuse is the result of an error or misunderstanding of program requirements. At a minimum, ascertain whether there have been similar complaints or warnings, and whether the provider has been the subject of Medical Review previously.
>
> The fraud unit often receives complaints alleging fraud that are determined to be abusive rather than fraudulent. When this occurs, the fraud unit will decide if it is more cost and time effective to complete the case or refer it to the Medical Review unit (3).

The message is that repetitive violations after notice(s) without any corrective action by the physician equates to fraud. Even though CMS is not interested in prosecuting billing errors, the local Medicare carrier can be instrumental in redefining such errors as fraud. Once that happens, the physician can be confronted with criminal, civil, and/or exclusionary sanctions. After this stage, the matter is no longer limited to negotiating an overpayment request with a carrier; but billing errors are translated to fraud and abuse.

FRAUD OR ABUSE?

The distinction between fraud and abuse can be very important in determining the potential fines and penalties that might apply. In this regard, fraud is much more serious than abuse. However, the distinction between fraud and abuse is not crystal clear. There is a significant grey area. The degree of intent by the individual or entity under investigation is often the determining factor. It may start as a billing error identified by a local Medicare carrier as an abusive billing pattern but could turn into a full blown fraud case turned over to the OIG and/or the Department of Justice (DOJ) for criminal prosecution, specifically if added billing irregularities or any evidence of intent to defraud is discovered.

Fraud, as defined by CMS, is an intentional deception or misrepresentation that someone makes, knowing it is false, that could result in the payment of unauthorized benefits.

In contrast, abuse involves actions that are inconsistent with sound medical, business, or fiscal practices.

Thus, the primary difference between fraud and abuse is a person's intent. Abuse directly or indirectly results in higher costs to the healthcare program through improper payments (3). For fraud, persons should be aware that they were committing a crime. However, for an activity or scheme to be judged fraudulent, it does not have to be successful.

In defining persons who have filed a false claim, federal legislation specifies that this includes (3):

> .... any person who engages in a pattern or practice of presenting or causing to be presented a claim for an item or service that is based on a (CPT™) code that the person *knows or should know* will result in a greater payment to the person than the code the person knows or should know is applicable to the item or service actually provided.

However, the problem with this statement is that there is always the danger that enforcement agencies could claim that there is sufficient evidence of fraudulent intent to pursue criminal sanctions.

The Health Insurance Portability and Accountability Act (HIPAA) also specifically includes the following language with regards to fraud (3): "... the term *should know* means that a person .. (A) acts in deliberate ignorance of the truth or falsity of the information; or (B) acts in reckless disregard of the truth or falsity of the information, and no proof of specific intent to defraud is required."

PREVALENCE OF FRAUD AND ABUSE

No one questions the need to identify and prosecute individuals involved in fraudulent activities. However, it is believed that the vast majority of physicians are honest and make attempts to comply with the very complex laws and regulations of modern healthcare, in addition to attending to patients' medical needs. Thus, honest mistakes by physicians are no more indicative of fraudulent billing than a healthcare carrier's failure to issue a correct payment in response to a clean health insurance claim form is indicative of fraud, either on the part of the government or private insurer. It has been estimated that the annual incidence of healthcare fraud is approximately 10%, which translates to over $100 billion annually in the United States (4). However, this has been questioned by many authorities. This is another instance of random estimations. The implication of $100 billion or $100,000 million fraud is serious. If physician services constitute 30% of the entire healthcare expenditures, physician fraud will be $30,000 million (4) with 750,000 doctors in the United States, and 450,000 of them in office based practice each doctor would be committing $40,000 or $70,000 fraud, unless most of the fraud is coming from hospitals and major corporations. If the entire fraud is attributed to physician payments each physician of 750,000 is responsible for $133,333 or each physician of 450,000 is responsible for $222,222, of fraudulent activity.

While the federal government has become far more aggressive in identifying and prosecuting healthcare professionals and entities for fraud and abuse, private insurance also are becoming not only more active but are also pursuing fraud and abuse. Recent Federal Bureau of Investigation statistics show that 75% of investigations are related to government agencies, either Medicare or Medicaid; whereas 25% of the cases are investigated secondary to the complaints of private insurers.

FRAUD DETECTION

The error rate methodology does not detect fraud, such as kickbacks, deliberate forgery of bills or supporting documents, or violations of the Stark law regarding the financial relationship between an entity and a physician or an immediate family member. To fulfill this function of OIGs legislative mandate, OIG looks to sources and techniques outside the error rate process. From investigations and from complaints they receive OIG knows that waste, fraud, and abuse are still pervasive in the health care sector. OIG is therefore continuing to watch all areas of Medicare through our audits, inspections, and investigations, as well as to encourage and receive support from industry and beneficiary groups in their efforts (2).

The Government's primary enforcement tool, the civil False Claims Act, covers only offenses that are committed with *actual knowledge* of the falsity of the claim, *reckless disregard* of the truth or falsity of the claim, or *deliberate ignorance* of the truth or falsity of the claim. The other major civil remedy available to the Government, the Civil Monetary Penalties Law, has the same standard of proof. Neither statute covers mistakes, errors, misunderstanding of the rules or negligence, and OIG is very mindful of the difference between innocent errors ("erroneous claims") and reckless or intentional conduct "fraudulent claims" (2).

To actually determine fraud, OIG typically obtains information through a combination of investigative techniques tailored to each case. These tools include subpoenas of medical and billing records, use of search warrants, investigative interviews of provider employees, surveillance, and undercover operations. For example, establishing that a claim is tainted by an illegal kickback often requires an analysis of contracts in the context of safe harbors as well as a review of the provider's Medicare and private billings over time. Once this information is gathered, it is presented to a U.S. Attorney whose office will evaluate the information and, with input from the OIG, make a final decision on whether the conduct constitutes criminal or civil fraud. If the evidence demonstrates an intentional violation of the law, the U.S. Attorney may opt to present the case to a Federal grand jury for potential criminal action. If no criminal intent can be shown, but there is evidence of provider knowledge that false claims were submitted, a civil False Claims Act case may be authorized.

IMPLICATIONS

Implications are much less serious if the issues are handled at local carrier level; however, once the issue is referred to law enforcement agencies, it becomes serious.

Identification of improper billing practices by a Medicare carrier requires the physician to repay any monies received inappropriately, along with interest. This is based on the carrier's discretion, which may include a return of funds for a relatively small number of services or calculation of the overpayment percentage from a small sample of patient encounters to determine the amounts to be recouped for payments received over several years for similar services.

For example, simplifying the sampling process, assume a Medicare carrier audited documentation of 20 patient encounters and determined that a physician upcoded seven claims, which resulted in an overpayment of $175 or $25 per claim. If a physician is lucky, the carrier may simply ask for repayment of $175 plus interest for the above encounters reviewed. In addition, the carrier may also offer education with regards to proper billing practices. However, more commonly than uncommonly with increasing frequency, Medicare carriers are asking for repayment of $25 each on 28.5% of similar services provided by the physician billed to that carrier over the past 5 years, which could result in a repayment request of hundreds of thousands of dollars.

That is the good news. The bad news is that carriers can also refer the case to the OIG or DOJ for further investigations, and that they are doing it frequently. Once it is referred to law-enforcement agencies, the government may pursue criminal prosecution, civil monetary penalties or exclusion from participation in the federal health programs. Where fraudulent intent is established, exclusion will not stop there, but could then lead to loss of hospital and other facility privileges and denial of participation in managed care plans.

Chart of Centers for Medicare and Medicaid Services Progressive Corrective Action is depicted in Table.1, based on program memorandam based on program memorandum AB-00-72(5)

FRAUD AND ABUSE STATUTES

Fraud and abuse statutes not only include various federal laws but also state laws, as well as antikickback statutes and Stark regulations. A number of federal statutes may be used as the basis for healthcare fraud prosecution. In addition, many states also have independently enacted legislation aimed at healthcare fraud and abuse. The most commonly used statutes for prosecuting or facilitating such a prosecution of healthcare fraud or abuse include (6):

- HIPAA of 1996,
- The False Claims Act,
- Health Care Fraud,
- Theft or embezzlement,
- Obstruction of criminal investigations of healthcare offenders,
- The False Statement Statute,
- Mail and wire fraud statutes,
- The Social Security Act,
- Civil monetary penalties,
- Criminal penalties, and/or
- Stark laws.

In addition, federal legislation such as the Racketeer Influenced and Corrupt Organization Act may be used to prosecute healthcare fraud. Antikickback statutes and Stark regulations are quite frequently used to facilitate prosecution of fraud and abuse.

Health Insurance Portability and Accountability Act of 1996

The HIPAA is the most significant legislative initiative with substantial implications for the to healthcare industry on issues of fraud and abuse. The HIPAA added substantial funding for fraud and abuse activities for several agencies, which included the CMS, FBI and OIG. The act not only provides the funding and also lets the agencies utilize recoveries from successfully prosecuted cases but also provides incentives to the various enforcement agencies to identify and prosecute fraud cases.

The HIPAA expanded the powers of the government with

Table 1. *Progressive Corrective Action Flow Chart*

POTENTIAL ERROR DETECTED

WIDESPREAD PROBLEM

If needed, for each service at risk, validate the potential error by pre or post pay review of 100 potential problem claims from a representative sample of providers. Deny or collect money.

Take service-specific actions

- √ Contact medical and speciality societies to assist in education and
- √ Develop new/revised LMRPs if needed &/or
- √ Issue bulletin article clarifying existing NCPs and LMRPs &/ or -initiate service-specific prepay edits.

LIMITED PROBLEM

For each provider-at-risk, validate the potential error by pre or post pay review of 20-40 potential problem claims. Deny or collect money. Determine level of concern considering error rate (net out undercoded $) and past history of the provider

Provider Feedback and Education Must be given

PRINCIPLES

- √ Data driven
- √ Test hypothesis
- √ Prioritize/target work load
- √ Collect money when errors are identified
- √ Make fraud referral when indicated
- √ Feedback to providers is always a part of corrective action
- √ Medical review resources should be used efficiently

MINOR CONCERNS IDENTIFIED

Scenario 1: Low error rate with no provider history of patterns of errors.
Scenario 2: Few dollers improperly paid.

MODERATE CONCERNS IDENTIFIED

Scenario 3: Low error rate but total dollers improperly paid substantial.
Scenario 4: Moderate error rate with mitigating circumstances.

MAJOR CONCERNS IDENTIFIED

Scenario 5: Moderate error rate despite documented educational interventions.
Scenario 6: Very high error rate. Mitigating circumstances considered but supports need for stringent administrative action.

PROVIDER EDUCATION AND FEEDBACK MUST BE GIVEN AT ALL LEVELS OF CONCERN

When the level of concern is minor, the mandated activities of provider education and feedback and collection of overpayments identified may be sufficient. Reevaluation may be appropriate at a later date.

When there is a moderate level of concern some level of prepayment medical review should be considered. adjust or eliminate prepayment review according to provider responce to actions taken.

A major level of concern should prompt stringent administrative action. Consideration of a high level of prepayment medical review &/or SVRS projected to the universe &/or payment suspension &/or referral to the Fraud unit (when appropriate) are examples of administrative actions which may be appropriate. Frequent feedback/provider education should be given to assure an understanding of the billing errors. Administrative actions should be adjusted or eliminated according to provider response to actions taken.

ALL EVIDENCE OF FRAUD MUST BE REFERRED TO THE FRAUD UNIT

PROGRESSIVE CORRECTIVE ACTION

Source: HCFA(5)

respect to healthcare fraud and abuse. It appears that, based on this act, the OIG can exclude from Medicare or Medicaid responsible owners, officers, and managing employees of companies that have committed fraud or have been excluded from Medicare, even if the investor, officer, or employee had no knowledge of the wrongdoing. Further, the DOJ can subpoena or seize the records in any healthcare fraud investigation regardless of whether the investigation involves a federal agency such as Medicare or Medicaid. The HIPAA also expands fraud and abuse actions to certain offenses against nongovernmental payors. Further, it increases penalties for fraud and abuse and offers incentives payable to informants and government departments participating in fraud cases.

In summary, the HIPAA creates a new category of offense, known as federal healthcare offense, which includes the following:

- Healthcare fraud,
- Making false statements,
- Theft and embezzlement,
- Obstruction of criminal investigations,
- Money laundering.

However, under HIPAA, unfortunately, these categories of crimes not only apply to all governmental agencies, but also to private payors.

Provisions

Provisions of HIPAA include the following:

- Civil monetary penalties of $10,000 per infraction plus three times the amount of the overpayment;
    - Consideration of an infraction as a line item on a claim form, resulting in a $10,000 or more penalty every time a fraudulent claim is filed;
- Imposition of $10,000 per day fines for organizations that continue any "investor" relationship or continue employing a person who has been excluded from any federal healthcare program;
- Mandatory exclusion from Medicare for 5 to 10 years for certain offenses;
- Application of Medicare and Medicaid exclusion penal ties to all other federal healthcare programs, including Civilian Health and Medical Program of the Uniformed Services, Veteran's Affairs, Blackland, and Federal Em ployee Health Benefits Program.
    - Consideration of "Deliberate ignorance" or "reckless disregard of the truth" as the test to whether an individual should have known that an activity was fraudulent;
- Specific definition of upcoding of evaluation and man agement services;
- Penalties for offering inducements to Medicare benefi ciaries or Medicaid recipients;
- Penalty of $5,000 or three times the cost of services for any physician who certifies unneeded home healthcare;
- Forfeiture and confiscation of any assets, including per sonal property, acquired directly or indirectly from funds related to fraudulent activity;
- A $25,000 penalty per infraction for health maintenance organizations (HMOs) that fail to comply with Medicare contracts or federal regulations.

Federal False Claims Act

The Federal False Claims Act permits not only the government, but also citizens civil action against physicians and other providers filing fraudulent claims. The False Claims Act provides for a civil penalty of $5,000 to $10,000 per false claim, plus three times the amount of damage that the government sustains (6).

This act is often used when a physician bills for services which were not actually rendered.

According to the law, any person is subject to penalty who commits one of the following actions:

1. Knowingly presents, or causes to be presented, to an officer or employee of the US government or a member of the armed forces . . a false or fraudulent claim for payment or approval (the term *knowingly* includes "acting in reckless disregard . . ." or in "deliberate ignorance of the truth or falsity of information");
2. Knowingly makes, uses, or causes to be made or used, a false record or statement to get a false or fraudulent claim paid or approved by the government;
3. Conspires to defraud the government by getting a false or fraudulent claim allowed or paid;
4. Has possession, custody, or control of property or money used, or to be used, by the government and, intending to defraud the government or willfully to conceal the property, delivers, or causes to be delivered, less property than the amount for which the person receives a certificate or receipt;
5. Is authorized to make or deliver a document certifying receipt of property used, or to be used, by the government and, intending to defraud the government, makes or delivers the receipt with-

out completely knowing that the information on the receipt is true;

6. Knowingly buys, or receives as a pledge of an obligation or debt, public property from an officer or employee of the government, or a member of the armed forces, who lawfully may not sell or pledge the property; or
7. Knowingly makes, uses, or causes to be used, a false record or statement to conceal, avoid, or decrease an obligation to pay or transmit money or property to the government; such an individual is liable to the US government for a civil penalty of not less than $5,000 and not more than $10,000, plus three times the amount of damages which the government sustains because of the acts. Note that the $5,000 to $10,000 penalty is per false claim.

The bad news is that the act also states: "the United States shall be required to prove all the essential elements of the cause of action, including damages, by a preponderance of the evidence." Thus, the government does not have to prove its false claims allegations beyond a reasonable doubt.

Private citizens often bring suit(s) on behalf of themselves and the government against fraudulent healthcare provider(s) by alleging violation(s) of the False Claims Act. These types of suits are called *qui tam* suits, also known as "whistle-blower" suits, with persons receiving 10% to 30% of the total recovery plus reasonable attorney fees. The only recourse for the physician or another provider is that if the *qui tam* plaintiff is the employee and if it were demonstrated that the employee intentionally filed an action knowing that the allegations were not true, this plaintiff might be responsible for legal fees to the extent that the government does not participate in the case and where the action is not successful. *Qui tam* suits generally are very expensive and long-lasting.

The OIG promulgated the provider self-disclosure protocol in 1999, which provides detailed guidance to healthcare providers that decide voluntarily to disclose irregularities in their dealings with federal healthcare programs. However, the protocol does not include any assurance that would prevent a *qui tam* plaintiff's filing an action, even after repayment has been made subject to the self-disclosure guidelines.

The statute of limitations under the False Claims Act runs for 6 years after the commission of an offense. However, this period may be extended to approximately 10 years when certain facts do not come to light within the normal 6-year period.

Health Care Fraud

Description of unlawful conduct: It is a crime to knowingly and willfully execute (or attempt to execute) a scheme to defraud any health care benefit program, or to obtain money or property from a health care benefit program through false representations. Note that this law applies not only to Federal health care programs as well.

Penalty for unlawful conduct: The penalty may include the imposition of fines, imprisonment of up to 10 years, or both. If the violation results in serious bodily injury, the prison term may be increased to a maximum of 20 years. If the violation results in death, the prison term may be expanded to include any number of years, or life imprisonment.

Description of unlawful conduct: It is a crime to knowingly and willfully embezzle, steal or intentionally misapply any of the assets of a health care benefit program. Note that this law applies not only to Federal health care programs, but to most other types of health care benefit programs as well.

Penalty for unlawful conduct: The penalty may include the imposition of a fine, imprisonment of up to 10 years, or both. If the value of the asset is $100 or less, the penalty is a fine, imprisonment of up to a year, or both.

Description of unlawful conduct: It is a crime to knowingly and willfully falsify or conceal a material fact, or make any materially false statement or use any materially false writing or document in connection with the delivery of or payment for health care benefits, items or services. Note that this law applies not only to Federal health care programs, but to most other types of health care benefit programs as well.

Penalty for unlawful conduct: The penalty may include the imposition of a fine, imprisonment of up to 5 years, or both.

Description of unlawful conduct: It is a crime to willfully prevent, obstruct, mislead, delay or attempt to prevent, obstruct, mislead, or delay the communication of records relating to a Federal health care offense to a criminal investigator. Note that this law applies not only to Federal health care programs, but to most other types of health care benefit programs as well.

Penalty for unlawful conduct: The penalty may include the imposition of a fine, imprisonment of up to 5 years, or both.

False Statements

The penalty for making false statements is imprisonment up to 5 years and fines up to $250,000 for individuals, and possibly more if the amount of gain is large.

However, once again, unfortunately, HIPAA extended Section 1001 of the False Claims Act, which is similar to 287, to private healthcare plans in addition to government programs.

This section is commonly used to prosecute physicians for billing services not rendered, and hospitals for knowingly including improper expenditures on their cost reports, and, finally, for billing services not personally performed.

Mail and Wire Fraud

Mail and wire fraud statutes allow for imprisonment for up to 5 years, and fines of not more than $1,000 per occurrence for a fraudulent scheme in which claims or statements are sent by mail, telephone, radio waves, etc. Many providers believe that private carriers such as Fed Express do not fall under this law. However, transmittal of almost any fraudulent claim might violate mail or wire fraud provisions, which includes using private or commercial interstate carriers.

Once again, HIPAA extended section 1341 and 1343 to private healthcare programs in addition to government programs.

Social Security Act Civil Monetary Penalties

The government may impose civil monetary penalties of up to $10,000 per claim if the physician knew or should have known the claim was false. In addition, a civil monetary action may be brought after successful criminal prosecution. The *Medicare Carrier's Manual* illustrates that penalties may be imposed where the secretary determines that a person presents or causes to be presented a claim for:

- An item or service not provided as claimed;
- An item or service that is false or fraudulent;
- A physician's service provided by a person who was not a licensed physician, whose license had been obtained through misrepresentation, or who improperly represented he/she was a certified specialist; or
- An item or service furnished by an excluded person.

The secretary may also impose a civil monetary penalty against a person who presents or causes to be presented a request for payment in violation of:

- A Medicare assignment agreement;
- An agreement with a state Medicaid agency not to charge a person in excess of permitted limits;
- A Medicare participating physician/supplier agreement; or
- An agreement not to charge patients for services denied as a result of a determination of an abuse of the prospective payment system (PPS). A person that gives false or misleading information regarding PPS that could reasonably be expected to influence a discharge decision is also subject to imposition of a civil monetary penalty.

Other situations where civil monetary penalties may be applied include:

- Violation of assignment requirements for certain diagnostic clinical lab tests;
- Violation of assignment requirements for nurse anesthetist services;
- Any supplier who refuses to supply rented durable medical equipment supplies without charge after rental payments may no longer be made (effective January 1, 1989);
- Nonparticipating physician or supplier violation of charge limitation provisions for radiology services (effective January 1, 1989);
- Violation of assignment requirement for physician assistant services;
- Medicare nonparticipating physician's violation of limiting charge limits;
- Nonparticipating physician's violation of charge limitations;
- Physician billing for assistants at cataract surgery without prior approval of Peer Review Organization;
- Nonparticipating physician's violation of refund requirements for medically unnecessary services;
- Nonparticipating physician's violation of refund provision for unassigned claims for elective surgery (where an elective surgical form was not provided);
- Physician charges in violation of assignment provision for certain purchased diagnostic procedures where markup is prohibited or where a payment is prohibited for these procedures due to failure to disclose required information;
- Hospital unbundling of outpatient surgery costs; and
- Hospital and responsible physician "dumping" of patients.

Antikickback Statute

The antikickback statute has prohibited payments for referrals since the 1970s. The antikickback statute prohibits:

1. The knowing and willful offer or making of payment (including a kickback, bribe or rebate) to induce a referral of a Medicare or Medicaid patient;
2. Solicitation or receipt of such payments;
3. Knowingly and willfully inducing, making, or causing to be made any false statement or material misrepresentation in an application for Medicare or Medicaid payment; and
4. Any payment to a physician as an inducement to limit or reduce necessary medical services to Medicare or Medicaid beneficiaries.

Violation of this statute is a felony. The violator is not only subject to civil penalties but also subject to criminal penalties, along with exclusion from Medicare, Medicaid and other federal healthcare programs.

Original Safe Harbors: Congress created safe harbors to describe activities in which one can safely engage without violating antikickback laws. The first 13 safe harbors were originally promulgated in 1991 and 1992. Subsequently, in 1999, some of the original ones were clarified or modified slightly. The list of safe harbors is as follows (6):

1. Investment interests in large publicly held healthcare companies,
2. Investments in small health care joint ventures,
3. Space rental,
4. Equipment rental,
5. Personal services and management contract,
6. Sales of retiring physicians' practices to other physicians,
7. Patient referral services (such as those maintained by a hospital),
8. Discounts,
9. Warranties,
10. Employee compensation,
11. Group purchasing,
12. Hospitals waiving coinsurance and deductibles for indigents, and
13. Inducements offered to potential enrollees by HMOs and similar discounts offered to HMOs, etc., by participating providers.

New Safe Harbors: New safe harbors include the following:

1. Investments in ambulatory surgical centers,
2. Joint ventures in underserved areas,
3. Practitioner recruitment in underserved areas,
4. Sales of physician practices to hospitals in underserved areas,
5. Subsidies for obstetric malpractice insurance in underserved areas,
6. Investments in group practices,
7. Specialty referral arrangements between providers, and
8. Cooperative hospital services organizations.

Stark Regulations

Limits on self referral were first enacted into a law known as the Stark Amendment as part of the Omnibus Budget Reconciliation Act of 1989. Referrals of Medicare or Medicaid beneficiaries for multiple designated services are prohibited under Stark II, if the physician has a financial relationship (not just ownership) with the entity providing the services. Some of these categories are extremely broad, which include the following but one not limited to (6):

1. Clinical laboratory services;
2. Physical therapy services;
3. Occupational therapy services;
4. Radiology or other diagnostic services;
5. Radiation therapy services and supplies;
6. Durable medical equipment and supplies;
7. Parenteral and enteral nutrients, equipment, and supplies;
8. Prosthetics, orthotics and prosthetic devices and supplies;
9. Home health services;
10. Outpatient prescription drugs; and
11. Inpatient and outpatient hospital services.

Often physicians are confused about the antikickback statute and Stark legislation. The following are the differences (6):

- The Stark Law is a civil statute that generally prohibits physicians from making referrals for clinical laboratory or other designated health services to entities in which the physicians have ownership or other financial interests and prohibits entities from presenting or causing to be presented claims or bills to any individual, third-party payor, or other entity for designated health services furnished pursuant to a prohibited referral.
- The antikickback statute, on the other hand, is a criminal statute that prohibits the knowing and willful offer, payment, solicitation, or receipt of remuneration to induce federal health care program business.
- Both laws are directed at the problem of inappropriate financial incentives' influencing medical decision-making. This similarity notwithstanding, the statutes are different in scope and structural approach. Under the Stark Law, physicians may not refer patients for certain designated health services to entities from which the physicians receive financial benefits, except as allowed in enumerated exceptions. A transaction must fall entirely within an exception to be lawful under the Stark Law.
- The antikickback statute, on the other hand, establishes an intent-based criminal prohibition with optional statutory and regulatory safe harbors that do not purport to define the full range of lawful activity. Rather, safe harbors provide a means of assuring that payment practices are not illegal. Payment practices that do not fully comply with a safe harbor may still be lawful if no purpose of the payment practice is to induce referrals of federal health care program business.

General exceptions to both ownership and compensation arrangements have been identified. These include physician services, in-office ancillary services, prepaid plans, and other permissible exceptions.

Description of Unlawful Conduct

False Statements and Representations: It is a crime to knowingly and willfully:

- make, or cause to be made, false statements or representations in applying for benefits or payments under all Federal health care programs;
- make, or cause to be made, any false statement or representation for use in determining rights to such benefit or payment;
- conceal any event affecting an individual's initial or continued right to receive a benefit or payment with the intent to fraudulently receive the benefit or payment either in an amount or quantity greater than that which is due or authorized;
- convert a benefit or a payment to a use other than for the use and benefit of the person for whom it was intended;
- present, or cause to be presented, a claim for a physician's service when the service was not furnished by a licensed physician;
- for a fee, counsel an individual to dispose of assets in order to become eligible for medical assistance under a State health program, if disposing of the assets results in the imposition of an ineligibility period for the individual.

Anti-Kickback Statute: It is a crime to knowingly and willfully solicit, receive, offer or pay remuneration of any kind (eg, money, goods, services):

- for the referral of an individual to another for the purpose of supplying items or services that are covered by a Federal health care program; or
- for purchasing, leasing, ordering or arranging for any good, facility, service or item that is covered by a Federal health care program.

There are a number of limited exceptions to the law, also known as "safe harbors," which provide immunity from criminal prosecution and which are described in greater detail in the statue and related regulations (found at 42 CFR 1001.952 and at www.hhs.gov/oig/ak/index.htm#OIG Safe Harbor Regulations). Current safe harbors include:

- investment interests;
- space rental;
- equipment rental;
- personal services and management contracts;
- sale of practice;
- referral services;
- warranties;
- discounts;
- employment relationships;
- waiver of Part A co-insurance and deductible amounts;
- group purchasing organizations;
- increased coverage or reduced cost sharing under a risk-basis or prepaid plan; and
- charge reduction agreements with health plans.

Penalty for Unlawful Conduct: The penalty may include the imposition of a fine of up to $25,000, imprisonment of up to 5 years, or both. In addition, the provider can be excluded from participation in Federal health care programs. The regulations defining the aggravating and mitigating circumstances that must be reviewed b the OIG in making an exclusion determination are set forth in 42 CFR Part 1001.

ENTITIES AND INVESTIGATIONS

A multitude of organizations and entities are involved in a fraud and/or abuse investigation (7).

1. The OIG,
2. The DOJ,
3. The FBI,
4. The state agency for healthcare administration,
5. State Licensing Boards,
6. Medicare/Medicaid carriers and intermediaries,
7. The HHS Office of Audit Services,
8. The HHS Office of Investigations,
9. The Drug Enforcement Administration,
10. The Internal Revenue Service,
11. The US Postal Service,
12. The CMS,
13. Utilization and quality control peer review organizations,
14. State attorney generals,
15. The US Attorney General,
16. State Medicare fraud units,
17. State bureau of investigation,
18. Private payors,
19. Self-insured companies,
20. Beneficiaries,
21. Competitors, and
22. Present and previous employees.

FEDERAL COMPREHENSIVE STRATEGY

The federal government has enacted over the years a comprehensive strategy to fight healthcare waste, fraud, and abuse. The Clinton Administration focused unprecedented attention on the fight against fraud, abuse and waste in the Medicare and Medicaid programs beginning in 1993. As a

Table 2. *Fraud and abuse budget of US government*

US Government Fraud and Abuse Budget			
	2000 actual (in $ millions)	**2001 enacted** (in $ millions)	**2002 request** (in $ millions)
Total CMS	316,007	354,485	386,527
Total Medicare	196,866	219,119	229,744
Total OIG	151	164	186
Health care fraud and abuse control (HCFAC)	715	820	860
CMS's Medicare integrity program	630	680	700
FBI refunds for health care fraud investigations	76	88	101
Other fraud and abuse control	158	182	209

Source: FY 2002 HHS Budget

result of this focus, in 1999, the OIG announced that improper Medicare payments to doctors, hospitals, and other healthcare providers declined 45% from fiscal year 1996 to fiscal year 1998. Federal authorities also have claimed that, due to this investigation, a new, more detailed picture of fraudulent activities at the Medicare and Medicaid systems has emerged. It was also claimed that new service and audits have helped investigators pinpoint areas of vulnerability and ongoing patterns of abuse, which in turn are leading to changes in law enforcement and administrative actions. Further, the government has gone so far that it is recruiting beneficiaries themselves to spot and report fraud and misspending. Former HHS Secretary, Donna Shalala, launched Operation Restore Trust, a ground-breaking project aimed at coordinating federal, state, local and private resources and targeting them on areas most plagued by abuse. During its 2-year demonstration phase, the project apparently identified $23 in overpayments for every dollar of project cost. In addition, the former Secretary also led the way to steady, guaranteed funding for anti-fraud efforts by the HHS Inspector General, by including these provisions in the HIPAA of 1996 (Table 2).

Under HIPAA's Healthcare Fraud and Abuse Control Program, HHS has reported more than $1.9 billion in fines and restitution returned to the Medicare trust fund during fiscal

Table 3. *Medicare exclusions and sanctions as of December 2001.*

Provider Type	**Total Exclusions**
Private citizen	4,075
Hospital (employee)	1,545
Chiropractic practice	1,703
Skilled nursing facility	2,643
Medical practice	3,552
Home health agency	602
All others	9,366
Total	**23,486**
Sanction Type	**Total Exclusions**
License revocation or suspension	8,741
Default on health education loan	2,444
Program-related conviction	6,454
Patient abuse or neglect	2,877
Conviction: controlled substance	266
All others	2,699
Total	**23,486**

Source: Office of Inspector General.

years 1997, 1998 and 1999. The HHS also excluded more than 23,186 individuals and entities from doing business with Medicare, Medicaid and other federal and state healthcare programs for engaging in fraud or other professional misconduct (Table 3). There was a substantial increase from 1996 to 2001 compared to previous years. The HHS has stated that, since 1993, these actions have saved HHS healthcare programs more than $38 billion and have increased convictions and other successful legal actions by more than 240%.

Various efforts by the Clinton Administration in fighting waste, fraud and abuse in Medicare and Medicaid included the following (1):

1. Decline of improper payments by 50%,
2. Operation Restore Trust,
3. A fraud and abuse hotline,
4. The administration on Aging Ombudsman Program,
5. Guaranteed and expanded funding,
6. An expanded OIG,
7. Increased efforts by the DOJ,
8. Rewards for fraud and abuse information,
9. Tightening of standards for home healthcare providers,
10. New requirements for durable medical equipment suppliers,
11. Targeting of fraud in community mental health centers,
12. The Medical Integrity Program and payment safeguards,
13. Improving healthcare industry compliance,
14. Correct coding initiatives,
15. Substantive claims testing,
16. Education efforts,
17. Tough new requirements for Medicare and Medicaid participants,
18. Budget 2000 anti-fraud and abuse legislative package, and
19. The administration on aging "fraud-buster projects."

POTENTIAL FRAUD AND ABUSE

Various categories of potential fraudulent or abusive billing practices relevant to interventional pain management include the following:

I. 1. Intentional misrepresentation of services rendered;

- Using covered CPT codes for noncovered services,
- Misuse of modifiers,
- Improper use of place-of-service indicators,
- Using a covered ICD-9 code, and
- Otherwise altering claim forms;

2. Billing for services not rendered or supplies not provided;

- Upcoding evaluation and management codes or other CPT codes;

3. Billing for services that were performed, but that may be questioned in terms of medical necessity;
4. Referrals billed with high-paying CPT consultation codes, rather than office or hospital visit codes;
5. Deliberately changing dates of service to circumvent correct coding edits;
6. Presentation of a claim for physician services performed by a nonphysician (unless the "incident to" provisions apply);
7. Alteration of claims to obtain payment;
8. Deliberate false diagnosis coding to obtain payment.
9. Falsifying medical records to justify payments;
10. Billing a noncovered service – by using covered CPT and ICD-9 codes –provided to patients in nursing homes or other facilities by podiatrists, psychologists, psychiatrists, ophthalmologists, optometrists, or others;
11. Misuse of misrepresentation of modifiers, or other codes, to circumvent carrier payment edits;
12. Billing for services rendered under another physician's provider number;
13. Falsely applying for Medicare or Medicaid certification by falsification of address, or misrepresentation of credentials or other pertinent facts;
14. Filing two or more claims for same date of service (without –51 or similar modifier) in an attempt to achieve greater payment for multiple surgical procedures (from payers that reduce payments for multiple procedures);
15. Deliberately applying for duplicate payment, eg, billing both Medicare and the beneficiary for the full amount for the same service or billing Medicare and another insurer in an attempt to get paid twice;
16. Billing for a more costly procedure, when a less costly one is considered a prerequisite to the more costly one;
17. Misrepresenting the identity of the person receiving the services;
18. Participating in schemes that involve collusion with a beneficiary or a supplier that results in higher costs or charges to the Medicare program;
19. Billing for services rendered to one beneficiary under the Medicare number of another.

II. 1. Unbundling or fragmenting CPT codes;

2. Billing based on what is often referred to as "gang visits," eg, a physician visits a nursing home and bills an evaluation and management code for each

vice to, or on behalf of, each patient;

3. Improper billing with individual psychotherapy codes when group psychotherapy was performed;
4. Significant occupational therapy, physical therapy, speech therapy, psychiatric services, and various forms of psychotherapy for patients with senile dementia or Alzheimer's disease who are deemed to be unable to benefit from the service;
5. Misrepresenting time for anesthesia, psychotherapy, various testing/ evaluation and management counseling, etc, where time is a component of the CPT code description;
6. Billing services of a teaching physician when not all supervisory requirements have been met or documented appropriately;
7. Billing laboratory tests incorrectly, including unbundling, manual vs automated tests, or failure to use panel codes when appropriate;
8. Completing certificates of medical necessity for patients not personally and professionally known by the physician (and signing blank prescriptions or certificates of medical necessity for durable medical equipment or home health services);
9. Improper billing with CPT code 90862 (pharmacologic management) when Medicare's special code M0064 (brief office visit for the sole purpose of monitoring or changing drug prescriptions used in treatment of mental, psychoneurotic and personality disorders) is descriptive of the service performed.

III. 1. Billing an evaluation and management code in the place of a minor surgical code or other minor procedure that would likely be denied (such as a lesionremoval);
2. Billing evaluation and management codes in addition to a minor surgical procedure when a significant, separately identifiable evaluation and management service is not performed, (ie, inappropriately appending the –25 modifier to the evaluation and management code when documentation does not indicate a separately identifiable evaluation and management service was performed);

IV. 1. Fee splitting, such as a chiropractor's splitting payment with a physician for evaluation and management codes billed under the physician's provider number;
2. Being associated with an organization or individual who has been prosecuted or cited for fraudulent activity;
3. Acceptance of kickbacks, bribes, rebates or other remuneration in exchange for referrals; payments made by hospitals, nursing homes, durable medical equipment suppliers, home health agencies, laboratories, or others for referrals; soliciting, offering, or receiving a kickback, bribe, rebate or other remuneration, eg, paying for a referral of patients in exchange for the ordering of diagnostic tests and other services or medical equipment;
4. Routine waiver of coinsurance and deductibles.

FRAUD AND ABUSE TARGETS

For the past 3 years, physician practices have been aggressively audited by the federal and state governments, along with major third-party payors across the nation. Since 1993, when President Clinton's administration began to delve into healthcare fraud and abuse, there have been a record number of investigations, indictments, convictions and settlements in almost every segment of the healthcare community. Thus, when the federal government stated that in 1999 alone, it recovered nearly $500,000,000 as a result of auditing providers for fraud, abuse and/or healthcare waste and when it said that federal officials have recovered an estimated $1.9 billion since 1996, with another $60,000,000 saved in improper and wasteful spending prevention, it was not an overstatement. Provider exclusions as of March 2000 since the inception of the program were $16,167 compared to $21,644 by May of 2001 and $23,186 by October 2001. Table 3 shows Medicare exclusions and sanctions.

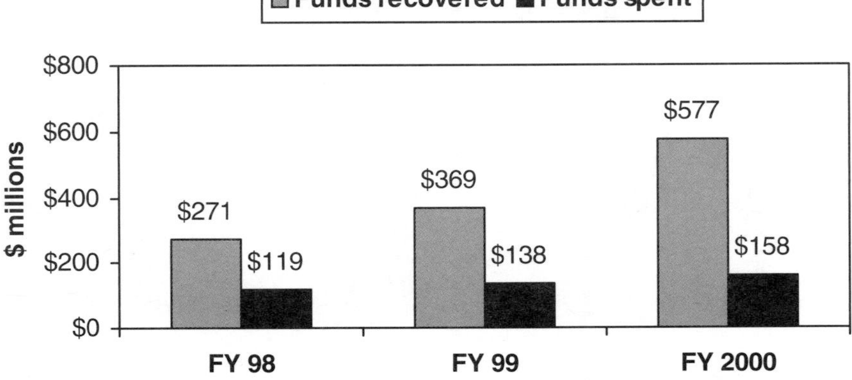

Fig 1. *Health Care fraud enforcement: Funds returned to the Medicare trust funds vs. Funds appropriated from federal budget*

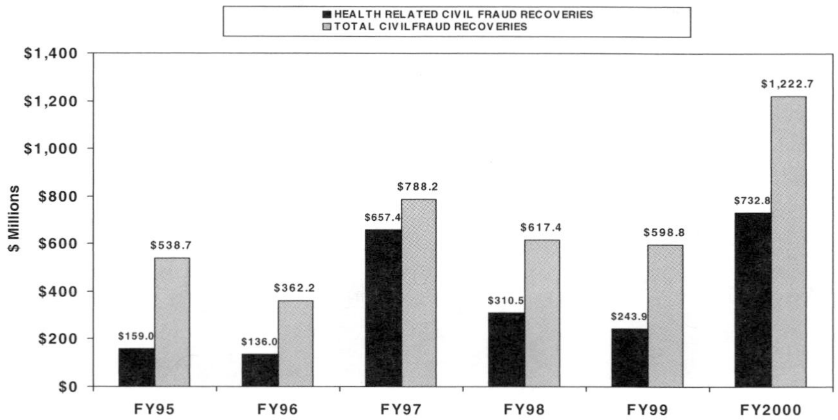

Fig 2. *Comparison of health-related civil fraud recoveries with other civil fraud recoveries*

Similarly, the government also has recovered significant amounts and returned the funds to the Medicare trust fund compared to the funds appropriated from the federal budget on fraud and abuse, as shown in Fig. 1. It also has been illustrated that government's health related civil fraud recoveries have been gradually increasing not only in the amount, but also in proportion compared to total civil fraud recoveries (Fig. 2).

THE OIG 2002 WORK PLAN

The OIG's 2002 work plan encompasses significantly increased levels of activity compared to 2001. The number of initiatives in 2001, 19 has been increased to 25 in 2002. Further, 13 of those 25 initiatives are new. Three of the new projects on the OIG's list have to do with the outpatient prospective payment system. Of these, nine projects concern physicians. Table 4 shows OIG descriptions of the 2002 work plan.

Not surprisingly, evaluation and management coding, as well as documentation, makeup the most important facet of the 2002 work plan. Once again, the federal government is going to focus on the level of coding, office visits versus consultations and billing for residents' services.

In addition, the topic of human subject research protection also is becoming an important subject for the OIG. Recent debts and clinical trials have heightened the scrutiny in this area. The OIG believes that investigators have received reports that some physicians are coercing their patients into trials to meet recruitment protocols. In addition, it is also believed that, at some sites, physicians are rushing their way through the consent process; thus, physician abuse in clinical trials is an upcoming "hot" area. The OIG also believes that physicians are not well educated about and are also unfamiliar with their federal obligations regarding clinical trials, such as Food and Drug Administration (FDA) regulations in terms of good clinical practices, they may be unknowingly violating FDA guidelines in various arenas of clinical research. The OIG also is looking at Medicare payments to drug trial participants to see if physicians may be crossing the medical necessity criteria. However, most of the focus is at the present time on drug trials.

Another issue is advanced beneficiary notices. Evidence continues to mount on physician offices all over the country over the use of advanced beneficiary notices. Practices will be required to use a new advanced beneficiary notice form (CMS' R–131) beginning September 2002. The OIG will not only be paying more attention to this area, but will be tough and less forgiving of those practices that fail to use the forms correctly. Noncovered laboratory tests are the greatest source of confusion with advanced beneficiary notices. The CMS believes that it is the physician's responsibility to issue an advanced beneficiary notice even when physicians' offices only draw the specimens and ship them to the labs for processing. This is because many believe that the physician has the rapport with the patient; thus he/she should be getting the advanced beneficiary notices signed. Further, the OIG is also concerned about why physician practices are failing to estimate the cost of each service. In the opinion of CMS, grossly underestimated cost estimates are extremely problematic.

The OIG's oversight is also increasing on mental health cases, as these services are increasing. A percentage of the exclusions of mental health providers are also increasing. Considering that many interventional practices also provide mental health services, this is of a crucial issue. Thus, the OIG is expecting to release guidelines to help mental health professionals comply with federal regulations. However, these guidelines once again will not be mandatory. Statistics show that in 1999, Medicare allowed $185 million in medically unnecessary mental health services. According to the OIG report, a year later, the program paid approximately $4.85 billion for mental health services. While the OIG continues to scrutinize and heighten its oversight, the CMS believes that mental health services are extremely important for the community. According to its work plan, the OIG will assess the role of the sub-

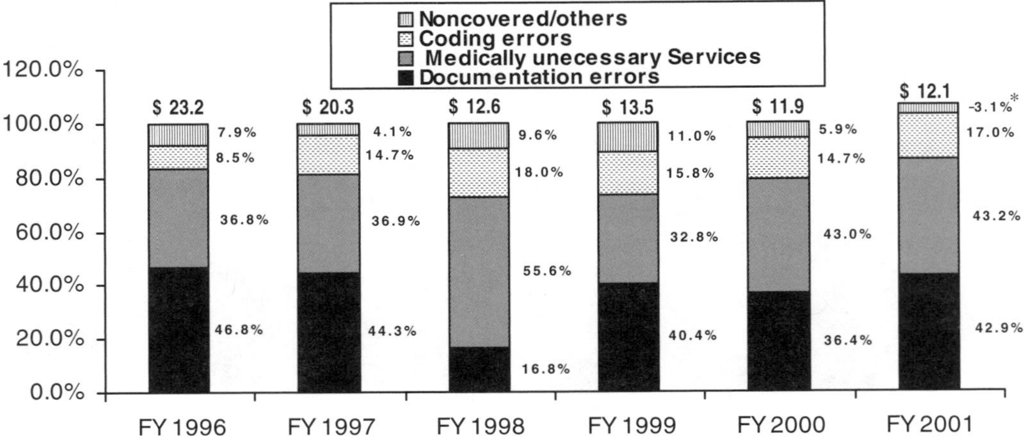

* - The –3.1% applied primarily to "other" errors. In these cases, medical reviewers determined that the amounts billed should have been higher or that amounts previously denied were correct.

Fig 3. *Improper payments by type of error (In Billions)*

Table 4. *Identification of various projects of the OIG 2002 plan*

New projects in OIG 2002 plan	Continued Projects From 2001	Deleted Projects From 2001
Outpatient Prospective Payment System	One-day hospital stays	Payments for related hospital and skilled nursing stays
Outpatient services delivered on the same day as a discharge and a readmission	Hospital discharges and subsequent readmissions	Prospective payment transfers
Procedure coding of outpatient and physician services	Satellite hospitals	Prospective payment transfers between chain members
Outlier payments under the outpatient prospective payment system	PPS transfers during hospital mergers or consolidations	Prospective payment transfers; administrative recovery
Inpatient Prospective Payment System	DRG payment limits	Postacute services for DRGs considered transfers
Consecutive inpatient stays	Outlier payments for expanded services	DRG payment windows: hospitals
Payments to acute-care hospitals operating under the Medicare prospective payment system	DRG payment window for Part B providers	Follow-up on peer review organizations' complaint process
Expansion of DRG payment window	Uncollected beneficiary deductibles and coinsurance	
Other payment issues	Hospital reporting of restraint-related deaths	
Payment Error Prevention Program	Outpatient prospective payment systems	
Periodic interim payments	Outpatient pharmacy services at acute-care hospitals	
Payments for medical education	Outpatient medical supplies at acute-care hospitals	
Implementation of the Medicare program for critical-access hospitals		
Miscellaneous issues		
Hospital privileging activities		
Peer review organizations' sanction authority		
Reporting of restraint and seclusion in psychiatric hospitals		

stance abuse and mental health services administration in treating mental illness. In addition, Congress also may be working on bills that would mandate health plans to offer the same deductibles, copayments and scope of coverage for mental health services as offered for other healthcare services.

The OIG also calls for increased scrutiny of documents and documentation of medical necessity. As per the OIG, in fiscal year 2000, the CMS processed $11.9 billion in claims that were incorrectly coded, not backed by documents or fraudulent. However, that is the lowest figure since the measurements began in 1996 and represents a 6.8% error rate. The total for 2000 is down $1.6 billion from fiscal year 1999, which was $13.5 billion. It was also down from 1998 with an error rate of $12.6 billion, 1997 with an error rate of $20.3 billion and 1996 with an error rate of $23.2 billion. In arriving at these calculations, the OIG looked at 5,234 Medicare claims from 610 beneficiaries and projected its findings nationally. The OIG attributed the waste primarily to physicians, skilled nursing and durable medical equipment manufacturers. Further, bad charges associated with inpatient hospitals were also significant. Finally, the OIG estimated that in fiscal year 2001, medically unnecessary services cost Medicare $5.23 billion; incomplete or missing documentation cost the program $5.19 billion; and coding errors cost at $2.06 billion; totalling $12.1 billion in errors (Fig. 3). The OIG also alluded to CPT codes 99232 and 99233 (subsequent hospital care); as well as 99214 (office or other outpatient visit for an established patient) as the most problematic areas. However, the most smallest error category was billing for noncovered services, accounting for $800 million; which included prescription drugs, examinations to prescribe eyeglasses, and chiropractic services.

In 1997, the OIG estimated that 50% of the rehab payments were improper. In a March 21, 2000, audit report, the OIG found that more than half the outpatient rehabilitation payments CMS made in the year ending June 30, 1998, were not necessary, badly documented or not provided by licensed professionals. In response, the OIG and CMS are "turning up the heat" on outpatient rehabilitation facilities by various means. To arrive at this decision, the OIG reviewed 200 paid claims from outpatient rehabilitation facilities in Florida, Louisiana, Michigan, New Jersey, Pennsylvania, and Texas. Of the 200 claims, 108, or 54%, contained unallowable or highly questionable services. Extrapolating the 54% error rate, the agency estimated that outpatient rehabilitation facilities in these six states improperly billed Medicare $173 million during the review and Medicare overpaid outpatient rehabilitation facilities in these six states by $277 million in calendar year 1997 out of a total national expenditure of $572 million. The OIG identified three main reasons for the unnecessary payments:

- Records did not indicate patients' functional impairment;
- There was no evidence of a therapist actively participating in care of the patient; and
- Rehabilitation therapy was continued even after the patient had reached a plateau and no further progress was seen or expected.

Finally, one silver lining is that the CMS says not to worry about fee waivers. Physicians are concerned that unusual charitable practices could be considered illegal and would result in fraud police visiting their offices for waiving the copayments for poor patients. It appears that the OIG has changed its heart on this issue. The OIG, at least for now, does not plan any type of organized investigation into copay waiver practices. Providers are also permitted under Medicare Part B to waive copayments once they have made a good-faith effort to determine the financial condition of the beneficiary. The OIG has always been concerned about the routine waiver of copayments, which could be associated with serious violations of reimbursement rules. It is best to use an objective standard, preferably one set by one entity, to develop a workable definition of financial hardship to justify waiving a copay. Theoretically, one could use the Medicaid eligibility standards, food-stamp program standards, or federal poverty guidelines. However, financial hardship becomes extremely difficult to decide in temporary situations involving personal circumstances with a loss of job, divorce, or unfortunate catastrophic illness. In addition, waiving medical fees for services provided to other physicians, family, employees, and friends, is considered as courteous and has been a common practice among most practices. With evolving emphasis on fraud, or even the appearance of fraud, the appearance of inappropriateness has discouraged all such professional courtesies. The physicians should take into consideration that this practice is not automatically considered illegal as long as the decision is not based directly or indirectly on that person's ability to refer patients covered by federal healthcare programs to the practice, and it is not a consistent practice of waiving the entire fee for services to a group of people, including employees, physicians, or their family members. Thus, the important facts are that the recipient of the benefit should be in a position to directly or indirectly affect past or future referrals, and the act should not create a financial relationship that violates the self-referral restrictions. Finally, waiving the copayments for federal healthcare program patients who are not financially needy can put interventional pain practitioners in potential violation of the False Claims Act, because the government views the routine waiver of deductibles or copayments as a misrepresentation of the actual charge, which can be construed as a false claim.

REFERENCES

1. *Health Care Fraud and Abuse. A Physician's Guide to Compliance,* AMA Press, Chicago, 2001.
2. Statement for the record to the house budget committee healthcare task force: Medicare program: *Reducing improper payments and Fraud,* Office of Inspector General, Department of Health and Human Services:July, 2000.
3. Health care fraud and abuse. In *Health Care Fraud and Abuse. A*

Physician's Guide to Compliance, AMA Press, Chicago, 2001, pp 1-26.
4. Orient JM. Can "Health care fraud" be ended? Medical Sentinel, July/ Aug 1998, pp. 124-130.
5. HCFA Program Memorandum AB-00-72.
6. Fraud and abuse statutes. In *Health Care Fraud and Abuse. A Physician's Guide to Compliance*, AMA Press, Chicago, 2001 pp 49-78.
7. Entities involved in fraud and abuse investigations. In *Health Care Fraud and Abuse.* A Physician's Guide to Compliance, AMA Press, Chicago, 2001 pp 121-130.

DIAGNOSTIC CODING SYSTEMS

Laxmaiah Manchikanti, MD
Vijay Singh, MD
Bert Fellows, MA

If you want to get paid for what you do, you have to speak the language and establish medical necessity. Medical necessity of any physician or provider encounter requires appropriate diagnosis and coding by ICD-9-CM to justify services rendered and indicates the severity of the patient's condition (1-3). From January 1, 1998, the Balanced Budget Act (HR.20515, Section 4317) requires all physicians to provide diagnostic information for all Medicare/Medicaid patients (2, 3). Failure to comply with this regulation can result in disastrous consequences, including prosecution. Thus, physicians or providers should code by listing ICD-9-CM diagnostic codes shown in the medical record to be chiefly responsible for the services provided. Coding should be to the highest degree of certainty for each encounter. Coding also should correlate with multiple components of the patient's medical record, including initial evaluation or follow-up visits, and the billing statement. Thus, practices use multiple coding systems to communicate the procedures and services provided to patients. While CPT-4 is the most commonly used physician and provider encounter coding system, ICD-9-CM is the most common diagnostic coding system in the United States and across the world. Similar to CPT, ICD-9 is unique and serves a specific purpose in communicating to third-party payors what the physician did and why the physician did it.

International Classification of Diseases, Ninth Revision, Clinical Modification (ICD-9-CM) is a coding system used to report patient illnesses, injuries, complaints, and/or symptoms, referred to as diagnoses. ICD-9-CM communicates to third-party payors the need for medical services, or why the physician performed the service. ICD-9-CM system consists of code numbers and narrative descriptions similar to CPT-4, even though two systems are distinctly separate and different.

In addition to the ICD-9-CM diagnostic coding systems, other diagnostic coding systems are also available. *Diagnostic and Statistical Manual of Mental Disorders*, Fourth Edition (DSM-IV) for psychiatric and mental health services is one such system. In addition, CDT-3 is also available for dental services. In 1976, the College of American Pathologists also published a diagnostic coding classification titled "SNOMED." The International Association for the study of pain also has published a diagnostic classification of pain disorders, which is entirely different from ICD-9-CM and DSM-IV (1, 4, 5).

The fourth edition of the American Psychiatric Associations *Diagnostic and Statistical Manual of Mental Disorders*, or DSM-IV (4) provides clear descriptions of diagnostic categories in order to enable clinicians and investigators to diagnose, communicate about, study, and treat people with various mental disorders. This manual offers the specified diagnostic criteria for each mental disorder as guidelines for making diagnoses, because it has been demonstrated that the use of such criteria enhances agreement among clinicians and investigators. However, the DSM-IV cautions that the proper use of these criteria requires specialized clinical training that provides both a body of knowledge and clinical skills. In addition to DSM-IV, *DSM-IV Source Book*, published in five volumes, is intended to provide a comprehensive and convenient reference record of the clinical and research support for the various decisions reached by the work groups and the task force. The first three volumes of the *Source Book* contained condensed versions of the 150 DMS-IV literature reviews. The fourth volume contains reports of the data analysis, and the fifth volume contains reports of the field trials and a final executive summary of the rationale for the decisions made by each working group (4).

HISTORY

Interestingly, ICD coding system was developed as a statistics gathering tool, rather than diagnostic-reporting system. In 1948 World Health Organization started statistics on morbidity and mortality.

In 1950, the U.S. Public Health Service and the Veterans Administration began independent tests of the *International Classification of Diseases* for hospital indexing purposes (1). The following year, the Columbia Presbyterian Medical Center in New York City adapted the *International Classification of Diseases*, Sixth Revision, with some modifications for use in its medical record department. A few years later, the Commission on Professional and Hospital Activities (CPHA) in Ann Arbor, Michigan, adapted the *International Classification of Diseases* with similar modifications for use in hospitals participating in the professionals activities studied.

In view of the growing interest in the use of *International Classification of Diseases* for hospital indexing, a study was undertaken in 1956 by the American Hospital Association and the American Medical Record Association of the relative efficiencies of coding systems for diagnosis in diagnostic indexing. This study indicated that *International Classification of Diseases* provided a suitable and efficient framework for indexing hospital records (1). The major users of *International Classification of Diseases* for hospital indexing purposes then consolidated their experiences, and an adaption was first published in December 1959. A revision was issued in 1962 and the first "Classification of Operations and Treatments" was included.

Subsequently in 1966, the international conference for revising the *International Classification of Diseases* noted the eight revision of ICD had been constructed with hospital indexing in mind and considered the revised classification suitable, in itself, for hospital use in some countries. At the same time, it was also recognized that the basic classification might provide inadequate detail for the diagnostic indexing in other countries. Consequently, a group of consultants was asked to study the eighth revision of ICD for applicability to various users in the United States. This group recommended that further detail be provided for coding of hospital and morbidity data. Thus, the American Hospital Association was requested to develop the needed adaptation proposals. An advisory committee was appointed. In 1968, the United States Public Health Service published a product, Eight Revision *International Classification of Diseases*, adapted for use in the United States. This became commonly known as ICDA-8, and beginning in 1968 it served as the basis for coding diagnostic data for both official morbidity and mortality statistics in the United States. In 1973, a revision of H-ICDA, referred to as H-ICDA-2 was published.

In February 1977, a steering committee was convened by the National Center for Health Statistics to provide advice and counsel in developing a clinical modification of ICD-9. The organizations represented on the steering committee included the American Association of Health Data Systems, American Hospital Association, American Medical Record Association, Association for Health Records, the Counsel and Clinical Classifications, Healthcare Financing Administration, and World Health Organization. This counsel was sponsored by the American Academy of Pediatrics, American College of Obstetricians and Gynecologists, American College of Physicians, American College of Surgeons, American Psychiatric Association, and Commission on Professional and Hospital Activities. The steering committee met periodically in 1977. Clinical guidance and technical input were provided by task forces on classification from the counsel on clinical classifications sponsoring organizations. Thus, ICD-9-CM became a clinical modification of the World Health Organizations ICD-9 to be used in the United States. The term "clinical" is used to emphasize the modifications intent: To serve as useful tool to classify morbidity data for indexing medical records, medical care review, and ambulatory and other medical care programs, as well as for basic health statistics (1). To describe the clinical picture of the patient, the code must be more precise than those needed only for statistical groupings and trend analysis.

Finally, in January 1979, ICD-9-CM was made the single classification intended primarily for use in the United States, replacing various earlier related, but somewhat dissimilar, classifications.

Thus, physicians have been required by law to submit diagnosis codes for Medicare reimbursement since the passage of the Medicare Catastrophic Coverage Act of 1988. This act requires physician offices to include the appropriate diagnosis codes when billing for services provided to Medicare beneficiaries on or after April 1, 1989. The Centers for Medicare and Medicaid Services (CMS), formerly known as Healthcare Financing Administration (HCFA) designated ICD-9-CM as the coding system physicians must use.

In 1993, the World Health Organization published the newest version of the *International Classification of Diseases*, Tenth Revision, ICD-10. This version contains the greatest number of changes in the history of ICD. There are more codes exceeding ICD-9 by approximately 5,500 to allow more specific reporting of diseases and newly recognized conditions. ICD-9 is currently used in some European countries with implementation expected after some time in the new millennium in the United States.

The historical background of development of the *Diagnostic and Statistical Manual of Mental Disorders* is also interesting. The need for a classification of mental disorders has been clear throughout the history of medicine, but there has been little agreement on which disorders should be included and the optimal method for their organization (4). The many nomenclatures that have been developed during the past two millennia have differed in their relative emphasis on phenomenonology, etiology, and course as defining features. Some systems have included only a handful of diagnostic categories; others have included thousands. Moreover, the various systems for categorizing mental disorders have differed with respect to whether their principle objective was for use in clinical research, or statistical settings.

In the United States, the initial impetus for developing a classification of mental disorders was the need to collect statistical information (4). The first official attempt to gather information about mental illness in the United States was the recording of the frequency of "–idiocy/insanity" in the 1840 census. By the 1880 census, seven categories of mental illness were distinguished which included mania, melancholia, monomania, paresis, dementia, dipsomania, and epilepsy. In 1917, the Committee on Statistics of the American Medico-Psychological Association, together with the National Commission on Mental Hygiene, formulated a plan that was adapted by the bureau of the census for gathering uniform statistics across mental hospitals. In 1921, the name of the American Medico-Psychological Association was changed to the American Psychiatric Association. The American Psychiatric Association subsequently collaborated with the New York Academy of Medicine to develop a nationally acceptable psychiatric nomenclature that would be incorporated within the first edition of the American Medical Association's Standard Classified Nomenclature of Disease. This nomenclature was designed primarily for diagnosing inpatients with severe psychiatric and neurological disorders. Later on, the U.S. Army developed a much broader nomenclature to better incorporate the outpatient presentations of World War II servicemen and veterans, which included not only personality disorders, but also psychophysiological and acute disorders. Around the same time, the World Health Organization (WHO) published the sixth edition of ICD, which, for the first time, included a section for mental disorders. ICD-6 was heavily influenced by Veterans Administration nomenclature and included 10 categories for psychoses, 9 for psychoneuroses, and 7 for disorders of character, behavior, and intelligence. In 1952, the American Psychiatric Association Committee on Nomenclature and Statistics developed a variant of the ICD-9 which was published at the first edition of the *Diagnostic and Statistical Manual: Mental Disorders* (DSM-I). WHO sponsored a comprehensive review of diagnostic issues that was conducted by the British psychiatrist, Stengel, because of the lack of widespread acceptance of the mental disorder, taxonomy contained in ICD-6 and ICD-7 (4). Subsequently, DSM-II and ICD-9 were published which were similar to DSM-I and ICD-7. Publication of DSM-III in 1974 and ICD-9 in 1977 introduced a number of important methodological innovations, including explicit diagnostic criteria, a multi-axial system, and a descriptive approach that attempted to be neutral with respect to theories of etiology. Subsequently, extensive revision process was undertaken with literature reviews, data re-analysis, field trials, and DSM-IV was published along with five volumes of extensive DSM-IV source books.

CHARACTERISTICS OF ICD-9-CM

ICD-9-CM contains classification of numerous health-related conditions and provides specificity at the fifth-digit level of detail. Thus, the fifth digits are not optional; they are intended for use in recording the information substantiated in the clinical record. Thus, the physician should code to the highest level of the specificity. All ICD-9-CM codes are numeric except for E and V codes. E codes are used to report environmental events as the cause of an injury, poisoning, or other adverse effect and are used in addition to other ICD-9-CM codes. V codes are used for: healthcare encounters when the person is not sick; person with a known disease obtaining a treatment for that disease; and circumstances that influence a person's health status but is not in itself a current injury or illness.

ICD-9-CM also contains five appendixes labeled from appendix A to appendix E listing morphology of neoplasms, glossary of mental disorders, classification of drugs, classification of industrial accidents according to agency, and list of three-digit categories. These appendixes are included as a reference to provide further information about the patient's clinical picture, to further define a diagnostic statement, to aid in classifying new drugs or to reference three-digit categories (1). In addition, alphabetic index of ICD-9-CM also contains many diagnostic terms that do not appear in tabular lists or volume I since the index includes most diagnostic terms currently in use.

CHARACTERISTICS OF DSM-IV

DSM-IV is acategorical classification that divides mental disorders into types based on criteria sets with the defining features. In DSM-IV, there is no assumption that each category of mental disorder is a completely discrete entity with absolute boundaries dividing it from other mental disorders or from no mental disorder. In addition, DSM-IV does not assume that all individuals described as having the same mental disorder are alike in all important ways. Thus, a clinician using DSM-IV should therefore consider that individuals sharing a diagnosis are likely to be heterogeneous even in regard to the defining features of diagnosis and that boundary cases will be difficult to diagnose in any probabilistic fashion (4). Thus, this type of outlook allows greater flexibility in the use of the system, encourages more specific attention to boundary cases, and emphasizes the need to capture additional clinical information that goes beyond diagnosis.

The manual states that it is important that DSM-IV not be applied mechanically by untrained individuals. The specific diagnostic criteria included in DSM-IV are meant to serve as guidelines to be informed by clinical judgment and are not meant to be used in a cookbook fashion.

The terms *mental disorder* and *general medical condition* are used throughout DSM-IV. The term *mental disorder* implies, rather unfortunately, a distinction between "mental" disorders and "physical" disorders that is a reductionistic anachronism of mind-body dualism. The concept of mental disorder, like many other concepts in medicine and science, lacks a consistent operational definition that covers all situations. Thus, each mental disorder is conceptualized as a clinically significant behavioral or psychological syndrome or pattern that occurs in an individual and that is associated with present distress or disability or with a significantly increased risk of suffering death, pain, disability, or an important loss of freedom. In contrast, the term *general medical condition* is used merely as a convenient shorthand to refer to conditions and disorders that are listed outside the mental and behavioral disorders chapters of ICD.

The manual begins with instructions concerning the use of the manual, followed by the DSM-IV classification, which provides a systematic listing of the official codes and categories. This is followed by a description of DSM-IV multi-axial system for diagnosis, followed by the diagnostic criteria for each of the DSM-IV disorders accompanied by descriptive text (4). In addition, DSM-IV also includes 10 appendixes.

INTERRELATIONSHIP OF ICD AND DSM

Preparation of ICD-9 and DSM-IV was coordinated with mutual efforts. ICD-9 consists of an official coding system and other related clinical and research documents and instruments, which was published in 1992, however, it is not expected to come into use in the United States until 2002, 2003 or even 2004. The codes and terms provided in DSM-IV are fully compatible not only with ICD-10, but also with ICD-9-CM.

PRACTICAL USE OF ICD-9-CM

To code accurately, it is necessary to have a working knowledge of medical terminology and to understand the characteristics, terminology, and conventions of ICD-9-CM (1). Transforming description of disease, injuries, conditions and procedures into numerical designations is a complex activity, and should not be undertaken without proper training. Following are the ten steps described in St. Anthony's ICD-9-CM code book for physician compliance and shown in table .

Table 1. *Ten steps to correct coding*

Step 1: Identify the reason for the visit
Step 2: Consult the alphabetic index before the tabular list
Step 3: Locate the main entry term
Step 4: Read and interpret any notes listed with the main term
Step 5: Review entries for modifiers
Step 6: Interpret abbreviations, cross-references, and brackets
Step 7: Choose a tentative code and locate it in the tabular list
Step 8: Determine whether the code is at the highest level of specificity
Step 9: Consult St. Anthony's color coding and reimbursement prompts
Step 10: Assign the code

Step 1

Identify the reason for the visit. In medical practices, providers describe the patient's condition using terminology that includes specific diagnosis, as well as symptoms, problems or reasons for the encounter or intervention. Thus, the reason for the visit could be a sign, symptom, diagnosis, or a condition. If symptoms are present but a definitive diagnosis has not yet been determined, a provider can code the symptoms. However, do not code conditions that are referred to as "rule out," "suspected," "probable," or "questionable."

Step 2

Consult the alphabetic index before the tabular list. As described earlier, ICD-9-CM consists of volume I, the tabular list, and volume II, alphabetic index. Volume II, or alphabetic index, contains many diagnostic terms that do not appear in volume I or tabular list since the index includes most diagnostic terms currently in use. Thus, always consult the alphabetic index, volume II, before turning to the tabular list (volume 1). This is considered as the most critical rule in coding. Turning first to the tabular list (volume I), may lead to coding errors and reduced specificity in assigning a code. Thus, to prevent coding errors in diagnosis, use both the alphabetic index and the tabular list when locating and assigning a code (1).

Step 3

Locate the main entry term. The alphabetic index is arranged by condition. Conditions may be expressed as nouns, adjectives, and eponyms (1). Some conditions have multiple entries under their synonyms. Main terms are identified using bold face type.

Step 4

Read and interpret any notes listed with the main term. Notes are always identified using italicized type.

Step 5

Review entries for modifiers. Certain non-essential modifiers are described in parenthesis. These parenthetical terms are supplementary words or explanatory information that may either be present or absent in the diagnostic statement.

Step 6

Interpret abbreviations, cross-references, and brackets.

NEC, also known as not elsewhere classified, indicates that there is no specific code for the condition even though the medical documentation may be very specific.

The $\sqrt{5^{th}}$ box indicates the code requires a fifth digit, however, if the appropriate fifth digits are not found in the index, in a box beneath the main term, you must refer to the tabular list.

Italicized brackets [ ] are used to enclose a second code number that must be used with the code immediately preceding it and in that sequence.

Cross-references used are "see," "see category", or "see also."

Step 7

Choose a tentative code and locate it in the tabular list. As described in Step 2, after consulting the alphabetic index, go to the tabular list. Always be guided by an inclusion or exclusion terms, notes or other instructions, such as "code first" and "use additional code" that would direct the use of a different or additional code from that selected in the index for a particular diagnosis, condition, or disease.

Step 8

Determine whether the code is at the highest level of specificity. A provider is always expected to code at the highest level of specificity, hence, assign five-digit codes for all the categories where they are available. However, if five-digit codes are not available, assign either three-digit codes, also known as category codes, or four-digit, or subcategory codes.

Step 9

Consult St. Anthony's color coding and reimbursement prompts.

Step 10

Assign the code.

PRACTICAL USE OF DSM-IV

The official coding system in use in the United States at the present time is ICD-9-CM. Most DSM-IV disorders have a numerical ICD-9-CM code that appears several times:

1. Preceding the name of the disorder in the classification,
2. At the beginning of the text section for each disorder, and
3. Accompanying the criteria set for each disorder.

Subtypes (some of which are coded in fifth digit) and specifiers are provided for increased specificity. *Subtypes* define mutually exclusive and jointly exhaustive phenomenological subgroupings within a diagnosis and are indicated by the instruction "specify type" in the criteria set (4). *Specifiers* are not intended to be mutually exclusive or jointly exhaustive and are indicated by the instruction "specify" or "specify if" in the criteria set.

The DSM-IV disorders are grouped into 16 major diagnostic classes and one additional section, other conditions that may be a focus of clinical attention. These are as follows (4):

- Disorders Usually First Diagnosed in Infancy, Childhood, or Adolescence
- Delirium, Dementia, and Amnestic and Other Cognitive Disorders
- Mental Disorders Due to a General Medical Condition
- Substance-Related Disorders
- Schizophrenia and Other Psychotic Disorders
- Mood Disorders
- Anxiety Disorders
- Somatoform Disorders
- Factitious Disorders
- Dissociative Disorders
- Sexual and Gender Identity Disorders
- Eating Disorders
- Sleep Disorders
- Impulse-Control Disorders Not Elsewhere Classified
- Adjustment Disorders
- Personality Disorders
- Other Conditions That May Be a Focus of Clinical Attention

DSM-IV also includes 10 appendixes as follows (4):

- *Appendix A* Decision Trees for Differential Diagnosis
- *Appendix B* Criteria Sets and Axes Provided for Furt her Study
- *Appendix C* Glossary of Technical Terms
- *Appendix D* Annotated Listing of Changes in DMS-IV
- *Appendix E* Alphabetical Listing of DSM-IV Diagnoses and Codes
- *Appendix F* Numerical Listing of DSM-IV Diagnoses and Codes
- *Appendix G* ICD-9-CM Codes for Selected General Medical Conditions and Medication-In duced Disorders
- *Appendix H* DSM-IV Classification With ICD-10 Codes
- *Appendix I* Outline for Cultural Formulation and Glos sary of Culture-Bound Syndromes
- *Appendix J* DSM-IV Contributors

REFERENCES

1. *International Classification of Diseases, Ninth Revision, Clinical Modification*, ICD-9-CM. St. Anthony Publishing, Reston, 1998.
2. Manchikanti L. The role of evaluation and management services in pain management. *Pain Physician* 1999; 2:10-32.
3. Manchikanti L. Evaluation and management services in interventional pain practice: Doing it right? *Pain Physician* 2000; 3:322-341.
4. American Psychiatric Association. *Diagnostic and Statistical Manual for Mental Disorders.* Fourth Edition (DSM-IV). American Psychiatric Press, Washington, DC, 1994.
5. *Classification of Chronic Pain.* Merskey H, Bogduk N (eds). International Association for the Study of Pain, Second Edition. IASP Press, Seattle, 1994.

PROCEDURAL CODING SYSTEMS

Laxmaiah Manchikanti, MD
Bert Fellows, MA

Physicians in the United States provide various types of services to their patients, which not only include evaluation and management services, but also include multiple procedures, psychological, radiological, physical medicine and rehabilitation services, and supplies. Almost all practices in the United States use coding systems to communicate the procedures and services provided to patients and the reasons they were provided. Thus, the majority of the practices in the United States require to understand procedural coding systems for not only proper reimbursement, and for appropriate record keeping, but also to avoid fraud and abuse implications. In addition, procedural coding in the United States has become not only an extremely important facet of medical practice, but has become a rapidly changing dynamic field secondary to development of new technology with advances in medicine, resulting in development of new codes, as well as changing dynamics of the population. Further, advent of Medicare resource-based relative value scale replacing the long existing usual, reasonable and customary charge; impact of fraud and abuse regulations on medical practices; and finally, economic impact of improper coding and the positive results of accurate documentation and coding have made it mandatory for providers to understand procedural coding systems, along with diagnostic coding systems. Procedural coding systems consist of Current Procedural Terminology® (CPT), International Classification of Diseases® (ICD-9) and HCPCS.

Current Procedural Terminology® (CPT), developed and updated by the American Medical Association (AMA), is the most commonly used coding system not only in the United States, but also in other countries. CPT is a tabular listing of "most known encounters" with patients. These encounters vary in location, as well as intensity, and include both "cognitive" and "procedural" services. Thus, CPT provides a uniform nomenclature and a logical sequence of codes for describing all medical encounters, specifically interventional pain medicine encounters not only in an accurate and comprehensive manner, but also functions as a short hand for understanding the service. Beginning in 2002, CPT also has adapted a three level coding system. The second popular coding systems is HCFA's (now known as CMS) common procedure coding system known as HCPCS. HCPCS is a three-level coding system with level I coding incorporating the CPT codes, level II incorporating the system of national alphanumeric codes that begin with a letter followed by four numbers generally used to report supplies and injections to Medicare and other payors, and level III incorporating five-digit alphanumeric codes applicable only specific localities or states used by local Medicare carriers for very unusual procedures for which there is no other level I or level II code available.

In addition to the CPT coding systems, HCPCS, other attempts also have been made at procedural coding and medical nomenclature. In 1974, the California Medical Society published its relative value schedule for procedural coding, which used five-digit coding with modifiers and other refinements. In addition, state by state Workers Compensation carriers also have utilized their own system of coding, however, mostly derived either from CPT coding system or HCPCS system, the differences being that these systems lag much behind the updated CPT or HCPCS coding systems as compensation systems in each state update them only once in several years during which time CPT would have published several editions.

Some insurers and government agencies use ICD-9 system. ICD9 system is mainly meant as diagnostic coding system. In contrast, CPT and HCPCS are procedural coding systems.

HISTORY

Until 1966, American Medical Association published current medical information and terminology, which was followed by the providers, as well as the insurers. In 1966, the AMA published its first edition of the Current Procedural Terminology as a companion volume to current medical information and terminology. Subsequently, AMA updated this manual with a second edition in 1970 and a third edition in 1973. The fourth edition, CPT-4, was first printed in 1977. Since then it has been updated periodically.

In 1983, the AMA and U.S. Department of Health and Human Services signed a contract making CPT-4 the standard coding system describing physician services for Medicare and Medicaid. At the same time, AMA established the CPT Editorial Panel. Initially, quarterly updates were provided. But, soon it was recognized that quarterly updating was not only inefficient, but also ineffective, as these updates were too frequent to follow through and it was creating too much confusion as to which update was being used. Thus, it was agreed upon that updates will be changed to a yearly basis and finalized each year in August.

AMA published its first series of mini books, in 1988. These were short versions of the CPT manual, containing excerpts from selected quotes frequently used in particular specialty or subspecialty. The mini books include and incorporate information, individually for Dermatology, Plastic & Reconstructive Surgery; General Surgery; Gynecology, Obstetrics & Urology; Head, Neck, Oral & Maxillofacial Surgery; Ophthalmology & Otorhinolaryngology; Medical Specialties; Radiology; Neurological & Orthopedic Surgery; and Pathology and Laboratory Medicine. In addition, various societies also have developed their own guides which are sort of mini books, including the relative value guides published each year by various societies, including the American Society of Anesthesiologists. Unfortunately, no such assistance is available for interventional pain physicians, except for partial and fragmented information provided by orthopedics and neurosurgery minibook, ASA relative value guide, and coding book published by the North American Spine Society.

As part of "administrative simplification" of the Health Insurance Portability and Accessibility Act of 1996 (HIPAA), legislation signed into law on August 12, 1996, by President Clinton, AMA has launched development of CPT-5.

NOMENCLATURE

CPT nomenclature is a listing of descriptive terms, guidelines and identifying codes for reporting medical services and procedures. The purpose of nomenclature is to provide a uniform language that accurately describes medical, surgical and diagnostic services – serving as an effective means for reliable nationwide communication among physicians, patients and third parties.

Inclusion of Category I CPT code descriptor and its associated specific five-digit identifying code number in CPT coding is generally based on the procedure being consistent with contemporary medical practice and performed by many physicians in clinical practice in multiple locations. Inclusion of a procedure/service in CPT coding does not represent endorsement by the American Medical Association (AMA) of any particular diagnostic or therapeutic procedure, nor does it imply any health insurance coverage or reimbursement policy.

The AMA first developed and published the CPT nomenclature in 1966. The first edition helped encourage the use of standard terms and descriptors to document procedures in the medical record; helped communicate accurate information on procedures and services to agencies concerned with insurance claims; provided the basis for a computer-oriented system to evaluate operative procedures; and contributed basic information for actuarial and statistical purposes.

The first edition of Current Procedural Terminology® published in 1966 contained primarily surgical procedures, with limited sections on medicine, radiology, and laboratory procedures. When first published, CPT coding used a four-digit system. The second edition, published in 1970, presented an expanded system of terms and codes to designate diagnostic and therapeutic procedures in surgery, medicine and the specialties. It was at that time that the five-digit codes were introduced, replacing the former four-digit system. Another significant change to the book was to list procedures related to internal medicine.

In the mid to late 1970s, the third and fourth editions of CPT nomenclature were introduced. The fourth edition, published in 1977, represented significant updates in medical technology, and a system of periodic updating was introduced to keep pace with the rapidly changing medical environment.

In 1983, CPT nomenclature was adapted as part of the Centers for Medicare and Medicaid Services (CMS), formerly Health Care Financing Administration (HCFA), Healthcare Common Procedure Coding System (HCPCS). With this adaption, the CMS mandated the use of HCPCS to report services for Part B of the -Medicare program. In October 1986, CMS also required state Medicaid agencies to use HCPCS in the Medicaid Management Information System. In July 1987, as part of the Omnibus Budget Reconciliation Act, CMS mandated the use of CPT codes for reporting outpatient hospital surgical procedures.

Today, in addition to use in federal programs (Medicare and Medicaid), the CPT nomenclature is used extensively throughout the United States as the preferred system of coding to describe health care services. In August 2000, the CPT code was named as a national standard under the Health Insurance Portability and Accessibility Act of 1996 (HIPAA).

Level I -CPT Nomenclature

Level I, is the American Medical Association's CPT nomenclature. CPT nomenclature makes up the majority of the HCPCS coding system. Most of the procedures and services performed by physicians and other health care professionals, even with respect to Medicare patients, are reported with CPT codes.

Highlights of the CPT nomenclature are as follows:

- Each procedure or service is identified with a five-digit numeric code or a five-character alpha-numeric code
- Two-digit modifiers are used
- Codes are revised and updated on an annual basis
- Updates and revisions become effective in January
- Revisions, additions, and deletions are prepared by the AMA's CPT Editorial Panel

Level II - National Codes

Level II, are the national codes are assigned, updated, and maintained by CMS. These codes describe services and supplies not found in the CPT code set. Some examples of the procedures and services described by Level II national codes include durable medical equipment, ambulance services, medical/surgical supplies, drugs, orthotics and prosthetics, dental procedures, and vision services.

Highlights of the Level II national codes are as follows:

- Five-character alphanumeric codes are used – first character is a letter (A through V, except I and S), followed by four numeric digits.
- Alpha (eg, -LT) and alphanumeric (eg, -E1) modifiers are used
- The codes are updated annually by CMS
- They are required for reporting most medical services and supplies provided to Medicare and Medicaid patients

The "I" codes are reserved for use by the Health Insurance Association of America to fulfill their member companies' unique coding needs. The "S" codes are created and maintained by the Blue Cross and Blue Shield Association for their needs.

Level III - Local Codes

These codes are assigned by local Medicare carriers to describe procedures and services not identified in the other two levels of HCPCS codes. These codes are also five-character alphanumeric codes beginning with a single letter W through Z. Updates and revisions to these codes may occur at any time.

Highlights of the Level III local codes include the following:

- Five-character alphanumeric codes are used – first character is a letter (W through Z) followed by four numeric digits
- Codes are assigned by local Medicare carriers
- They are not consistent from state to state
- Updates and revisions are available from local Medicare carrier

This nomenclature should not be confused with introduction of 3 categories of codes (code categories) effective January 2002.

CPT nomenclature has expanded to include 3 categories of codes, namely category I, II and III.

Category I CPT Codes

Inclusion of a code in Category I, is generally based on the procedure being consistent with contemporary medical practice and being performed by many physicians in clinical practice in multiple locations. CPT codes in Category I, describe a procedure or service identified with a five-digit CPT code, which also includes a descriptor nomenclature.

Category II CPT Codes

Category II codes are intended to facilitate data collection by coding certain services and/or test results that are agreed upon as contributing to positive health outcomes and quality patient care. These codes may be services that are typically included in an Evaluation and Management (E/M) service or other component part of a service and are not appropriate for regular Category I CPT codes. Thus, Category II codes are a set of optional tracking codes, developed principally for performance measurement.

Category II codes for performance measures were developed to standardize the collection of data for performance measurement, seeking improvement from current methods, which are based on antiquated techniques of chart reviews, site surveys, which are ineffective and costly. In this way, CPT Category II codes will ease the burden on physicians' offices to complete surveys and reduce the intrusion caused by chart review, by having administrative record to code performance improvement measures. In addition, CPT Category II codes will concentrate on measurements that are developed and tested by national organizations, such as the National Committee for Quality Assurance, and those that are well established and currently being used by large segments of the health care industry.

CPT Category II codes are assigned an alphanumeric identifier with the letter "F" in the last field (eg, 1234F), to distinguish them from Category I CPT codes, and are located in a separate section of the CPT book. *The use of these codes is optional and not required for correct coding.*

The Editorial Panel established a Performance Measures Advisory Group in February 2000. In October 2000, the AMA Board of Trustees appointed a total of six physicians from the Centers for Medicare and Medicaid Services, the Agency for Healthcare Research and quality, the AMA Physician Consortium for Performance Improvement, the Joint Commission on Accreditation of Healthcare Organizations, the National Committee on Quality Assurance.

Category III CPT Codes

CPT Category III (Emerging Technology) codes are a set of temporary codes for emerging technology, services and procedures. Category III CPT codes will allow data collection for these services/procedures. These codes are intended to be used for data collection purposes to substantiate widespread usage or in the FDA approval process.

An important part of the reasoning behind the development of Category III codes was the length and requirements of the CPT approval process, which conflicted with the needs of researchers for coded data to track emerging technology services throughout the research process. The CPT Editorial Panel at a minimum requires that:

- services/procedures be performed by many health care professionals across the country;
- FDA approval be documented or be imminent within a given CPT cycle; and
- the service/procedure has proven clinical efficacy.

As such, the Category III CPT codes may *not* conform to these usual CPT code requirements. For services/procedures to be eligible for Category III codes, the service/procedure must have relevance for research, either ongoing or planned. Another important consideration in the development of Category III codes is the elimination of local codes under HIPAA. The August 17, 2000 *Final Rule* supports the elimination of local codes and the transition to national standard code sets. Many of the local codes were temporary codes used by payers until services/procedures were more fully substantiated through research and received a CPT code. Thus, Category III codes can take the place of temporary, local codes used for this purpose.

Category III codes are assigned an alphanumeric identifier with the "T" letter in the last field (0027T). These codes are located in a separate section of the CPT book.

Category III CPT codes are not referred to the AMA/Specialty RVS Update Committee (RUC) for evaluation because no relative value units (RVUs) will be assigned. Payment for these services/procedures is based on the policies of payers and not on a yearly fee schedule.

These codes will be archived after 5 years if the code has not been accepted for placement in the Category I section of the CPT book, unless it is demonstrated that a Category III code is still needed. These archived codes will not be reused. Of particular interest to interventional pain physicians is development of a Category III code for spinal endoscopy (0027T) effective January 1, 2001.

HIERARCHY OF PANELS AND COMMITTEES

The Editorial Panel

The American Medical Association's CPT Editorial Panel is responsible for maintaining the CPT nomenclature. This panel is authorized to revise, update, or modify the CPT codes. The panel is made up of 16 members as follows:

- Eleven are nominated by the AMA Board of Trustees, with one of the seats designated for a physician to present managed care viewpoint.
- One member is a nonphysician, representing the Health Care Professionals Advisory Committee (HCPAC)
- One is nominated by the Centers for Medicare and Medicaid Services
- One is nominated by the Blue Cross and Blue Shield Association
- One is nominated by the Health Insurance Association of America
- One is nominated by the American Hospital Association

Five members of the Editorial Panel serve as the panel's Executive Committee. The Executive Committee includes the chairman, the vice chairman, and three panel members-at-large, as elected by the entire panel. One of the three members-at-large of the executive committee must be a third-party payer representative.

The Advisory Committee

There is a larger body of CPT advisors that supports the CPT Editorial Panel in its work, the CPT Advisory Committee members are primarily physicians nominated by the national medical specialty societies represented in the AMA House of Delegates. Currently, the Advisory Committee is limited to national medical specialty societies seated in the AMA House of Delegates and to the AMA Health Care Professionals Advisory Committee (HCPAC), organizations representing limited-license practitioners and other allied health professionals. Additionally, a group of individuals, the Performance Measures Advisory Committee (PMAC), who represent various organizations concerned with performance measures, also provide expertise.

The described primary objectives of the Advisory Committee are to serve as a resource to the CPT Editorial Panel by providing documentation and advice on procedure coding and appropriate nomenclature, revisions to the CPT nomenclature, assist in the review and further development of relevant coding issues, and promote the education.

Health Care Professionals Advisory Committee

Many codes contained in the current CPT nomenclature are used by not only physicians, but also their providers. Further, use of CPT codes by non-MD/DOs is required by legislation and regulation in some instances. Third-party payors also have additionally retained limiting policies that govern how non-physician providers report their services by means of CPT codes.

The American Medical Association Board of Trustees in 1992 concluded to establish a Health Care Professionals Advisory Committee (HCPAC) for the CPT Editorial Panel and the RVS Update Committee (RUC) to open up these processes to all the groups required to use CPT codes. The American Medical Association invited organizations representing physician assistants, nurses, occupational and physical therapists, optometrists, podiatrists, psychologists, social workers, audiologists, speech pathologists, chiropractors, and dietitians to nominate representatives to the HCPAC.

UPDATE PROCESS

CPT Update Process

The CPT coding system is updated on an ongoing basis, based on input from various member organizations. For interventional pain medicine specialists, it is obvious that there have been substantial changes in our specialty, specifically with CPT 2000 publication. Additional codes were created in 2001 and some new codes are expected in 2002, as well as 2003, with assis-

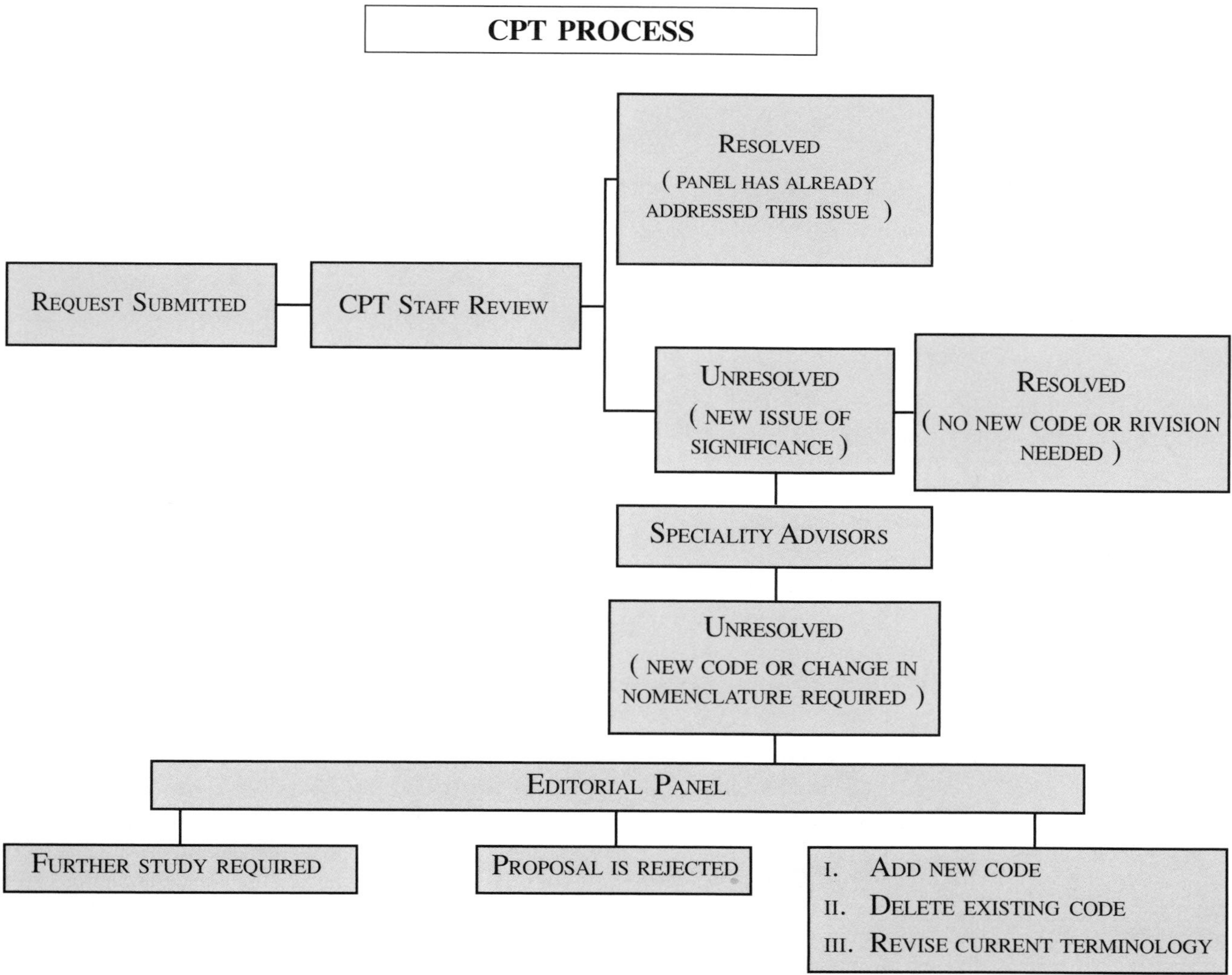

Fig 1. *Depiction of a multistep CPT decision process*

tance from multiple organizations, including the American Society of Anesthesiologists, the North American Spine Society, the American Academy of Physical Medicine and Rehabilitation, and the American Academy of Pain Medicine, and finally, the American Society of Interventional Pain Physicians. The American Society of Interventional Pain Physicians thus far is not a member of either AMA, any of the CPT committees, or RVS Update Committee (RUC).

In 2000, with the assistance of multiple organizations in an effort spearheaded by Samuel Hassenbusch, MD, multiple Interventional Procedure codes were revised with additions, deletions, and replacements. The American Society of Interventional Pain Physicians also has played a substantial role in revision and addition of various injection codes. The American Society of Interventional Pain Physicians is constantly monitoring the evolution of interventional pain medicine, and requirements for revisions and updates, as well as additions to interventional pain medicine coding.

The effectiveness of the CPT nomenclature depends on constant updating to reflect changes in medical practice. Suggestions of physicians, medical specialty societies, state medical associations, and those who deal regularly with health care information are the only way to ensure that CPT nomenclature reflects current practice.

The AMA welcomes correspondence, inquiries, and suggestions concerning old and new procedures. Specific procedures exist for addressing suggestions to revise CPT coding or modify existing nomenclature. Coding change request forms are available through the AMA and are required to initiate a review of a proposed coding change by the CPT Advisory Committee. These forms play a vital role in maintaining and increasing the efficiency of the CPT process. You may obtain this information from the CPT Web site at www.ama-assn.org/cpt.

The CPT Editorial Panel meets quarterly, addressing the complexities associated with new and emerging technologies, as well as effectively managing outdated procedures. CPT process is described in Fig. 1.

Resource Value Update Process

Medicare changed the way it pays for physicians' services. In 1992, Medicare established a standardized physician payment schedule based on a resource-based relative value scale (RBRVS). In the RBRVS system, payments for services are determined by the resource costs needed to provide them. The cost of providing each service is divided into three components: physician work, practice expense and professional liability insurance. Payments are calculated by multiplying the combined costs of a service by a conversion factor and payments are adjusted for geographic differences in resource costs (3).

On average, 55% of the total relative value for each service is the physician work component. The initial physician work relative values were based on the results of a Harvard University study. The factors used to determine physician work include the time it takes to perform the service; the technical skill and physical effort; the required mental effort and judgment; and stress due to the potential risk to the patient. The physician work relative values are updated each year to account for changes in medical practice. In addition, the legislation enacting the RBRVS requires the Centers for Medicare and Medicaid Services (CMS) to review the whole scale at least every five years (3).

The practice expense component of the RBRVS accounts for an average of 42% of the total relative value for each service. Up until recently, practice expense relative values were based on a formula using average Medicare approved charges from 1991 (the year before the RBRVS was implemented) and the proportion of each specialty's revenues that is attributable to practice expenses. However, in January 1999, CMS began a transition to resource-based practice expense relative values for each CPT code that differ based on the site of service. In 2002, the resource-based practice expenses will be fully transitioned.

On January 1, 2000, CMS implemented the resource-based professional liability insurance (PLI) relative value units. With this implementation and final transition of the resource-based practice expense relative units on January 2, 2002, all components of the RBRVS will be resource-based.

Annual updates to the physician work relative values are based on recommendations from a committee involving the American Medical Association (AMA) and national medical specialty societies. The AMA/Specialty RVS Update Committee (RUC) was formed in 1991 to make recommendations to CMS on the relative values to be assigned to new or revised codes in *Physicians' Current Procedural Terminology* (CPT). The relative value update process is described in Fig. 2.

Relative Value Update Committee

The RUC constitutes 29 members, twenty-three of its 29 members are appointed by major national medical specialty societies.

RUC consists of a representation from American Medical Association, CPT Editorial Panel, American Osteopathic Association, Health Care Professionals Advisory Committee and Practice Expense Advisory Committee. In addition, the societies appointing one member each include: Anesthesiology, Cardiology, Dermatology, Emergency Medicine, General Surgery, Geriatric Medicine, Internal Medicine, Neurology, Neurosurgery, Obstetrics/Gynecology, Ophthalmology, Orthopaedic Surgery, Otolaryngology, Pathology, Pediatrics, Plastic Surgery, Psychiatry, Radiation Oncology, Radiology, Rheumatology, Thoracic Surgery and Urology.

RUC Advisory Committee

The Advisory Committee consists of one physician representative from each of over 100 specialty societies seated in the AMA House of Delegates. However, specialty societies that are not in the House of Delegates also may be invited to participate in developing relative values for coding changes of particular relevance to their members. Specialties represented on both the RUC and the Advisory Committee are required to appoint different physicians to each committee to distinguish the role of advocate from that of evaluator.

Practice Expense Advisory Committee

Since there is not a single universally accepted cost allocation methodology, it is especially important that CMS base its methodology on actual practice expense data. The decisions reached by CMS have enormous implications for physicians and all their patients, not just those on Medicare (3). Since many other payment systems use the Medicare RBRVS, the change to resource-based practice expense relative values has broad implications for the entire health care system. Due to the significance of this issue, the RUC has established a special subcommittee called the Practice Expense Advisory Committee (PEAC) to monitor this process. The composition of the PEAC mirrors the RUC with addi-

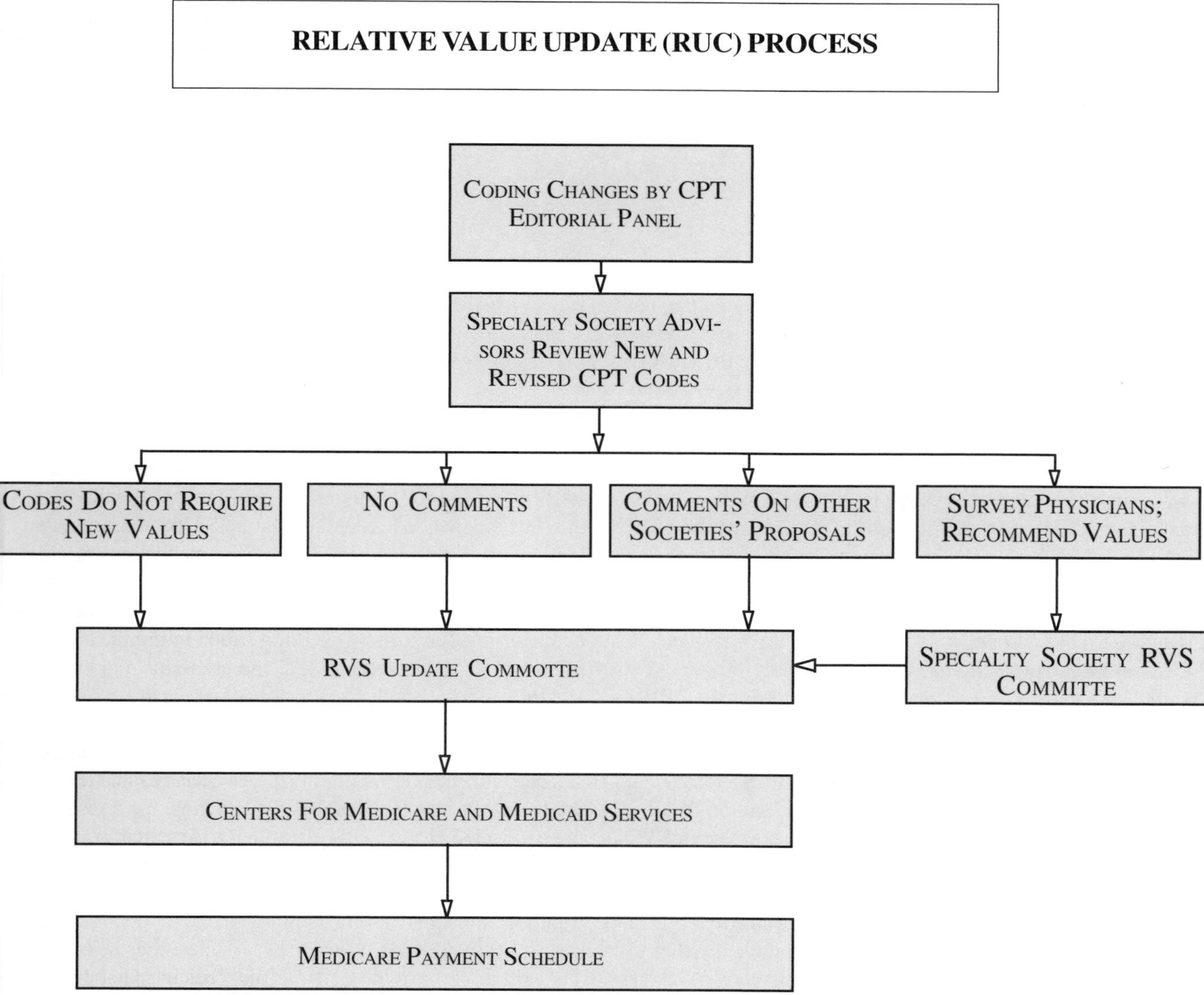

Fig 2. *Depiction of various steps in RUC process*
Adapted and modified from AMA/Speciality Society RVS Update Process(3)

tional representation added from nursing. The PEAC is charged to review direct expense inputs (clinical time, medical supplies, and equipment) used to calculate practice expense relative values, and makes code-specific recommendations to the RUC. The RUC then makes the final recommendation to CMS.

The RBRVS Five-Year Review

In addition to annual updates reflecting changes in CPT, Section 1848(C)2 (B) of the Omnibus Budget Reconciliation Act of 1990 requires CMS to comprehensively review all relative values at least every five years and make any needed adjustments. The changes resulting from the first Five-Year review of the RBRVS became effective January 2, 1997. Relative value changes from the second Five-Year Review of the RBRVS will be implemented on January 1, 2002. The success of the RUC's role in the annual updates led CMS to seek assistance from the RUC in both Five-Year review processes. Because a separate process was ongoing to develop and refine new resource-based practice expense relative values, the Five-Year reviews have been limited to the physician work relative values.

Non-Medicare Use of the RBRVS

It is important to understand the extent to which the RBRVS has been adapted outside of Medicare, the different payment policies used by payers, and the use of Medicare payment policies. While many payers may claim to use the RBRVS, adjustments to payment policies, large numbers of conversion factors, and other adjustments may result in a payment system that differs from Medicare's RBRVS system.

In a survey conducted by AMA in 2001 involving 226 payers, results showed that, 74% of the respondents currently use the RBRVS (4). Of this group using the RBRVS, 83% have adapted and fully implemented it, and 17% have decided to adapt the system and are in the process of implementation. Additionally, 7% of the survey respondents are examining the potential use of the Medicare RVRVS. This indicates that 81% of respondents are either using the RBRVS or considering its use. Alternatively, only 9% have considered, but decided not to adapt, and 10% have not considered it at all. Also of those using the RBRVS, 95% use all three components (work, practice expense, and professional liability insurance) while only 5% use either the work RVUs only or a combination of the work and PE RVUs.

Historically, the RBRVS has been used primarily by traditional fee-for-service insurers, but the data show that use of RBRVS is now widespread by various types of payers. Part of this can be due to the continued dominance of fee-for-service payment mechanisms, even by managed care companies (4). This survey showed adaption of RBRVS as follows:

Fee-for-service	44%
HMO	55%
PPO	54%
POS	47%

Thus, managed care organizations continue to use the RBRVS to a greater extent than traditional fee-for-service payers. This indicates that the RBRVS is applicable not only to fee-for-service insurers, but to a wide range of product lines. As long as a managed care plan continues to base some payments on a fee-for-service basis, it can effectively utilize the RBRVS to determine payments within a managed care framework. In addition, 79% of insurers use the RBRVS for at least 75% of the physicians. In fact, for 53% of the respondents who use the RBRVS, all of the physicians under contract are reimbursed with an RVBRS methodology (4). The AMA survey showed that with the exception of Medicaid, the conversion factor amounts were generally in excess of Medicare.

- Sixty percent of survey respondents had more than once conversion factor. The distribution of the number of conversion factors is as follows:
- For all payers, the average conversion factor was \$41.70, with a minimum of \$10.75 and a maximum of \$78.49. At the time of the survey, Medicare had a single conversion factor of \$38.26.

CURRENT PROCEDURAL TERMINOLOGY - 5

On August 12, 1996, President Clinton signed into law the HIPAA legislation. "Administrative Simplification," a part of this law is intended to reduce the costs and administrative burdens of health care this is achieved by the standardized, electronic transmission of certain administrative and financial transactions that are currently carried out manually on paper claim forms. The purpose of administrative simplification is to improve the Medicare and Medicaid programs, in particular, and the efficiency and effectiveness of the health care system in general. To accomplish this goal, the law requires the Secretary of Health and Human Services to adapt a national uniform standard for these transactions. It also requires that the standards that the standards be followed anytime the transactions are conducted electronically. Among the standards are code sets and classification systems. The code set criteria include cost-effective implementation and use low-cost efficient distribution, and applicability to all users.

The primary goal of the CPT-5 Project has been to have *Current Procedural Terminology* chosen by the Secretary of Health and Human Services as the national standard procedure code set for physicians services under HIPAA. A Final Rule, issued in the August 17, 2000 *Federal Register,* named

CPT nomenclature as the national standard code set for physician services. CPT modifiers were also designated as part of the code set. This means that by October 16, 2002, anyone who sends or receives health care information electronically, must be able to accept CPT codes and modifiers. However, CPT guidelines were not named as the standard for implementing the CPT nomenclature.

The CPT-5 Project used a workgroup process, with six workgroups (Managed Care; Research; Non-Physician Practitioners; Maintenance and Education; Structure and Hierarchy; and Sites of Service) and an Executive Project Advisory Group (PAG), participating in the process. The workgroups consisted of payment and health systems experts from a variety of backgrounds including clinical practice, data management, government, organized medicine, and coding. Each workgroup reviewed public and private sector reports, oral and written expert testimony, and other appropriate material to assess the capacity of CPT to address these issues. The workgroups made recommendations to the PAG for their review, evaluation, and transmission to the CPT Editorial Panel. The CPT Editorial Panel makes all final decisions regarding changes to the CPT codes and decides on the implementation process.

The workgroups and PAG examined issues such as coding for non-physician professionals; coding to facilitate the collection of data for quality health services and public health research; the elimination of ambiguity and enhanced specificity; the development of uniform coding rules; and changes to the editorial process to allow greater participation and efficient development of new descriptions of service. New ways to maintain the CPT nomenclature were also examined, including enhanced databases and other new technologies.

Methodology

The workgroups' activities were organized into four major components:

- Requirements definition – identification of the needs, uses, sources and types of coded data that is required by the health care industry
- Capacity assessment – analysis of the present and future capabilities of the CPT nomenclature to meet the coding demands of the health care system and the necessary steps to remedy capacity shortfalls
- Recommendation development – articulation of recommended changes in the structure or process of CPT coding to enable its goals
- Impact analysis – study of the interactive effects as well as intentional and unintentional consequences of recommended changes to the CPT nomenclature

The objectives of the CPT-5 Project and the activities of the workgroups and PAG have resulted in a preference for enhancing the existing functionality of the CPT nomenclature, correcting problem areas, and expanding the codes and descriptors to accommodate emerging demands in the provision of health care. The workgroups and PAG have concluded that an evolutionary approach is preferable and that the CPT nomenclature should be a code set for all health care services. Thus, the CPT nomenclature will not seek to accommodate all the needs of the health care system for data, but will concentrate on providing unambiguous definitions, descriptors, and rules for reporting administrative and clinical data. To support practitioners and other CPT coding users, implementation is likely to take place incrementally with a transition plan for a final product in 2003.

These changes will preserve the core elements that define CPT nomenclature as the language to communicate clinical information for administrative and financial purposes. This includes:

- Descriptions of clinically recognized and generally accepted health care services
- Five-character core with concept extenders (modifiers)
- Professional responsibility for a mechanism for periodic review and updating

The CPT Editorial Panel, proceeding with these core elements, will also stimulate progress to evolve in step with health care to accommodate changes in the health care environment and the needs of users. This includes:

- Accurate and up-to-date communication of clinical services
- Needs of providers, payers, and researchers for tools to support evidence-based clinical practice.

Based on the activities of the workgroups and PAG, as well as on the objectives of the CPT-5 Project and the guiding philosophy, the following are CPT nomenclature attributes under consideration or development:

- Provisional codes for new technology
- Tracking codes for performance measures
- Codes to capture preventive medicine/screening services
- Codes to capture education/counseling services
- Development of non-physician health professional evaluation services
- Expanded Editorial Panel process
- Decrease the timeframe involved in obtaining a CPT code through web and Internet communications
- Expansion of CPT Advisory Committee
- Improvement of CPT nomenclature instructions/guidelines to be more comprehensive, user-friendly, and specific
- Development of a CPT glossary to standardize definitions and differentiate use of synonymous terms
- Maintenance of the CPT code set through a database that incorporates data modeling tools and vocabulary structures to formalize the hierarchical re-

lationships within the CPT code set

- Computer management of intellectual content data and transition into various print publication processes
- Development of CPT educational material and training for postgraduate medical education, health care professional societies, and others

INTRODUCTION TO THE MANUAL

CPT is a systematic listing and coding of procedures and services performed by physicians (1). Each procedure or service is identified with a five-digit code. The use of CPT codes simplifies the reporting of services. With this coding and recording system, the procedure or service rendered by the physician is accurately identified (1).

Inclusion of a descriptor and its associated specific five-digit identifying code number in CPT is generally based upon the procedure being consistent with contemporary medical practice and being performed by many physicians in clinical practice in multiple locations. However, the CPT manual says that inclusion in CPT does not represent endorsement by the American Medical Association of any particular diagnostic or therapeutic procedure. In addition, the manual also states that inclusion or exclusion of a procedure does not imply any health insurance coverage or reimbursement policy. Even then, exclusion of a code is automatically considered by many as "experimental", "investigational", or "non-covered procedure", even though acceptance or coverage is not automatic or mandatory with an inclusion in CPT manual.

The purpose of the terminology is to provide a uniform language that will accurately describe medical, surgical, and diagnostic services, and will thereby provide an effective means for reliable nationwide communication among physicians, patients, and third parties. CPT 2002 is the most current edition. CPT descriptive terms, along with identification of various codes serve a wide variety of important functions in the field of medical nomenclature, as the CPT apparently is the most widely accepted nomenclature for the reporting of physician procedures and services not only under government, but also under private health insurance programs. In addition, CPT is also useful for administrative management purposes, including claims processing, guideline development, medical care review, education, research, and providing a useful basis for local, regional, and national utilization comparisons (1).

CPT code for each patient visit or procedure reflect:

- skill and effort required
- complexity
- responsibility
- medical knowledge
- counseling
- work resources

SECTIONS AND SUBSECTIONS

CPT is divided into five major groups. These consist of:

- evaluation and management services
- anesthesia
- surgery
- radiology
- pathology and laboratory medicine

Most interventional pain procedures are located in the surgery section under the musculoskeletal system and nervous system; radiology section; medicine section for physical therapy and occupational therapy services, as well as psychiatry and biofeedback services; apart from evaluation and management services. Further, all these sections also have various subsections describing either various types of interventions or regions.

APPENDICES

The manual consists of six appendices describing:

- appendix A-modifiers
- appendix B-summary of additions, deletions, and revisions
- appendix C -update to short descriptors
- appendix D-clinical examples
- appendix E-summary of CPT add-on codes
- appendix F-summary of CPT codes exempt from modifier -51

Appendix A

Appendix A lists modifiers applicable to CPT 2002 codes:

- 21 - prolonged evaluation and management services
- 22 - unusual procedural services
- 23 - unusual anesthesia
- 24 - unrelated evaluation and management service by the same physician during A postoperative period
- 25 - significant, separately identifiable evaluation and management service by the same physician on the same day of the procedure or other service
- 26 - professional component
- 32 - mandated services
- 47 - anesthesia by surgeon
- 50 - bilateral procedure
- 51 - multiple procedures
- 52 - reduced services
- 53 - discontinued procedure
- 54 - surgical care only
- 55 - postoperative managements only
- 56 - preoperative management only
- 57 - decision for surgery

- 58 - staged or related procedure or service by the same physician during the postoperative period
- 59 - distinct procedural service
- 62 - two surgeons
- 66 - surgical team
- 76 - repeat procedure by same physician
- 77 - repeat procedure by another physician
- 78 - return to the operating room for a related procedure during the postoperative period
- 79 - unrelated procedure or service by the same physician during the postoperative period
- 80 - assistant surgeon
- 81 - minimum assistant surgeon
- 82 - assistant surgeon (when qualified resident surgeon not available)
- 90 - reference (outside) laboratory
- 91 - repeat clinical diagnostic laboratory test
- 99 - multiple modifiers (1).

Modifiers for Ambulatory Surgery Centers and Hospital Outpatient Services

These modifiers include CPT level I modifiers, as well as level II or HCPCS/national modifiers:

- 25 - significant, separately identifiable evaluation and management service by the same physician on the same day of the procedure or other service
- 27 - multiple outpatient hospital E/M encounters on the same date
- 50 - bilateral procedure
- 52 - reduced services
- 58 - staged or related procedure or service by the same physician during the postoperative period
- 59 - distinct procedural service
- 73 - discontinued outpatient hospital/ambulatory surgery center (ASC) procedure prior to the administration of anesthesia
- 74 - discontinued outpatient hospital/ambulatory surgery center (ASC) procedure after administration of anesthesia
- 76 - repeat procedure by same physician
- 77 - repeat procedure by another physician
- 78 - return to the operating room for a related procedure during the postoperative period
- 79 - unrelated procedure or service by the same physician during the postoperative period
- 91 - repeat clinical diagnostic laboratory test, RT-right side, LT – left side

Appendices B, C, D

Appendix B is a listing of summary of additions, deletions and revisions applicable to CPT 2002 codes (2).

Appendix C lists all the changes necessary to update the short descriptors on the CPT 2002 data file. The descriptors have been changed to reflect additions, revisions, or deletions to the CPT 2002 codes, or to enhance or correct the data file (2).

Appendix D describes various clinical examples for evaluation and management services.

Appendix E

Appendix E provides a summary of CPT add-on codes for CPT 2002. The codes relevant to interventional pain management are as follows indicated with a + symbol (2)

- +22522 - percutaneous vertebroplasty, one vertebral body, unilateral or bilateral injection; each additional thoracic or lumbar vertebral body
- +64472 - injection, anesthetic agent and/or steroid, paravertebral facet joint or facet joint nerve; cervical or thoracic, each additional level
- +64476 - injection, anesthetic agent and/or steroid, paravertebral facet joint or facet joint nerve; lumbar or sacral, each additional level
- +64480 - injection, anesthetic agent and/or steroid, transforaminal epidural; cervical or thoracic, each additional level
- +64484 - injection, anesthetic agent and/or steroid, transforaminal epidural; lumbar or sacral, each additional level
- +64623 – destruction by neurolytic agent, paravertebral facet joint nerve; lumbar or sacral, each additional level
- +64627 – destruction by neurolytic agent, paravertebral facet joint nerve; cervical or thoracic, each additional level

The significance of add-on codes, and relevance to physician and ASC services is described below under 'Guidelines.'

Appendix F

Appendix F describes a listing of summary of CPT codes that are exempt from the use of modifier -51, but have not been designed as CPT add-on procedures or services. As shown in appendix E, the add-on codes do not require modifier -51. However, none of these codes are relevant to interventional pain medicine.

DEFINITIONS

Current Procedural Terminology is filled with terms such as guidelines, starred procedures, unlisted procedural service, and separate procedures, etc. Thus, while some terms in CPT require in depth explanation, others need brief explanation. We will only discuss the terminology relevant to interventional pain management.

Guidelines

Specific guidelines are presented at the beginning of each of the six sections as described earlier in Current Procedural Terminology (2). These guidelines define items that are necessary to appropriately interpret and report the procedures and services contained in that section. For example:

- The evaluation and management services guidelines describe classification of evaluation and management services, definitions of commonly used terms, unlisted services, special reports, clinical examples, and instructions for selecting a level of evaluation and management service. Further, definitions of commonly used terms in evaluation and management services define new and established patient, chief complaint, concurrent care, counseling, family history, history of present illness, levels of E/M services, nature of presenting problem, past history, social history, system review, and time inclusion.

- The surgery guidelines provide definitions and clarifications for listed surgical procedures, follow-up care for diagnostic procedures, follow-up care for therapeutic surgical procedures, materials supplied by physician, reporting more than one procedure or service, separate procedures, and add-on codes, etc.

- The radiology guidelines provide various definitions and items unique to radiology with definitions of multiple procedures, separate procedures, with special clarification of rules of supervision and interpretation. These guidelines indicate that for radiology section of supervision and interpretation, if a procedure is performed by two physicians, the radiologic portion of the procedure is designated as "radiological supervision and interpretation." However, when a physician performs both the procedure and provides imaging supervision and interpretation, a combination of procedure codes outside the 70000 series and imaging supervision and interpretation codes are used. In addition, the radiological supervision and interpretation codes are not applicable to the radiation oncology subsection. This is crucial for interventional pain physicians as impact extends to all radiology codes used in interventional pain medicine for this purpose including supervision and interpretation of epidurography (CPT 72275), discography (CPT 72285 and 72295), and sacroiliac joint arthrography (CPT 73542).

Separate Procedures

Separate procedures are procedures commonly carried out as an integral part of a "larger procedure" and as such should not be coded separately or in addition to the procedure of which it is a part. In the past, epidural injections were considered as separate procedures, thus, they were excluded to be coded separately or in addition to the procedure of which it is a part. However, when the epidural injection procedures were revised, this designation was eliminated. Thus, at the present time, for interventional pain medicine procedures, none of the procedures are listed as separate procedures, however, we should remember the correct coding policies which do include component and mutually exclusive procedures for each procedure.

Unlisted Procedure Service

It is common in interventional pain medicine to perform a procedure that is not listed in the current edition of the CPT manual. Thus, CPT manual recognizes that there may be services or procedures performed by physicians that are not found in CPT. This is more so with interventional pain medicine with development of new procedures. Generally, CPT code development lags several years behind the technology. Hence, a number of specific code numbers have been designated for reporting such unlisted procedures. However, when an unlisted procedure code is used, the service or procedure should be described and a special report or copy of the operative report should be submitted with the appropriate claim form. The unlisted procedure codes for interventional pain medicine are at the end of each anatomic section and end in the numbers –99.

Special Report

Current Procedural Terminology also describes a "special report." It is a service that is rarely provided, unusual, variable, or new may require a special report in determining medical appropriateness of the service (1, 2). Hence, pertinent information in this special report should include an adequate definition or description of the nature, extent, and need for the procedure; and the time, effort, and equipment necessary to provide the service. Further, special report may encompass complexity of symptoms, final diagnosis, pertinent physical findings, diagnostic and therapeutic procedures, concurrent problems, and follow-up care.

It is common to enclose a special report whenever an unlisted procedure or service code is utilized.

Add-on Codes

Add-on codes are codes that are never used by themselves. For example, subsequent facet joint nerve block would always be used with the facet joint nerve block, a single level. Similarly it applies to subsequent transforaminal epidural injections, and neurolytic blocks of facet joint nerves. The work values for add-on codes have been determined to represent the work of add-on code only, and so, when an add-on code is used, the modifier -51 used to designate additional procedure or multiple procedures is not used.

While this is followed for physician services by some, it is rarely followed for surgical center services as carriers routinely apply modifier -51. In addition, most private carriers do not follow add-on code rules and they generally reduce by addition of a modifier –51, both for physician and facility services.

Starred Procedures

The "*" is used to identify certain surgical procedures. Certain relatively small surgical services involve a readily identifiable surgical procedure but include variable preoperative and postoperative services. Most of the interventional pain medicine procedures are categorized with a * except codes such as CPT 62263 – percutaneous lysis of epidural adhesions, CPT 62287 – aspiration or decompression procedure, implantation codes (CPT 62350 to 62368), cervical and lumbar facet joint nerve blocks (CPT 64470 to 64476), transforaminal epidural injections (CPT 64479 to 64484) and all neurolytic blocks.

Because of the indefinite pre- and post-operative services, the "usual package" concept for surgical services is not applied. Thus, when a * follows a surgical procedure code number, the following rules apply:

1. The service listed includes the surgical procedure only. Associated pre- and post-operative services are not included in the service as listed.
2. Preoperative services are considered as one of the following:
    - When the starred procedure is carried out at the time of an initial visit (new patient) and this procedure constitutes the major service at that visit, procedure number 99025 is listed in lieu of the usual initial visit as an additional service (1, 2).
    - When the starred procedure is carried out at the time of an initial or established patient visit involving significant identifiable services, the appropriate visit is listed with the modifier –25 appended in addition to the starred procedure and its follow-up care.
    - When the starred procedure requires hospitalization, an appropriate hospital visit is listed in addition to the starred procedure and its follow-up care.
3. All postoperative care is added on a service-by-service basis.
4. Complications are added on a service-by-service basis.

However, in practice, almost all evaluation and management services are denied for starred procedure – while performing a procedure and billing for an E/M service and procedure(s) is acceptable most carriers, including Medicare and Medicaid; billing for an established patient with modifier –25, while not reimbursed, may also lead to fraud and abuse investigation(s). Definition of modifier –25 is as follows:

- ♦ significant, separately identifiable evaluation and management service by the same physician on the same day of the procedure or other service

Thus, E/M service has to be not only a significant service (not routine), but also a separately identifiable E/M service (separate from the evaluation required for the procedure). If a patient presents for a lumbar transforaminal epidural injection, but also presents with a new onset (onset after the last visit) neck pain (never documented on any of the evaluations), a physician may conduct an evaluation and bill for an appropriate level of E/M service, in addition to the procedure. In some circumstances, the level and complexity of E/M service may be higher than the procedural service; in such cases physician may only bill for E/M service, instead of the procedure.

CONCLUSION

Physicians' *Current Procedural Terminology* is a listing of descriptive terms and identifying codes for reporting medical services and procedures that physicians perform. The purpose of CPT is to provide a uniform language that accurately describes medical, surgical, and diagnostic services and thereby services and effective means of reliable nationwide communication among physicians, patients, and payors.

CPT is organized in six sections. Within each section or subsections with anatomic, procedural, condition or descriptor subheadings. Specific guidelines are presented at the beginning of each section. These guidelines define items that are necessary to appropriately interpret and report the procedures and services contained in each section.

The American Medical Association first developed and published CPT in 1966. The CPT Editorial Panel is responsible for maintaining CPT. This panel is authorized to revise, update or modify CPT. Specific procedures have been developed for addressing suggestions to revise CPT, adding or deleting a code, or modifying existing nomenclature.

Numerous changes in CPT coding development include revision of various existing codes and addition of multiple codes for interventional pain procedures over the last three years. Further, CPT also has developed Category III codes describing a set of temporary codes for emerging technology, services and procedures. Category III codes will allow data collection for these services. An important part of the reasoning behind the development of Category III codes was the length and requirements of the CPT approval process, which conflicted with the needs of researchers for coded data to track emerging technology services throughout the research process.

REFERENCES

1. *Current Procedural Terminology. CPT 2001*, American Medical Association, Chicago, 2000.
2. *Current Procedural Terminology. CPT 2002*, American Medical Association, Chicago, 2001.
3. AMA/Specialty Society RVS Update Process, American Medical Association, Chicago, 2001.
4. Non-Medicare Use of the RBRVS. In *Medicare RBRVS*: The Physicians' Guide 2001.

GENERAL CORRECT CODING POLICIES

Laxmaiah Manchikanti, MD

It is impossible to discuss interventional pain medicine without mentioning correct coding, billing, appropriate documentation, fraud and abuse. Compliance with the laws and regulations encompassing documentation with coding, billing, and collections, along with documentation of medical records, is of crucial importance in today's interventional pain medicine practices.The Balanced Budget Act of 1997 empowered and directed the Health Care Financing Administration (HCFA), now Centers for Medicare and Medicaid Services (CMS), to develop a payment system based upon physician work, and guidelines to document that work. The Health Insurance Portability and Accountability Act (HIPAA) or the Kennedy-Kassebaum Health Reform Bill of 1996 provided the Office of Inspector General and the Federal Bureau of Investigations with broad powers to identify and prosecute health-care fraud and abuse. Thus, it is the responsibility of CMS (HCFA) to institute uniform payment policies and procedures. However, in those instances where carriers are authorized to make local medical review policy, payment policies may vary. Hence, providers across various jurisdictions to receive similar payments for the same services (altered only by mandated geographic adjustments), to use the same codes and to provide similar documentation for services performed, CMS (HCFA) created the National Correct Coding Council (NCCC).

HISTORY

Omnibus Budget Reconciliation Act (OBRA) was enacted in 1989. OBRA of 1989, Section 6102 of P.L. 101-239 amended title XVIII of the Social Security Act, dealing with payment for physicians' services. Addition of this new section (section 1848), provided a resource based relative value scale (RBRVS) fee schedule in 1992. RBRVS, thus replaced reasonable charge mechanism of actual, customary, and prevailing charges. The National Correct Coding Council was created by CMS (HCFA), which initiated the National Correct Coding Committee (NCCC) to develop strategies for HCFA's Bureau of Program Operations to control improper coding leading to inappropriate or increased payments in Part B claims. As a direct outgrowth of NCCC's work, CMS (HCFA) established the National Correct Coding Policy in 1996 and eventually implemented the Medicare Correct Coding Initiative (CCI) to identify and isolate inappropriate coding, unbundling, and other irregularities in coding. Multiple versions of National Correct Coding Policies have been released in the form of a National Correct Coding manuals starting with version 5.0 to most recent publication 8.0 in Jan 2002. CCI audits are developed by Administar Federal. In addition, HCFA also has utilized unpublished coding edits referred to as "black-box ed

Table 1. *History of development of correct coding policies*

1985	
1989	OBRA - Ominibus Budget Reconciliation Act Ammendement of Social Security Act With Addition of Section 1848
1990	
1992	RBRVS - Resource Based Relative Value Scale, replacing reasonable charge
1995	
1996	Birth of National Correct Coding Policy Black Box Audits HIPAA (HR 3103) makes correct coding mandatory
2000	Extinction of Black Box Audits
1996-2002	CCI - 5.0 to 8.0
2005	

its," which, essentially, are a system of payment denials to be used by carriers based on commercial guidelines. With a multitude of arguments on the issue of black-box edits, they were finally eliminated in the year 2000. Historical development of National Correct Coding Policy is listed in Table 1. Prior to development of CCI edits, Medicare Part B carriers included in their claims-processing systems various computerized edits to detect improper coding of procedures, which at the time was designated as *fragmentation.*

NATIONAL CORRECT CODING POLICY

In consideration of monumental changes in outpatient coding with multiple proposals in 1999, 2000, 2001 and 2002 by CMS (HCFA), development of multiple new codes and revision of codes along with deletion of codes by AMA for *CPT 2000, 2001* and *2002* and use of modifiers and ambulatory payment classifications by CMS (HCFA), CMS officials have acknowledged that they have assigned over 105,000 coding edits to edit approximately 5,600 CPT codes Part B carriers use to analyze claims. These edits will be applied to physician services, services provided in ambulatory surgical centers, and hospital outpatient department claims.

The NCCC's policies are based on established coding conventions defined in the American Medical Association's (AMA's) Current Procedural Terminology (CPT) manual, national and local policies and edits, coding guidelines developed by national societies, analysis of standard medical and surgical practice, and reviews of current coding practices.

Correct coding essentially means reporting a group of procedures with appropriate comprehensive code. Under the CCI, CMS (HCFA) has developed general policies that define the coding principles and edits that apply to procedure and service codes.

Correct coding policies have influenced, patterns of billing and coding of all facets of medicine, specifically interventional pain medicine. Installation of the Correct Coding edits went into effect January 1, 1996. Since then, Medicare claims of inappropriate coding by providers and, thus, rejections have multiplied, resulting in substantial cost savings for the Medicare program. With the passage of the Health Insurance Portability and Accountability Act of 1996 (HR 3103), correct coding practices have become part of the requirement to obtain proper payment from Medicare, rather than an option. The CMS's (HCFA's) current coding policies and edits apply when the same provider bills for all the procedures involved, or when the services for the same beneficiary were provided on the same day.

CORRECT CODING POLICIES

In order for the CCI to be effective, it is essential that the coding description accurately describes what actually transpired at each patient encounter. A multitude of codes reflect the wide spectrum of services provided by various medical providers, and many medical services can be rendered by different methods and combinations of various procedures. Hence, multiple codes describing similar services are frequently necessary to accurately reflect the particular service a physician performs. However, when multiple procedures are performed at the same session, the procedure and postprocedure work do not have to be repeated for each procedure; and, therefore, a comprehensive code describing the multiple services commonly performed together can be used. Many activities which are integral to a procedure are considered as generic activities and are assumed to be included as acceptable medical/surgical practice and, while they could be performed separately, they should not be considered as such when a code narrative is defined. Hence, all services integral to accomplishing a procedure will be considered to be included in that procedure and, therefore, will be considered a component and part of the comprehensive code (2, 3).

Standards of Medical/Surgical Practice

Many of the provider activities during a procedure are integral to a procedure and termed as generic activities, which are assumed to be included as acceptable medical/surgical practice, considered included in that procedure and considered a component of the procedure. Some generic services integral to standard medical/surgical services include:

- Cleansing, shaving, and prepping of the skin;
- Draping of the patient;
- Positioning of the patient;
- Insertion of intravenous access;
- Administration of sedation;
- Local, topical, or regional anesthetic administration;
- Identification the of surgical approach;
- Surgical cultures;
- Wound irrigation;
- Insertion and removal of drains, suction devices, dressings, and pumps;
- Application, management and removal of postoperative dressings, including transcutaneous electrical nerve stimulation units and institution of patient-controlled analgesia;
- Preoperative, intraoperative, and postoperative documentation; and
- Surgical supplies, unless excepted by existing HCFA policy.

Medical/Surgical Package

Over the years the CPT manual has grown to accommodate the expanding variety of surgical, diagnostic, and therapeutic surgical, as well as nonsurgical, procedures performed. In general, most services include associated preprocedure and postprocedure work; when performed at a single patient encounter, the preprocedure and postprocedure work is relatively fixed, regardless of the number of services actually performed at each session. For interventional pain procedures, some general guidelines can be developed. Thus, the following services are considered integral to an interventional procedure and are included in the CPT code description for the primary or comprehensive procedure. Such component services are:

- Intravenous access, e.g., CPT codes 36000, 36140, 36400, 36410, 37201, and 90780 to 90784;
- Cardiopulmonary monitoring, e.g., CPT codes 93000, 93005, 93040, 93041, 94656, 94760, 94761, or 94770;
- Billing of successful service only;
- Anesthesia by physician or conscious sedation, e.g., CPT codes 99141 and 99142.

Add-on Codes

The CPT coding system identifies certain codes that are submitted with other codes. These codes are identified generally with a statement such as, "List separately in addition to code for primary procedure" in parentheses. The supplemental code is to be used only with certain primary codes that are identified in parentheses. The purpose of these CPT codes is to enable providers to separately identify a service that is performed in certain situations as an additional service (3-5). Incidental services that are necessary to accomplish the primary procedure, such as injection of contrast, are not separately reported. Iatrogenic complications arising in the course of a procedure such as a catheter kink or malfunction requiring a replacement are not separately reported.

Add – on codes relevant to interventional pain management are: subsequent transforaminal epidural injections (CPT codes 64480 and 64484), facet joint blocks (CPT codes 64472 and 64476), and facet joint neurolysis (CPT codes 64623 and 64627).

Modifiers

In order to expand the information provided by the five-digit CPT codes, a number of modifiers have been created by the AMA, CMS (HCFA), and local Medicare carriers. These modifiers, in the form of two digits, either numbers, letters, or a combination of each, are intended to convey specific information regarding the procedure or service to which they are appended (1-5). Modifiers are attached to the end of a code to indicate that a service or procedure described in the code definition has been modified by some circumstance. However, explicit understanding of the purpose of each modifier is required prior to its usage. It is also essential to recognize that modifiers may be different for each locality. In addition, it is essential to understand the specific meaning of the modifier for the payor to which a claim is being submitted before using it. For example, all modifiers described in the CPT code manual are not accepted by CMS, third-party payors, Compensation carriers, and local carriers. Similarly, modifiers developed by CMS or local Medicare carriers are not accepted by third-party carriers or Worker's Compensation carriers. Meanwhile, Compensation carriers and third-party carriers also have developed their own modifiers in some jurisdictions.

Within the context of multiple-services reporting, without the addition of an appropriate modifier, it will appear that providers are engaging in the practice of "unbundling." The appropriate use of modifiers indicates that the services were performed under circumstances which did not involve this practice at all.

The CMS (HCFA) identified modifier - 59 for use when several procedures are performed on different anatomic sites, or at different sessions on the same day (formerly known as the "GB" modifier) (3). This is considered as a distinct procedural service and the specific proposed language is: "Under certain circumstances, the physician may need to indicate that a procedure or service was distinct or independent from other services performed on the same day." Modifier - 59 is used to identify procedures/services that are not normally reported together, but are appropriate under the circumstances. However, modifier - 59 should be used only when no more descriptive modifiers such as an anatomic modifier or the staged-procedure modifier is available.

Modifier - 50 is used to report bilateral procedures. Until April 1, 2000, CMS (HCFA's) took a position that facet joint injections and neurolytic blocks and transforaminal injection codes were unilateral. However, in April 2000, CMS (HCFA) recognized that these are bilateral codes, both for physicians services and ambulatory surgical centers

Excluded Services

Even though Medicare program has identified some services as "excluded services," they have not been included in CCI audits.

CPT Procedure Code Definition

All procedures described by the CPT code narrative for the comprehensive code should have been performed, and only the single CPT code most accurately describing the procedure should be reported (1-5).

Thus, in interventional pain management, if a percutaneous lysis of adhesions is performed, CPT code 62263 with a description of the code, percutaneous lysis of epidural adhesions using solution injection, e.g., hypertonic saline, enzyme, or mechanical means, e.g., spring–guide catheter, including radiologic localization (includes contrast when administered) is used. It will be considered as unbundling, also fraud, if, in addition to 62263, other codes such as 62310 or

62311, 62318 or 62319, 64479 or 64483, 64722, 62281, 62282 or 76005 are used.

Similarly, facet joint nerve blocks performed with neurolysis are considered as an integral part of the procedure. If epidural injection via indwelling catheter is utilized, separate codes for epidural injections are not advisable.

In addition, a code description may define a correct coding relationship where one code is a part of another based on the language used in the descriptor. Some examples of this type of correct coding in interventional pain medicine by code definition are: "single" and "multiple" codes – the single procedure is included in the multiple procedure, e.g., CPT 64420 intercostal nerve, single – CPT 64421 intercostal nerves, multiple.

Other examples, though not specific to interventional pain medicine, are:

- "Partial" and "complete" CPT codes; partial is included in complete
- "Partial" and "total" CPT codes; partial is included in total.
- "Unilateral" and "bilateral" CPT codes; unilateral procedure is included in bilateral.

Coding Guidelines

Each section of the CPT coding manual includes instructions that are unique to that section, in addition to the general instructions provided. These directions are not all inclusive of, nor limited to, definitions of terms, modifiers, unlisted procedures or services, special or written reports, details about reporting separate, multiple or starred procedures and qualifying circumstances (2, 4, 5). These instructions define items or provide explanations that are necessary to appropriately interpret and report the procedures or services and to define terms that apply to a particular section.

Many changes have occurred in interventional pain procedure coding in 2000, 2001 and 2002 CPT procedure manuals. Hence, it is imperative that an interventional pain physician thoroughly understand each procedure code used in describing interventional pain procedures to avoid misunderstanding, incorrect coding or unbundling.

Separate Procedures

The "separate procedure" notation in the CPT manual identifies a procedure or service that can be performed independently but that, when performed as an integral part of the comprehensive procedure, should not be reported separately. In previous CPT manuals, all epidural codes were considered as separate procedures; however, 2000 CPT codes with new epidural codes are not considered as separate procedures, since CPT code definitions have been expanded to clearly delineate what the CPT panel meant to include in that code without any ambiguity.

Designation of Sex

Many procedure codes have a sex designation within their narrative; however, these codes do not apply to the practice of interventional pain medicine.

Family of Codes

The CPT manual describes certain codes that include two or more component codes that should not be reported separately, as these are considered members of a code family and included in a more comprehensive code. As such, comprehensive codes include certain services that are separately identified by other component codes. Although, component codes as members of the comprehensive code family represent parts of the procedure, that should not be listed separately when the complete procedure is performed, the component codes are considered individually if the procedures they describe are performed independently of the complete procedure. If this is not the case, all services listed in the comprehensive codes will be considered to make up the total service.

The example in interventional pain procedures would include epidural catheterization, epidural steroid injection, epidural local anesthetic injection, injection of enzyme or neurolytic solution such as hypertonic saline or contrast, and needle localization for percutaneous lysis of adhesions, which are all component codes to describe the comprehensive procedure, namely, percutaneous lysis of adhesions.

Similarly, a comprehensive code is available describing epidural catheterization, hence, injection into the epidural space of local anesthetic steroid, contrast, etc., is not reportable separately.

Most Extensive Procedures

The CMS-established policy is that, for a code which applies to a procedure that can be performed at different levels of complexity, only the most extensive service, encompassing the comprehensive code actually performed, should be reported. Thus, when procedures are performed together that are basically the same, or performed on the same side but qualified by an increased level of complexity, the less extensive procedure is included in the more extensive procedure. Hence, the procedure viewed as the most complex should be reported.

Sequential Procedures

Sequential procedure or a successful procedure is identified in this policy. It identifies codes for procedures that are often performed in sequence or for procedures involving an initial approach followed by a more invasive procedure during the same encounter. Only the procedure that successfully accomplishes the expected result is reported, with a less extensive procedure bundled into the more extensive one.

An example of this situation in interventional pain medicine would be a caudal epidural injection followed by percutaneous lysis of adhesions on the same day, in which case only the code for the successful procedure, that is, percutaneous lysis of adhesions, may be reported.

With or Without Procedures

Certain codes in the CPT manual identify a procedure that can be performed with or without certain services. It is contradictory to report code combinations in which one code represents a procedure that includes a certain service and the other code represents the procedure without that service.

As a practical matter in interventional pain management, multiple codes are described with or without contrast, or with or without radiological guidance.

Laboratory Panels

Medical necessity for laboratory evaluation must be established. In addition, an interventional pain specialist should pay close attention to comprehensive panel codes that include multiple component tests.

Unlisted Services or Procedures

Multiple sections in the CPT manual list certain codes that end in "99" or "9," in a few cases used to report a service that is not described in any code listed elsewhere in the CPT manual. This facilitates advances in technology, or physician expertise with new procedures when a CPT code may not have been assigned to a procedure when it is first introduced as accepted treatment. In these cases, at least initially, the unlisted service or procedure codes are necessary to describe the procedure. However, every effort should be made to find the appropriate code to describe the service, and frequent use of these unlisted codes instead of proper codes is not appropriate. Under this policy, the correct code would be assigned after the documentation has been reviewed, and then code pairs would be bundled based on this initial code. Thus far, the unlisted service or procedure has not been included in the CCI because of the multiple procedures that can be assigned to these codes.

It is interesting to note that, whenever a code is not available, well-meaning attorneys advise to use an unlisted code; however, this may result not only in denial of payment for such a service, but also in raising a red flag if this code is repeatedly used. The advice of manufacturers and the opinion of AMA has differed on multiple occasions regarding the description of spinal endoscopy, as well as electrothermal annuloplasty in interventional pain practices. A further disadvantage of using an unlisted code is that, even if reimbursement comes through for physician services, there will not be facility reimbursement for ambulatory surgery centers and hospital outpatient departments. Prior to development of CPT 2000 codes, many also have advised using unlisted codes to describe cervical facet joint nerve blocks, cervical facet joint neurolysis, and transforaminal epidural injections.

Misuse of Column 2 Code with Column 1 Code

This policy indicates that CPT codes are written precisely and are not to be used out of context. At the same time, the policy also indicates that inappropriate interpretation of the CPT code definitions must not be performed. Thus, according to this policy, component codes cannot be billed with a comprehensive code.

Mutually exclusive codes are codes for procedures that cannot reasonably be performed in the same session.

Correct Coding and its Modifier Indicator

An appropriate modifier must be used with a code for which a modifier is appropriate. This code may be a column 1 or column 2 code. The definition of a modifier according to the CPT manual is as follows: "a modifier provides the means by which the reporting physician or provider can indicate that a service or procedure that has been performed has been altered by some specific circumstance but not changed in its definition or code."

Thus, the correct coding file formats have been presumably expanded to include a modified indicator for both the mutually exclusive code and the comprehensive component code tables. The Correct Coding Edits modifier indicators are "0", "1", or "9."

- A "0" indicates that there are no circumstances in which a modifier would be appropriate. The services represented by the code combination will not be paid separately.
- A "1" indicates that a modifier is allowed in order to differentiate between the services provided.
- A "9" indicator is used for all code pays having a deletion date the same as their effective date.

INCORRECT CODING

Incorrect coding is defined as the intentional or unintentional billing of multiple procedure codes for a group of procedures that are covered by a single comprehensive code.

Incorrect coding includes both unbundling and upcoding. Various types of incorrect coding examples include:

- Fragmenting one service into component parts and coding each component as if it were a separate service;
- Reporting separate codes for related services when the comprehensive code includes all related services;
- Breaking out bilateral procedures when one code is appropriate;
- Downcoding a service in order to use an additional code when one higher-level, more comprehensive code is appropriate; and
- Separating a surgical approach from a major surgical service.

Consequences of inaccurate coding are disastrous as shown in Table 2.

Table 2. *Consequences of inaccurate coding and billing in order of importance*

1.	Prison	6.	Denied claims
2.	Exclusion	7.	Triggering review(s)
3.	Sanctions	8.	Returned claims
4.	Fines	9.	Suspended claims
5.	False Claims Prosecution	10.	Downcoding

CONCLUSION

The CMS (HCFA), to help ensure that providers across various jurisdictions receive like payments for the same services, use the same codes and provide similar documentation for services performed, created the NCCC. Subsequently, CMS (HCFA) established the National Correct Coding Policy in 1996 and eventually implemented the "Medicare Correct Coding Initiative" to identify and isolate inappropriate coding, unbundling, and other irregularities in coding. Correct coding policies encompass coding based on standards of medical/surgical practice; medical/surgical packages; add–on codes; modifiers; excluded services; CPT procedure-code definitions; CPT coding manual instructions/guidelines; separate procedures; designation of sex; family of codes; most extensive procedures; sequential procedures; with or without procedures; laboratory panels; unlisted services or procedures; misuse of column 2 code with column 1 code; mutually exclusive procedures; and, finally, Correct Coding Edits modifier indicated. Interventional pain physicians, like the rest of the medical community, are deeply entangled in National Correct Coding Policy and CCI. It is imperative for interventional pain physicians to avoid incorrect coding, either by unbundling or upcoding, and to understand National Correct Coding Policy and Correct Coding Edits, some of which are described here.

References

1. Manchikanti L. The impact of National Correct Coding Policy on interventional pain management. *Pain Physician* 1999; 2:33-45.
2. National Correct Coding Primer with Correct Code Check 2002: United Communications Group, Rockville, 2002.
3. CCI edits require expertise in the face of voluminous outpatient, coding changes. *HCPCS Report* 2000; 14:1-5.
4. *Current Procedural Terminology. CPT 1999*, American Medical Association, Chicago, 1998.
5. *Current Procedural Terminology. CPT 2000*, American Medical Association, Chicago, 1999.
6. Manchikanti L. Evaluation and management services in interventional pain practice: Doing it right! *Pain Physician* 2000; 3:322-341
7. Manchikanti L. The role of evaluation and management services in pain management. *Pain Physician* 1999; 2:10-32.
8. Manchikanti L. Appropriate documentation, billing and coding in interventional pain practice. *Pain Physician* 2000; 3:218-236.
9. CCI version 6.1 Errata. Coding and Medicare updates. 2000: May 1-2.
10. Manchikanti L. CPT 2000: Interventional pain management coding in the new millennium. *Pain Physician* 2000; 3:73-85.

COMPLIANCE FOR INTERVENTIONAL PAIN MEDICINE CODING

Laxmaiah Manchikanti, MD
Vijay Singh, MD

With the release of the *Office of Inspector General (OIG) Compliance Guidelines for third party billing companies and physician practices*, it is crystal clear that providers of interventional pain medicine and vendors providing billing and coding services to interventional pain practices are mandated to take steps to ensure that both perform their jobs with appropriate documentation, coding and billing in a manner compliant with rules and regulations. Although any service may be assigned to others or contracted out, interventional pain physicians and ambulatory surgery centers (ASCs) unfortunately, are unable to contract out the liability, and should remember that "the buck" stops with them. Further, primary responsibility rests with the provider, either the interventional pain physician or the ASC, regardless or in spite of the numerous outside contracts or firms involved not only in documentation, billing and coding, but also in auditing. Thus, it is extremely important for interventional pain practices to understand the compliance guidelines pertaining to documentation, billing and coding. This can only be achieved by active participation of the provider rather than delegating and contracting it out.

RATIONALE

Compliance auditing is essential to meet regulations of the government, as well as those of accrediting agencies and it is becoming necessary for almost all third party payors. However, providers should understand that compliance not only meets federal and state accreditation regulations but also improves medical care and the efficiency of the practice. Once providers realize and appreciate the positive aspects of compliance, it is easy to sell the compliance to staff in a positive manner. Multiple benefits compliance with billing and coding are listed in Table 1. The most important benefits of compliance include improvement of overall quality, efficiency of the medical practice, relations and an improved bottom line.

1. Improvement of Quality of Data

Various aspects of compliance may initially be a grueling tasks and very uncomfortable in terms of opposition from staff members. However, if compliance is instituted and auditing for compliance is performed appropriately with required education, follow-up and feedback, it results not only in improvement of quality of data, but also in enjoyment of staff. Appropriate data collection is a pivotal aspect of the organization not only for billing and coding, but also for quality management; planning; research; and, finally, cash flow.

2. Improvement of Knowledge

The desire to implement and be compliant with proper documentation, coding and billing will invariably result in improvement of knowledge of not only the physician, and the billing and coding staff, but also of the administrative and patient-care staff. This will initiate the most pleasant experience in learning the code appropriately for proper billing purposes. At the same time, documentation compliance leads administrative and patient-care staff to concentrate on the most cru

Table 1. *Top 10 benefits of compliance.*

1.	Improvement of quality of data
2.	Improvement of knowledge
3.	Creation of efficient medical practice
4.	Improved relations between staff
5.	Improved and correct reimbursement
6.	Protection against fraud and abuse
7.	Availability of proper data for evaluation purposes
8.	Improved quality management and improvement with enhanced availability of data
9.	Improved relations with public and payors
10.	Peace of mind and comfort with enhanced medical practice

cial aspects of documentation compliance. Even though medical schools and training programs teach appropriate patient-care aspects and various medical technology, they fail to teach medical students and physicians appropriate documentation guidelines, specifically, for billing and coding. Most practitioners learn billing, coding and documentation in the first few weeks of practice if they are careful and start appropriately. However, unfortunately, some of them learn during the process of auditing by an external agency or during an investigation. Initiation of auditing for proper compliance and compliance with various regulations is the best incentive for appropriate learning and improving knowledge.

3. Creation of Efficient Medical Practice

Appropriate compliance with documentation, billing and coding will lead to improved and efficient cooperation of the medical practice. Properly performed audits will identify all types of errors and lead to compliance. The appropriate auditing process for compliance addresses all errors by type and cause. Once errors are identified by type and cause and categorized, it will direct the providers and staff to the root of any coding problems. Following this, practice will develop process improvements and, finally, correction of the deficiency, which in turn will help the organization to operate more efficiently. Improved and efficient medical practice will result in efficient functioning of staff; efficient functioning of providers with time savings; an improved practice with more patients; and, finally, improved returns by appropriate coding in a "win-win" situation.

Appropriate compliance and auditing can increase productivity, as when employees consider compliance as part of their jobs, rather than as an activity which threatens their job security. Employees will be able to function in comfortably with a higher degree of safety and effectiveness, which translates into savings of time and money for the organization, leading to efficient practice. However, these benefits are not automatically generated from compliance, as improvement depends on many factors, including the organization's approach to the process of compliance; the management of audits; and, finally, the type, frequency and utilization of audit results, education and follow-up.

4. Improved Relations Between Physicians and Staff

Compliance with rules and regulations and the auditing required to maintain compliance not only can bring physicians and staff together for a single purpose of improving care and staying out of prison, but also improve relations between billing, administrative and nursing staff for the single purpose of compliance, which is common to the entire organization. The physician should initiate compliance, thus, becoming the leading force with proper knowledge of documentation, billing and coding. Physicians are not only involved in each step of compliance but are also in the best position to interact with and educate other physicians if poor documentation, billing and coding practices exist within the organization. This should be an interactive phenomenon with ongoing monitoring, follow-up and feedback. The billing and auditing staff should be able to communicate directly with physicians to ensure that actual problems are understood and efficiently addressed in the future. Auditing is a three-pronged process involving physicians, billing staff and other staff in identification of the issues, correction of the issues, and follow-up with re-auditing to ensure that each provider has taken appropriate remedial action and continues to follow compliance guidelines appropriately.

5. Improved and Accurate Reimbursement to the Organization

Appropriate billing, coding and documentation, along with compliance with guidelines at federal and state levels, in addition to the third-party guidelines, should result in correct, or even improved, reimbursement. The basic intent of correct billing, coding and documentation is correct, if not improved, reimbursement. Compliance should not be limited to only the type of errors, that will increase reimbursement: but should include all types of errors, even if it means decreased reimbursement or refunding the excess reimbursement. Thus, organizations should focus on underpayments, as well as overpayments. However, proper understanding and compliance with guidelines in many instances will result in an increase in overall revenue, even though it is quite possible that on occasions, overall reimbursement may decrease; and this is more so the case in terms of individual items. Thus, the goal of auditing should not be improved or increased overall reimbursement; it should be accurate and correct reimbursement, finally leading to an efficient organizational process.

6. Protection Against Fraud and Abuse

The OIG Compliance Program Guidance in all its regulations conveys to the provider community that the government will look upon the existence of an effective compliance program as a potential mitigating factor in the event of an investigation. The most important and pivotal word in this sentence is effective. An organization cannot and will not operate an effective compliance program without an effective auditing mechanism for documentation, billing and coding. Thus, a compliance program must address all issues that are the focus of compliance investigations, but in this case with an exceeding focus on all and any functions affecting documentation, billing, coding and reimbursement

An effective compliance program in the process of appropriate auditing will likely uncover potential issues of noncompliance related to all aspects of coding and reimbursement, which could not only develop into legal issues, but also essentially become issues of quality of care and risk management. Early identification of these issues will lead through appropriate audit to effective management of compliance before a full-blown fraud or abuse exposure can develop.

7. Reliable Data for Evaluation Purposes

Proper data collection, auditing and compliance with regulations not only lead to all the above described benefits, but also to appropriate evaluation of internal processes, patient satisfaction, clinical outcomes, and cost effectiveness of various modalities of treatments. Quality and reliable data reporting outcomes may even lead to research and government funds. Thus, a provider can move from providing proper medical care into the research arena. However, above all, they will provide an armamentarium to improve patient care in an efficient manner.

8. Improved Quality Management and Improvement with Enhanced Data

Once again, appropriate compliance and required auditing have many benefits, not only in terms of overall improvement of organizational function, but also in terms of improved functioning of quality management and improvement in terms of enhanced auditing and available data. In addition, auditing can be incorporated into many of the quality management and improvement data already in effect with auditing of medical records, billing, coding and documentation. Thus, many of the functions of quality management and improvement can be incorporated or will become part of a compliance audit.

9. Improved Relations with Public and Payors

An effective compliance program with successful auditing systems will not only improve practice efficiency but also can become a public relations tool not only with patients, but also with third party payors. This is an achievement an organization can use to attract more patients in the form of new patients with self-referrals and also with new contracts with third party payors.

Appropriate data will also enable the organization to provide outcomes and cost effectiveness data to third party payors.

10. Peace of Mind and Comfort With Enhanced Medical Practice

As described above, the multiple benefits of proper compliance will result in a practice and an organization in which physicians and staff can be comfortable, with improved practice patterns which are not only efficient, but also attracting new patients; attracting third party payors and contracts; and, finally, improving the bottom line with improved cash flow.

AUDITING FOR COMPLIANCE

The main and fundamental goal of the audit is to improve the coding, billing and documentation process so that the entire reimbursement to the organization is not only accurate, but also appropriate. Thus:

- Do not focus only on coding errors that affect reimbursement; organizations should focus on identifying all types of coding errors.
- Do not focus only on coding errors but also focus on and identify documentation errors.
- Do not identify a single procedure and extrapolate the results to all procedures.
- Do not identify a single individual and extrapolate to all individuals.
- Do not focus on every area of coding and documentation; focus mainly on areas of OIG interest and other areas such as local Medicare Review Policy and third party payor focus areas.

If this is an external audit, you must contract with an outside firm, preferably through your attorney, to retain at least part of attorney-client privilege. The audit process should start with defining its purpose and limitations, followed by selection of the sample, then, by review of the records, analysis of the data, preparation of the report, and reaudit.

Purpose

An organization may identify a purpose of the compliance audit and arrive with a statement such as: the purpose of our compliance audit is to identify documentation, coding and billing errors, with a goal to have a 100% proficiency rate for reimbursement and a 98% proficiency rate for coding.

To achieve excellence, one can also have a goal of a 100% accuracy or proficiency rating.

Sample Selection

As shown earlier, sample selection is a crucial process and also one of the pivotal pieces of the auditing and compliance process. Sample selection not only shapes the entire audit process by determining exactly what records need to be reviewed to influence the overall audit findings but also shapes the entire outcome and the effectiveness of the audit itself.

It is best to have a good sample; however, this does not need to meet criteria at a statistically significant level. If a statistician is available, the sample selection can be improved significantly, and the results can be reliable. Another way of being certain is to review 100% of the patients or 100% of the records. This may be time consuming and expensive and occasionally, may be impossible to do. Thus, it may be necessary to draw some statistical inferences, by which a conclusion is reached about a population on the basis of the information in the sample. However, to project the data to the entire organization, a scientific sample is required.

To obtain reliable information in a sample selection, definition of the sample should be identified. This may include all interventional pain procedures performed in the office or in the surgery center; all follow-up visits, either consultations or established office outpatients; all types of epidurals; or all facet joint injections. In interventional pain practices, it will be easy to audit and analyze the data because data are stored based on the CPT coding system.

Inclusion is not the only important issue; one should also define the exclusion criteria. Exclusion automatically puts a shadow on the reliability of data. In addition, the OIG also recommends that, in sample selection and analysis of data, compliance plans should apply to all payors equally. Fundamentally, once again, it reinforces the issue that accuracy should be the same for all payors, not just for Medicare or Medicaid. However, a focused selection of the sample can be performed for either Medicare, Medicaid or a particular third party payor or particular provider or even a particular procedure or service.

Sample selection may be performed by random tables or by computer programming. Surprisingly, the OIG's self-disclosure protocol endorses random sampling, which can be performed by using the government's Regional Advanced Technique Staff program. However, whatever type of random sampling, is used in case of an investigation, one should be in a position to explain to the OIG the rationale for selecting such a technique. Another type of random sampling is stratified random sampling in which the population is divided into two or more strata based on a specific characteristic. Thus, in interventional pain practices, sampling may be performed either only for behavioral medicine visits, physical therapy visits, or interventional procedure visits.

Finally, a sample size is also an important factor. How much is enough? An organization based on the number of patients encountered can choose a sample size of from 2% to 100%. For small practices, a higher sample is required; whereas for larger practices, a small sample is required. An ideal sample size is approximately 5% or 10%.

Review of Records

Once sample selection is completed, all charts and documents are collected and reviewed for accuracy and correctness. This also may be incorporated with chart review performed for quality management and improvement purposes. Some data are mutual. The basic data which need to be evaluated are as follows:

- ♦ Patient demographic data,
- ♦ Diagnosis code,
- ♦ Procedure code, and
- ♦ Documentation to support the coding (this includes initial evaluation, preoperative evaluation, intraoperative evaluation, postoperative evaluation, discharge, follow-up, operative report and various other forms used in performing procedures, billing and coding.

Compilation of Data

After reviewing the charts, appropriate data are compiled and analyzed. Data should never be analyzed by the same person who is performing the primary function of documentation, coding and billing. After analysis of the data, all the deficiencies must be identified and presented to the relevant staff. Whenever deficiencies exist in any aspect, appropriate recommendations must be made.

Follow-up review and data analysis should be conducted and results should be evaluated.

CONCLUSION

Compliance for interventional pain medicine coding is a complex, and time consuming, intense, self-evaluation which may protect the providers from disastrous consequences. In addition to protecting physicians from fraud and abuse, this activity will also be beneficial in many ways, including improving the practice, efficiency and reimbursement. In summary, the following is a list of important items of internal control for safe, efficient, and effective practice.

1 Check out all employees with the OIG exclusion list.
2 Assign individual passwords to access the computer system; these should not be shared.
3 Reconcile sheets, patient schedules, sign-in patient/ procedure data sheets, and charge sheets with daily report of charges.
4 Different people should:
   - Open the mail and prepare and make deposits,
   - Sign the checks,
   - Reconcile the accounts and bank statements, and
   - Do write-offs.
5 Review daily reports of payments for unposted patient's charges.
6 Check monthly:
   - Contractual adjustments
   - Sample payments, tracing from explanation of benefits to patient account and deposit slips,
   - Charges,
   - Payments,
   - Write-offs, and
   - Balance sheet.

LOCAL MEDICAL REVIEW POLICY AND CARRIER ADVISORY COMMITTEE

Laxmaiah Manchikanti, MD

The centers for Medicare and Medicaid publishes Medicare program integrity manual with multiple policies, rules and regulations, along with exhibits. These include types of claims for which contractors are responsible; and the Medicare medical review program which consists of national coverage decisions, coverage provisions and interpretative manuals, local medical review policy and individual claim determinations; local Medical review policy; Carrier Advisory Committee; Medicare fraud program; coordination of medical review and benefit integrity units; and various other program integrity requirements.

The carrier is an entity that has entered into a contract with CMS to process medical claims under Part B for non-facility providers (eg, physicians, suppliers, laboratories). Durable medical equipment regional carriers are those carriers that CMS designated to process durable medical equipment claims. The term contractor includes all intermediaries, carriers, durable medical equipment regional carriers, program safeguard contractors and others.

Local medical review policies (LMRPs) are those policies used to make coverage and coding decisions in the absence of specific statute, regulations, national coverage policy, national coding policy, or as an adjunct to a national coverage policy. Thus, local medical review policies are the most crucial compliance tools for pain practitioners promulgated by local medical carrier. LMRPs are developed by local Medicare carrier directors with assistance of Carrier Advisory Committee, thus, the purpose of the Carrier Advisory Committee is to provide:

- A formal mechanism for physicians in the state to be informed of and participate in the development of LMRP in an advisory capacity;
- A mechanism to discuss and improve administrative policies that are within carrier discretion; and
- A form for information exchanged between carriers and physicians

Thus, the focus of the CAC is local medical review policies and administrative policies and not issues and policies related to private insurance business. In addition, CAC is not a forum for peer review, discussion of individual cases or individual providers. Even though CAC must review all draft LMRPs, the final implementation decision about LMRPs rests with the carrier medical director (CMD).

THE CARRIER ADVISORY COMMITTEE

Each carrier must establish one CAC per state, however, when there is more than one carrier in a state, the carriers must jointly establish a CAC. If there is one carrier for many states, each state shall have a full committee and the opportunity to discuss draft LMRPs and issues presented in their state. However, the carriers that develop identical policies within a single region may establish a single CAC with permission from the regional office. In order to obtain a waiver from the regional office, contractors must obtain consensus agreement from all CAC members within the region.

Composition

The CAC is to be composed of physicians, a beneficiary representative and other medical organizations. Medicare defines physicians as, doctors of medicine, doctors of osteopathy, doctors of dental surgery or dental medicine, chiropractors, doctors of podiatry or surgical chiropody, and doctors of optometry. Thus, other practitioners such as physical therapists and nurse practitioners are not considered as physicians. Other practitioners are not included on this committee.

Carriers select committee representatives from names recommended by *state medical societies and specialty societies*. As the name implies, these are local medical review policies and are developed locally. CMS has clearly defined that the representatives must also be local. However, if there is no organized specialty society for a particular specialty, the carrier medical director should work with the state medical society to determine how the specialty is to be represented. Carrier Medicare directors are instructed to encourage each state medical society and specialty society to nominate representatives to the CAC. If there are multiple specialty societies representing a specialty, carrier medical director has the discretion to select only one representative. However, carrier medical directors also are instructed to encourage specialty societies to work together to determine how a representative is selected and how that representative communicates with each society. However, once again, it is emphasized that it is limited to state medical societies and specialty societies rather than national societies.

CMS instructs carrier medical directors to attempt to include, as members of their CACs, physician representatives from each of the following groups;

- State medical and osteopathic societies;
- National medical association (representative of either the local or state chapter or its equallant, if one exists); and
- Medicare managed care organizations. However, the number of managed care representatives on the CAC is based on the medicare penetration rates for the states; one representative for those states with penetration rates of less than 5% and two representative for those states with penetration rates of 5% or higher.
- Physician representatives for each of the following;
    - Chiropractic
    - Maxillofacial/oral surgery
    - Optometry
    - Podiatry
- One physician representative of each of the following clinical specialties and sub-specialties;
    - Allergy
    - Anesthesia
    - Cardiology
    - Cardiovascular/Thoracic Surgery
    - Dermatology
    - Emergency Medicine
    - Family Practice
    - Gastroenterology
    - Gerontology
    - General Surgery
    - Hematology
    - Internal Medicine
    - Infectious Disease
    - Medical Oncology
    - Nephrology
    - Neurology
    - Neurosurgery
    - Nuclear Medicine
    - Obstetrics/Gynecology
    - Ophthalmology
    - Orthopedic Surgery
    - Otolaryngology
    - Pathology
    - Pediatrics
    - Peripheral Vascular Surgery
    - Physical Medicine and Rehabilitation
    - Plastic and Reconstructive Surgery
    - Psychiatry
    - Pulmonary Medicine
    - Radiation Oncology
    - Radiology
    - Rheumatology and
    - Urology

The CMD must work with the societies to ensure that committee members or representative of the entire service area and represent a variety of practice settings. As of now, Medicare only has instructions encouraging them to appoint representatives or state society members from pain management societies, specifically state society of interventional pain physicians. Some carrier medical directors have misunderstood these directions. In multiple areas including with interpretation of state medical societies and specialty societies, their obligation is only to appoint one or two physicians with the alternate representative from the above listed 33 specialties, with regards to the establishment of advisory committees and, finally, the size of the Carrier Advisory Committee. In February of 2002, CMS at the request of the American Society of Interventional Pain Physicians has issued a program memorandum clarifying the issue with removal of any such misunderstanding that pain management representative can serve on the Carrier Advisory Committee. CMS in its letter also emphasized importance of interventional pain physicians serving on the Carrier Advisory Committees and their role in developing local medical review policies.

The Role of Membership

CAC members serve to improve the relations and communication between Medicare and the physician community. Specifically, they:

- Disseminate proposed LMRPs to colleagues in their

respective State and specialty societies to solicit comments;
- Disseminate information about the Medicare program obtained at CAC meetings to their respective State and specialty societies; and
- Discuss inconsistent or conflicting medical review policies.

The Carrier Advisory Committee membership should also include clinical laboratory representative, beneficiaries, and representative from other organizations including state hospital association, PRO medical director, intermediary medical director, Medicaid medical director, and a representative of an association representing administrative practices, such as American Group Practice Association or the Medical Group Management Association. The Medicare manual also suggests that congressional staff must be welcomed to attend as observers. The Medicare manual further suggests that carrier medicare directors to send notices to them of the agenda, as well as dates. Further, the manual suggests carrier medical directors to invite representatives of the regional office to attend and participate.

Structure and Process

The Medicare manual defines the number of representatives to serve on the CAC and the tenure of these representatives. It also describes the role of co-chairs, staff participation, and the location of meeting should be selected. In addition, the manual also describes the process of the Carrier Advisory Committee with frequency of meetings and record keeping.

The manual describes that each specialty shall have only one member and a designated alternate with the approval of committee co-chairs. Additional members may attend and policies that require their expertise are under discussion. Carriers maintain a current local directory of CAC members and that is available to various officials including the provider community on request. Even though carriers have discretion to establish the duration of membership on the committee, the manual recommends that the term should balance the duration of time needed to learn about the process to enhance the level of participation and functioning with the desire to allow a variety of physicians to participate. The manual recommends to consider a two to three year term.

The CAC should be co-chaired by the medical director and one physician selected by the committee. Thus, co-chairs are responsible to run the meetings and determine the agendas; provide the full agenda and background material to each committee at least fourteen days in advance; and encourage committee members to discuss the material and disseminate it to interested colleagues within their specialty and to clinic or hospital colleagues for whom the item may be pertinent. In addition, the members may bring comments back to the meeting or request that their colleagues send written comments to the carrier medical director separately. However, the attendance at the meeting is at the discretion of the committee members. If the item is of importance to their specialty, members are encouraged to attend or they should send an alternate. However, physicians must remember that this is the primary forum for discussion of proposed LMRPs developed by the CMD. The forty-five day comment process required for all LMRPs starts when the proposed LMRP is distributed to the committee members. However, if the need arises to develop and implement LMRPs before the next scheduled meeting, co-chairs solicit comments from committee members by mail or e-mail.

Recommended frequency of meetings is a minimum of 3 meetings a year, with no more than 4 months between meetings. Each meeting should include a discussion and presentation of comparative utilization data that has undergone preliminary analysis by the carrier and relates to discussion of the proposed LMRP. Carriers also solicit input from CAC members to help explain or interpret the data and give advice on how overutilization should be addressed. The use of data to illustrate the extent of problem billing may help justify the need for a particular policy. The comparative data is presented using graphs, charts, and other visual methods of presenting data. In addition, carriers may present egregious individual providers data. However, the identity of the provider or providers is not disclosed or cannot be deduced. Carriers also keep minutes of the meeting and distribute them to the members. Even though carrier medical directors should encourage CAC members to work through their respective organizations and practicing physicians advisory counsel to affect national policy, the CAC is not precluded from commenting on these issues. Thus, when it is appropriate, carrier Medicare director may forward a formal letter to cover a section through the regional office.

Development Process

The process for developing the LMRP includes developing a draft LMRP based on review of medical literature and the contractor's understanding of the local practice. In addition, contractors solicit comments from the medical community, carriers solicit comments from the Carrier Advisory Committee, contractors respond to comments and, where appropriate incorporate them into the final LMRP. Contractors notify providers of the LMRP effective date. New LMRP may not be implemented retroactively.

The Medicare manual strongly recommends for the contractors with LMRP jurisdiction for two or more states to develop uniform LMRP across all its jurisdictions. However, the contractor must continue to maintain and utilize CACs in accordance with the Medicare integrity manual. In a program memorandum released on 7/11/01, CMS clarified that multi-state contractors may develop uniform LMRP across all its jurisdictions even if data analysis indicated that the problem existed only in one state. The use of LMRP helps to avoid situations in which claims are paid or denied without a provider having a full understanding of the basis for payment and denial. Thus, contractors shall develop LMRPs when they have identified an item or service that is never covered under certain circumstances and wish to establish automated review in the absence of a national coverage decision that supports automated review. Contractors may develop LMRPs under following circumstances:

- A validated widespread problem demonstrates a significant risk to the Medicare trust funds (identified or potentially high dollar and/or high volume services);
- LMRP is needed to assure beneficiary access to care;
- A contractor has assumed the LMRP development workload of another contractor and is undertaking an initiative to create uniform LMRPs across its multiple jurisdictions; or
- Frequent denials are issued (following routine or complex review) or frequent denials are anticipated.
- Further, contractors must review and appropriately revise affected LMRP within 90 days of the publication of;
- A program instruction containing a new or revised national coverage decision;
- A program instruction containing a new or revised coverage provision and interpretive manual;
- A program instruction containing a change to national payment policy.

In addition, contractors must all review and appropriately revise affected LMRP within 120 days of the publication of an update of the ICD-9 or CPT coding systems.

CMS in a program memorandum issued on 7/11/01 instructed all carriers the following: effective October 2001, to ensure that all LMRPs remain accurate and up-to-date at all times; at least annually, contractors must review and appropriately revise LMRPs based upon HCFA's NCD; coverage provisions in interpretive manuals; national payment policies and national coding policies. If an LMRP has been rendered useless by a superseding national policy, it must be retired. This process must include a review of the policies at www.LMRP.net.

The above program memorandum also advises contractors should ensure that LMRPs are developed for services only within their jurisdiction. The requirements for LMRP are that it should be clear, concise and not restrict or conflict with national coverage decisions or coverage provisions in the interpretative manuals. When a national coverage decision or coverage provision in an interpretative manual does not exclude coverage for other diagnoses/conditions, contractors must allow for individual consideration unless the LMRP supports automatic denial for some or all of those other diagnoses/conditions.

Contents of LMRPs

The Medicare manual describes certain policies, procedures and wording to be included or not to be included, along with coding provisions and LMRPs.

Contractors may use phrases such as "rarely medically necessary" or "not usually medically necessary" in proposed LMRPs to describe situations where a service is considered to be, in almost instances, not reasonable and necessary. However, Medicare also advises that to limit unsolicited documentation, the LMRP should clearly state what specific documentation or clinical situation would have to exist to be considered reasonable and necessary. The manual also specifies that if a contractor chooses to apply policies from NCD, national coverage provisions and interpretive manuals, or LMRPs during prepay review, they may not do so via automated review if documentation is submitted with a claim. However, they must manually review such claims.

The program memorandum dated 7/11/01 also permits carriers to develop LMRPs that contain absolute words such as "is never covered" or "is only covered for." Thus, when phrases with absolute words are clearly stated in LMRPs, contractors are not required to make any exceptions or give individual consideration based on evidence. Thus, contractors create edits/parameters that are as specific and narrow as possible to separate cases that can be automatically denied from those requiring individual review.

In addition to the above, contractors may incorporate into LMRPs a concept, which is termed as "prerequisite." They may incorporate into LMRPs that the use of an alternative item or service precedes the use of another item or service. However, contractors must base any requirement on evidence that a particular alternative is safe, more effective, or more appropriate for a given condition without exceeding the patient's medical needs. Further, prerequisites must be based on medical appropriateness, not on cost effectiveness. However, any prerequisite for drug therapy must be consistent with the national coverage decisions for label uses. Whenever national policy bases coverage on assessment of need by the beneficiary's provider, prerequisite should not be included in LMRPs. The memo provides guidance to the contractors that as an alternative, they may use phrases and proposed LMRPs like "the provider should consider . . ."

LMRP Coverage Provisions

A service may be covered by a contractor if it meets all of the conditions which include that it is one of the benefit categories described in the social security act, it is not excluded by the social security act, and it is reasonable and necessary under the act. Thus, a service must meet the definition of the benefit category listed in the CMS's manual, should not include such exclusions which are not limited to, routine physical checkups, immunizations, cosmetic surgery, hearing aids, eyeglasses, routine foot care, and most dental care; and service should be considered reasonable and necessary as per the contractor. The guidance from CMS states that contractors shall consider a service to be reasonable and necessary if the contractor determines that the service is safe and effective, not experimental or investigational, and appropriate, including the duration and frequency. In addition, the service must be furnished in accordance with accepted standards of medical practice for the diagnosis or treatment of the patient's condition or to improve the function of a malformed body member, furnished in a setting appropriate the patient's medical needs and condition, ordered and are furnished by qualified personnel, one that only meets the patient's medical needs but does not exceed them, and at least as beneficial as an existing and available medically appropriate alternative.

However, multiple exceptions apply to the requirement that a service be reasonable and necessary for diagnosis or treatment of illness or injury. These include care of pneumococcal, influenza, and hepatitis vaccines; hospice care; screening mammography, screening pap smears, prostate cancer screening tests, colorectal screening tests; and eyeglasses subsequent to cataract surgery with insertion of intraocular lens.

CMS provides the guidance with regards to experimental or investigational. It also provides exception that routine clinical trial services with dates of service on or after September 19, 2000, which met requirements of clinical trials, NCD are considered reasonable and necessary.

LMRPs also incorporate coding provisions in them. A contractor may describe the national or local coding rules that pertain to a given service. However, it should be remembered that the presence and use of billing codes, either describing a specific category of product/ service or describing products/services not otherwise categorized, does not automatically guarantee coverage or payment. Once the appropriate billing code for a service has been identified, contractors must still determine if the service meets Medicare coverage criteria and how much pay for that service.

LMRP Notice and Comment Process

Contractors must provide a minimum comment period of 45 days. For LMRPs that affect services submitted to carriers, the comment period begins at the time the policy is distributed to the CAC either at the regularly scheduled meeting or in writing to all members of the CAC. Contractors may distribute these draft LMRPs to the CAC members via hardcopy or via e-mail.

Further, when developing an LMRP, all contractors must solicit comments and recommendations on the policy and get input from, at least appropriate groups of health professionals and provider organizations that may be affected by the LMRP, representatives of specialty societies, other intermediaries/carriers, professional review organizations within the region and other carrier medical directors within the region, as well as the general public. An effort should be made to ensure that providers who have a history of billing for the service are informed of the proposed LMRP and have the opportunity to comment carriers. Carriers should send and solicit comments from regional office. Carriers are also required to obtain input from the CAC, and providers of service. CAC, as well as providers of service, are encouraged to submit evidence-based data, professional consensus opinions or any other relevant information.

Carriers also should provide open LMRP meetings for the purpose of discussion of draft LMRPs. These meetings are held prior to presenting the policy to the CAC. Interested parties including providers, physicians, vendors, manufacturers, beneficiaries, and caregivers can make presentations of information related to draft policies. Contractors must remain sensitive to organizations or groups which may have an interest in an issue and should invite them to participate in meetings in which a related LMRP is to be specifically discussed. Contractors are required to post a summary of comments concerning the draft LMRP with the contractor's response.

Contractors must make final LMRPs public via a special bulletin, update to a provider manual, or inclusion in a newsletter, and through their website. However, these requirements vary with substantial changes with restricting an existing LMRP, or liberalizing a policy; nonsubstantial changes with clarification or correction. Contractors are provided with ability to bypassing the notice and comment process if a new/revised LMRP is developed and there are compelling reasons to forego the notice and comment process, with regional office approval. However, contractors simultaneously initiate the notice and comment period and implement the new/revised policy.

CMS provided carriers with newly developed policies to use a standard format. All new LMRPs must be written in hypertext markup language. The LMRPs on the website must be also in hypertext markup language. This does not prohibit a contractor from writing policies in word or another application and then translating them into HTML. All LMRPs should include the following:

- Contractor policy number
- Contractor name
- Contractor number
- Contractor type
- LMRP title
- AMA CPT copyright statement

- CMS national coverage policy
- Primary geographic jurisdiction
- Secondary geographic jurisdiction
- CMS region
- CMS consortium
- Original policy effective date
- Original policy ending date
- Revision effective
- Revision ending date
- LMRP description
- Indications and limitations of coverage and/or medical necessity
- CPT/HCPC S section & benefit category
- Type of bill code
- Revenue codes
- CPT/HCPCS codes
- Not otherwise classified (NOC)
- ICD-9 codes that support medical necessity
- Diagnosis that support medical necessity
- ICD-9 codes that DO NOT support medical necessity
- Diagnosis that DO NOT support medical necessity
- Reasons for denial
- Noncovered ICD-9 code(s)
- Noncovered diagnosis
- Coding guidelines
- Documentation requirements
- Utilization guidelines
- Other comments
- Sources of information and basis for decision
- Advisory committee notes
- Start date of comment period
- End date of comment period
- Start date of notice period
- Revision history

Finally, LMRPs must include the following paragraph: "this policy does not reflect the sole opinion of the contractor or contractor medical director. Although the final decision rests with the contractor, this policy was developed in cooperation with the advisory groups, which includes representatives from . . ."

SECTION 2

NON-INTERVENTIONAL SERVICES

EVALUATION AND MANAGEMENT SERVICES IN INTERVENTIONAL PAIN MEDICINE

Laxmaiah Manchikanti, MD

"It is as important to know the person who has the disease as to know the disease the person has."

Sir William Osler

"A doctor who cannot take a good history, and a patient who cannot give one are in danger of giving and receiving bad treatment."

Anonymous

"More mistakes are made from want of proper examination than for any other reason."

Russell Howard

Evaluation of new patients and established patients is an integral part of interventional pain medicine. Over the last few years there has been significant confusion over the proper documentation for evaluation and management services in general and interventional pain medicine in particular. The confusion has been made worse by numerous articles published in a multitude of advisory publications and misguided advice by well-meaning consultants (1). Interventional pain physicians have learned basic evaluation of patients presenting with pain based on their specialty training. While modern training programs are introducing residents and fellows to the intricacies of evaluation and management services and federal regulations, this has not always been the case. Multiple textbooks of pain management, physiatry, and neurology and numerous journal articles have described the evaluation of pain patients, but they have not met the regulatory perspective (2-9). While these publications were written by well-meaning, well-read academicians, it is unfortunate that none of them meet the current evaluation and management documentation criteria according to the level of service established by Health Care Financing Administration (HCFA), now known as The Centers for Medicare and Medicaid Services (CMS), and herein after referred to as CMS (HCFA) (10-14).

HISTORICAL CONSIDERATIONS

The medical evaluation of patients has been a fact of life since the beginnings of medical history. Over the years, advances in medicine, increasing knowledge, and understanding of the physiologic concepts of pain have dramatically improved the evaluation process. While medicine was always influenced by federal regulations, the influence of these laws and regulations has become much more intrusive since the enactment of Medicare. In the evolution of numerous regulations governing the practice of medicine by the CMS (HCFA), implementation of evaluation and management guidelines started in the 1990s. The latest guidelines utilized in the U.S. were developed in 1997. The new proposed guidelines were awaiting pilot testing and were expected to be released in the later part of 2001 or early 2002. Consequently, CMS (HCFA) has permitted providers to use either the 1997 or 1995 versions of the guidelines in the interim. Meanwhile, on July 19, 2001, Secretary of HHS, announced that he has directed stoppage on further work on these proposed guidelines.

In the past, physicians followed a simple format characterized by an acronym, SOAP, which stands for *subjective, objective, assessment, and plan*. This was later expanded, presumably to meet the criteria of CMS (HCFA's) evaluation and management services, to SOAPER to also include *education and return instructions*. Other variations of the same theme include SOAPIE, which stands for *subjective, objective, assessment, plan, intervention and evaluation*; and SNOCAMP, which stands for *subjective, nature of presenting problem, counseling, assessment, medical decision making and plan*. However, due to the complicated nature of the documentation guidelines proposed by CMS (HCFA), SOAP and SOAPER no longer meet the criteria in most cases. Other variations are as complicated as CMS (HCFA) guidelines.

The CMS (HCFA) and multiple specialty societies continue to struggle with differing opinions, in favor of and against the various components of evaluation and management guidelines.

The most important aspect of billing and coding for evaluation and management services includes appropriate documentation of the level of service by documentation of history, which includes chief complaint, history of present illness, review of systems, past, family, and social history; physical examination, which includes either single-system or multisystem examination; and complexity of decision making, which includes straightforward, low-complexity, moderate complexity, or high complexity.

The latest in the saga of development of guidelines:

- Secretary Tommy Thompson halted development of guidelines on July 19, 2001.
- AMA formed a new workgroup, expected to keep CMSs Advisory Council on payment issues Practicing Physi cians' Advisory Council (PPAC), informed about the di rection of discussion on E/M Guidelines, modification of CPT codes, with target dates of recommendations by end of 2002, and pilot testing in 2003 or 2004.
- There is no guarantee that CMS would use what the AMA work group recommends.
- CMS asserted that the proposed E/M Guidelines need to come from people who use these codes and not the administrative agency.
- CMS staff is discussing about:
  - collapsing the 5 E/M codes down to 4 or 3
  - doing away with guidelines
  - necessity of new guidelines
- On December 4, 2001, US House of Representatives passed a bill which requires:
  - HHS to develop new E/M Guidelines in collaboration with practicing physicians
  - Subject any such guidelines to appropriate pilot tests – peer review method and time based method
  - Provide physician education on use of the guidelines.

MEDICAL NECESSITY

Medical necessity requires appropriate diagnosis and coding by ICD-9-CM to justify services rendered and indicates the severity of the patient's condition (15). The Balanced Budget Act (HR 2015, Section 4317) requires all physicians to provide diagnostic information for all Medicare/Medicaid patients starting from January 1, 1998 (12, 13). Further, failure to comply with this regulation can result in prosecution. Physicians should code by listing the ICD-9-CM diagnostic codes shown in the medical record to be chiefly responsible for the services provided. Coding should be to the highest degree of certainty for each encounter. Coding also should correlate with multiple components of the patient's medical record, including initial evaluation or follow-up visits, and the billing statement. One "silver lining" for interventional pain practices is that chronic conditions treated on an ongoing basis may be reported as many times as the patient receives care for the condition. If proper diagnosis is not established, codes that describe symptoms and signs, as opposed to the diagnosis, are acceptable for reporting purposes until the diagnosis is confirmed. Medical necessity is defined in numerous ways:

- The Centers for Medicare and Medicaid Services defines medical necessity as, ... "no payment may be made under part A of part B for any expense incurred for items or services which ... are not reasonable and necessary for the diagnosis or treatment of illness or injury or to improve the functioning of a malformed body member."
- The American Medical Association defines medical necessity as, " Health care services or products that a prudent physician would provide to a patient for the purpose of preventing, diagnosing or treating an illness, injury, disease or its symptoms in a manner that is: 1) in accordance with generally accepted standards of medical practice; 2) clinically appropriate in terms of type, frequency, extent, site and duration; and 3) not primarily for the convenience of the patient, physician or other healthcare provider."
- According to Black's Dictionary of Law, Medical necessity is defined as, " An absolute physical necessity, an inevitability, or convenient, useful, appropriate, suitable, proper or conductive to the end sought" (16).
- According to Quinn (17), who offered a common sense formulation of how the matter of medical necessity should be handled in individual cases defined medical necessity as, "Ideally, it encompasses the shortest least expensive, or least intense level of treatment, care or service rendered, or supply provided, as determined to the extent required to diagnose or treat an injury or sickness".
- One insurer defined medical necessity as, "Health care services and supplies which are determined by the carrier to satisfy all of the following requirements:
  - Necessary to meet basic health needs of the Covered Person;
  - Rendered in the most cost-effective manner and type of setting appropriate for the delivery of the service or supply;
  - Consistent in type, frequency and duration of

treatment with scientifically based guidelines of national medical, research, or health care cover age organizations or governmental agencies that are accepted by the company;
- Consistent with the diagnosis of the condition;
- Required for reasons other than the conveniece of the Covered Person or his or her Physician;and
- Demonstrated through prevailing peer-reviewed medical literature to be either:
    - Safe and effective for treating or diagnosing the condition or illness for which their use is proposed; and or
    - Safe with promising efficacy.
        - For treating a life threatening illness or condition;
        - In a clinically controlled research setting; and
        - Using a specific research protocol that meets standards equivalent to those defined by the National Institutes of Health.

- Another insurer defined medical necessity as, "medically necessary means the shortest, least expensive, or least intense level of treatment, care, or service rendered, or supply provided, as determined by us, the extent required to diagnose or treat an injury or sickness. The service or supply must be consistent with the insured persons medical condition, is know to be safe and effective by most doctors who are licensed to treat the condition at the time the service is rendered, and is not provided primarily for the convenience of the insured person or doctor."

WIDE ARENA OF DOCUMENTATION

Medical record documentation is required to record pertinent facts, findings, and observations about an individual's health history including the past and present illnesses, examinations, tests, treatments, and outcomes. The medical record facilitates (2, 3):

- The ability of a physician and other health care professionals to evaluate and plan the patient's treatment and to monitor his or her health care over a period of time;
- Communication and continuity of care among physicians and other health care professionals involved in the patient's care;
- Accurate and timely claims review and payment;
- Appropriate utilization review and quality of care evaluations; and
- Collection of data that may be useful for research and education.

MEDICAL RECORD

A medical record is a document with confidential information that functions as a clinical record, as well as a business record. A properly executed medical record facilitates and provides information with regards to:

- Why did the patient present for care?
- What was done?
- Where were the services rendered?
- When is the patient to return or what is the plan of action?
- Will there be follow-up tests or procedures ordered?

Functions of a Medical Record are as follows:

- Supports "medical necessity"
- Reduces professional liability exposure
- Reduces audit exposure
- Facilitates claim review
- Supports insurance billing
- Provides clinical data for education
- Provides clinical data for research
- Promotes continuity of care
- Indicates quality care

Specific requirements of a Medical Record Documentation of CMS (HCFA) are as follows:

- Supports " medical necessity "
- Complete
- Legible
- Signed

Table 1. *Functions and requirements of patient's medical record*

Clinical Record	Business Record	CMS's (HCFA's) Requirements
Indicates quality of care	Supports insurance billing	Supports "medical necessity"
Promotes continuity of care among physicians	Facilitates claim review	Complete
Provides clinical data for research	Reduces audit exposure	Legible
Provides clinical data for education	Reduces professional liability exposure	Signed

Table 2. *Various types of CPT codes utilized for evaluation and management services relevant to interventional pain medicine*

New Patient Office Visit(s)	Established Outpatient(s)	Office Consult (s) New or Established Patient(s)	Initial Inpatient New or Established Patient(s)	Subsequent Equipment Hospital Care	Observation or in Patient Care services	Initial Inpatient Consult(s)	Follow-Up Impatient Consult(s)
99201	99211	99241	99221	99231	99234	99251	99261
99202	99212	99242	99222	99232	99235	99252	99262
99203	99213	99243	99223	99233	99236	99253	99263
99204	99214	99244				99254	
99205	99215	99245				99255	

Table 3. *Common CPT codes for evaluation and management services in pain management*

A. Office Outpatients

i. New Patients

99201 - Problem Focused
99202 – Expanded Problem Focused
99203 - Detailed/Low Complexity
99204 - Comprehensive/Moderate Complexity
99205 - Comprehensive/High Complexity

ii. Established Patients

99211 – Brief
99212 – Problem Focused
99213 – Expanded Problem Focused
99214 - Detailed/Moderate Complexity
99215 - Comprehensive/High Complexity

iii.Office Consultations (New or Established Patients)

99241 - Problem Focused
99242 - Expanded Problem Focused
99243 - Detailed/Low Complexity
99244 - Comprehensive/Moderate Complexity
99245 - Comprehensive/High Complexity

B. Hospital Services

i. Initial Inpatient (New or Established Patient)

99221 - Detailed/Low Complexity
99222 - Comprehensive/Moderate Complexity
99223 - Comprehensive/High Complexity

ii. Subsequent Hospital Care

99231 - Problem Focused/Low Complexity
99232 - Expanded Problem Focused/Moderate Complexity
99233 - Detailed/High Complexity

iii. Initial Inpatients (Consultations)

99251 – Problem Focused
99252 – Expanded Problem Focused
99253 – Detailed/Low Complexity
99254 – Comprehensive/Moderate Complexity
99255 – Comprehensive/High Complexity

iv. Follow-up Inpatient (Consultations)

99261 – Problem Focused
99262 – Expanded Problem Focused
99263 – Detailed/High Complexity

Essential functions and requirements of a patient's medical record are listed in Table 1.

LEVELS OF SERVICE

Evaluation and management services in pain management are office outpatient services and hospital inpatient services (Tables 1 to 3). Five levels of services are available for office outpatients. Four levels for established office outpatients (for established office outpatient, CPT 99211 does not involve physician services and comprehensive/high complexity not available), and five levels for consultations and new patient visits that include:

Level 1 – Problem focused
Level 2 – Expanded problem focused
Level 3 – Detailed/low complexity
Level 4 – Comprehensive/moderate complexity
Level 5 – Comprehensive/high complexity

Hospital services include initial inpatient, either new or established patients; subsequent inpatient hospital care; initial inpatient consultations; and follow-up inpatient consultations. Initial inpatient and subsequent inpatient hospital care is divided into three levels encompassing:

Level 1 – Detailed/low complexity
Level 2 – Comprehensive/moderate complexity
Level 3 – Comprehensive/high complexity

Initial and follow-up inpatient consultations, however, differ in that initial inpatient consultations are at five levels similar to new patient consultations but follow-up inpatient consultations are only at three levels.

The descriptors for the levels of evaluation and management services recognize seven components, of which three components are considered crucial in defining the levels of evalu-

Table 4. *CMS (HCFA) guidelines differantiating features of consultation and a referral visit*

	Consultation	Referral Visit
1. Problem	Suspected	Known
2. Request Language	"Please examine patient and provide me with your opinion and recommendation on his/her condition."	"Patient is referred for treatment or management of his/her condition."
3. Request	Written request for opinion or advice received from attending physician, including the *specific* reason the consultation is requested.	Patient appointment made for the purpose of providing treatment or management or other diagnostic or therapeutic services.
4. Report Language	"I was asked to see Mr. Jones in consultation by Dr. Johnson."	"Mr. Jones was seen following a referral from Dr. Johnson."
5. Patient Care	*Only* opinion or advice sought. Subsequent to the opinion, treatment may be initiated in the same encounter.	Transfer of total patient care for management of the specified condition.
6. Treatment	Undetermined course	Prescribed and known course
7. Correspondence	Written opinion returned to attending physician.	No further communication (or limited contact) with referring physician is required.
8. Diagnosis	Final diagnosis is probably unknown.	Final diagnosis is typically known at the time of referral.
9. Follow-up	Patient advised to follow up with attending physician.	Patient advised to return for additional discussion, testing, treatment, or continuation of treatment and management.
10. Further Follow-up	Confirmatory or follow-up consultation or established patient based on specific situation.	Always established patient for 3 years.

ation and management services in interventional pain medicine. Three crucial components are:

- History
- Physical examination
- Medical decision making

Other components include:

- Counseling
- Coordination of care
- Nature of presenting problem
- Time

Because the level of evaluation and management service is dependent on two or three components, performance and documentation of one component at the highest level does not necessarily mean that the encounter in its entirety qualifies for the highest level of evaluation and management service.

If counseling or coordination of care are provided as the predominant service constituting more than 50% of the time by the physician, then time may be considered the key or controlling factor to qualify for a particular level of evaluation and management service.

CONSULT VERSUS VISIT

Interpretation of the guidelines for consultations versus visits and billing for these services, along with the level of service, are contentious issues. Guidelines by CMS (HCFA) have clarified some of the issues involved in the confusion with regards to this issue. The guidelines suggest that any time a physician sees a patient at the request of another physician, the visit may be a consultation (1). However, there are three "R's" for considerations for the visit to qualify for a consultation.

- First "R", the requesting physician must be seeking the advice or opinion of the consulting physician, not transferring care. Documentation of such a request for consultation is essential.
- Second "R", you must be render the service / opinion.
- Third "R", there must be documentation that the consulting physician has communicated his or her findings to the requesting physician in writing or report back.

Table 4 shows the differences between a consultation and visit. The CPT and CMS (HCFA) guidelines have always stated that a physician may order laboratory tests and/or institute treatment at the time of a consultation. Hence, if an interventional pain medicine physician is asked to see a patient with back pain, either in the hospital or in the office, the interventional pain specialist may institute treatment and the visit may still be a consultation, however, it becomes a visit if the referring physician arranges for the receiving physician to take over part or all of the care prior to the receiving physician seeing the patient. Another misunderstood issue with regards to consultation is that if the receiving physician assumes part or all of the care of the patient, then subsequent visits must not be coded as a consultation but as subsequent outpatient or hospital care. This is somewhat confused with initial visits in some cases. Follow-up consultations would be appropriate only when there is a period of time between visits. For example, an interventional pain physician sees a patient in consultation, makes recommendations and signs off and then later is asked to see the patient because the recommended treatment did not work; that may be considered a follow-up consultation. One of the major requirements of consultation is that of documentation in the patient's record that the consultation in fact was requested. This can be accomplished by a letter from the requesting physician asking for the consultation, or a consultation request slip followed by documentation by the consulting physician something similar to: "I was asked to see this patient for consultation by Dr. Smith." Documentation that findings of the consulting physician were communicated in writing to the requesting physician is also crucial. This may be accomplished by sending the requesting physician a copy of the patient record, and a thank you letter. Unfortunately, recently published guidelines require that it be in writing, contradicting the earlier guidelines where communication by telephone was sufficient. Coding for a large number of consultations raises red flags to CMS (HCFA) medical directors who are monitoring each physician's coding profile. Thus, abnormal coding profiles are likely to bring on audits. Therefore, interventional pain medicine specialists must weigh the increased revenue from a consultation versus the possible consequences of audit, which may include not only the evaluation and management services, but may be extended to any other area of the practice.

THE EVALUATION PROCESS

History

History constitutes one of the three crucial components of evaluation and management, the other two being physical examination and medical decision making. All patients, whether new or established, seen in the office or in the hospital setting, for visits or consultation, require documentation of history based on level of service. The history includes:

- Chief complaint
- History of present illness
- Review of systems
- Past, family, and/or social history

The extent of history obtained and documented is dependent upon the clinical judgment of the physician and the nature of the presenting problem of the patient (Table 5). Nevertheless, the required documentation is progressively detailed and complex, with brief and problem pertinent for problem focused and extended problem focused to extended and complete for detailed comprehensive and comprehensive/complex services.

Chief Complaint: The chief complaint is a concise statement describing the symptom, problem, condition, diagnosis, physician-recommended return, or other factor that is the reason for the encounter, usually stated in the patient's words. This should be clearly documented in the medical record.

The chief complaint should always be the first thing in initial evaluation, history and physical, progress note, and consultation report. Examples of chief complaint or statement include:

- Low back pain
- Pain in the neck
- Headache
- Can't move shoulder
- Hurting for the past week

Table 5. *Documentation of level of history*

	Problem focused	Expanded Problem	Detailed/Low Complexity	Comprehensive
Chief complaint	Yes	Yes	Yes	Yes
History of present illness	Brief (1-3)	Brief (1-3)	Extended or >3 chronic conditions	Extended or >3 chronic conditions
System review	NA	Problem pertinent (1system)	Extended (2-9 systems)	Complete (10+ systems)
Past family social history	NA	NA	Pertinent (1 area)	Complete (2 or 3 areas)

- Pain in the spine
- Management of back pain
- Back still hurts
- Follow-up for back pain
- Head still hurts
- Can't walk
- Here for evaluation and management
- Here for injection therapy
- Reason for appointment: evaluation and management
- Here for medicine refills
- Here to discuss my test results

However, chief statements such as:

- Doing fine
- No problems
- Feeling fine
- History of back pain
- Blocks helped well
- Can't work, etc.,

will not suffice. It is critical that the chief complaint establishes medical necessity. However, if medical necessity of the visit is not established with the chief complaint, this can be established in the history of present illness by a statement to explain the purpose of the patient's visit, such as:

- Mr. Jones is here for further evaluation and management with injection therapy,
- Mr. Jones is here for further evaluation and prescription refills.

History of Present Illness: History of present illness is a chronological description of the development of the patient's present illness from the first sign and/or symptom or from the previous encounter to the present. It includes the following elements:

- Location – Describing the area of the body
- Quality – Sensation or pattern that will be satisfied by the McGill Pain Questionnaire (MPQ), either short form or long form
- Severity – Satisfied by pain-rating scale, either visual analog, verbal or numerical scale describing the level of pain
- Duration – Symptom duration from onset to the present encounter
- Timing – Description of the pain pattern:
- continuous, intermittent, in the evening or afternoon, etc.
- Context – Specific circumstances, conditions, and activities surrounding the present condition
- Modifying factors – Measures taken to relieve symptoms or discomfort, such as physical therapy, surgery, injection therapy, drug therapy, etc., and results with these measures
- Associated signs and symptoms – Such as numbness, weakness, blurred vision, disturbed sleep pattern, or difficulty with activities of daily living, etc.

Brief and extended history of present illness are distinguished by the amount of detail needed to accurately characterize the clinical problem(s) (10, 12, 13). Brief history of present illness requires documentation of one to three elements of the present illness, whereas extended history of present illness requires documentation of at least four elements of the history of present illness or the status of at least three chronic or inactive conditions. Further, a brief history of present illness suffices for problem-focused and expanded-problem-focused visits, whereas extended with at least four elements or status of three inactive or chronic conditions is required for detailed comprehensive and comprehensive complex levels of services (10, 12, 13). Examples of brief history of present illness with one to three elements include:

- Intermittent low back pain with radiation into leg
- Intermittent neck pain with headache and radiation to both upper extremities
- Throbbing headache for two months

Examples of extended history of present illness with four elements or status of three chronic or inactive elements may be achieved with careful articulation of patient symptomatology with one or more conditions, for example:

Intermittent midline and bilateral neck pain with radiation into both upper extremities; associated with headaches; associated with occasional numbness, tingling, and weakness since 1984, which started following a fall from a roof; which failed to respond to various conservative modalities of treatment with physical therapy, medical therapy, and three sugical interventions; with arm pain and neck pain equal.

Review of Systems: Review of systems is an inventory of body systems obtained through a series of questions seeking to identify signs and/or symptoms that the patient may be experiencing or has experienced (10, 12, 13). Guidelines recognize the following 14 systems for purposes of review of systems, also known as medical review. These systems include:

- Constitutional
- Eyes
- Ears, nose, mouth, throat
- Cardiovascular
- Respiratory
- Gastrointestinal
- Genitourinary
- Musculoskeletal
- Integumentary (skin and/or breast)

- Neurological
- Psychiatric
- Endocrine
- Hematologic/lymphatic
- Allergy/immunologic

Review of systems is described at three levels, which include problem pertinent, extended, and complete. Problem pertinent involves the documentation of the patient's pertinent responses, both positive as well as negative, for the system related to the problem. In contrast, an extended review of systems includes positive and pertinent negatives for two to nine systems, as listed above. For complete review of systems, at least 10 systems must be reviewed and documented; however, while those systems with positive or pertinent negative responses must be individually documented, a notation indicating that the remaining systems are negative is acceptable. In the absence of such a notation, at least 10 systems must be individually documented.

Review of systems is not required for problem-focused visits, either for new patients or established patients. For the expanded-problem focused level, problem-pertinent review of system with positives and negatives is required. However, for detailed, ie, level 3, for new patients as well as established patients, extended review of systems with positive and pertinent negatives for two to nine systems is required. For comprehensive levels, complete review of systems with at least 10 systems is required.

Information for review of systems is obtained through a series of questions, either by a questionnaire or through recording by ancillary staff. However, physicians should document that the information was reviewed. Hence, there must be notation supplementing or confirming the information recorded by others. If the physician is unable to obtain a history from the patient or other source, the record should describe the patient's condition or other circumstance which precludes obtaining a history.

Review of systems may be listed as separate elements of the history, or they may be included in the description of the history of present illness.

A review of history obtained during an earlier encounter does not need to be rerecorded if there is evidence that the physician reviewed and updated the previous information. This may occur when a physician updates his or her own record or when many physicians use a common record in an institutional setting or group practice. The review and update may be documented by:

- Describing any new information or noting that there has been no change in the information; and
- Noting the date and location of the earlier review of system documentation.

Appropriate levels of system reviews can be met by using a comprehensive questionnaire enabling the patient or the ancillary staff to record all the systems; thus, during the documentation pertinent positives and negatives and all positives may be recorded, followed by a statement that all other systems were negative.

Past, Family, and/or Social History: The past, family, and/or social history consists of:

- A review of the past history of the patient including past experiences, illnesses, operations, injuries, and treatments
- Family history, including a review of medical events in the patient's family, hereditary diseases, and other factors
- Social history appropriate for age reflecting past and current activities

There are two levels of past, family, and/or social history: pertinent to problems identified in history of present illness; and complete, which includes at least one specific history of present illness item from three of the three history areas. A problem-focused or expanded problem-focused visit does not require past, family, and/or social history; however, a detailed visit requires at least one specific item from one of three areas of the history to be pertinent, in contrast to comprehensive, which requires complete past, family, and/or social history with at least one specific history of present illness from three of the three history areas for new patients and at least two specific items from three history areas for established patients.

Past, family, and/or social history may be listed as a separate element of the history, or it may be included in the description of the history of the present illness; it may be recorded by ancillary staff or on a questionnaire or a form completed by the patient. To document that a physician, in fact, reviewed the information, there must be notation supplementing or confirming the information recorded by others.

If the physician is unable to obtain a history from the patient or other source, the record should describe the patient's condition or other circumstance, which precludes obtaining a history.

Past, family, and/or social history obtained during an earlier encounter does not need to be rerecorded if there is evidence that the physician reviewed and updated the previous information. This may occur when a physician updates his or her own record or when many physicians use a common record in an institutional setting or group practice. The review and update may be documented by describing any new information or noting there has been no change in the information and noting the date and location of the earlier past, family, and/or social history.

Past history in interventional pain medicine includes history of past pain problems, ranging from headaches to numbness or tingling in the feet, motor vehicle injuries, occupational, or non-occupational injuries; history of headache, neck pain, upper extremity pain, pain in the upper, mid back or chest wall, pain in low back or lower extremities, and pain in joints; and disorders such as arthritis, fibromyalgia, or systemic lupus erythematosus.

Family history includes history of pain problems in the family such as low back pain, neck pain, mid back or upper back pain, chest wall pain, extremity pain, headaches, migraine, arthritis, fibromyalgia, multiple sclerosis, and systemic lupus erythematosus; drug dependency, alcoholism, drug abuse; and psychological disorders such as depression, anxiety, schizophrenia, and suicidal tendencies, etc.

Social history includes environmental information, education, marital status, children, habits, hobbies, and occupational history whenever available.

An example of documentation of past history is as follows: Mr. Jones suffered with low back pain in the past, and sustained a work-related injury in 1995, which resulted in neck pain. He was involved in a motor vehicle injury in 1984. He denied any history of any other pain problems, injuries, fibromyalgia, or arthritis.

An example of documentation of family history includes that the history was positive for migraine, arthritis, and low back pain in the family; but that it was negative for fibromyalgia, systemic lupus erythematosus, alcoholism, drug dependency, depression, schizophrenia, and epilepsy.

Social history may be documented as follows: lives in any town, is a high school graduate, is married with three children, works as a carpenter, has smoked three packs of cigarettes since 1978, does not drink alcohol, and plays golf for recreation. All of these may be separated into various sections indicating environment, occupation, habits, and hobbies.

Physical Examination

Various levels of evaluation and management services are based on four types of examination (Table 6). However, the type of examination is dependent upon the nature of the presenting problem(s) and clinical judgment of the physician.

- Problem focused – It is a limited examination of the affected body area or organ system(s), includes examination of one to five bullet-point elements from a single-system examination such as musculoskeletal.
- Expanded problem focused – It is a limited examination of the affected body area or organ system, and any other symptomic or related body areas or organ systems, documentation of at least six of the bullet-point elements from one of the ten single-organ system examinations.
- Detailed – This is an extended examination of the affected body area(s) or organ system(s) and any other symptomatic or related body area(s) or organ system(s), documentation of at least 12 bullet points or elements from one of the ten single-system examinations.
- Comprehensive – This is a general multisystem examination, a complete examination of a single organ system and other symptomatic or related areas or organ systems, documentation of all elements identified by a bullet.

Various types of examinations include either general multi-system examination or single-organ-system examination. Single-organ-system examinations include examination of any of the 10 organ systems:

- Musculoskeletal
- Neurological
- Cardiovascular
- Ears, nose, mouth, and throat
- Eyes

Table 6. *CMS (HCFA) Documentation requirements for various levels of examination*

	Problem focused	Expanded problem focused	Detailed	Comprehensive
Multi-system	Perform and document 1-5 elements	Perform and document > 6 elements	Perform and document 12 elements in > 2 areas	Perform all elements in >9 areas. Document >2 elements in 9 areas
Single-system	Perform and document 1-5 elements	Perform and document > 6 elements	Perform and document 12 elements	Perform all elements. Document every element in shaded box and >1 element in unshaded box

- Genitourinary – female
- Genitourinary – male
- Hematologic/lymphatic/immunologic
- Psychiatric
- Respiratory
- Skin

A general multisystem examination or a single-organ-system examination may be performed by any physician, regardless of the specialty. The type of the examination, however, whether it is general multisystem or single-organ-system and its content(s) are selected by the examining or consulting physician and are based upon clinical judgment, the patient's history, and the nature of the presenting problem or problems(s).

In interventional pain medicine, the following types of examinations are suitable.

- General multisystem examination,
- A single organ system examination consisting of either musculoskeletal or neurological systems.

The content in documentation requirements for each type and level of examination are summarized and described in Table 6. Some of the important aspects of the evaluation and management and physical examination are as follows:

- Performance and documentation of one component at the highest level does not necessarily mean that the encounter in its entirety qualifies for the highest level of service.
- The three key components are history, examination, and complexity of medical decision making.
- The chief complaint, review of systems, and past, family, or social history may be listed as separate elements of history, or they may be included in the description of the history of the present illness.
- The review of systems and the past, family, and social history may be recorded by ancillary staff or on a form completed by the patient. However, the physician must document that the information was reviewed by making a notation supplementing or confirming the information recorded by others. If the history is unobtainable, either from the patient or other source, the record should describe the patient's condition or other circumstance, which precludes obtaining a history.
- "Abnormal" – A notation without elaboration is insufficient. Specific abnormal and relevant findings of the examination of the affected or symptomatic body area or areas or organ system or systems should be documented.
- Abnormal or unexpected findings of the examination of any asymptomatic body area or areas or organ system or organ systems should be described.
- "Negative" or "normal" is sufficient to document normal findings related to unaffected area or areas of asymptomatic organ system (s).
- Documentation for each element must satisfy any numeric requirements.

General Multisystem Examination(s): General multisystem examination(s), although they appear simpler and may fit universal needs, are somewhat complex. To qualify for a given level of multisystem examination, the documentation should include:

- Problem-focused examination – Should include performance and documentation of one to five elements in one or more organ system(s) or body area(s)
- Expanded problem focused – Should include performance and documentation of at least six elements in one or more organ system(s) or body area(s).
- Detailed examination – Should include at least six organ systems or body areas for each system/area selected; performance and documentation of at least two elements is expected. However, alternatively, a detailed examination may include performance and documentation of at least 12 elements in two or more organ systems or body areas.
- Comprehensive – Comprehensive examinations should include at least nine organ systems or body areas. For each system/area selected, all elements of the examination should be performed unless specific directions limit the content of the examination. For each area or system, documentation of at least two elements identified by a bullet is expected.

Even though criteria can be met by examining each area or system and documenting at least two elements, the difficulties with general multisystem examination include:

- Ophthalmoscopic examination of the optic discs and posterior segments
- Otoscopic examination of the external auditory canals and tympanic membranes
- Inspection and palpation of breasts
- Examination of genitourinary system

However, comprehensive examination can be met by examination of only nine out of 12 organ systems or body areas.

Single-System Examination(s): Single-system examination(s) include an examination of any of the 12 systems. However, variations among these examinations in the organ systems and body areas reflect differing emphasis among specialties. To qualify for a given level of single-system examination, the following content and documentation requirement should be met.

- Problem focused – This examination should include performance and documentation of one to five elements.
- Expanded problem focused – This examination should include performance and documentation of at least six elements.
- Detailed examination – Examinations other than the eye and psychiatric examination should include performance and documentation of at least 12 elements.
- Eye and psychiatric examination – Should include the performance and documentation of at least nine elements
- Comprehensive – This examination should include documentation of all elements.

Musculoskeletal Examination: Musculoskeletal examination includes the musculoskeletal system as the single primary organ system and multiple other systems. Various systems capable of contributing a number of elements to the evaluation in musculoskeletal examination, single system, are as follows:

Constitutional Two elements:

- Measurement of any three of the seven vital signs
- General appearance of the patient

Cardiovascular One element

- Examination of the peripheral/vascular system

Lymphatic One element

- Palpation of lymph nodes

Skin One element

- Inspection and palpation of the skin in subcutaneous tissue

Neurologic/psychiatric Four elements

- Test coordination
- Deep tendon reflexes
- Sensation
- Assessment of mental status – orientation to time, place, and person
- Mood and effect

Musculoskeletal Five elements

- Gait and station
- Inspection, percussion, and palpation
- Range of motion
- Assessment of stability
- Muscle strength and tone

Thus, the musculoskeletal system has, potentially, a total of 15 elements, 12 from shaded, bordered systems, and 3 from unshaded bordered systems (Table 7). The problem-focused examination may be satisfied by examining only the musculoskeletal system. However, expanded problem-focused examination requires at least six elements that will require complete examination of the musculoskeletal system with five elements and at least one other system with one element, either constitutional, neurological, lymphatic, cardiac, or skin. Detailed examination requires 12 elements, which will require examination of multiple systems to meet the criteria of 12 elements. This can be met by five elements from the musculoskeletal system; five from the neurologic and psychiatric examination; and an additional two from either the constitutional, skin, cardiovascular, or lymphatic systems. Comprehensive requires complete examination or performance of all elements and documentation of every element in each box with a shaded border, and at least one element in each box with an unshaded border, which means examination and documentation of two elements from the constitutional, five elements from the musculoskeletal system examination, one element from the skin examination, and five elements from the neurologic/psychiatric examination; and at least one element from the peripheral vascular and lymphatic, which is all elements.

Neurologic Examination: Specific areas in neurological examination include:

Constitutionial Two elements

- Three of the seven vital signs
- General appearance

Eyes One element

- Ophthalmoscopic examination

Cardiovascular Three elements

- Examination of carotid arteries
- Auscultation of the heart
- Examination of the peripheral/vascular system

Musculoskeletal Three elements

- Examination of gait and station
- Muscle strength in upper and lower ex tremities
- Muscle tone in upper and lower extremities

Neurological Sixteen elements

Table 7. *Comparison of musculoskeletal and neurological - single system examinations for interventional pain practice, with general multisystem - physical examination.*

Systems	Multisystem	Single System	
		Musculoskeletal	Neurologic
Constitutional	2 Elements	2 Elements	2 Elements
Musculoskeletal	6 Elements	5 Elements	3 Elements
Neurological	3 Elements	2 Elements	16 Elements
Cardiovascular	7 Elements	1 Element (Peripheral)	3 Elements
Chest/Breasts	2 Elements	------	------
Ears, Nose, Mouth and Throat	6 Elements	------	------
Eyes	3 Elements	------	1 Element Ophthalmoscopy
Genitourinary	4 Elements - Male 7 Elements - Female	------	------
Gastrointestinal	5 Elements	------	------
Lymphatic	4 Elements	1 Element Lymphatic	------
Psychiatric	4 Elements	2 Elements	------
Respiratory	4 Elements	------	------
Skin	2 Elements	1 Element	------

- Orientation
- Memory
- Attention span and concentration
- Language
- Knowledge
- Second cranial nerve
- Third, fourth, and sixth cranial nerves
- Fifth cranial nerve
- Seventh cranial nerve
- Eighth cranial nerve
- Ninth cranial nerve
- 11th cranial nerve
- 12th cranial nerve
- Sensation
- Tendon reflexes
- Test coordination

Hence, problem focused, which requires one to five elements, and expanded problem focused, which requires six elements, are easily met by examination of the neurological system. Similarly, a detailed examination (which requires 12 elements) can also be met by examination of the neurological system alone. However, a comprehensive examination should include all elements from systems with shaded borders, namely constitutional, musculoskeletal, neurological, and eyes; and one element from the cardiovascular, totaling 23 elements. The major disadvantage of the neurological examination in chronic pain involves ophthalmoscopic examination of the optic discs and posterior segments, and detailed examination of all cranial nerves. If ophthalmoscopic examination is not performed, the physical examination will not meet the criteria for comprehensive.

Differences between musculoskeletal and neurological examination, along with similarities in comparison to general multisystem examination, are illustrated in Table 7.

Medical Decision Making

Documentation of the complexity of medical decision making involves four types of medical decision making to accommodate all levels of evaluation and management services.

The four types of medical decision making options include:

- Straightforward
- Low complexity
- Moderate complexity

- High complexity

Medical decision making refers to the complexity of establishing a diagnosis and/or selecting a management option as measured by three components, including:

- diagnosis/management options, with number of possible diagnoses and/or the number of management options;
- review of records/investigations, with number and/or complexity of medical records, diagnostic tests, and other information that must be obtained, reviewed, and analyzed; and
- risk(s) of significant complications, morbidity and mortality, as well as comorbidities associated with the patient's presenting problem(s), the diagnostic procedure(s), and/or the possible management options.

Table 8 shows the progression of elements required for each level of medical decision making. To qualify for a given type of decision making, at least two of the three elements in the table must be either met or exceeded.

Diagnosis or Management Options: The number of possible diagnoses and/or the number of management options that must be considered is based on the number and types of problems addressed during the encounter, the complexity of establishing a diagnosis, and management decisions that are made by the physician (Table 8). The number and type of diagnostic tests employed may be an indicator of the number of possible diagnoses (Table 9). Problems, that are improving or resolving, are less complex than those that are worsening or failing to change as expected. The need for further consultations or advice from others is another indicator of complexity of diagnostic or management problems.

Following are some important aspects in documenting diagnosis and/or management options.

Table 8. *Progression of elements required for each level of medical decision making*

Type of decision making	Number of diagnoses or management options	Amount and/or complexity of data to be reviewed	Risk of complications and/or morbidity or mortality
Straightforward	Minimal	Minimal or None	Minimal
Low Complexity	Limited	Limited	Low
Moderate Complexity	Multiple	Moderate	Moderate
High Complexity	Extensive	Extensive	High

Table 9. *Required documentation of REVIEW and/or ORDER of diagnostic testing and reporting*

- Clinical lab tests
- Radiology: Review of reports or interpretation
- Medical diagnostic tests
- Any discussion with interpreting physician
- Old record request
- Review of records

- For each encounter, an assessment, clinical impression, or diagnosis should be documented. It may be explicitly stated or implied in documented decisions regarding management plans and/or further evaluation.
- For a presenting problem with an established diagnosis, the records should reflect whether the problem is:
  - Improved, well-controlled, resolving, or resolved;
  - Inadequately controlled, worsening, or failing to change as expected
- For a presenting problem without an established diagnosis, the assessment or clinical impression may be stated in the form of differential diagnosis or as a possible, probable, or rule-out diagnosis.
- The initiation of, or changes in, treatment should be documented.
- The treatment includes a wide range of management options, including patient instructions, nursing instructions, therapies, and medications.
- If referrals are made, consultations are requested or advice is sought, they must be indicated on the record with details as to whom or where the referral or consultation is made.

Review of Records/Investigations: The nature, amount, and complexity of data to be reviewed is based on the types of diagnostic testing ordered or reviewed (Tables 10 and 11). A decision to obtain and review old medical records and/or obtain history from sources other than the patient increases the amount and complexity of data to be reviewed.

Discussion of contradictory or unexpected test results with the physician who performed or interpreted the tests is an indication of the complexity of the date being reviewed. It is not uncommon for an interventional pain physician to personally review the images to supplement the reports of other physicians or include an independent report. The following documentation is important:

- Whenever a diagnostic service, test, or procedure is ordered, planned, scheduled, or performed at the time of the encounter, the type of service should be documented.
- The review of investigations including radiology and/or other diagnostic tests should be docu-

Table 10. *Relevant diagnostics tests in medicine section of CPT*
1. Psychological testing
2. Neurology and neuromuscular testing
• Sleep testing
• EEG
• Needle EMG
• Nerve conduction
• SSEP
3. Non-invasive vascular studies
4. Electrocardiography/echocardiography
5. Pulmonary function studies
6. Allergy testing
7. Audiologic function tests
8. Vestibular function tests

mented. A simple notation such as, "MRI showed disc herniation at L5/S1 level," or "MRI was grossly within normal limits" is acceptable. Alternatively, the review may be documented by initialing and dating the report containing the test results.

- Documentation should be made with regards to the decision to obtain old records or additional history from the family or other sources to supplement that obtained from the patient.
- Documentation of relevant findings from the review of the old records, additional history from the family, or other sources is important; however, if there is no relevant information beyond that already obtained, that fact should be documented.
- A notation of old records reviewed or additional history obtained from the family without elaboration of the facts of what was reviewed and the result of the review is insufficient.
- The results of discussion of radiology or other diagnostic tests with either the radiologist or neurologist or any other physician who performed or interpreted the study should be documented.
- The independent interpretation of imaging studies should be documented.

Table 11. *Amount/complexity of data reviewed*	
Categories of data to be reviewed	**Points**
Review and/or order clinical tests	1
Review and/or order of tests in the radiology section CPT	1
Review and/or order of tests in the medicine section of CPT	1
Discussion of test results with performing physician	1
Decision to obtain old records and/or history from someone other than patient	1
Review and summarization of old records and/or obtaining history from someone other than patient and/or discussion of case with another health provider	2
Independent visualization of image, tracing, or specimen itself (not simply review of report)	2

Risks: The risks of significant complications, morbidity, and/or mortality are based on the risks associated with:

- The presenting problem(s)
- The diagnostic procedure(s)
- Possible management options

Some important aspects of the risks in interventional pain medicine are:

- Co-morbidity, underlying disease, or other factors that increase the complexity of medical decision making by increasing the risk of complications, morbidity, and/or mortality should be documented.
- Planned or scheduled invasive diagnostic or therapeutic procedures or surgical procedures at the time of the encounter should be documented, with the type of procedure.
- If an invasive diagnostic, therapeutic or surgical procedure is performed at the time of the encounter, the specific procedure should be documented.
- If the patient is referred for an emergency, invasive diagnostic, therapeutic procedure, or surgical intervention, such referrals should be documented.

Table 12 shows some salient aspects in the determination of risks, whether minimal, low, moderate, or high. However, the determination of risks is complex and not readily quantifiable in low back pain evaluation and is also variable with each specialty. In addition, the assessment of risk of the presenting problems is based on the risks related to the disease process anticipated between the immediate and the next encounter. The assessment of risk of selecting diagnostic procedures and management options is also based on the risk during and immediately following any procedures or treatments. The highest level of risk in any one category of the three described determines the overall risks. Table 13 shows risk of complications and/or mortality/morbidity relevant to interventional pain medicine.

Counseling and/or Coordination of Care: If either counseling and/or coordination of care dominates the physician/patient and/or family encounter (face-to-face time in the office or other outpatient setting exceeding 50% of the time), time is considered the key or controlling factor to qualify for a particular level of evaluation and management service. The codes are shown in Table 14. However, if the physician elects to report the level of service based on counseling and coordination of care, the total length of time of the encounter (face-to-face or floor time,

Table 12. *Illustration of Risk based on the diagnosis and/or management options, amount and/or complexity of data to be reviewed, risk of complications and type of decision-making*

Risk of complications and/or morbidity or mortality	Number of diagnosis and/or management options	Amount and/or complexity of data to be reviewed	Type of decision making
Minimal	Minimal 1	Minimal or Low 1	Straightforward
Low	Limited 2	Limited 2	Low Complexity
Moderate	Multiple 3	Moderate 3	ModerateComplexity
High	Extensive 4	Extensive 4	High Complexity

Table 13. *Risk of complications and/or morbidity/mortality*

Level of risk	Presenting problem(s)	Diagnostic procedure(s) ordered	Management option selected
Minimal	One self-limited or minor problem (eg. post -procedure follow up, post-procedure pain)	Laboratory tests requiring venipuncture Single area x-rays, CT, MRI without contrast, bone scan	Rest Elastic bandages
Low	Two or more self-limited or minor problems One stable chronic illness Acute uncomplicated illness or injury, simple sprain (Myofascial syndrome, Intra-articular disorders synovitis)	CT with contrast MRI with contrast	Over-the counter drugs Physical therapy Occupational therapy Psychotherapy Interventional procedureswith no identified risk factors (Trigger point injections)
Moderate	One ore more chronic illness with mild exacerbation (Chronic low back pain) Two or more stable chronic illnesses (Chronic low back pain, neck pain, headache) Acute illness with systemic symptoms(Discitis, epidural abscess) Acute complicated injury (Disc herniation) Undiagnosed new problem	Obtain fluid from body cavity (eg, joint, lumbar puncture)	Interventional procedures with identified risk factors Elective major surgery(percutaneous or endoscopic) Prescription drug management Closed treatment or fracture of dislocation without manipulation
High	One or more chronic illness(s) with severe exacerbation Acute or chronic illness or injuries that pose a threat to life or bodily function (eg, acute MI, pulmonary embolus, progressive rheumatoid arthritis, psychiatric illness with threat to self or others, acute renal failure, severe respiratory distress) Abrupt change in neurological status (eg, weakness, sensory loss, TIA, caudaequina-syndrome)	Discography Myelography	Elective major surgery(percutaneous or endoscopic) with identified risk factors Parenteral controlled substances Drug therapy requiring intensive monitoring for toxicity Do not resituate

Table 14. *Services based on time*	
Hospital discharge	99238 & 99239
Critical care codes	99291 & 99292
Prolonged services	99375 & 99378
Care plan oversight	99374 - 99378

as appropriate) should be documented and the records should describe the counseling and/or activities. Summary Table 15 shows an abbreviated summary of the process and requirements for various levels of service in multiple regions. Tables 16 shows various services requiring 3 of 3 key components, whereas Table 17 shows services requiring at least 2 of 3 components. Table 18 and Fig 1 illustrate self assessment of E/M guideline documentation for various levels of services This, not only complies with the regulations, but also improves patient care.

Table 16. *Specific CPT codes requiring 3 of 3 components*					
Office, new	99201	99202	99203	99240	99205
Consult, Out patient (New or Est.)	99241	99242	99243	99244	99245
Consult, Initial-Hosp (New or Est.)	99251	99252	99253	99254	99255
Confirm, Consult (New or Est.)	99271	99272	99273	99274	99275

NEW GUIDELINES

In the evolution of numerous regulations by CMS (HCFA) regarding the practice of medicine, implementation of evaluation and management guidelines started in the 1990s. The latest guidelines utilized at the present time were implemented in 1997. Since then, new guidelines were released in 1998

Table 15. *Illustration of CMS requirements for various levels of service*

Type of visit	**Documentation of History**				**Physical Examination**		**Complexity of Decision Making**
	Chief Complaint	History of Present illness(HPI)	Review of Systems (ROS)	Past, Family, and Social History (PFSH)	General Multisystem	Single System	
Problem-Focused Level 1	✓	**Brief** One to three Elements	N/A	N/A	**Limited** to affected body areas one to five elements	**Limited** to affected body areas one to five elements	Straightforward
Expanded - Problem Focused Level 2	✓	**Brief** One to three Elements	**Problem Pertinent** Positives and Negatives	N/A	**Limited** to symptomatic or related systems six elements	**Limited** to symptomatic or related systems six elements	Straightforward
Detailed Level 3	✓	**Extended** At least four elements or status of three chronic or inactive conditions	**Extended** Positive and Pertinent negatives two to nine systems	**Pertinent** To problems identified in HPI	**Extended** At least two elements from six systems or twelve in two or more systems	**Extended** examination of symptomatic and related systems at least twelve elements	Low Complexity
Comprehensive Level 4	✓	**Extended** At least four elements or status of three chronic or inactive conditions	**Complete** At least ten systems	**Complete** At least one specific HPI from three of three history areas	**Comprehensive** At least two elements from nine systems eighteen elements	**Complete** Every element in each box with a shaded border and at least one element in each box with unshaded border	Moderate Complexity
Comprehensive Complex Level 5	✓	**Extended** At least four elements or status of three chronic or inactive conditions	**Complete** At least ten systems	**Complete** At least one specific HPI from three of three history areas	**Comprehensive** At least two elements from nine systems eighteen elements	**Complete** Every element in each box with a shaded border and at least one element in each box with unshaded border	High Complexity

Table 17. *Various services requiring at least 2 of 3 key components*

- Outpatient visit – Established 99211, 99212, 99213
- Follow-up inpatient consultation(s) 99261, 99262, 99263
- Subsequent hospital care 99231, 99232, 9923

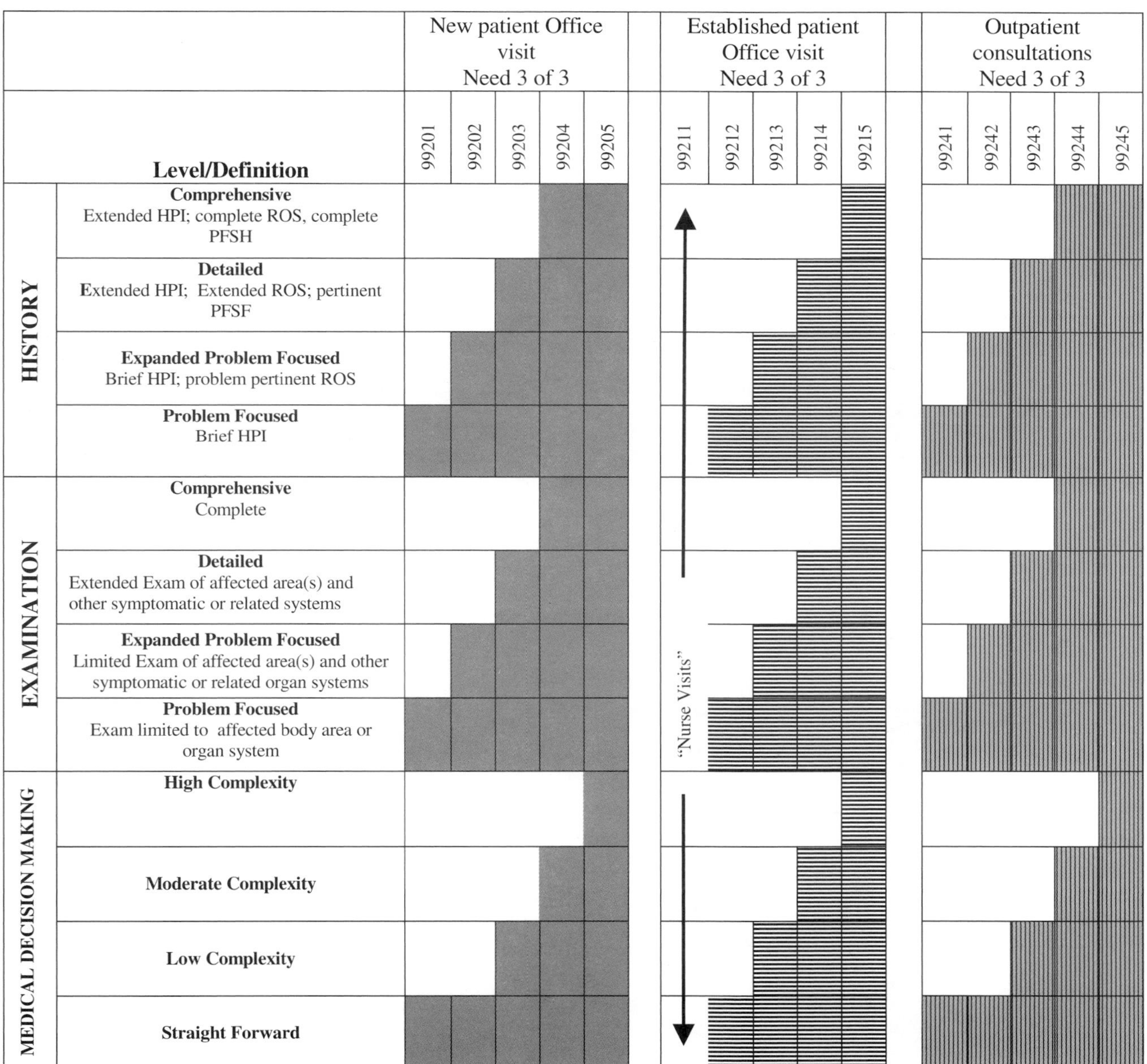

Fig 1. *Graphic depiction of multiple requirements for various levels of services*

Table 18. *Assessment of level of E/M service based on 1997 Guidelines*

HISTORY					
Chief Complaint		√	√	√	√
HPI (History of present illness) ☐Location ☐Severity ☐Timing ☐Modifying factors ☐Quality ☐Duration ☐Context ☐Associated signs and symptoms		Brief *1-3 elements*	Brief *1-3 elements*	Extended *≥ 4 elements or status of ≥ 3 chronic or inactive (conditions)*	Extended *≥ 4 elements or status of ≥ 3 chronic or inactive (conditions)*
ROS (Review of systems) ☐Constitutional ☐NA ☐GI ☐NA ☐Neuro ☐NA ☐Eyes ☐NA ☐GU ☐NA ☐Psych ☐NA ☐ENT ☐NA ☐Musculo ☐NA ☐Endo ☐NA ☐Cardiovasc ☐NA ☐Integumentary (skin, breast) ☐NA ☐Hem/lymph ☐NA ☐Resp ☐NA ☐"All others negative		None	Pertinent to problem *1 system*	Extended *2-9 systems*	Complete *10 or systems, or pertinent systems with statement "all other systems if reviewed negative"*
PFSH (Past family and social history) ☐ Past medical history ☐ Past pain history ☐ Family history ☐ Social history	Established	None	None	One history area	Two or three history areas
	New	None	None	One or two history area(s)	Three history areas
PHYSICAL EXAMINATION		**PROBLEM FOCUSED**	**EXPANDED PROBLEM FOCUSED**	**DETAILED**	**COMPRE-HENSIVE**

Multi-system Exam		Single System Exam
1-5 elements identified by bullets	PROBLEM FOCUSED	1-5 elements identified by bullets
≥6 elements identified by bullets	EXPANDED PROBLEM FOCUSED	≥6 elements identified by bullets
≥2 Elements identified by bullets from 6 areas/systems OR ≥12 elements identified by bullets from at least 2 areas/systems	DETAILED	≥12 elements identified by bullets
≥2 elements identified by bullets from 9 areas/systems	COMPREHENSIVE	Perform all elements identified by bullets, document all elements in shaded boxes, document ≥1 element in unshaded boxes

Number of Diagnoses or Treatment Options

Problems to Exam Physician	Number	X Points	= Result
Self-limited or minor (stable, improved, or worsening)	Max=2	1	
Established. Problem; stable improved		1	
Established problem; worsening		2	
New problem; no additional workup planned	Max=1	3	
		4	
		TOTAL	

Amount and/or Complexity of Data to Be Reviewed

Data to be reviewed	Points
Review and/or order of clinical lab tests	1
Review and/or order of tests in the radiology section of CPT	1
Review and/or order of tests in the medicine section of CPT	1
Discussion of test results with performing physician	1
Decision to obtain old records and.or obtain history from someone other than patient	2
Independent visualization of image	2
TOTAL	

Risk of complications and/or Morbidity or Mortality

Number of diagnoses or treatment options	≤1 Minimal	2 Limited	3 Multiple	≥4 Extensive
Amount and complexity of data	≤1 Minimal or low	2 Limited	3 Multiple	≥4 Extensive
Risk	Minimal	Low	Moderate	High
Type of decision making	Straightforward	Low complex	Moderate complex	High complex

Final Determination of level of service

Visit	History	Physical examination	Medical decision making
P. Focused			
P. Focused/ Expanded			
Detailed/Low Comp			
Compre/Mod. Comp.			
Compre/High Comp.			

followed by a review draft. Due to a multitude of complaints and differences in opinion between CMS (HCFA) and the American Medical Association (AMA) and various specialty medical societies and the inability of CMS (HCFA) to pilot-test these guidelines, CMS (HCFA) unveiled new, draft documentation guidelines for evaluation and management services in June 2000, which was preceded by an article by the administrator of HCFA in JAMA (18, 19).

The "new framework" evaluation and management documentation guidelines were released in June 1998. It was stated that these guidelines, in some form, would eventually replace the 1995 and 1997 guidelines. However, when the newest version of evaluation and management services guidelines was released on June 22, 2000, it did not resemble the so-called "new framework" (20). Even though 1998 guidelines were reported as a significant improvement over 1995 and 1997 guidelines, in the 2 years since the release of the 1998 guidelines many flaws were recognized:

- The 1998 proposed guidelines were not work equal and across the various specialties for a given level of service. The current law does not allow for differentials among various specialties, making this a great stumbling block in the implementation of the 1998 proposed guidelines (20). Similar to 1997 guidelines, proposed guidelines for 1999 deviated significantly from the qualitative definitions for examinations and medical decision making (20). It was noted that it was possible under the 1999 draft guidelines to satisfy the numerous requirements for a physical examination while not meeting the qualitative requirements of the CPT definition to examine affected organ systems or body areas. According to CMS (HCFA), breaking down the physical examination into a list of elements and then requiring documentation of a subset of those elements to achieve a level of service creates an incentive to perform unnecessary examinations and to record clinically irrelevant information.
- Medical decision making tables for the 1997 and 1999 guidelines deviated from the CPT definition of medical decision making. The factors that comprise medical decision making, such as patient risk, and amount of data to be reviewed, are significantly rearranged or altered (20). The list of examples for each factor is confusing and often will be clinically irrelevant to the physician and biller attempting to assign a level of service (20). Finally, the assigned level of decision making was determined by only a single factor in the decision–making process (20).
- These are wide discrepancies in the assessment of various codes under 1995, 1996, 1997 and 1999 guidelines by a non-physician reviewer (registered record analyst, and physician reviewer), and carrier medical director under all three sets of guidelines.

To remedy all of the above issues, CMS (HCFA) released the new 2000 guidelines. The CMS (HCFA) plans to examine the differences in the visit leveling between physician and non-physician reviewers under the new 2000 guidelines. The HCFA stated that, in the new guidelines:

- Physical examination has been simplified to three levels based on the number of organ systems examined. For example, a detailed examination includes findings from three to eight organ systems, rather than the total number of items examined (18).
- The requirements for review of systems are also based on organ systems.
- Counting of elements in an examination is virtually eliminated, as are incentives to perform unnecessary examinations
- Medical decision making has been simplified to three levels, with clear requirements that will be cross-referenced to specialty-specific vignettes to aid reviewers in making accurate determinations. The vignettes will capture the nuances of each medical specialty and prevent arbitrary application of and dependence upon generative, flexible, and often meaningless lists of elements.
- The HCFA believes that new, simpler guidelines will provide clear and unambiguous guidance and streamline the documentation required for clinically appropriate record keeping and verification that services were medically necessary and rendered as billed.
- However, HCFA wants to make sure that these guidelines will work in the real world of clinical practice. Hence, vigorous testing of the simplified guidelines is planned. The testing is planned at three levels:
    - Pilot testing focusing on the basic region of the original 1995 guidelines that is designed to minimize counting of elements and the uses of a series of physical examination and medical decision-making scenarios to help physicians and reviewers assign a level of service;
    - A second version that focuses more on how physicians make medical decisions and less on history and physical examination, involving little or no counting and including medical de cision-making scenarios; and
    - Testing of training mechanisms.

The CMS (HCFA) hoped to begin pilot testing in year 2000, with results available as early as summer 2001, and new guidelines in place in 2002. The HCFA also concedes that, if test results demonstrate that further work is needed, it will make additional adjustments. However, HCFA must know before proceeding whether it has indeed found a simpler, clinically meaningful, and nonintrusive approach to documentation that all can live with.

However, these new guidelines may not go into effect at all. With multitude of complaints from physicians and numerous organizations, HHS Secretary, Hon. Tommy Thompson, has ordered a stop to work on controversial proposed draft guidelines.

On July 19, in a testimony before the House Ways and Means Committee, Hon. Tommy Thompson stated that he told Aspen Systems which created the E/M guidelines to stop work on the current draft. He stated that "after 6 years of confusion, I think it makes sense to try to step back and assess what we are trying to achieve". He also stated that physicians primary work is to provide clinical care, not "documentation". He felt that for the system to work effectively, the codes for billing for visits need to be simple and unambiguous.

This not only opens a whole avenue of new guidelines which may be physician friendly but also delays the proposed guidelines from implementation and physicians may continue to use either 1995 or 1997 guidelines.

CONCLUSION

Evaluation and management services are part and parcel of the practice of interventional pain medicine, and management of chronic low back pain. Consequences of inappropriate coding and insufficient documentation to support charges billed to Medicare include, not only penalties, but also exclusion from the Medicare program, and finally, prison terms. Understanding appropriate documentation issues of medical necessity and rules and regulations governing evaluation and management coding is extremely crucial. Appropriate documentation not only will meet the criteria for billing and coding at an appropriate level, but also will result in higher reimbursement, providing a safety net to avoid fraud and abuse. The new regulations will not only clarify a multitude of issues but will also make it easier for physicians, not only to document appropriate level of service, but also to do this with less confusion and fear.

References

1. Haralson R. Consultation coding tips. *NASS News* 2000; XIV(II):1-6.
2. Masquelier E, Plaghki L, Gizisart J et al. Tutorial 42: History taking Examination and management of low back pain. *Pain Digest* 1999; 9:258-275.
3. Portenoy RK, Kanner RM. Definition and assessment of pain. In Portenoy RK, Kanner RM (eds). *Pain Management: Theory and Practice.* Philadelphia, FA Davis Company, 1996; pp 3-18.
4. Donohoe CD. Targeted history and physical examination. In Waldman SD (eds). *Interventional Pain Management.* Second Edition, W.B. Saunders Company, Philadelphia, 2000; pp 83-94.
5. Loeser JD. Medical evaluation of the patient with pain in Loeser JD, Butler SH, Chapman CR et al (eds), *Bonica's Management of Pain.* Third Edition, Lippincott Williams and Wilkins, New York, 2001:pp267-278.
6. Abrams BM. History taking in the patient in pain. In Raj PP, Abrams BM, Hahn MB (eds), *Practical Management of Pain.* Third Edition, Mosby, St. Louis, 2000:pp.333-338.
7. Wall PD, Melzack R (eds). *Textbook of Pain.* Third Edition, New York, Churchill Livingstone, 1994.
8. McPeak LA. Physiatric history and examination. In Braddom RL (ed). *Physical Medicine and Rehabilitation. Philadelphia,* W.B. Saunders Co., 1996; pp 3-42.
9. Turk DC, Melzack R (eds). *Handbook of Clinical Assessment of Pain.* New York, Guilford Press, 1992.
10. Evaluation and management services: *Anesthesia Answer Book 1999*; Rockville, MD pp 13501-13594.
11. Manchikanti L. Appropriate documentation, billing and coding of interventional pain procedures. *Pain Physician* 2000; 3:218-236.
12. Manchikanti L. The role of evaluation and management services in pain management. *Pain Physician* 1999; 2:10-32.
13. Manchikanti L. Evaluation and management services in interventional pain practice: Doing it right! *Pain Physician* 2000; 3:322-341.
14. Manchikanti L, Singh V, Kloth D et al. Interventional techniques in the management of chronic pain: Part 2.0. *Pain Physician* 2001; 4:24-96.
15. *International Classification of Diseases, Ninth Revision, Clinical Modification,* ICD-9-CM. St. Anthony Publishing, Reston, 1998.
16. Quinn C. Issues of medical necessity. A medical director's guide to good faith adjudication. *Am J Managed Care* 1997; 3:883-888.
17. Jacobson PD, Asch S, Glassman PA et al. Defining and implementing medical necessity in Washington State and Oregon. *Inquiry* 1997; 34:143-154.
18. DeParle NA. Evaluation and management services guidelines. *JAMA* 2000; 283:3061.
19. *Evaluation and Management Services Guidelines.* Washington, D.C. Health Care Financing Administration, June 22, 2000.
20. *History and Future of New Evaluation and Management Guidelines. Coding and Medicare Updates.* A publication of the Medical Management Institute ®, SSN 1524-6442; 2000; 4:5-7.

CORRECT CODING POLICIES FOR COMMONLY USED EVALUATION AND MANAGEMENT, PHYSICAL MEDICINE, PSYCHOLOGICAL, NEURODIAGNOSTIC AND RADIOLOGICAL SERVICES

Laxmaiah Manchikanti, MD
Trish Burks, LPT
Bert Fellows, MA

Among the numerous risk areas for practice of interventional pain medicine, the risks associated with evaluation and management (E and M services) is just behind interventional procedures. Based on some of the practices, it may even be the number one risk area for an interventional pain physician. Details and importance of general correct coding policies, as well as evaluation and management services in interventional pain medicine have been described (1-10). There has been significant confusion over the proper documentation for evaluation and management services in interventional pain medicine (2). Further, the confusion has been made worse by numerous articles published in a multitude of advisory publications and often misguided advice by consultants, though well meaning.

For evaluation and management services, it is essential not only to perform the appropriate service to meet the criteria and code appropriate level of service, but also to follow correct coding policies. Correct coding policies for evaluation and management services along with other Part B Medicare services have been published in National Correct Coding manuals over the years with the latest version 8.0 published in Jan 2002. There has been a continuous evolution of numerous component and mutually exclusive codes for almost all evaluation and management services. Thus, it is imperative for interventional pain physicians not only properly understand various pertinent correct coding policies in relation to evaluation and management services, but it is mandatory.

In addition to E/M services, a physician should be aware of various issues involved with not only documentation and correct coding of various ancillary services, but also with correct coding policies relevant to these services. Some of the services provided by interventional pain medicine services independently or in conjunction with other specialists have been included as high risk for fraudulent activities, hence, it is extremely crucial for an interventional to understand the evolution of numerous component and mutually exclusive codes for almost all services. Various services are listed under the medicine section of CPT Manual. Other services provided by interventional pain physicians include laboratory testing, however, since this is not a common occurrence, no descriptions are provided on laboratory testing, which is described in pathology and laboratory testing of the CPT Manual. In addition, occasionally medical nutrition therapy, osteopathic manipulative treatment, chiropractic manipulative treatment and various other modalities of treatments are provided by interventional pain physicians due to the minor nature of these procedures provided, they are not described here.

EVALUATION AND MANAGEMENT SERVICES

Table 1 illustrates various types of CPT codes utilized for evaluation and management services, specifically relevant to interventional pain medicine. An interventional pain medicine physician should realize that there are other codes other than the ones described in this table. However, if there is a question about coding, its comprehensive nature, or mutual exclusion, physicians and other providers are urged to contact local Medicare carriers or third party payors. Table 2 illustrates the most commonly used evaluation and management services in interventional pain medicine and correct coding policies. Table 3 shows an easy cross-walk listing of comprehensive, component and mutually exclusive codes.

Table 1. *Various types of CPT codes utilized for evaluation and management services relevent to interventional pain medicine*

New Patient Office visit(s)	Established Outpatient(s)	Office Consult (s) New or Established Patient(s)	Initial Inpatient New or Established Patient(s)	Subsequent Equipment Hospital Care	Observation or inpatient care services	Initial Inpatient Consult(s)	Follow-Up Impatient Consult(s)
99201	99211	99241	99221	99231	99234	99251	99261
99202	99212	99242	99222	99232	99235	99252	99262
99203	99213	99243	99223	99233	99236	99253	99263
99204	99214	99244				99254	
99205	99215	99245				99255	

Table 2. *Illustration of most commonly used evaluation and management services showing component and mutually exclusive codes*

Comprehensive Code	Component Codes and Mutually Exclusive Codes
99201 – office or other outpatient visit; requiring these three key components: a problem focused history; a problem focused examination; and straightforward medical decision making	80500, 80502, 90862, 94656, 94657, 94660, 94662, 95831, 95832, 95833, 95834, 95851, 95852, 96115, 96150, 96151, 96152, 96153, 96154, 96155, 97802, 97803, 97804, G0102, G0117, G0118, 99239, 99435
99202– office or other outpatient visit; requiring these three key components: an expanded problem focused history; an expanded problem focused examination; and straightforward medical decision making	80500, 80502, 90862, 94656, 94657, 94660, 94662, 95831, 95832, 95833, 95834, 95851, 95852, 96115, 96150, 96151, 96152, 96153, 96154, 96155, 97802, 97803, 97804, G0102, G0117, G0118, 99239, 99435
99203 – office or other outpatient visit; requiring these three key components: a detailed history; a detailed examination; and medical decision making of low complexity	80500, 80502, 90862, 94656, 94657, 94660, 94662, 95831, 95832, 95833, 95834, 95851, 95852, 96115, 96150, 96151, 96152, 96153, 96154, 96155, 97802, 97803, 97804, G0102, G0117, G0118, 99239, 99435
99204 – office or other outpatient visit; requiring these three key components: a comprehensive history; a comprehensive examination; and medical decision making of moderate complexity	80500, 80502, 90862, 94656, 94657, 94660, 94662, 95831, 95832, 95833, 95834, 95851, 95852, 96115, 96150, 96151, 96152, 96153, 96154, 96155, 97802, 97803, 97804, G0102, G0117, G0118, 99435
99205 – office or other outpatient visit requiring these three key components: a comprehensive history; a comprehensive examination; and medical decision making of high complexity	80500, 80502, 90862, 94656, 94657, 94660, 94662, 95831, 95832, 95833, 95834, 95851, 95852, 96115, 96150, 96151, 96152, 96153, 96154, 96155, 97802, 97803, 97804, G0102, G0117, G0118
99211 – office or other outpatient visit; may not require the presence of a physician. Usually, the presenting problem(s) are minimal	80500, 80502, 90862, 94656, 94657, 94660, 94662, 95831, 95832, 95833, 95834, 95851, 95852, 96115, 96150, 96151, 96152, 96153, 96154, 96155, 97802, 97803, 97804, G0102, G0117, G0118, Q0081, Q0083, Q0084, Q0085, 99239, 99435
99212 – office or other outpatient visit; requiring at least two of these three key components: a problem focused history; a problem focused examination; straightforward medical decision making	80500, 80502, 90862, 94656, 94657, 94660, 94662, 95831, 95832, 95833, 95834, 95851, 95852, 96115, 96150, 96151, 96152, 96153, 96154, 96155, 97802, 97803, 97804, G0102, G0117, G0118, 99239, 99435
99213 – office or other outpatient visit; requiring at least two of these three key components: an expanded problem focused history; an expanded problem focused examination; medical decision making of low complexity	80500, 80502, 90862, 94656, 94657, 94660, 94662, 95831, 95832, 95833, 95834, 95851, 95852, 96115, 96150, 96151, 96152, 96153, 96154, 96155, 97802, 97803, 97804, G0102, G0117, G0118, Q0081, Q0084, 99239, 99435
99214 – office or other outpatient visit; requiring at least two of these three key components: a detailed history; a detailed examination; medical decision making of moderate complexity	80500, 80502, 90862, 94656, 94657, 94660, 94662, 95831, 95832, 95833, 95834, 95851, 95852, 96115, 96150, 96151, 96152, 96153, 96154, 96155, 97802, 97803, 97804, G0102, G0117, G0118, Q0081, Q0083, Q0084, Q0085, 99239, 99435

Table 2. *Continued.....*

Comprehensive Code	Component Codes and Mutually Exclusive Codes
99215 – office or other outpatient visit; requiring at least two of these three key components: a comprehensive history; a comprehensive examination; medical decision making of high complexity	80500, 80502, 90862, 94656, 94657, 94660, 94662, 95831, 95832, 95833, 95834, 95851, 95852, 96115, 96150, 96151, 96152, 96153, 96154, 96155, 97802, 97803, 97804, G0102, G0117, G0118, Q0084, 99435
99241 – office consultation for a new or established patient; requiring these three key components: a problem focused history; a problem focused examination; and straightforward medical decision making	80500, 80502, 90862, 94656, 94657, 94660, 94662, 95831, 95832, 95833, 95834, 95851, 95852, 96115, 96150, 96151, 96152, 96153, 96154, 96155, 97802, 97803, 97804, G0102, G0117, G0118, 99435
99242 – office consultation for a new or established patient; requiring these three key components: an expanded problem focused history; an expanded problem focused examination; and straightforward medical decision making	80500, 80502, 90862, 94656, 94657, 94660, 94662, 95831, 95832, 95833, 95834, 95851, 95852, 96115, 96150, 96151, 96152, 96153, 96154, 96155, 97802, 97803, 97804, G0102, G0117, G0118, 99435
99243 – office consultation for a new or established patient; requiring these three key components: a detailed history; a detailed examination; and medical decision making of low complexity	80500, 80502, 90862, 94656, 94657, 94660, 94662, 95831, 95832, 95833, 95834, 95851, 95852, 96115, 96150, 96151, 96152, 96153, 96154, 96155, 97802, 97803, 97804, G0102, G0117, G0118, 99435
99244 – office consultation for a new or established patient; requiring these three key components: a comprehensive history; a comprehensive examination; and medical decision making of moderate complexity	80500, 80502, 90862, 94656, 94657, 94660, 94662, 95831, 95832, 95833, 95834, 95851, 95852, 96115, 96150, 96151, 96152, 96153, 96154, 96155, 97802, 97803, 97804, G0102, G0117, G0118
99245 – office consultation for a new or established patient; requiring these three key components: a comprehensive history; a comprehensive examination; and medical decision making of high complexity	80500, 80502, 90862, 94656, 94657, 94660, 94662, 95831, 95832, 95833, 95834, 95851, 95852, 96115, 96150, 96151, 96152, 96153, 96154, 96155, 97802, 97803, 97804, G0102, G0117, G0118
99221 – initial hospital care, per day; requiring these three key components: a detailed or comprehensive history; a detailed or comprehensive examination; and medical decision making that is straightforward or of low complexity	80500, 80502, 90862, 94656, 94657, 94660, 94662, 95831, 95832, 95833, 95834, 95851, 95852, 96115, 96150, 96151, 96152, 96153, 96154, 96155, 97802, 97803, 97804, 99238, 99239, G0102, 99435
99222 – initial hospital care, per day; requiring these three key components: a comprehensive history; a comprehensive examination; and medical decision of moderate complexity	80500, 80502, 90862, 94656, 94657, 94660, 94662, 95831, 95832, 95833, 95834, 95851, 95852, 96115, 96150, 96151, 96152, 96153, 96154, 96155, 97802, 97803, 97804, 99238, 99239, G0102, 99435
99223 – initial hospital care, per day; requiring these three key components: a comprehensive history; a comprehensive examination; and medical decision of high complexity	80500, 80502, 90862, 94656, 94657, 94660, 94662, 95831, 95832, 95833, 95834, 95851, 95852, 96115, 96150, 96151, 96152, 96153, 96154, 96155, 97802, 97803, 97804, 99238, 99239, G0102

Table 3. *Crosswalk of most commonly used evaluation and management services showing comprehensive, component and mutually exclusive codes*

Comprehensive Codes	Component Codes									Mutually exclusive code
	80500	90862	95831	95832	95833	95834	95851	95852	G0102	99239
99201 office or other outpatient visit for the evaluation and management of a new patient	X	X	X	X	X	X	X	X	X	Y
99202 office or other outpatient visit for the evaluation and management of a new patient	X	X	X	X	X	X	X	X	X	Y
99203 office or other outpatient visit for the evaluation and management of a new patient	X	X	X	X	X	X	X	X	X	Y
99204 office or other outpatient visit for the evaluation and management of a new patient	X	X	X	X	X	X	X	X	X	
99205 office or other outpatient visit for the evaluation and management of a new patient	X	X	X	X	X	X	X	X	X	
99211 office or other outpatient visit for the evaluation and management of an established patient	X	X	X	X	X	X	X	X	X	Y
99212 office or other outpatient visit for the evaluation and management of an established patient	X	X	X	X	X	X	X	X	X	Y
99213 office or other outpatient visit for the evaluation and management of an established patient	X	X	X	X	X	X	X	X	X	Y
99214 office or other outpatient visit for the evaluation and management of an established patient	X	X	X	X	X	X	X	X	X	Y
99215 office or other outpatient visit for the evaluation and management of an established patient	X	X	X	X	X	X	X	X	X	
99241 office consultation for a new or established patient	X	X	X	X	X	X	X	X	X	
99242 office consultation for a new or established patient	X	X	X	X	X	X	X	X	X	
99243 office consultation for a new or established patient	X	X	X	X	X	X	X	X	X	
99244 office consultation for a new or established patient	X	X	X	X	X	X	X	X	X	
99245 office consultation for a new or established patient	X	X	X	X	X	X	X	X	X	
99221 initial hospital care, per day, for the evaluation and management of a patient	X	X	X	X	X	X	X	X	X	
99222 initial hospital care, per day, for the evaluation and management of a patient	X	X	X	X	X	X	X	X	X	
99223 hospital care, per day, for the evaluation and management of a patient	X	X	X	X	X	X	X	X	X	

X - Component Codes
Y – Mutually Exclusive Codes

COMPREHENSIVE CODES

New Patient Office Visit(s)

- 99201 – office or other outpatient visit for the evaluation and management of a new patient
- 99202 – office or other outpatient visit for the evaluation and management of a new patient
- 99203 – office or other outpatient visit for the evaluation and management of a new patient
- 99204 – office or other outpatient visit for the evaluation and management of a new patient
- 99205 – office or other outpatient visit for the evaluation and management of a new patient

Established Outpatient(s)

- 99211 – office or other outpatient visit for the evaluation and management of an established patient
- 99212 – office or other outpatient visit for the evaluation and management of an established patient
- 99213 – office or other outpatient visit for the evaluation and management of an established patient
- 99214 – office or other outpatient visit for the evaluation and management of an established patient
- 99215 – office or other outpatient visit for the evaluation and management of an established patient

Office Consult(s) New or Established Patient(s)

- 99241 – office consultation for a new or established patient
- 99242 – office consultation for a new or established patient
- 99243 – office consultation for a new or established patient
- 99244 – office consultation for a new or established patient
- 99245 – office consultation for a new or established patient

Initial Inpatient New or Established Patient(s)

- 99221 – initial hospital care, per day, for the evaluation and management of a patient
- 99222 – initial hospital care, per day, for the evaluation and management of a patient
- 99223 – hospital care, per day, for the evaluation and management of a patient

Subsequent Inpatient Hospital Care

- 99231 – subsequent hospital care, per day, for the evaluation and management of a patient
- 99232 – subsequent hospital care, per day, for the evaluation and management of a patient
- 99233 – subsequent hospital care, per day, for the evaluation and management of a patient

Observation or Inpatient Care Service(s)

- 99234 – observation or inpatient hospital care, for the evaluation and management of a patient
- 99235 – observation or inpatient hospital care, for the evaluation and management of a patient
- 99236 – observation or inpatient hospital care, for the evaluation and management of a patient

Initial Inpatient Consult(s)

- 99251 – initial inpatient consultation for a new or established patient
- 99252 – initial inpatient consultation for a new or established patient
- 99253 – initial inpatient consultation for a new or established patient
- 99254 – initial inpatient consultation for a new or established patient
- 99255 – initial inpatient consultation for a new or established patient

Follow-Up Inpatient Consult(s)

- 99261 – follow-up inpatient consultation for an established patient
- 99262 – follow-up inpatient consultation for an established patient
- 99263 – follow-up inpatient consultation for an established patient

Component Codes

All of the above codes are comprehensive codes with the following common component codes. For a complete list of component codes, please refer to appropriate manuals:

- 80500 General Health Panel
- 80502 Clinical pathology consultation
- 90862 Pharmacologic management
- 94656 Ventilation assist and management, first day
- 94657 Ventilation assist and management, subsequent days
- 94660 Continuous positive airway pressure ventilation
- 94662 Continuous negative pressure ventilation
- 95831 Muscle testing, manual (separate procedure) with report; extremity (excluding hand) or trunk
- 95832 Muscle testing, manual (separate procedure)

with report; hand, with or without comparison with normal side

- 95833 Muscle testing, manual (separate procedure) with report; total evaluation of body, excluding hands
- 95834 Muscle testing, manual (separate procedure) with report; total evaluation of body, including hands
- 95851 Range of motion measurements and report (separate procedure); each extremity (excluding hand) or each trunk section (spine)
- 95852 Range of motion measurements and report (separate procedure); hand, with or without comparison with normal side
- G0102 Prostate cancer screening; digital rectal examination

Mutually exclusive codes

- 99239 Hospital discharge day management; more than 30 minutes

PHYSICAL MEDICINE AND REHABILIATION SERVICES

Following is the illustration of the most commonly used physical medicine and rehabilitation codes showing component and mutually exclusive codes. Due to the extensive nature of the text, only CPT codes are utilized for component and mutually exclusive codes. For definitions or descriptions, please refer to CPT 2002 (8).

COMPREHENSIVE CODE	COMPONENT CODES	MUTUALLY EXCLUSIVE CODES
97001 – physical therapy evaluation	95831, 95832, 95833, 95834, 95851, 95852, 97703, 97750, 97802, 97803, 97804	99201, 99202, 99203, 99204, 99205, 99211, 99212, 99213, 99214, 99215, 99217, 99218, 99219, 99220, 99221, 99222, 99223, 99231, 99232, 99233, 99234, 99235, 99236, 99238, 99239, 99241, 99242, 99243, 99244, 99245, 99251, 99252, 99253, 99254, 99255, 99261, 99262, 99263, 99271, 99272, 99273, 99274, 99275, 99291, 99292, 99295, 99296, 99297, 99298, 99301, 99302, 99303, 99311, 99312, 99313, 99315, 99316, 99321, 99322, 99323, 99331, 99332, 99333, 99341, 99342, 99343, 99344, 99345, 99347, 99348, 99349, 99350, 99354, 99355, 99356, 99357, 99431, 99432, 99433, 99435, 99440, 99455, 99456
97002 – physical therapy re-evaluation	95831, 95832, 95833, 95834, 95851, 95852, 97703, 97750, 97802, 97803, 97804	97001, 99201, 99202, 99203, 99204, 99205, 99211, 99212, 99213, 99214, 99215, 99217, 99218, 99219, 99220, 99221, 99222, 99223, 99231, 99232, 99233, 99234, 99235, 99236, 99238, 99239, 99241, 99242, 99243, 99244, 99245, 99251, 99252, 99253, 99254, 99255, 99261, 99262, 99263, 99271, 99272, 99273, 99274, 99275, 99291, 99292, 99295, 99296, 99297, 99298, 99301, 99302, 99303, 99311, 99312, 99313, 99315, 99316, 99321, 99322, 99323, 99331, 99332, 99333, 99341, 99342, 99343, 99344, 99345, 99347, 99348, 99349, 99350, 99354, 99355, 99356, 99357, 99431, 99432, 99433, 99435, 99440, 99455, 99456
97003 – occupational therapy evaluation	95831, 95832, 95833, 95834, 95851, 95852, 97703, 97750, 97802, 97803, 97804	99201, 99202, 99203, 99204, 99205, 99211, 99212, 99213, 99214, 99215, 99217, 99218, 99219, 99220, 99221, 99222, 99223, 99231, 99232, 99233, 99234, 99235, 99236, 99238, 99239, 99241, 99242, 99243, 99244, 99245, 99251, 99252, 99253, 99254, 99255, 99261, 99262, 99263, 99271, 99272, 99273, 99274, 99275, 99291, 99292, 99295, 99296, 99297, 99298, 99301, 99302, 99303, 99311, 99312, 99313, 99315, 99316, 99321, 99322, 99323, 99331, 99332, 99333, 99341, 99342, 99343, 99344, 99345, 99347, 99348, 99349, 99350, 99354, 99355, 99356, 99357, 99431, 99432, 99433, 99435, 99440, 99455, 99456

COMPREHENSIVE CODE	COMPONENT CODES	MUTUALLY EXCLUSIVE CODES
97004 – occupational therapy re-evaluation	95831, 95832, 95833, 95834, 95851, 95852, 97703, 97750, 97802, 97803, 97804	97003, 99201, 99202, 99203, 99204, 99205, 99211, 99212, 99213, 99214, 99215, 99217, 99218, 99219, 99220, 99221, 99222, 99223, 99231, 99232, 99233, 99234, 99235, 99236, 99238, 99239, 99241, 99242, 99243, 99244, 99245, 99251, 99252, 99253, 99254, 99255, 99261, 99262, 99263, 99271, 99272, 99273, 99274, 99275, 99291, 99292, 99295, 99296, 99297, 99298, 99301, 99302, 99303, 99311, 99312, 99313, 99315, 99316, 99321, 99322, 99323, 99331, 99332, 99333, 99341, 99342, 99343, 99344, 99345, 99347, 99348, 99349, 99350, 99354, 99355, 99356, 99357, 99431, 99432, 99433, 99435, 99440, 99455, 99456
97012 -supervised application of traction, mechanical	97002, 97004, 97018	97140, 99186
97014 - supervised application of electrical stimulation	64550, 67002, 97004	99186
97016 - supervised application of vasopneumatic devices	97002, 97004, 97018, 97026	99186
97018 - supervised application of paraffin bath	97002, 97004, 99186	97022
97020 - supervised application of microwave	97002, 97004, 97018, 97026, 99186	NA
97022 - supervised application of whirlpool	97002, 97004, 99186	NA
97024 - supervised application of diathermy	97002, 97004, 97018, 97026, 99186	97020
97026 - supervised application of infrared	97002, 97004, 99186	97018, 97022
97028 - supervised application of ultraviolet	97002, 97004, 97018, 97026, 99186	96910, 96912, 96913, 97022
97032 – constant attendance application of a modality	64550, 97002, 97004, 97014,	NA
97033 - constant attendance application of iontophoresis	97002, 97004	NA
97034 - constant attendance application of contrast baths	97002, 97004, 97018, 97020, 97022, 97024, 97026	NA

COMPREHENSIVE CODE	COMPONENT CODES	MUTUALLY EXCLUSIVE CODES
97035 - constant attendance application of ultrasound	97002, 97004, 97018, 97020, 97022, 97024, 97026	NA
97036 - constant attendance application of Hubbard tank	97002, 97004, 97018, 97020, 97022, 97024, 97026	NA
97039 - constant attendance application of unlisted modality	97002, 97004	NA
97110 – therapeutic procedure, one or more areas, each 15 minutes	97002, 97004, 99186	NA
97112 - therapeutic procedure, one or more areas, each 15 minutes; neuromuscular reeducation	97002, 97004, 99186	NA
97113 - therapeutic procedure, one or more areas, each 15 minutes; aquatic therapy	97002, 97004, 97110	NA
97116 - therapeutic procedure, one or more areas, each 15 minutes; gait training	97002, 97004, 99186	NA
97124 therapeutic procedure, one or more areas, each 15 minutes; massage	97002, 97004, 99186	NA
97139 – unlisted therapeutic procedure	97002, 97004	NA
97140 – manual therapy techniques	95851, 95852, 97002, 97004, 97018, 97124, 97750, 99186	97530
97150 – therapeutic procedures	95831, 95834, 95851, 97002, 97004, 97124, 97504, 97520, 97535, 97537, 97542	97110, 97112, 97113, 97116, 97140, 97530
97504 – orthotics fitting and training	29044, 29046, 29049, 29055, 29058, 29065, 29075, 29085, 29105, 29125, 29126, 29130, 29131, 29200, 29220, 29240, 29260, 29280, 29305, 29325, 29345, 29355, 29358, 29365, 29405, 29425, 29435, 29440, 29445, 29450, 29505, 29515, 29520, 29530, 29540, 29550, 29580, 29700, 29705, 29710, 29720, 29730, 29740, 29750, 97002, 97004, 97016, 97110, 97112, 97116, 97124, 97140	NA
97520 – prosthetic training	97002, 97004, 97016, 97110, 97112, 97116, 97124, 97140, 97504	NA
97530 – therapeutic activities	95831, 95832, 95833, 95834, 95851, 95852, 97002, 97004, 97113, 97116, 97535, 97537, 97542, 97750, 99186	NA

COMPREHENSIVE CODE	COMPONENT CODES	MUTUALLY EXCLUSIVE CODES
97535 - self care/home management	97002, 97004	NA
97537 – community work reintegration training	97002, 97004	NA
97542 – wheelchair management/propulsion training	97002, 97004	NA
97545 – work hardening/conditioning	97002, 97004, 97140	NA
97601 – removal of devitalized tissue from wound; selective debridement	00300, 00400, 00402, 00404, 00406, 00410, 01250, 01320, 01462, 01470, 01480, 11900, 11901, 64400, 64402, 64405, 64408, 64410, 64412, 64413, 64415, 64417, 64418, 64420, 64421, 64425, 64430, 64435, 64445, 64450, 64470, 64472, 64475, 64476, 64479, 64480, 64483, 69990, 90782, 97022	NA
97703 – checkout for orthotic/prosthetic use	NA	97504, 97520
97750 – physical performance test or measurement	95831, 95832, 95833, 95834, 97150	NA

PSYCHOLOGICAL SERVICES

Following is the illustration of the most commonly used psychological services codes showing component and mutually exclusive codes. Description of each component and mutually exclusive code is not provided due to large number of codes occupying several hundred pages. For code definitions or descriptions, please refer to CPT 2002 (8).

COMPREHENSIVE CODE	COMPONENT CODES	MUTUALLY EXCLUSIVE CODES
90804 – individual psychotherapy, insight oriented, office or outpatient facility, 20-30 minutes	36640, 90801, 90802, 90862, 96115, 96150, 96151, 96152, 96153, 96154, 96155, 97802, 97803, 97804, G0176, G0177, M0064	90810, 90811, 90812, 90813, 90814, 90815, 90816, 90817, 90818, 90821, 90822, 90823, 90824, 90826, 90827, 90828, 90829, 90845, 90865, 90880, 99201, 99202, 99203, 99205, 99211, 99212, 99213, 99214, 99215, 99217, 99218, 99219, 99220, 99221, 99222, 99223, 99231, 99232, 99233, 99234, 99235, 99236, 99238, 99239, 99241, 99242, 99243, 99244, 99245, 99251, 99252, 99253, 99254, 99255, 99261, 99262, 99263, 99271, 99272, 99273, 99274, 99275, 99281, 99282, 99283, 99284, 99285, 99291, 99295, 99296, 99297, 99301, 99302, 99303, 99311, 99312, 99313, 99321, 99322, 99323, 99331, 99332, 99333, 99341, 99342, 99343, 99344, 99345, 99350, 99354, 99355, 99356, 99357, 99360, 99431, 99432, 99433, 99435, 99440, 99455, 99456

COMPREHENSIVE CODE	COMPONENT CODES	MUTUALLY EXCLUSIVE CODES
90805 - individual psychotherapy; insight oriented, office or outpatient facility, 20-30 minutes with medical evaluation and management services	36640, 90801, 90802, 90804, 90862,96115, 96150, 96151, 96152, 96153, 96154, 96155, 97802, 97803, 97804, 99201, 99202, 99203, 99204, 99205, 99211, 99212, 99213, 99214, 99215, 99217, 99218, 99219, 99220, 99221, 99222, 99223, 99231, 99232, 99233, 99234, 99235, 99236, 99238, 99239, 99241, 99242, 99243, 99244, 99245, 99251, 99252, 99253, 99254, 99255, 99261, 99262, 99263, 99271, 99272, 99273, 99274, 99275, 99281, 99282, 99283, 99284, 99285, 99301, 99302, 99303, 99311, 99312, 99313, 99321, 99322, 99323, 99331, 99332, 99333, 99341, 99342, 99343, 99344, 99345, 99347, 99348, 99349, 99350, 99354, 99355, 99356, 99357,G0176, G0177,M0064	90811, 90812, 90813, 90814, 90815, 90816, 90817, 90818, 90821, 90822, 90824, 90826, 90827, 90828, 90829, 90845, 90865, 90880, 99291,
90806 - individual psychotherapy; insight oriented, office or outpatient facility, 45-50 minutes	36640, 90801, 90802, 90804, 90805, 90862, 96115, 96150, 96151, 96152, 96153, 96154, 96155, 97802, 97803, 97804,G0176, G0177, M0064	90813, 90814, 90816, 90817, 90818, 90819, 90821, 90822, 90824, 90826, 90827, 90828, 90829, 90845, 90865, 99201, 99202, 99203, 99204, 99205, 99211, 99212, 99213, 99214, 99215, 99217, 99218, 99219, 99220, 99221, 99222, 99223, 99231, 99232, 99233, 99234, 99235, 99236, 99238, 99239, 99241, 99242, 99243, 99244, 99245, 99251, 99252, 99253, 99254, 99255, 99261, 99262, 99263, 99271, 99272, 99273, 99274, 99275, 99281, 99282, 99283, 99284, 99285, 99291, 99295, 99296, 99297, 99301, 99302, 99303, 99311, 99312, 99313, 99321, 99322, 99323, 99331, 99333, 99341, 99342, 99343, 99344, 99345, 99350, 99354, 99355, 99356, 99357, 99360, 99431, 99432, 99433, 99435, 99440, 99455, 99456
90807 - individual psychotherapy, insight oriented; office or outpatient facility, 45-50 minutes, with medical evaluation and management services	36640, 90801, 90802, 90804, 90805, 90806, 90862,96115, 96150, 96151, 96152, 96153, 96154, 96155, 97802, 97803, 97804, 99201, 99202, 99203, 99204, 99205, 99211, 99212, 99213, 99214, 99215, 99217, 99218, 99219, 99220, 99221, 99222, 99223, 99231, 99232, 99233, 99234, 99235, 99236, 99238, 99239, 99241, 99242, 99243, 99244, 99245, 99251, 99252, 99253, 99254, 99255, 99261, 99262, 99263, 99271, 99272, 99273, 99274, 99275, 99281, 99282, 99283, 99284, 99285, 99295, 99296, 99297, 99301, 99302, 99303, 99311, 99312, 99313, 99321, 99322, 99323, 99331, 99332, 99333, 99341, 99342, 99343, 99344, 99345, 99347, 99348, 99349, 99350, 99354, 99355, 99356, 99357, 99360, 99431, 99432, 99433, 99435, 99440, 99455, 99456, G0176,G0177,M0064	90813, 90814, 90815, 90816, 90817, 90818, 90819, 90821, 90822, 90826, 90827, 90828, 90829, 90865, 90880, 99291,
90808 - individual psychotherapy, insight oriented, office or outpatient facility, 75-80 minutes	36640, 90801, 90802, 90804, 90805, 90806, 90807, 90862,96115, 96150, 96151, 96152, 96153, 96154, 96155, 97802, 97803, 97804,G0176, G0177, M0064	90814, 90815, 90816, 90817, 90818, 90819, 90821, 90822, 90828, 90829, 90865, 90880, 99201, 99202, 99203, 99204, 99205, 99211, 99212, 99213, 99214, 99215, 99217, 99218, 99219, 99220, 99221, 99222, 99223, 99231, 99232, 99233, 99234, 99235, 99236, 99238, 99239, 99241, 99242, 99243, 99244, 99245, 99251, 99252, 99253, 99254, 99255, 99261, 99262, 99263, 99271, 99272, 99273, 99274, 99275, 99281, 99282, 99283, 99284, 99285, 99291, 99295, 99296, 99297, 99301, 99302, 99303, 99311, 99312, 99313, 99321, 99322, 99323, 99331, 99332, 99333, 99341, 99342, 99343, 99344, 99345, 99350, 99354, 99355, 99356, 99357, 99360, 99431, 99432, 99433, 99435, 99440, 99455, 99456

COMPREHENSIVE CODE	COMPONENT CODES	MUTUALLY EXCLUSIVE CODES
90809 - individual psychotherapy, insight oriented; office or outpatient facility, 75-80 minutes; with medical evaluation and management services	36640, 90801, 90802, 90804, 90805, 90806, 90807, 90808, 90862,96115, 96150, 96151, 96152, 96153, 96154, 96155, 97802, 97803, 97804, 99201, 99202, 99203, 99204, 99205, 99211, 99212, 99213, 99214, 99215, 99217, 99218, 99219, 99220, 99221, 99222, 99223, 99231, 99232, 99233, 99234, 99235, 99236, 99238, 99239, 99241, 99242, 99243, 99244, 99245, 99251, 99252, 99253, 99254, 99255, 99261, 99262, 99263, 99271, 99272, 99273, 99274, 99275, 99281, 99282, 99283, 99284, 99285, 99295, 99296, 99297, 99301, 99302, 99303, 99311, 99312, 99313, 99321, 99322, 99323, 99331, 99332, 99333, 99341, 99342, 99343, 99344, 99345, 99347, 99348, 99349, 99350, 99354, 99355, 99356, 99357, 99360, 99431, 99432, 99433, 99435, 99440, 99455, 99456, G0176, G0177, M0064	90815, 90821, 90822, 90828, 90829, 90865, 90880, 99291
90810 - individual psychotherapy, interactive; office or outpatient facility, 20-30 minutes	36640, 90801, 90802, 90862, 96115, 96150, 96151, 96152, 96153, 96154, 96155, 97802, 97803, 97804,G0176, G0177, M0064	90805, 90806, 90807, 90808, 90809, 90812, 90813, 90814, 90815, 90816, 90817, 90818, 90819, 90821, 90822, 90823, 90824, 90826, 90827, 90828, 90829, 90845, 90865, 90880, 99201, 99202, 99203, 99204, 99205, 99211, 99212, 99213, 99214, 99215, 99217, 99218, 99219, 99220, 99221, 99222, 99223, 99231, 99232, 99233, 99234, 99235, 99236, 99238, 99239, 99241, 99242, 99243, 99244, 99245, 99251, 99252, 99253, 99254, 99255, 99261, 99262, 99263, 99271, 99272, 99273, 99274, 99275, 99281, 99282, 99283, 99284, 99285, 99291, 99295, 99296, 99297, 99301, 99302, 99303, 99311, 99312, 99313, 99321, 99322, 99323, 99331, 99332, 99333, 99341, 99342, 99343, 99344, 99345, 99350, 99354, 99355, 99356, 99357, 99360, 99431, 99432, 99433, 99435, 99440, 99455, 99456
90811 - individual psychotherapy, interactive; office or outpatient facility, 20-30 minutes; with medical evaluation and management services	36640, 90801, 90802, 90810, 90862,96115, 96150, 96151, 96152, 96153, 96154, 96155, 97802, 97803, 97804, 99201, 99202, 99203, 99204, 99205, 99211, 99212, 99213, 99214, 99215, 99217, 99218, 99219, 99220, 99221, 99222, 99223, 99231, 99232, 99233, 99234, 99235, 99236, 99238, 99239, 99241, 99242, 99243, 99244, 99245, 99251, 99252, 99253, 99254, 99255, 99261, 99262, 99263, 99271, 99272, 99273, 99274, 99275, 99281, 99282, 99283, 99284, 99285, 99295, 99296, 99297, 99301, 99302, 99303, 99311, 99312, 99313, 99321, 99322, 99323, 99331, 99332, 99333, 99341, 99342, 99343, 99344, 99345, 99347, 99348, 99349, 99350, 99354, 99355, 99356, 99357, 99360, 99431, 99432, 99433, 99435, 99440, 99455, 99456, G0176, G0177, M0064	90806, 90807, 90808, 90809, 90814, 90815, 90817, 90818, 90819, 90821, 90822, 90823, 90824, 90826, 90827, 90828, 90829, 90845, 90865, 90880, 99291,
90812 - individual psychotherapy, interactive, office or outpatient facility, 45-50 minutes	36640, 90801, 90802, 90811, 90862,96115, 96150, 96151, 96152, 96153, 96154, 96155, 97802, 97803, 97804,G0176, G0177, M0064	90806, 90807, 90808, 90809, 90818, 90819, 90821, 90822, 90823, 90824, 90826, 90827, 90828, 90829, 90865, 90880, 99201, 99202, 99203, 99204, 99205, 99211, 99212, 99213, 99214, 99215, 99217, 99218, 99219, 99220, 99221, 99222, 99223, 99231, 99232, 99233, 99234, 99235, 99236, 99238, 99239, 99241, 99242, 99243, 99244, 99245, 99251, 99252, 99253, 99254, 99255, 99261, 99262, 99263, 99271, 99272, 99273, 99274, 99275, 99281, 99282, 99283, 99284, 99285, 99291, 99295, 99296, 99297, 99301, 99302, 99303, 99311, 99312, 99313, 99321, 99322, 99323, 99333, 99341, 99342, 99343, 99344, 99345, 99350, 99354, 99355, 99356, 99357, 99360, 99431, 99432, 99433, 99435, 99440, 99455, 99456

COMPREHENSIVE CODE	COMPONENT CODES	MUTUALLY EXCLUSIVE CODES
90813 - individual psychotherapy, interactive; office or outpatient facility, 45-50 minutes, with medical evaluation and management services	36640, 90801, 90802, 90811, 90812, 90862, 96115, 96150, 96151, 96152, 96153, 96154, 96155, 97802, 97803, 97804, 99201, 99202, 99203, 99204, 99205, 99211, 99212, 99213, 99214, 99215, 99217, 99218, 99219, 99220, 99221, 99222, 99223, 99231, 99232, 99233, 99234, 99235, 99236, 99238, 99239, 99241, 99242, 99243, 99244, 99245, 99251, 99252, 99253, 99254, 99255, 99261, 99262, 99263, 99271, 99272, 99273, 99274, 99275, 99281, 99282, 99283, 99284, 99285, 99295, 99296, 99297, 99301, 99302, 99303, 99311, 99312, 99313, 99321, 99322, 99323, 99331, 99332, 99333, 99341, 99342, 99343, 99344, 99345, 99347, 99348, 99349, 99350, 99354, 99355, 99356, 99357, 99360, 99431, 99432, 99433, 99435, 99440, 99455, 99456, G0176, G0177, M0064	90808, 90809, 90814, 90819, 90821, 90822, 90823, 90824, 90826, 90827, 90828, 90829, 90865, 90880, 99291
90814 - individual psychotherapy, interactive, office or outpatient facility, 75-80 minutes	36640, 90801, 90802, 90812, 90862, 96115, 96150, 96151, 96152, 96153, 96154, 96155, 97802, 97803, 97804, G0176, G0177, M0064	90809, 90821, 90822, 90823, 90824, 90826, 90827, 90828, 90829, 90865, 90880, 99201, 99202, 99203, 99204, 99205, 99211, 99212, 99213, 99214, 99215, 99217, 99218, 99219, 99220, 99221, 99222, 99223, 99231, 99232, 99233, 99234, 99235, 99236, 99238, 99239, 99241, 99242, 99243, 99244, 99245, 99251, 99252, 99253, 99254, 99255, 99261, 99262, 99263, 99271, 99272, 99273, 99274, 99275, 99281, 99282, 99283, 99284, 99285, 99291, 99295, 99296, 99297, 99301, 99302, 99303, 99311, 99312, 99313, 99321, 99322, 99323, 99331, 99332, 99333, 99341, 99342, 99343, 99344, 99345, 99350, 99354, 99355, 99356, 99357, 99360, 99431, 99432, 99433, 99435, 99440, 99455, 99456
90815 - individual psychotherapy, interactive; office or outpatient facility, 75-80 minutes, with medical evaluation and management services	36640, 90801, 90802, 90812, 90813, 90814, 90862, 96115, 96150, 96151, 96152, 96153, 96154, 96155, 97802, 97803, 97804, 99201, 99202, 99203, 99204, 99205, 99211, 99212, 99213, 99214, 99215, 99217, 99218, 99219, 99220, 99221, 99222, 99223, 99231, 99232, 99233, 99234, 99235, 99236, 99238, 99239, 99241, 99242, 99243, 99244, 99245, 99251, 99252, 99253, 99254, 99255, 99261, 99262, 99263, 99271, 99272, 99273, 99274, 99275, 99281, 99282, 99283, 99284, 99285, 99295, 99296, 99297, 99301, 99302, 99303, 99311, 99312, 99313, 99321, 99322, 99323, 99331, 99332, 99333, 99341, 99342, 99343, 99344, 99345, 99347, 99348, 99349, 99350, 99354, 99355, 99356, 99357, 99360, 99431, 99432, 99433, 99435, 99440, 99455, 99456, G0176, G0177, M0064	90806, 90822, 90823, 90824, 90826, 90827, 90828, 90829, 90865, 90880, 99291
90816- individual psychotherapy, insight oriented; inpatient hospital, partial hospital or residential care setting, 20-30 minutes	36640, 90801, 90802, 90862, 96115, 96150, 96151, 96152, 96153, 96154, 96155, 97802, 97803, 97804, G0176, G0177, M0064	90809, 90811, 90812, 90813, 90814, 90815, 90823, 90824, 90826, 90827, 90828, 90829, 90845, 90865, 90880, 99201, 99202, 99203, 99204, 99205, 99211, 99212, 99213, 99214, 99215, 99217, 99218, 99219, 99220, 99221, 99222, 99223, 99231, 99232, 99233, 99234, 99235, 99236, 99238, 99239, 99241, 99242, 99243, 99244, 99245, 99251, 99252, 99253, 99254, 99255, 99261, 99262, 99263, 99271, 99272, 99273, 99274, 99275, 99281, 99282, 99283, 99284, 99285, 99291, 99295, 99296, 99297, 99301, 99302, 99303, 99311, 99312, 99313, 99321, 99322, 99323, 99331, 99333, 99341, 99342, 99343, 99344, 99345, 99350, 99354, 99355, 99356, 99357, 99360, 99431, 99432, 99433, 99435, 99440, 99455, 99456

COMPREHENSIVE CODE	COMPONENT CODES	MUTUALLY EXCLUSIVE CODES
90817 - individual psychotherapy, insight oriented; inpatient hospital, partial hospital or residential care setting, 20-30 minutes, with medical evaluation and management services	36640, 90801, 90802, 90816, 90862, 96115, 96150, 96151, 96152, 96153, 96154, 96155, 97802, 97803, 97804, 99201, 99202, 99203, 99204, 99205, 99211, 99212, 99213, 99214, 99215, 99217, 99218, 99219, 99220, 99221, 99222, 99223, 99231, 99232, 99233, 99234, 99235, 99236, 99238, 99239, 99241, 99242, 99243, 99244, 99245, 99251, 99252, 99253, 99254, 99255, 99261, 99262, 99263, 99271, 99272, 99273, 99274, 99275, 99281, 99282, 99283, 99284, 99285, 99295, 99296, 99297, 99301, 99302, 99303, 99311, 99312, 99313, 99321, 99322, 99323, 99331, 99332, 99333, 99341, 99342, 99343, 99344, 99345, 99347, 99348, 99349, 99350, 99354, 99355, 99356, 99357, 99360, 99431, 99432, 99433, 99435, 99440, 99455, 99456, G0176, G0177, M0064	90809, 90812, 90813, 90814, 90815, 90824, 90826, 90827, 90828, 90829, 90845, 90865, 99291
90818 - individual psychotherapy, insight oriented; inpatient hospital, partial hospital or residential care setting, 45-50 minutes	36640, 90801, 90802, 90816, 90817, 90862, 96115, 96150, 96151, 96152, 96153, 96154, 96155, 97802, 97803, 97804,G0176, G0177, M0064	90809, 90813, 90814, 90815, 90826, 90827, 90828, 90829, 90865, 90880, 99201, 99202, 99203, 99204, 99205, 99211, 99212, 99213, 99214, 99215, 99217, 99218, 99219, 99220, 99221, 99222, 99223, 99231, 99232, 99233, 99234, 99235, 99236, 99238, 99239, 99241, 99242, 99243, 99244, 99245, 99251, 99252, 99253, 99254, 99255, 99261, 99262, 99263, 99271, 99272, 99273, 99274, 99275, 99281, 99282, 99283, 99284, 99285, 99291, 99295, 99296, 99297, 99301, 99302, 99303, 99311, 99312, 99313, 99321, 99322, 99323, 99331, 99332, 99333, 99341, 99342, 99343, 99344, 99345, 99350, 99354, 99355, 99356, 99357, 99360, 99431, 99432, 99433, 99435, 99440, 99455, 99456
90819 - individual psychotherapy, insight oriented; inpatient hospital, partial hospital or residential care setting, 45-50 minutes, with medical evaluation and management services	36640, 90801, 90802, 90804, 90805, 90816, 90817, 90818, 90862, 96115, 96150, 96151, 96152, 96153, 96154, 96155, 97802, 97803, 97804, 99201, 99202, 99203, 99204, 99205, 99211, 99212, 99213, 99214, 99215, 99217, 99218, 99219, 99220, 99221, 99222, 99223, 99231, 99232, 99233, 99234, 99235, 99236, 99238, 99239, 99241, 99242, 99243, 99244, 99245, 99251, 99252, 99253, 99254, 99255, 99261, 99262, 99263, 99271, 99272, 99273, 99274, 99275, 99281, 99282, 99283, 99284, 99285, 99295, 99296, 99297, 99301, 99302, 99303, 99311, 99312, 99313, 99321, 99322, 99323, 99331, 99332, 99333, 99341, 99342, 99343, 99344, 99345, 99347, 99348, 99349, 99350, 99354, 99355, 99356, 99357, 99360, 99431, 99432, 99433, 99435, 99440, 99455, 99456, G0176, G0177, M0064	90809, 90814, 90815, 90827, 90828, 90829, 90865, 90880, 99291
90821-individual psychotherapy, insight oriented; inpatient hospital, partial hospital or residential care setting, 75-80 minutes	36640, 90801, 90802, 90816, 90817, 90818, 90819, 90862, 96115, 96150, 96151, 96152, 96153, 96154, 96155, 97802, 97803, 97804, G0176, G0177, M0064	90815, 90828, 90829, 90865, 90880, 99201, 99202, 99203, 99204, 99205, 99211, 99212, 99213, 99214, 99215, 99217, 99218, 99219, 99220, 99221, 99222, 99223, 99231, 99232, 99233, 99234, 99235, 99236, 99238, 99241, 99242, 99243, 99244, 99245, 99251, 99252, 99253, 99254, 99255, 99261, 99262, 99263, 99271, 99272, 99273, 99274, 99275, 99281, 99282, 99283, 99284, 99285, 99291, 99295, 99296, 99297, 99301, 99302, 99303, 99311, 99312, 99313, 99321, 99322, 99323, 99331, 99332, 99333, 99341, 99342, 99343, 99344, 99345, 99350, 99354, 99355, 99356, 99357, 99360, 99431, 99432, 99433, 99435, 99440, 99455, 99456

COMPREHENSIVE CODE	COMPONENT CODES	MUTUALLY EXCLUSIVE CODES
90822 - individual psychotherapy, insight oriented; inpatient hospital, partial hospital or residential care setting, 75-80 minutes, with medical evaluation and management services	36640, 90801, 90802, 90816, 90817, 90818, 90819, 90821, 90862, 96115, 96150, 96151, 96152, 96153, 96154, 96155, 97802, 97803, 97804, 99201, 99202, 99203, 99204, 99205, 99211, 99212, 99213, 99214, 99215, 99217, 99218, 99219, 99220, 99221, 99222, 99223, 99231, 99232, 99233, 99234, 99235, 99236, 99238, 99239, 99241, 99242, 99243, 99244, 99245, 99251, 99252, 99253, 99254, 99255, 99261, 99262, 99263, 99271, 99272, 99273, 99274, 99275, 99281, 99282, 99283, 99284, 99285, 99295, 99296, 99297, 99301, 99302, 99303, 99311, 99312, 99313, 99321, 99322, 99323, 99331, 99332, 99333, 99341, 99342, 99343, 99344, 99345, 99347, 99348, 99349, 99350, 99354, 99355, 99356, 99357, 99360, 99431, 99432, 99433, 99435, 99440, 99455, 99456, G0176, G0177, M0064	90829, 90865, 90880, 99291
90823 - individual psychotherapy, interactive, inpatient hospital, partial hospital or residential care setting, 20-30 minutes	36640, 90801, 90802, 90862, 96115, 96150, 96151, 96152, 96153, 96154, 96155, 97802, 97803, 97804, G0176, G0177, M0064	90805, 90806, 90807, 90808, 90809, 90817, 90818, 90819, 90821, 90822, 90827, 90828, 90829, 90845, 90865, 90880, 99201, 99202, 99203, 99204, 99205, 99211, 99212, 99213, 99214, 99215, 99217, 99218, 99219, 99220, 99221, 99222, 99223, 99231, 99232, 99233, 99234, 99235, 99236, 99238, 99239, 99241, 99242, 99243, 99244, 99245, 99251, 99252, 99253, 99254, 99255, 99261, 99262, 99263, 99271, 99272, 99273, 99274, 99275, 99281, 99282, 99283, 99284, 99285, 99291, 99295, 99296, 99297, 99301, 99302, 99303, 99311, 99312, 99313, 99321, 99322, 99323, 99331, 99332, 99333, 99341, 99342, 99343, 99344, 99345, 99350, 99354, 99355, 99356, 99357, 99360, 99431, 99432, 99433, 99435, 99440, 99455, 99456
90824 - individual psychotherapy, interactive, inpatient hospital, partial hospital or residential care setting, 20-30 minutes, with medical evaluation and management services	36640, 90801, 90802, 90823, 90862, 96115, 96150, 96151, 96152, 96153, 96154, 96155, 97802, 97803, 97804, 99201, 99202, 99203, 99204, 99205, 99211, 99212, 99213, 99214, 99215, 99217, 99218, 99219, 99220, 99221, 99222, 99223, 99231, 99232, 99233, 99234, 99235, 99236, 99238, 99239, 99241, 99242, 99243, 99244, 99245, 99251, 99252, 99253, 99254, 99255, 99261, 99262, 99263, 99271, 99272, 99273, 99274, 99275, 99281, 99282, 99283, 99284, 99285, 99295, 99296, 99297, 99301, 99302, 99303, 99311, 99312, 99313, 99321, 99322, 99323, 99331, 99332, 99333, 99341, 99342, 99343, 99344, 99345, 99347, 99348, 99349, 99350, 99354, 99355, 99356, 99357, 99360, 99431, 99432, 99433, 99435, 99440, 99455, 99456, G0176, G0177, M0064	90807, 90808, 90809, 90818, 90819, 90821, 90822, 90828, 90829, 90845, 90865, 90880, 99291
90826 - individual psychotherapy, interactive, inpatient hospital, partial hospital or residential care setting, 45-50 minutes	36640, 90801, 90802, 90823, 90824, 90862, 96115, 96150, 96151, 96152, 96153, 96154, 96155, 97802, 97803, 97804, G0176, G0177, M0064	90808, 90809, 90819, 90821, 90822, 90829, 90865, 90880, 99201, 99202, 99203, 99204, 99205, 99211, 99212, 99213, 99214, 99215, 99217, 99218, 99219, 99220, 99221, 99222, 99223, 99231, 99232, 99233, 99234, 99235, 99236, 99238, 99239, 99241, 99242, 99243, 99244, 99245, 99251, 99252, 99253, 99254, 99255, 99261, 99262, 99263, 99271, 99272, 99273, 99274, 99275, 99281, 99282, 99283, 99284, 99285, 99291, 99295, 99296, 99297, 99301, 99302, 99303, 99311, 99312, 99313, 99321, 99322, 99323, 99331, 99332, 99333, 99341, 99342, 99343, 99344, 99345, 99350, 99354, 99355, 99356, 99357, 99360, 99431, 99432, 99433, 99435, 99440, 99455, 99456

COMPREHENSIVE CODE	COMPONENT CODES	MUTUALLY EXCLUSIVE CODES
90827 - individual psychotherapy, interactive, inpatient hospital, partial hospital or residential care setting, 45-50 minutes, with medical evaluation and management services	36640, 90801, 90802, 90824, 90826, 90862, 96115, 96150, 96151, 96152, 96153, 96154, 96155, 97802, 97803, 97804, 99201, 99202, 99203, 99204, 99205, 99211, 99212, 99213, 99214, 99215, 99217, 99218, 99219, 99220, 99221, 99222, 99223, 99231, 99232, 99233, 99234, 99235, 99236, 99238, 99239, 99241, 99242, 99243, 99244, 99245, 99251, 99252, 99253, 99254, 99255, 99261, 99262, 99263, 99271, 99272, 99273, 99274, 99275, 99281, 99282, 99283, 99284, 99285, 99295, 99296, 99297, 99301, 99302, 99303, 99311, 99312, 99313, 99321, 99322, 99323, 99331, 99332, 99333, 99341, 99342, 99343, 99344, 99345, 99347, 99348, 99349, 99350, 99354, 99355, 99356, 99357, 99360, 99431, 99432, 99433, 99435, 99440, 99455, 99456, G0176, G0177, M0064	90808, 90809, 90821, 90822, 90828, 90829, 90865, 90880, 99291
90828 - individual psychotherapy, interactive, inpatient hospital, partial hospital or residential care setting, 75-80 minutes	36640, 90801, 90802, 90826, 90862, 96115, 96150, 96151, 96152, 96153, 96154, 96155, 97802, 97803, 97804, G0176, G0177, M0064	90822, 90865, 90880, 99201, 99202, 99203, 99205, 99211, 99212, 99213, 99214, 99215, 99217, 99218, 99219, 99220, 99221, 99222, 99223, 99231, 99232, 99233, 99234, 99235, 99236, 99238, 99239, 99241, 99242, 99243, 99244, 99245, 99251, 99252, 99253, 99254, 99255, 99261, 99262, 99263, 99271, 99272, 99273, 99274, 99275, 99281, 99282, 99283, 99284, 99285, 99291, 99295, 99296, 99297, 99301, 99302, 99303, 99311, 99312, 99313, 99321, 99322, 99323, 99331, 99332, 99333, 99341, 99342, 99343, 99344, 99345, 99350, 99354, 99355, 99356, 99357, 99360, 99431, 99432, 99433, 99435, 99440, 99455, 99456
90829 - individual psychotherapy, interactive, inpatient hospital, partial hospital or residential care setting, 75-80 minutes, with medical evaluation and management services	36640, 90801, 90802, 90828, 90862, 96115, 96150, 96151, 96152, 96153, 96154, 96155, 97802, 97803, 97804, 99201, 99202, 99203, 99204, 99205, 99211, 99212, 99213, 99214, 99215, 99217, 99218, 99219, 99220, 99221, 99222, 99223, 99231, 99232, 99233, 99234, 99235, 99236, 99238, 99239, 99241, 99242, 99243, 99244, 99245, 99251, 99252, 99253, 99254, 99255, 99261, 99262, 99263, 99271, 99272, 99273, 99274, 99275, 99281, 99282, 99283, 99284, 99285, 99295, 99296, 99297, 99301, 99302, 99303, 99311, 99312, 99313, 99321, 99322, 99323, 99331, 99332, 99333, 99341, 99342, 99343, 99344, 99345, 99347, 99348, 99349, 99350, 99354, 99355, 99356, 99357, 99360, 99431, 99432, 99433, 99435, 99440, 99455, 99456, G0176, G0177, M0064	90865, 90880, 99291
90845 – psychoanalysis	36640, 90801, 90802, 90862, 96115, 96150, 96151, 96152, 96153, 96154, 96155, 97802, 97803, 97804, 99201, 99202, 99203, 99204, 99205, 99211, 99212, 99213, 99214, 99215, 99217, 99218, 99219, 99220, 99221, 99222, 99223, 99231, 99232, 99233, 99234, 99235, 99236, 99238, 99239, 99241, 99242, 99243, 99244, 99245, 99251, 99252, 99253, 99254, 99255, 99261, 99262, 99263, 99271, 99272, 99273, 99274, 99275, 99281, 99282, 99283, 99284, 99285, 99291, 99292, 99301, 99302, 99303, 99311, 99312, 99313, 99321, 99322, 99323, 99331, 99332, 99333, 99341, 99342, 99343, 99344, 99345, 99347, 99348, 99349, 99350, 99354, 99355, 99356, 99357, G0176, G0177, M0064	90807, 90808, 90809, 90812, 90813, 90814, 90815, 90818, 90819, 90821, 90822, 90826, 90827, 90828, 90829, 90846, 90847, 90865, 90880

COMPREHENSIVE CODE	COMPONENT CODES	MUTUALLY EXCLUSIVE CODES
90846 – family psychotherapy (without patient present)	96115, 96150, 96151, 96152, 96153, 96154, 96155, 97802, 97803, 97804, 99201, 99202, 99203, 99204, 99205, 99211, 99212, 99213, 99214, 99215, 99217, 99218, 99219, 99220, 99221, 99222, 99223, 99231, 99232, 99233, 99234, 99235, 99236, 99238, 99239, 99241, 99242, 99243, 99244, 99245, 99251, 99252, 99253, 99254, 99255, 99261, 99262, 99263, 99271, 99272, 99273, 99274, 99275, 99281, 99282, 99283, 99284, 99285, 99301, 99302, 99303, 99311, 99312, 99313, 99315, 99316, 99321, 99322, 99323, 99331, 99332, 99333, 99341, 99342, 99343, 99344, 99345, 99347, 99348, 99349, 99350, 99354, 99355, 99356, 99357, G0176, G0177	90801, 90802, 90804, 90805, 90806, 90807, 90808, 90809, 90810, 90811, 90812, 90813, 90814, 90815, 90816, 90817, 90818, 90819, 90821, 90822, 90823, 90824, 90826, 90827, 90828, 90829, 90847, 90865, 90870, 90871, 90880
90847 – family psychotherapy (conjoint psychotherapy)	36640, 90802, 90862, 96115, 96150, 96151, 96152, 96153, 96154, 96155, 97802, 97803, 97804, 99201, 99202, 99203, 99204, 99205, 99211, 99212, 99213, 99214, 99215, 99217, 99218, 99219, 99220, 99221, 99222, 99223, 99231, 99232, 99233, 99234, 99235, 99236, 99238, 99239, 99241, 99242, 99243, 99244, 99245, 99251, 99252, 99253, 99254, 99255, 99261, 99262, 99263, 99271, 99272, 99273, 99274, 99275, 99281, 99282, 99283, 99284, 99285, 99291, 99292, 99301, 99302, 99303, 99311, 99312, 99313, 99315, 99316, 99321, 99322, 99323, 99331, 99332, 99333, 99341, 99342, 99343, 99344, 99345, 99347, 99348, 99349, 99350, 99354, 99355, 99356, 99357, G0176, G0177	90801, 90804, 90805, 90806, 90807, 90808, 90809, 90810, 90811, 90812, 90813, 90814, 90815, 90816, 90817, 90818, 90819, 90821, 90822, 90823, 90824, 90826, 90827, 90828, 90829, 90865, 90870, 90871, 90880
90849 – multiple –family group psychotherapy	90801, 90802, 90862, 96115, 96150, 96151, 96152, 96153, 96154, 96155, 97802, 97803, 97804, 99201, 99202, 99203, 99204, 99205, 99211, 99212, 99213, 99214, 99215, 99217, 99218, 99219, 99220, 99221, 99222, 99223, 99231, 99232, 99233, 99234, 99235, 99236, 99238, 99239, 99241, 99242, 99243, 99244, 99245, 99251, 99252, 99253, 99254, 99255, 99261, 99262, 99263, 99271, 99272, 99273, 99274, 99275, 99281, 99282, 99283, 99284, 99285, 99291, 99292, 99301, 99302, 99303, 99311, 99312, 99313, 99315, 99316, 99321, 99322, 99323, 99331, 99332, 99333, 99341, 99342, 99343, 99344, 99345, 99347, 99348, 99349, 99350, 99354, 99355, 99356, 99357, G0176, G0177	90804, 90805, 90806, 90807, 90808, 90809, 90810, 90811, 90812, 90813, 90814, 90815, 90816, 90817, 90818, 90819, 90821, 90822, 90823, 90824, 90826, 90827, 90828, 90829, 90845, 90846, 90847, 90865, 90870, 90871, 90880
90853 – group psychotherapy	36640, 90802, 90862, 96115, 96150, 96151, 96152, 96153, 96154, 96155, 97802, 97803, 97804, 99201, 99202, 99203, 99204, 99205, 99211, 99212, 99213, 99214, 99215, 99217, 99218, 99219, 99220, 99221, 99222, 99223, 99231, 99232, 99233, 99234, 99235, 99236, 99238, 99239, 99241, 99242, 99243, 99244, 99245, 99251, 99252, 99253, 99254, 99255, 99261, 99262, 99263, 99271, 99272, 99273, 99274, 99275, 99281, 99282, 99283, 99284, 99285, 99291, 99292, 99301, 99302, 99303, 99311, 99312, 99313, 99315, 99316, 99321, 99322, 99323, 99331, 99332, 99333, 99341, 99342, 99343, 99344, 99345, 99347, 99348, 99349, 99350, 99354, 99355, 99356, 99357, G0176, G0177	90801, 90804, 90805, 90806, 90807, 90808, 90809, 90810, 90811, 90812, 90813, 90814, 90815, 90816, 90817, 90818, 90819, 90821, 90822, 90823, 90824, 90826, 90827, 90828, 90829, 90845, 90846, 90847, 90849, 90865, 90870, 90871, 90880

COMPREHENSIVE CODE	COMPONENT CODE	MUTUALLY EXCLUSIVE CODES
90857 – interactive group psychotherapy	90801, 90802, 90853, 90862, 96115, 96150, 96151, 96152, 96153, 96154, 96155, 97802, 97803, 97804, 99201, 99202, 99203, 99204, 99205, 99211, 99212, 99213, 99214, 99215, 99217, 99218, 99219, 99220, 99221, 99222, 99223, 99231, 99232, 99233, 99234, 99235, 99236, 99238, 99239, 99241, 99242, 99243, 99244, 99245, 99251, 99252, 99253, 99254, 99255, 99261, 99262, 99263, 99271, 99272, 99273, 99274, 99275, 99281, 99282, 99283, 99284, 99285, 99291, 99292, 99301, 99302, 99303, 99311, 99312, 99313, 99315, 99316, 99321, 99322, 99323, 99331, 99332, 99333, 99341, 99342, 99343, 99344, 99345, 99347, 99348, 99349, 99350, 99354, 99355, 99356, 99357, G0176, G0177	90804, 90805, 90806, 90807, 90808, 90809, 90810, 90811, 90812, 90813, 90814, 90815, 90816, 90817, 90818, 90819, 90821, 90822, 90823, 90824, 90826, 90827, 90828, 90829, 90845, 90846, 90847, 90849, 90865, 90870, 90871, 90880
90862 – pharmacologic management	90782, 96150, 96151, 96152, 96153, 96154, 96155, 97802, 97803, 97804	NA
90865 – narcosynthesis for psychiatric diagnostic and therapeutic purposes	90801, 90802, 90862 96115, 96150, 96151, 96152, 96153, 96154, 96155, 97802, 97803, 97804, 99201, 99202, 99203, 99204, 99205, 99211, 99212, 99213, 99214, 99215, 99217, 99218, 99219, 99220, 99221, 99222, 99223, 99231, 99232, 99233, 99234, 99235, 99236, 99238, 99239, 99241, 99242, 99243, 99244, 99245, 99251, 99252, 99253, 99254, 99255, 99261, 99262, 99263, 99271, 99272, 99273, 99274, 99275, 99281, 99282, 99283, 99284, 99285, 99291, 99292, 99301, 99302, 99303, 99311, 99312, 99313, 99315, 99316, 99321, 99322, 99323, 99331, 99332, 99333, 99341, 99342, 99343, 99344, 99345, 99347, 99348, 99349, 99350, 99354, 99355, 99356, 99357	NA
90870 – electroconvulsive therapy; single seizure	00104, 90801, 90802, 90862, 96150, 96151, 96152, 96153, 96154, 96155, 97802, 97803, 97804	90804, 90805, 90806, 90807, 90808, 90809, 90810, 90811, 90812, 90813, 90814, 90815, 90816, 90817, 90818, 90819, 90821, 90822, 90823, 90824, 90826, 90827, 90828, 90829, 90865, 90880
90871 - electroconvulsive therapy; multiple seizure	90801, 90802, 90870, 96150, 96151, 96152, 96153, 96154, 96155, 97802, 97803, 97804	90804, 90805, 90806, 90807, 90808, 90809, 90810, 90811, 90812, 90813, 90814, 90815, 90816, 90817, 90818, 90819, 90821, 90822, 90823, 90824, 90826, 90827, 90828, 90829, 90865, 90880
90880 – hypnotherapy	90801, 90802, 96115, 96150, 96151, 96152, 96153, 96154, 96155, 97802, 97803, 97804, 99201, 99202, 99203, 99204, 99205, 99211, 99212, 99213, 99214, 99215, 99217, 99218, 99219, 99220, 99221, 99222, 99223, 99231, 99232, 99233, 99234, 99235, 99236, 99238, 99239, 99241, 99242, 99243, 99244, 99245, 99251, 99252, 99253, 99254, 99255, 99261, 99262, 99263, 99271, 99272, 99273, 99274, 99275, 99281, 99282, 99283, 99284, 99285, 99291, 99292, 99301, 99302, 99303, 99311, 99312, 99313, 99315, 99316, 99321, 99322, 99323, 99331, 99332, 99333, 99341, 99342, 99343, 99344, 99345, 99347, 99348, 99349, 99350, 99354, 99355, 99356, 99357, G0176, G0177	90806, 90817, 90865
90901 – biofeedback training by any modality	51784, 51785, 51795, 64550, 90804, 90805, 90806, 90807, 90808, 90809, 90810, 90811, 90812, 90813, 90814, 90815, 90816, 90817, 90818, 90819, 90821, 90822, 90823, 90824, 90826, 90827, 90828, 90829, 90845, 90846, 90847, 90849, 90853, 90857, 90865, 90880, 91122	NA
90911 – biofeedback training, perineal muscles, anorectal or urethral sphincter, including EMG and/or manometry	51784, 51785, 51795, 64550, 90804, 90805, 90806, 90807, 90808, 90809, 90810, 90811, 90812, 90813, 90814, 90815, 90816, 90817, 90818, 90819, 90821, 90822, 90823, 90824, 90826, 90827, 90828, 90829, 90845, 90846, 90847, 90849, 90853, 90857, 90865, 90880, 90901, 91122, 95860, 95861, 95863, 95864, 95867, 95868, 95869, 95870, 95872, 97032, 97110, 97112, 97530, 97535, 97750	NA

NEURODIAGNOSTIC TESTING

Table 4 illustrates most commonly used neurodiagnostic testing services, with comprehensive, component and mutually exclusive codes.

Comprehensive Codes

CPT 95831 Muscle testing, manual (separate procedure) with report; extremity (excluding hand) or trunk; a comprehensive code which also includes several component codes as follows:

- 95851 Range of motion measurements and report (separate procedure); each extremity (excluding hand) or each trunk section (spine)
- 97140 Manual therapy techniques (eg, mobilization/ manipulation, manual lymphatic drainage, manual traction), one or more regions, each 15 minutes

Mutually Exclusive Codes - None

CPT 95833 Muscle testing, total evaluation of body, excluding hands; a comprehensive code which also includes several component codes as follows:

- 95831 Muscle testing, manual (separate procedure) with report; extremity (excluding hand) or trunk
- 95851 Range of motion measurements and report (separate procedure); each extremity (excluding hand) or each trunk section (spine)
- 97140 Manual therapy techniques (eg, mobilization/ manipulation, manual lymphatic drainage, manual traction), one or more regions, each 15 minutes

Mutually Exclusive Codes - None

CPT 95834 Muscle testing, hand, including hands; a comprehensive code which also includes several component codes as follows:

- 95832 Muscle testing, hand, with or without comparison with normal side
- 95851 Range of motion measurements and report (separate procedure); each extremity (excluding hand) or each trunk section (spine)
- 95852 Range of motion measurements and report (separate procedure); hand, with or without comparison with normal side
- 97140 Manual therapy techniques (eg, mobilization/ manipulation, manual lymphatic drainage, manual traction), one or more regions, each 15 minutes

Mutually exclusive codes - None

Table 4. *Illustration of most commonly used neurodiagnostic techniques (comprehensive codes) showing component and mutually exclusive codes*

Comprehensive Code	Component Codes	Mutually Exclusive Codes
95831 – muscle testing, manual; extremity	95851, 97140	NA
95832 – muscle testing, hand	95852, 97140	NA
95833 – muscle testing, total evaluation of body	95831, 95851, 97140	NA
95834 – muscle testing, hand	95832, 95851, 95852, 97140	NA
95858 – Tensilon test for myasthenia gravis; with electromyographic recording	95857	NA
95860 – needle electromyography, one extremity	95869, 95870	NA
95861 – needle electromyography, two extremities	95860, 95869, 95870	NA
95863 – needle electromyography, three extremities	95860, 95861, 65869, 95870	NA
95864 – needle electromyography, four extremities	95860, 95861, 95863, 95869, 95870	NA
95867 – needle electromyography, cranial nerve supplied muscle, unilateral	95869, 95870	NA
95868 - needle electromyography, cranial nerve supplied muscle, bilateral	95867, 95869, 95870	NA
95869 - needle electromyography, thoracic paraspinal muscles	90901, 95870	NA
95875 – ischemic limb exercise with needle electromyography	95860, 95869	NA
95903 – nerve conduction, amplitude and latency/velocity study; with F-wave study	95900, 95920	NA
95937 – neuromuscular junction testing, each nerve	790	NA

CPT 95858 Tensilon test for myasthenia gravis; with electromyographic recording; a comprehensive code which also includes several component codes as follows:

- 95857 Tensilon test for myasthenia gravis

Mutually exclusive codes - None

CPT 95860 Needle electromyography, one extremity with or without related paraspinal areas; a comprehensive code which also includes several component codes as follows:

- 95869 Needle electromyography, thoracic paraspinal muscles
- 95870 Needle electromyography, limited study of muscle in one extremity or non-limb (axial) muscles (unilateral or bilateral), other than thoracic paraspinal, cranial nerve supplied muscles, or sphincters

Mutually exclusive codes - None

CPT 95861 Needle electromyography, two extremities with or without related paraspinal areas; a comprehensive code which also includes several component codes as follows:

- 95860 Needle electromyography, one extremity with or without related paraspinal areas
- 95869 Needle electromyography, thoracic paraspinal muscles
- 95870 Needle electromyography, limited study of muscle in one extremity or non-limb (axial) muscles (unilateral or bilateral), other than thoracic paraspinal, cranial nerve supplied muscles, or sphincters

Mutually exclusive codes - None

CPT 95863 Needle electromyography, three extremities with or without related paraspinal areas; a comprehensive code which also includes several component codes as follows:

- 95860 Needle electromyography, one extremity with or without related paraspinal areas
- 95861 Needle electromyography, two extremities with or without related paraspinal areas
- 95869 Needle electromyography, thoracic paraspinal muscles
- 95870 Needle electromyography, limited study of muscle in one extremity or non-limb (axial) muscles (unilateral or bilateral), other than thoracic paraspinal, cranial nerve supplied muscles, or sphincters

Mutually exclusive codes - None

CPT 95864 Needle electromyography, four extremities with or without related paraspinal areas; a comprehensive code which also includes several component codes as follows:

- 95860 Needle electromyography, one extremity with or without related paraspinal areas
- 95861 Needle electromyography, two extremities with or without related paraspinal areas
- 95863 Needle electromyography, three extremities with or without related paraspinal areas
- 95869 Needle electromyography, thoracic paraspinal muscles
- 95870 Needle electromyography, limited study of muscle in one extremity or non-limb (axial) muscles (unilateral or bilateral), other than thoracic paraspinal, cranial nerve supplied muscles, or sphincters

Mutually exclusive codes - None

CPT 95867 Needle electromyography, cranial nerve supplied muscles, unilateral; a comprehensive code which also includes several component codes as follows:

- 95869 Needle electromyography, thoracic paraspinal muscles
- 95870 Needle electromyography, limited study of muscle in one extremity or non-limb (axial) muscles (unilateral or bilateral), other than thoracic paraspinal, cranial nerve supplied muscles, or sphincters

Mutually exclusive codes - None

CPT 95868 Needle electromyography, cranial nerve supplied muscles, bilateral; a comprehensive code which also includes several component codes as follows:

- 95867 Needle electromyography, cranial nerve supplied muscles, unilateral
- 95869 Needle electromyography, thoracic paraspinal muscles
- 95870 Needle electromyography, limited study of muscle in one extremity or non-limb (axial) muscles (unilateral or bilateral), other than thoracic paraspinal, cranial nerve supplied muscles, or sphincters

Mutually exclusive codes - None

CPT 95869 Needle electromyography, thoracic paraspinal muscles; a comprehensive code which also includes several component codes as follows:

- 90901 Biofeedback training by any modality
- 95870 Needle electromyography, limited study of muscle in one extremity or non-limb (axial) muscles (unilateral or bilateral), other than thoracic paraspinal, cranial nerve supplied muscles, or sphincters

Mutually exclusive codes - None

CPT 95875 Ischemic limb exercise with needle electromyography, with lactic acid determination; a comprehensive code which also includes several component codes as follows:

- 95860 Needle electromyography, one extremity with or without related paraspinal areas
- 95869 Needle electromyography, thoracic paraspinal muscles

Mutually exclusive codes - None

CPT 95903 Nerve conduction, amplitude and latency/velocity study, each nerve; motor, with F-wave study; a comprehensive code which also includes several component codes as follows:

- 95900 Nerve conduction, amplitude and latency/velocity study, each nerve; motor, without F-wave study
- 95920 Intraoperative neurophysiology testing, per hour

Mutually exclusive codes - None

CPT 95937 Neuromuscular junction testing (repetitive stimulation, paired stimuli), each nerve, any one method; a comprehensive code which also includes several component codes as follows:

- 00790 Anesthesia for intraperitoneal procedures in upper abdomen including laparoscopy, not otherwise specified

Mutually exclusive codes - None

RADIOLOGICAL SERVICES

The radiology chapter includes multiple codes divided into regions extending from 70010 to 79999. This includes diagnostic imaging, interventional radiology, and nuclear medicine. We will only describe radiological services relevant to interventional pain medicine which include some of the services provided in evaluation of the chest, spine and pelvis, upper extremities, lower extremities, and procedures listed under other procedures.

Following is the illustration of most commonly used radiological services showing component and mutually exclusive codes. Due to extensive nature of descriptions, only comprehensive codes are described, whereas component and mutually exclusive codes are listed with CPT code, but without description.

Comprehensive Code	Component Codes	Mutually Exclusive Codes
71010 – radiologic examination, chest; single view, frontal	NA	71022, 71023, 71030, 71034
71015 – radiologic examination, chest; single view, stereo, frontal	71010	71023
71020 – radiologic examination, chest; two views, frontal and lateral	71010	71021, 71022, 71023, 71030, 71034, 71101, 71111
71021 – radiologic examination, chest; two views, frontal and lateral; with apical lordotic procedure	71010	71022, 71023, 71030, 71034, 71111
71022 - radiologic examination, chest; two views, frontal and lateral; with oblique projections	NA	71023, 71034, 71111
71023 - radiologic examination, chest; two views, frontal and lateral; with fluoroscopy	76000, 76001	71034
71030 - radiologic examination, chest; complete, minimum of four views	71022	71023, 71111
71034 - radiologic examination, chest; complete, minimum of four views, with fluoroscopy	71030, 76000, 76001	NA
72010 - radiologic examination, spine, entire, survey study, anteroposterior and lateral	72020, 72040, 72050, 72069, 72070, 72072, 72080, 72090, 72110, 72114, 72120	NA
72050 – radiologic examination, spine, cervical; minimum of four views	72020, 72040	NA
72052 – radiologic examination, spine, cervical; complete	72020, 72040, 72050	72010

Comprehensive Code	Component Codes	Mutually Exclusive Codes
72069 – radiologic examination, spine, thoracolumbar, standing (scoliosis)	NA	72090
72070 - radiologic examination, spine, thoracic; two views	NA	72090
72072 -radiologic examination, spine, thoracic; three views	72070	72090
72074 - radiologic examination, spine, thoracic; minimum of four views	72070, 72072	72010, 72069, 72090
72080 - radiologic examination, spine, thoracolumbar; two views	72070	72069, 72072, 72074
72090 - radiologic examination, spine, scoliosis study, including spine and erect studies	72080	NA
72100 - radiologic examination, spine, lumbosacral; two or three views	NA	72010
72110 - radiologic examination, spine, lumbosacral; minimum of four views	72020, 72100	72114
72114 - radiologic examination, spine, lumbosacral; complete, including bending views	72100, 72120	NA
72120 - radiologic examination, spine, lumbosacral; bending views only, minimum of four views	NA	72110
72126 – computerized axial tomography, cervical spine; with contrast	36000, 36011, 34606, 36410, 72125, 90782, 90783, 90784	NA
72127 – computerized axial tomography, cervical spine; without contrast, followed by contrast and further sections	36000, 36011, 36406, 36410, 72125, 72126, 90782, 90783, 90784	NA
72129 – computerized axial tomography, thoracic spine; with contrast	36000, 36011, 36406, 36410, 72128, 90782, 90783, 90784	NA
72130 - computerized axial tomography, thoracic spine; without contrast, followed by contrast and further sections	36000, 36011, 36406, 36410, 72128, 72129, 90782, 90783, 90784	NA
72132 -computerized axial tomography, lumbar spine; with contrast	36000, 36011, 36406, 36410, 72131, 90782, 90783, 90784	NA
72133 – computerized axial tomography, lumbar spine; without contrast	36000, 36011, 36406, 36410, 72131, 72132, 90782, 90783, 90784	NA
72142 –magnetic resonance imaging, spinal canal and contents, cervical; with contrast	36000, 36011, 36406, 36410, 72141	NA
72147 - magnetic resonance imaging, spinal canal and contents, thoracic; with contrast	36000, 36011, 36406, 36410, 72146, 90782, 90783, 90784	NA
72149 - magnetic resonance imaging, spinal canal and contents, lumbar; with contrast material	36000, 36011, 36406, 36410, 72148, 90782, 90783, 90784	NA
72156 - magnetic resonance imaging, spinal canal and contents, lumbar; without contrast material; followed by contrast and further sequences; cervical	36000, 36011, 36406, 36410, 72141, 72142, 90782, 90783, 90784	NA
72157 - magnetic resonance imaging, spinal canal and contents, lumbar; without contrast, followed by contrast and further sequences; thoracic	36000, 36011, 36406, 36410, 72146, 72147, 90782, 90783, 90784	NA
72158 - magnetic resonance imaging, spinal canal and contents, lumbar; without contrast, followed by contrast and further sequences; lumbar	36000, 36011, 36406, 36410, 72148, 72149, 90782, 90783, 90784	NA

Comprehensive Code	Component Codes	Mutually Exclusive Codes
72190 - radiologic examination, pelvis; complete minimum of three views	72170	NA
72193 - computed tomographic angiography, pelvis, with contrast	36000, 36011, 36406, 36410, 72192, 90782, 90783, 90784	NA
72194 – computerized axial tomography, pelvis, without contrast, followed by contrast material and further section	36000, 36011, 36406, 36410, 72192, 72193	NA
72196 – magnetic resonance (eg, proton) imaging, pelvis; with contrast	36000, 36011, 36406, 36410, 72195, 90782, 90783, 90780, 90784	NA
72200 – radiologic examination, sacroiliac joints; less than three views	NA	NA
72202 - radiologic examination, sacroiliac joints; three or more views	72200	NA
72240 – myelography, cervical, radiological supervision and interpretation	76000, 76001, 76003, 76005	NA
72225 – myelography, thoracic, radiological supervision and interpretation	76000, 76001, 76003, 76005	NA
72265 – myelography, lumbosacral, radiological supervision and interpretation	76000, 76001, 76003, 76005	NA
72270 – myelography, entire spinal canal, radiological supervision and interpretation	72240, 72255, 72265, 76000, 76001, 76003, 76005	NA
72275 – epidurography, radiological supervision and interpretation	76000, 76001, 76003, 76005	NA
72285 – diskography, cervical or thoracic, radiological supervision and interpretation	76005	NA
72295 – diskography, lumbar, radiological supervision and interpretation	76005	NA
76000 - fluoroscopy	36000, 36011, 36410, 36425	76120, 76125
76001 - fluoroscopy	76000	NA
76003 – fluoroscopic guidance	NA	76001, 76005, 76095, 76096, 76360, 76393, 76942
76005 – fluoroscopic guidance	76000	76001, 76393, 76942
76006 – radiologic examination, stress view(s), any joint	70328, 70330, 73020, 73030, 73070, 73080, 73090, 73092, 73130, 73140, 73500, 73510, 73520, 73540, 73550, 73560, 73564, 73565, 73590, 73592, 73620, 73630, 73650, 73660	NA
76010 - radiologic examination, from nose to rectum for foreign body, single view, child	71010, 71015, 71020, 71021, 71022, 71023, 71030, 71034, 71035, 74000	NA
76012 – radiologic supervision and interpretation, percutaneous vertebroplasty, per vertebral body	75872	76000, 76001, 76003, 76005, 76013
76013 – radiologic supervision and interpretation, percutaneous vertebroplasty, per vertebral body	75872	72128, 72129, 72130, 72131, 72132, 72133
76062 – radiologic examination, osseous survey; complete	76061	NA
76065 - radiologic examination, osseous survey, infant	NA	76061, 76062

REFERENCES

1. Manchikanti L. General correct coding policies. In Manchikanti L (ed). *Interventional Pain Medicine: Documentation, Coding, and Billing*. ASIPP Publishing, Paducah, 2001; pp. 51-56
2. Manchikanti L. Evaluation and management services in Interventional Pain Medicine. In Manchikanti L (ed). *Interventional Pain Medicine: Documentation, Coding, and Billing*. ASIPP Publishing, Paducah, 2001; pp. 69-88
3. Manchikanti L. The impact of National Correct Coding Policy on interventional pain management. *Pain Physician* 1999; 2:33-45.
4. *National Correct Coding Manual 2001*: Medical Management Institute, Alpharetta; 2001.
5. CCI edits require expertise in the face of voluminous outpatient, coding changes. *HCPCS Report* 2000; 14:1-5.
6. *Current Procedural Terminology. CPT 1999*, American Medical Association, Chicago, 1998.
7. *Current Procedural Terminology. CPT 2000*, American Medical Association, Chicago, 1999.
8. Manchikanti L. Evaluation and management services in interventional pain practice: Doing it right! *Pain Physician* 2000; 3:322-341
9. Manchikanti L. The role of evaluation and management services in pain management. *Pain Physician* 1999; 2:10-32.
10. Manchikanti L. Appropriate documentation, billing and coding in interventional pain practice. *Pain Physician* 2000; 3:218-236.

CODING FOR ANCILLARY SERVICES

Jo Anne E. Burkhardt

Many pain management centers struggle with whether to include ancillary services as part of their centers. It is an individual decision because the environment differs for each center. Factors that should be considered are:

a) Opportunities in the marketplace.
b) Political conflicts with referring physicians or hospital opportunities.
c) Competition in the marketplace.
d) Major payor reimbursement and coverage policies in your area. Be sure payors do not have carved out networks that provide these services on a mandated basis.

Once the decision is made to include these services it is critical that the processes are put in place to ensure payment for these services. Precertification of ancillary services is critical. Many times payors will have separate deductibles, coverage rules and other issues relating to coverage.

The following are the rules for Medicare for physical therapy and psychological services.

PHYSICAL THERAPY

Under the guidelines for physical and occupational therapy provided by physician employees, physician employees must meet the entire incident to requirements. To be covered incident to the service of the physician, services and supplies must be (1) an integral, although incidental, part of the physician's professional service; (2) commonly rendered without charge or included in the physician's bill; (3) of a type commonly furnished in a physician's office or clinic; (4) furnished under the physician's direct personal supervision; and (5) furnished by the physician or by an individual who qualifies as an employee or a leased/contracted employee of the physician.

The following standards apply to physical/occupational therapy services provided by physicians, physical/occupational therapy services provided by physical therapists or occupational therapists in independent practice:

A. The services must be provided by, or under the direct supervision of a physician (a doctor of medicine or osteopathy) who is legally authorized to practice physical/occupational therapy services by the State in which he/she performs such function or action. The patient must be under the care of the physician for a condition that is medically necessary, reasonable and appropriate for physical/occupational therapy treatment. The services must be considered under accepted standards of medical practice to be a specific and effective treatment for the patient's condition.
B. The services must be of a level of complexity that requires that they be performed by or under the direct supervision of the physician. Services that do not require the performance or supervision of the physician are not considered reasonable or necessary physical/occupational therapy services even if they are performed or supervised by a physician.
C. Services must be furnished under a plan of treatment that has been written and developed by the physician caring for the patient. The plan must be established prior to the initiation of treatment, must be signed by the physician, and must be incorporated into the physician's permanent record for the patient. The services provided must relate directly to the written regimen.

1. The plan of care contains the following information:
   - The patient's significant past history
   - Patient's diagnoses that require physical/occupational therapy;
   - Related physician orders
   - Therapy goals and potential for achievement
   - Any contraindications
   - Patient awareness and understanding of diagnoses, prognosis, treatment goals; and
   - When appropriate, the summary of treatment provided and results achieved during the previous periods of physical/occupational therapy services.
2. The plan of care indicates anticipated goals and specifies the type, amount frequency and duration of therapy services. The amount, frequency and duration of the physical/occupational therapy services must be reasonable and necessary.
3. The plan of care and results of treatment are reviewed every 30 days. When services are continued for more than 30 days, the physician must recertify the plan of treatment every 30 days. Any change in treatment plan must be noted in writing in the patient record.

D. The physical/occupational therapy services provided to the beneficiary must be restorative or for the purpose of designing and teaching maintenance program for the patient to conduct at home. There must be an expectation that the patient's condition will improve significantly in a reasonable and generally predictable period of time, or the services must be necessary for the establishment of a safe and effective maintenance program required in connection with a specific disease state. If the patient's expected restoration potential would be insignificant in relation to the extent and duration of physical/occupational therapy services required to achieve such potential, the physical/occupational therapy would not be considered reasonable and necessary. If at any point in the treatment it is determined that improvement in the patient's condition will not be achieved, the services will no longer be considered reasonable and necessary.

E. Services that are palliative in nature are not considered necessary and reasonable and are not covered services. These services maintain function and generally do not involve complex physical/occupational therapy procedures nor do they require physician judgment and skill for safety and effectiveness.

If physical therapy services are rendered in the home and billed as "incident to" services, the physician must be present in the home in order to bill these services.

The Physical Therapy codes are found in the Medicine Section beginning with 97001.

Some of the more common codes that are used for Physical Therapy are:

97001	Initial Evaluation
97002	Reevaluation
97010	Hot or Cold Pack
97014	Electric Stimulation (unattended)
97018	Paraffin Bath
97032	Electric Stimulation (manual)
97033	Iontophoresis
97035	Ultrasound
97039	Unlisted Modality
97110	Therapeutic Exercises, each 15 minutes
97112	Therapeutic Exercises/Neuromuscular reeducation of movement
97116	Gait Training
97124	Massage Therapy
97140	Manual Therapy
97535	ADLs/HEP or TENS/IFC Home Instruction

For billing commercial payors it is important to determine their rules for credentialing the physical/occupational therapy providers. Determine if they are covered under the physician or if they credential these providers independently. Contracts should be negotiated to include these services if they are part of the pain practice. It is important to understand the payor's requirements on treatment plans, prior preauthorization, coverage limits, separate deductibles, and medical necessity rules.

PSYCHOLOGY

Psychology services are covered when performed by an M.D. (may or may not be a psychiatrist), D.O., clinical psychologist (Ph.D), clinical social worker (NSW or Ph.D). Coding must be specific to psychological services, not Evaluation and Management services performed by a physician.

Psychology services documentation must include the date and length of session, major themes discussed, concurrent clinical status, summary statement of attempted therapeutic intervention, summary statement on degree of progress. The diagnosis codes must reflect medical necessity. There must be a signature and credential of the performing person.

Individual group and family psychotherapy are covered. Family medical (co-joint) psychotherapy is covered when the primary purpose is the treatment of the beneficiary's condition. Medicare does not cover family counseling principally covered with the effects of the beneficiary's condition. Medicare does not cover family counseling principally covered with the effects of the beneficiary's condition on family members.

Medicare pays for diagnostic and therapeutic services furnished by a physician or under a physician's supervision, for treatment of alcoholism and drug abuse. Services must be reasonable and necessary for the diagnosis or treatment.

The allowance for outpatient psychiatric services is reduced to 62.5% before the deductible and coinsurance are applied. This reduction applies to psychiatric therapeutic and follow up diagnostic services furnished on an outpatient basis. It does not apply to inpatient services or outpatient initial diagnostic services.

The clinical Psychologist must meet all the following qualification requirements:

- A doctoral degree in psychology from a program in clinical psychology of an educational institution that is accredited by an organization recognized by the council on post-secondary accreditation; or a doctoral degree in counseling psychology or educational psychology (Ed.D) where there is a health service orientation.
- Compliance with licensing or certification standards for psychologists in independent practice in the state in which he practices.
- Two years of supervised clinical experience, at least one of which is post-degree.

Clinical psychologist services are covered if the clinical psychologist practices independently or is employed by a physician who bills for them. These claims can be submitted in two ways:

1) If the clinical psychologist services are performed under the direct supervision of the physician and meet the requirements as "incident to" a physician's service under the Medicare program, the physician may bill these services in his or her name. It is not necessary to indicate that the clinical psychologist performed the services.
2) If the clinical psychologist services are not performed under the direct personal supervision of the physician and do not meet the "incident to" requirements, the AH modifier, *Clinical psychologist*, should be used.

Reimbursement for services of clinical psychologist's practicing independently is based on the clinical psychologist fee schedule. Reimbursement for services of a clinical psychologist incident to the services of a physician, clinical psychologist, or other health care practitioner is based on the Medicare reimbursement method of the employer.

Medicare B covers clinical psychologist services in all places of service. Claims for practitioner therapeutic services provided by clinical psychologists must be submitted on an assigned basis.

Clinical psychologists may bill for neurological test services in the clinical psychologist range 96100 - 96117. Payment is made in the same amount as that made under the physicians fee schedule. The time required to conduct these neurological testing services must be reported to ensure correct reimbursement. The actual number of test hours should be reported as the number of services, i.e., in the number of services field, for each test.

A clinical social worker must meet all of the following qualifications

- Master's or doctoral degree in social work
- Two years of supervised clinical social work
- Licensed or certified as a clinical social worker by the state in which the services are performed
  Or,
  If the state does not provide for licensure or certification, the clinical social worker has completed at least two years or 3,000 hours of post master's degree practice under the supervision of a master's level social worker in a setting such as a hospital, skilled nursing facility (SNF), or clinic.

Clinical social worker services are covered if the clinical social worker practices independently or is employed by a physician, CP or other health practitioner who bills for the clinical social worker. These claims can be submitted in two ways:

1. The physician may bill these services if the clinical social worker services are performed under the direct personal supervision of the employer and meet the requirements as "incident to" a physician's service. It is not necessary to indicate that the clinical social worker performed the services.
2. If the clinical social worker services are not performed under the direct personal supervision of the physician and do not meet the "incident to" requirements, the AJ modifier, *Clinical social worker,* should be used.

Reimbursement for services of an independent clinical social worker is based on the clinical social worker fee schedule. Reimbursement for services of a clinical social worker employed by a provider who bills for the clinical social worker is based on the clinical social worker fee schedule. Reimbursement for services of a clinical social worker incident to the services of a physician, CP, or other health care practitioner is based on the Medicare reimbursement of the employer.

Claims for services provided by clinical social workers must be submitted on an assigned basis. clinical social worker services are payable in all places of service except inpatient hospital (21) and inpatient psychiatric facility (51). A nursing facility *is* required to provide the services of a clinical social worker as a requirement for participation and payment by Medicare Part A. clinical social worker services in these places are covered only as incident to the services of a physician, CP, or other health care practitioner and therefore must be billed by the employer, in the employer's name. The employer must be on the premises when the services are provided.

Hospitals must bill Medicare Part B for all clinical social worker services performed in the hospital outpatient setting, whether the clinical social worker is a hospital employee, a hospital contractor, or practices independently. This is true whether independent practitioners performed the services or facility based practitioners. For facility-based practitioners, the hospital outpatient department bills the carrier directly.

The codes for billing behavioral health services are found in the Medicine Section of the CPT and range form 90801 through 90899.

Codes 96150-96155 may be reported to describe those services performed to address difficulties associated with an acute or chronic illness that do not meet the criteria for a psychiatric diagnosis. These codes are billed by a non-physician provider and are applicable for pain management.

Use of these codes eliminates inappropriate labeling of the patient as having a mental health disorder when the problem is actually a physical illness. It is important to note that the focus of these services is on the biopsychosocial factors affecting physical health problems and treatments.

These assessment codes do not include neuropsychological testing. Any testing performed in addition to codes 96150-96155 should be additionally reported based on the type of testing done.

Each commercial payor has their own rules regarding the credentialing of behavioral health providers. It is very important to precertify these services because these services usually require the provider to be in a network, to submit a treatment plan, and to have that plan monitored on a frequent basis. There is usually a coverage maximum, expressed in either dollars or duration of visits.

SECTION 3

INTERVENTIONAL TECHNIQUES

MEDICAL RECORD DOCUMENTATION GUIDELINES FOR AMBULATORY SURGICAL SERVICES

Laxmaiah Manchikanti, MD
Vijay Singh, MD
Bert Fellows, MA

The importance of documentation in providing interventional pain management services can never be stressed neither too much, nor too frequently. As described earlier, the medical record is one of the most important resources of a health care organization. Accurate and complete documentation in the medical record is essential for provision of patient care of high quality, to avoid errors in treatment, and avoid fraud and abuse allegations. Medical record documentation for ambulatory surgical services, while similar to hospital outpatient services, but are comprehensive requiring detailed documentation, compared to an office setting. These requirements encompass:

- History and physical
- Peri-operative documentation
- Discharge/disposition

Additionally, documentation requirements for ambulatory surgical services, also include:

- Preoperative medical record requirements
- Anesthesia requirements
- Post-operative medical record requirements
- Discharge documentation requirements

HISTORY AND PHYSICAL

The federal and many state administrative regulations state that the medical record must include a history and physical examination which documents any significant medical history and results of the physical examination (1-3). Further, regulations also require that the history and physical to be completed no more than 30 days prior to the date of surgery. While ambulatory surgery centers may accept history and physical documents from other practitioners or organizations if the results of the history and physical are confirmed by the practitioner who is accepting responsibility for the patient's care and the practitioner documents or confirms the conclusions or impressions that were drawn from the history and physical (3).

However, any significant changes in the patient's condition subsequent to these assessments are to be documented. In addition, a pre-procedure note by the practitioner is to be completed on the day of the procedure. Thus, the record should always document the physician's examination of the patient performed immediately prior to surgery (4-6). However, statements such as "see previous record" generally are not acceptable unless a copy of the previous report is included in the current record and also is timely.

HISTORY

The physician's history should include the following elements:

- Documentation of the identification and symptoms warranting the invasive procedure.
- A listing of the patient's current medications including dosages, route, and frequency of administration.
- Any existing co-morbid conditions and previous surgeries.
- Documentation of any social history or conditions which would have an impact on the patient's care upon discharge from the facility following the procedure.

PHYSICAL EXAMINATION

The physician's physical examination should not only reflect the interventional procedure, but also anesthesia planned:

- If no anesthesia is to be administered, or only topical or local anesthesia/regional block, there should be an assessment of the patient's mental status and an examination specific to the proposed procedure specific to any co-morbid conditions.

- However, if the planned anesthesia includes intravenous sedation, general anesthesia, major regional anesthesia, including spinal or epidural (not epidural or spinal as a therapeutic procedure), the physical examination should include the following:

  - An assessment of the patient's mental status
  - An examination specific to the proposed procedure and any co-morbid conditions,
  - Documentation of the results of an auscultatory examination of the heart and lungs, and
  - An assessment and written statement about the patient' s general health.

Thus, the level of anesthesia to be administered dictates the components of the physician's physical examination. However, any combination of the forms of anesthesia described above would necessitate a physical examination relevant to the highest level of anesthesia planned (Table 1).

PERI-OPERATIVE REQUIREMENTS

These include pre-operative, intra-operative, post-operative, anesthesia and discharge guidelines (Table 2).

Pre-operative Medical Record Requirements

The medical record should contain various elements in the pre-operative record.

- Date of admission and discharge
- Names of referring and attending physicians
- The pre-operative diagnosis
- Data to support the diagnosis and planned treatment
- Reports of any pre-operative diagnostic studies or consultations
- Diagnostic or therapeutic orders which must be dated and signed
- Documentation of allergies (if the patient has no history of allergies or adverse reactions, this should be noted in a prominent place)
- Informed consent
- Documentation of vital signs, assessments, and other findings
- Any evidence of advance directives
  Nurses' notes

Anesthesia Requirements

Anesthetic requirements include a pre-anesthesia evaluation by an individual qualified to administer anesthesia immediately before surgery to evaluate the risk of anesthesia and of the procedure to be performed (5). In addition, this pre-anesthesia evaluation should consider data from other assessments and collect information needed to complete selection and planning of anesthesia, safely administer anesthesia, and interpret findings of patient monitoring.

The medical record should also include all the entries reflect-

Table 1. *Medical record (history and physical) documentation guidelines for ambulatory surgical services.*

	History				Examination			
	Indications and symptoms	Current medications	Co-morbid conditions/-previous surgeries	Social history	Mental status	Specific to proposed procedure and co-morbid conditions	Auscultation of heart & lungs	General health
No anesthesia	√	√	√	√	√	√	_	_
Intravenous sedation	√	√	√	√	√	√	√	√
General	√	√	√	√	√	√	√	√

Table 2. *Medical record (peri-operative) documentation guidelines for ambulatory surgical services.*

- **Pre-operative medical record requirements**

  Date of admission and discharge
  Names of referring and attending physicians
  Pre-operative diagnosis
  Medical necessity data
  Pre-operative diagnostic studies or consultation
  Diagnostic or therapeutic orders
  Allergies
  Informed consent
  Vital signs
  Advance directives
  Nurse's notes

- **Anesthesia requirements**

  Pre-anesthesia evaluation
  Monitoring

- **Post-operative documentation requirements**

  Post-operative and discharge diagnosis
  Intraoperative and postoperative complications
  Vital signs
  Orders for drugs and biologicals
  Adverse reactions or complications
  Practitioners evaluation prior to discharge
  Compliance with discharge criteria
  Condition on discharge
  Copy of patient instructions
  Discharge summary

ing the monitoring of the patient's physiological status during the operative procedure.

Post-Operative Documentation Requirements

Post-operatively, medical records should contain appropriate documentation with the following:

- An operative note describing the techniques, findings, and any tissues removed or altered during the procedure (1, 5).
- The names of the clinicians involved, the post-operative diagnosis, and the condition of the patient at the end of the procedure.
- Documentation of any and all complications and evidence of the management of post-operative complications or unusual events.
- The operative note must be written or dictated immediately following surgery, and must be signed by the surgeon. However, when the operative report is not placed in the medical record immediately after surgery, a progress note should be entered.
- The record must contain a tissue diagnosis, by a pathologist, on any tissues removed during surgery excluding those exempted by the governing body (1, 5).
- Documentation of the patient's vital signs, level of consciousness, and medications, including IV fluids.
- Post-operatively orders for drugs and biologicals.
- A report of any adverse reactions to drugs or biologicals to the physician.
- Documentation of physician's evaluation of the patient to assess for proper anesthesia recovery prior to discharge,
- Assessment on admission to and discharge from the post anesthesia recovery area.
- Documentation of discharge from post-anesthesia care area by the responsible independent practitioner or according to discharge criteria.
- Documentation of compliance with discharge criteria.
- Condition of the patient on discharge.
- Documentation of the name of the licensed independent practitioner responsible for the discharge.
- Discharge diagnosis.
- A nursing note documenting post-operative abnormalities or complications, vital signs, and general condition of the patient.

DISCHARGE/DISPOSITION

The medical records should document discharge plans (eg, plans to discharge to home with the care of the family or if there is no family, adequate plans for home care).

- A description or copy of actual patient instructions and/or eduction should be included in the patient's medical record.
- A discharge summary, which includes the condition of the patient and any post-operative instructions to the patient should be completed at the time of discharge.

Thus, ambulatory surgical medical record is an important document. The medical record should be signed and completed by the physician as soon as possible after discharge, however, this time frame should not exceed ten days (2).

PROCEDURAL DOCUMENTATION

All interventional techniques are considered surgical procedures. Documentation requirements as listed in Table 3 include:

- History and physical
- Indications and medical necessity
- Intra-operative procedural description with consent,

Table 3. *Procedural documentation guidelines for interventional techniques in ambulatory surgery centers*

1. History and physical
2. Indications and medical necessity
3. Description of the procedure
   - consent
   - monitoring
   - sedation
   - positioning
   - site preparation
   - fluoroscopy
   - drugs utilized
   - needle placement complications
4. Post-operative monitoring
5. Discharge/disposition

monitoring, sedation, positioning, preparation of the site, local anesthetic infiltration, fluoroscopy, needle placement, contrast injection, type and volume of drugs injected, description of complications, and the names of assistants and radiological technologists

- Post-operative monitoring and ambulation
- Discharge/disposition including discharge status, and instructions.

REFERENCES

1. 42 Code of Federal Regulations 416.47, October 1, 1998.
2. Kentucky Administrative Regulations, 902 (20.106).
3. Comprehensive Accreditation Manual for Ambulatory Care, Joint Commission for the Accreditation of Hospitals, (IM. 7.2), 1998-99.
4. 42 Code of Federal Regulations 416.42, October 1, 1998.
5. Comprehensive Accreditation Manual for Ambulatory Care, Joint Commission on Accreditation of Healthcare Organizations, 2000-2001.

CODING FOR INTERVENTIONAL PROCEDURES

Laxmaiah Manchikanti, MD

In addition to multiple issues of documentation, billing, and coding that are facts of life for physicians practicing interventional pain management, emphasis continues to be placed on the description and definition of what the physician does for and to the patient. Various aspects of appropriate documentation, billing, and coding in interventional pain practice have been described (1-4). Focus on errors for the Medicare program, as well as errors in other insurance programs; exclusion and sanction of medical providers; Medicare fraud hotline hits; qui tam cases and recoveries: and sky-high settlements from institutions and individual physicians continue to increase. Recent developments include changes in CPT 2000, 2001 and 2002 (4-6); the final rule for 2000, 2001, and 2002 on physician payment policies (7, 8); the Medicare program prospective payment system for hospital outpatient services (9, 10); and ongoing development of correct coding initiatives (CCI), with publication of the latest CCI in Jan 2002, affecting almost all interventional techniques (3, 11-14).

Issues of correct coding and medical necessity and guidelines with regards to frequency and number of interventions, combination of blocks/interventions, and number of interventions per setting continue to remain contentious (11, 12, 14, 15). Table 1 illustrates payments in various settings for 2002.

Various descriptors of interventional pain procedures commonly utilized and examples for many of the situations encountered in interventional pain practices are reviewed here. However, this review will only provide generally accepted practice patterns in a safe, conservative and ethical manner. Essentially, the illustrations and information provide practical considerations for the use of interventional techniques in the management of chronic pain based on the current state of the art and signs of interventional pain management, rules and regulations. However, this article and its descriptions do not constitute practice management or legal advice. In addition, these guidelines do not constitute inflexible treatment recommendations. It is expected that a provider will establish a plan of care on a case-by-case basis, taking into account an individual patient's medical condition, personal needs, and preferences, and the physician's experience. Thus, based on an individual patient's needs, treatments provided, experience of the physician, billing and coding staff, and rules and regulation of local Medicare carriers, and other payors, various types of practice patterns including billing and coding are warranted.

FACET JOINT BLOCKS AND NEUROLYSIS

Procedure (CPT) Codes 2002

- 64470 – Injection, anesthetic agent and/or steroid, paravertebral facet joint or facet joint nerve, cervical or thoracic, single level
- 64472 – Injection, anesthetic agent and/or steroid, paravertebral facet joint or facet joint nerve, cervical or thoracic, each additional level
- 64475 – Injection, anesthetic agent and/or steroid, paravertebral facet joint or facet joint nerve, lumbar or sacral, single level
- 64476 – Injection, anesthetic agent and/or steroid, paravertebral facet joint or facet joint nerve, lumbar or sacral, each additional level
- 64626 – Destruction by neurolytic agent, paravertebral facet joint nerve; cervical or thoracic, single level
- 64627 – Destruction by neurolytic agent, paravertebral facet joint nerve; cervical or thoracic, each additional level
- 64622 – Destruction by neurolytic agent, paravertebral facet joint nerve; lumbar or sacral, single level
- 64623 – Destruction by neurolytic agent, paravertebral facet joint nerve; lumbar or sacral, each additional level

Table 1. *2002 Medicare Fee Schedule for Physicians, Ambulatory Surgery Centers (Based on 2001), and 2002 Hospital Outpatient Payment for interventional pain procedures.*

CPT CODE	Abbreviated Description of Procedure	Office setting			ASC		Hospital Outpatient	
		Professional or Physician Fee ($)	Office or Overhead Fee ($)	Total ($)	Professional or Physician Fee ($)	Facility or ASC ($)	Professional or Physician Fee ($)	Facility or Hospital ($)
20550	Tendon sheath, ligament, Inj	43.44	20.63	64.07	64.07	-0-	43.44	114.02
20551	Tendon origin/insertion Inj	47.42	14.11	61.53	61.53	-0-	47.42	114.02
20552	Single or Two T.P. Inj	47.42	14.11	61.53	61.53	-0-	47.42	114.02
20553	Multiple T.P. Inj Three or more	47.42	14.11	61.53	61.53	-0-	47.42	114.02
20600	Small-joint injection	39.46	10.86	50.32	50.32	-0-	39.46	114.02
20605	Intermediate-joint	40.54	14.48	55.02	55.02	-0-	40.54	114.02
20610	Large-joint injection	47.42	18.82	66.24	66.24	-0-	47.42	125.73
27096	SI-joint injection	66.24	308.06	374.3	374.3	-0-	66.24	-0-*
62263	Epidural adhesiolysis	312.4	111.49	423.89	312.4	323	312.4	803.77
62270	Spinal puncture	60.45	130.32	190.77	60.45	323	60.45	182.75
62273	Epidural blood patch	128.87	10.86	139.73	128.87	323	128.87	182.75
62280	Neurolytic subarachnoid	126.7	111.85	238.55	126.7	323	126.7	182.75
62281	Cervical / epi neurolytic	124.53	140.45	264.98	264.98	-0-	124.53	272.85
62282	Lumbar / epi neurolytic	111.86	179.18	291.04	111.86	323	111.86	272.85
62287	Decompression of nucleus pulposus	499.19	NA	NA	499.19	-0-	499.19	692.29
62290	Lumbar diskography	162.9	158.55	321.45	321.45	-0-	162.9	-0-
62291	Cervical/thoracic diskography	154.93	182.45	337.38	337.38	-0-	154.93	-0-
62310	Cervical/thoracic epidural	88.69	118.73	207.42	88.69	323	88.69	182.75
62311	Lumbar/caudal epidural	72.4	139.37	211.77	72.4	323	72.4	182.75
62318	Continuous C/T epi	94.12	122.71	216.83	94.12	323	94.12	182.75
62319	Continuous epi lumbar	86.15	118.38	204.53	86.15	323	86.15	182.75
62350	Implant of catheter	409.05	NA	NA	409.05	433	409.05	3837.65
62355	Removal of catheter	323.62	NA	NA	323.62	-0-	323.62	751.34
62361	Implant of non-programmable pump	347.15	NA	NA	347.15	433	347.15	7103.65
62362	Implant of programmable pump	439.54	NA	NA	439.54	433	439.54	7103.65
62365	Removal of reservoir	361.63	NA	NA	361.63	433	361.63	751.34
63650	Implant of neurostimulator	368.87	NA	NA	368.87	433	368.87	13619.87
63660	Removal of neurostimulator	379.37	NA	NA	379.37	323	379.37	2155.28
63685	Implant of pulse generator	439.82	NA	NA	439.82	433	439.82	15399.99
63688	Removal of pulse generator	354.03	NA	NA	354.03	323	354.03	7394.82
64400	Trigeminal nerve block	52.85	87.24	140.09	140.09	-0-	52.85	114.02
64402	Facial nerve block	64.07	142.27	206.34	206.34	-0-	64.07	114.02
64405	Greater occipital nerve block	64.07	35.12	99.19	99.19	-0-	64.07	114.02
64413	Cervical plexus blocks	66.24	90.41	156.65	156.65	-0-	66.24	114.02
64415	Brachial plexus block	68.05	84.35	152.4	68.05	323	68.05	114.02
64417	Axillary nerve block	69.14	102.44	171.58	69.14	323	69.14	114.02
64418	Suprascapular N.B.	60.81	79.64	140.45	140.45	-0-	60.81	114.02
64420	Intercostal N.B. single	55.02	76.02	131.04	55.02	323	55.02	272.85
64421	Intercostal N.B. multiple	78.19	91.58	169.77	78.19	323	78.19	272.85
64425	Ilioinguinal N.B.	82.17	69.5	151.67	151.67	-0-	82.17	114.02
64445	Sciatic nerve block	71.67	42.72	114.39	114.39	-0-	71.67	114.02
64450	Peripheral nerve block	60.81	52.86	113.67	113.67	-0-	60.81	114.02
64470	Facet injection-C/T -single	88.69	128.14	216.83	88.69	323	88.69	272.85
64472	Facet injection-C/T/-addi.	61.9	129.23	191.13	61.9	323	61.9	272.85
64475	Facet injection-lumbar/sacral-single	68.42	124.16	192.58	68.42	323	68.42	272.85
64476	Facet injection-L/S addi.	47.06	130.32	177.38	47.06	323	47.06	272.85
64479	C/T Transforaminal-single	107.87	136.11	243.98	107.87	323	107.87	272.85
64480	C/T Transforaminal -addi.	77.1	129.24	206.34	77.1	323	77.1	272.85
64483	L/S Transforaminal single	93.39	140.46	233.85	93.39	323	93.39	272.85
64484	L/S Transforaminal addi.	65.52	132.13	197.65	65.52	323	65.52	272.85

Table 1. *Continued......*

CPT CODE	Abbreviated Description of Procedure	Office setting			ASC		Hospital Outpatient	
		Professional or Physician Fee ($)	Office or Overhead Fee ($)	Total ($)	Professional or Physician Fee ($)	Facility or ASC ($)	Professional or Physician Fee ($)	Facility or Hospital ($)
64505	Sphenopalatine ganglion block	64.8	74.57	139.37	139.37	-0-	64.8	114.02
64510	Stellate ganglion block	56.11	82.17	138.28	56.11	323	56.11	272.85
64520	L/T sympathetic block	62.99	115.11	178.1	62.99	323	62.99	272.85
64530	Celiac plexus block	73.85	97.73	171.58	73.85	323	73.85	272.85
64600	Neurolytic-trigeminal-small branches	209.59	33.31	242.9	209.59	323	209.59	803.77
64605	Neurolytic-trigeminal-2/3 division	327.24	26.06	353.3	327.24	323	327.24	803.77
64610	Neurolytic-trigeminal-at foramen ovale	451.04	NA	NA	451.04	323	451.04	803.77
64612	Neurolytic block-muscles of facial nerve	133.94	48.87	182.81	182.81	-0-	133.94	114.02
64613	Neurolytic block-cervical spinal muscles	128.15	12.3	140.45	140.45	-0-	128.15	114.02
64620	Intercostal neurolysis	133.21	83.62	216.83	133.21	323	133.21	803.77
64622	L/S Facet neurolysis-single	141.54	145.88	287.42	141.54	323	141.54	803.77
64623	L/S Facet neurolysis-addi.	46.7	130.68	177.38	46.7	323	46.7	803.77
64626	C/T/ Facet neurolysis-single	155.66	128.14	283.8	155.66	323	155.66	803.77
64627	C/T Facet neurolysis- addi	55.38	124.89	180.27	55.38	323	55.38	803.77
64630	Pudendal nerve neurolysis	146.24	100.64	246.88	146.24	433	146.24	272.85
64640	Peripheral neurolysis	166.15	70.59	236.74	236.74	-0-	166.15	272.85
64680	Celiac plexus neurolysis	127.78	77.11	204.89	127.78	433	127.78	803.77
72275	Epidurography radiological S&I	36.2	78.55	114.75	114.75	-0-	36.2	266.74
72285	C/T Diskography, radiological S & I	58.28	301.18	359.46	359.46	-0-	58.28	266.74
72295	L/S Diskography, radiological S & I	41.99	282.35	324.34	324.34	-0-	41.99	266.74
73542	SI joint arthrography – radiological S&I	28.6	75.65	104.25	104.25	-0-	28.6	131.84
76005	Fluoroscopic guidance	28.96	47.06	76.02	28.96	-0-	28.96	-0-

NA – Not approved / Not applicable

* Reimbursed to Hospital Outpatient Department for supervision and interpretation of radiology codes

- 76005 – Fluoroscopic guidance

Tables 2 to 4 illustrate facet joint nerves required to be blocked for each joint.

Examples

i. Cervical facet joint injection, single level (C5/6 joint)

Physician

- 64470 – C/T facet joint injection, single level
- 76005 – Fluoroscopic guidance

Surgery Center

- 64470 – C/T facet joint injection, single level

ii. Multiple cervical facet joint injections (C4/5 through C6/7)

Physician

Table 2. *Facet joint nerves required to be blocked for each facet joint in cervical region*

Facet Joint	Facet Joint Nerves(Medial Branches) to be Blocked	Level of Transverse Process
C2/3	Third occipital nerve or C2 and C3 medial	At C2/3 joint
C3/4	C3 and C4 medial branches	At C3 and C4 articular pillars
C4/5	C4 and C5 medial branches	At C4 and C5 articular pillars
C5/6	C5 and C6 medial branches	At C5 and C6 articular pillars
C6/7	C6 and C7 medial branches	At C6 and C7 articular pillars
C7/T1	C7 and C8 medial branches	At C7 articular pillar At T1 transverse process for C8

Table 3. *Facet joint nerves required to be blocked for each facet joint in thoracic region*

Facet Joint	Facet Joint Nerves (Medial Branches) to be Blocked	Level of Transverse Process
T1/2	C8 and T1 medial branches	At T1 transverse process for C8 At T2 transverse process for T1
T2/3	T1 and T2 medial branches	At T2 transverse process for T1 At T3 transverse process for T2
T 3/4	T2 and T3 medial branches	At T3 transverse process for T2 At T4 transverse process for T3
T4/5	T3 and T4 medial branches	At T4 transverse process for T3 At T5 transverse process for T4
T5/6	T4 and T5 medial branches	At T5 transverse process for T4 At T6 transverse process for T5
T6/7	T5 and T6 medial branches	At T6 transverse process for T5 At T7 transverse process for T6
T7/8	T6 and T7 medial branches	At T7 transverse process for T6 At T8 transverse process for T7
T8/9	T7 and T8 medial branches	At T8 transverse process for T7 At T9 transverse process for T8
T9/10	T8 and T9 medial branches	At T9 transverse process for T8 At T10 transverse process for T9
T10/11	T9 and T10 medial branches	At T10 transverse process for T9 At T11 transverse process for T10
T11/12	T10 and T11 medial branches	At T11 transverse process for T10 At T12 transverse process for T11
T12/L1	T11 and T12 medial branches	At T12 transverse process for T11 At L1 transverse process forT12

Table 4. *Facet joint nerves required to be blocked for each facet joint in lumbar region*

Facet Joint	Facet Joint Nerves to be Blocked (Medial Branches or L5 Dorsal Ramus)	Level of Transverse Process or Sacral Ala
L1/2	T12 and L1 medial branches	At L1 transverse process for T12 At L2 transverse process for L1
L2/3	L1 and L2 medial branches	At L2 transverse process for L1 At L3 transverse process for L2
L3/4	L2 and L3 medial branches	At L3 transverse process for L2 At L4 transverse process for L3
L4/5	L3 and L4 medial branches	At L4 transverse process for L3 At L5 transverse process for L4
L5/S1	L4 medial branch L5 dorsal ramus	At L5 transverse process for L4 medial branch at sacral ala groove for L5 dorsal ramus

- 64470 – C/T facet joint injection, single level
- 64472 – (multiple units – 2 or 3) – C/T facet joint injection, each additional level
- 76005 – Fluoroscopic guidance

Surgery Center

- 64470 – C/T facet joint injection, single level
- 64472 – 51 (two units) – C/T facet joint injection, each additional level

iii. Bilateral cervical facet joint injections (C4/5 through C6/7)

Physician

- 64470-50 – C/T facet joint injection, single level (bilateral)
- 64472 – C/T facet joint injection, each additional level (right)
- 64472 – C/T facet joint injection, each additional

- 76005 – Fluoroscopic guidance

or

- 64470-50 – C/T facet joint injection, single level (bilateral)
- 64472–50 - C/T facet joint injection, each additional level (bilateral)
- 76005 – Fluoroscopic guidance

For carriers who do not permit bilateral coding

- 64470 – C/T facet joint injection, single level
- 64472 – (multiple units – 2 or 3) – C/T facet joint injection, each additional level
- 76005 – Fluoroscopic guidance

Surgery Center

- Cervical facet joint nerve block procedures are not approved for surgery centers.
- 64470-50 – C/T facet joint injection, single level (bilateral)
- 64472–50 - C/T facet joint injection, each additional level (bilateral)

For carriers who do not permit bilateral coding

- 64470 – C/T facet joint injection, single level
- 64472 – 51 (two units) – C/T facet joint injection, each additional level

iv. Cervical facet joint nerve blocks, single level (C5/6 joint – C5 and C6 medial branch nerves)

Physician

- 64470 – C/T facet joint nerve block, single level
- 76005 – Fluoroscopic guidance

Surgery Center

- 64470 – C/T facet joint nerve block, single level

v. Cervical facet joint nerve blocks, multiple levels (C3/4 and C4/5 joints – C3, C4, and C5 medial branch nerves)

Physician

- 64470 – C/T facet joint nerve block, single level
- 64472 – C/T Facet joint nerve block, each additional level
- 76005 – Fluoroscopic guidance

Surgery Center

- 64470 – C/T facet joint injection, single level
- 64472-51 – C/T facet joint injection, each additional level

vi. Cervical facet joint nerve blocks, multiple levels (C3/4 through C6/7 joints - C3 through C7 medial branches)

Physician

- 64470 – C/T facet joint nerve block, single level
- 64472 - (multiple units – 2 or 3) – C/T facet joint nerve blocks, each additional level
- 76005 – Fluoroscopic guidance

Surgery Center

- 64470 – C/T facet joint nerve block, single level
- 64472-51 (two units) – C/T facet joint nerve blocks, each additional level

vii. Bilateral cervical facet joint nerve blocks (C5/6 and C6/7 joints - C5 through C7 facet joint nerves or medial branches)

Physician

- 64470–50 - C/T facet joint nerve block, single level (bilateral)
- 64472 – C/T facet joint nerve block, each additional level (right)
- 64472 – C/T facet joint nerve block, each additional level (left)
- 76005 – Fluoroscopic guidance

or

- 64470-50 – C/T facet joint nerve block, single level (bilateral)
- 64472–50 - C/T facet joint nerve block, each additional level (bilateral)
- 76005 – Fluoroscopic guidance

For carriers who do not permit bilateral coding

- 64470 – C/T facet joint nerve block, single level
- 64472 – (two units) – C/T facet joint nerve block, each additional level
- 76005 – Fluoroscopic guidance

Surgery Center

- 64470-50 – C/T facet joint injection, single level (bilateral)
- 64472–50 - C/T facet joint injection, each additional level (bilateral)

For carriers who do not permit bilateral coding

- 64470 – C/T facet joint injection, single level
- 64472 – 51 (two units) – C/T facet joint injection, each additional level

viii. Thoracic facet joint injection, single level (T5/6 joint)

Physician

- 64470 – C/T facet joint injection, single level
- 76005 – Fluoroscopic guidance

Surgery Center

- 64470 – C/T facet joint injection, single level

ix. Multiple thoracic facet joint injections (T4/5 through T6/7)

Physician

- 64470 – C/T facet joint injection, single level
- 64472 - (two units) – C/T facet joint injection, each additional level
- 76005 – Fluoroscopic guidance

Surgery Center

- 64470 – C/T facet joint injection, single level
- 64472 – 51 (two units) – C/T facet joint injection, each additional level

x. Bilateral thoracic facet joint injections (T4/5 through T6/7)

Physician

- 64470-50 – C/T facet joint injection, single level (bilateral)
- 64472 – C/T facet joint injection, each additional level (right)
- 64472 – C/T facet joint injection, each additional level (left)
- 76005 – Fluoroscopic guidance

or

- 64470-50 – C/T facet joint injection, single level (bilateral)
- 64472–50 - C/T facet joint injection, each additional level (bilateral)
- 76005 – Fluoroscopic guidance

For carriers who do not permit bilateral coding

- 64470 – C/T facet joint injection, single level
- 64472 – (two units) – C/T facet joint injection, each additional level
- 76005 – Fluoroscopic guidance

Surgery Center

- 64470-50 – C/T facet joint injection, single level (bilateral)
- 64472–50 - C/T facet joint injection, each additional level (bilateral)

For carriers who do not permit bilateral coding

- 64470 – C/T facet joint injection, single level
- 64472 – 51 (two units) – C/T facet joint injection, each additional level

xi. Thoracic facet joint nerve blocks, single level (T5/6 joint – T5 and T6 medial branch nerves)

Physician

- 64470 – C/T facet joint nerve block, single level
- 76005 – Fluoroscopic guidance

Surgery Center

- 64470 – C/T facet joint nerve block, single level

xii Thoracic facet joint nerve blocks, multiple levels (T3/4 through T6/7 joints - T3 through T7 medial branches)

Physician

- 64470 – C/T facet joint nerve block, single level
- 64472- (multiple units- 2 or 3) – C/T facet joint nerve blocks, each additional level
- 76005 – Fluoroscopic guidance

Surgery Center

- 64470 – C/T facet joint nerve block, single level
- 64472-51 (two units) – C/T facet joint nerve blocks, each additional level

xiii. Bilateral thoracic facet joint nerve blocks (T5/6 and T6/7 joints - T5 through T7 facet joint nerves or medial branch nerves)

Physician

- 64470-50 – C/T facet joint nerve block, single level (bilateral)

- 64472 – C/T facet joint nerve block, single level (right)
- 64472 – C/T facet joint nerve block, single level (left)
- 76005 – Fluoroscopic guidance

or

- 64470-50 – C/T facet joint nerve block, single level (bilateral)
- 64472–50 - C/T facet joint nerve block, each additional level (bilateral)
- 76005 – Fluoroscopic guidance

For carriers who do not permit bilateral coding

- 64470 – C/T facet joint nerve block, single level
- 64472 – (multiple units- 2 or 3) – C/T facet joint nerve block, subsequent levels
- 76005 – Fluoroscopic guidance

Surgery Center

- 64470-50 – C/T facet joint injection, single level (bilateral)
- 64472–50 - C/T facet joint injection, each additional level (bilateral)

For carriers who do not permit bilateral coding

- 64470 – C/T facet joint injection, single level
- 64472 – 51 (two units) – C/T facet joint injection, each additional level

xiv. Lumbosacral facet joint injection, single level (L3/4 joint)

Physician

- 64475 – L/S facet joint injection, single level
- 76005 – Fluoroscopic guidance

Surgery Center

- 64475 – L/S facet joint injection, single level

xv. Lumbosacral facet joint injection, multiple levels (L2/3 - L5/S1)

Physician

- 64475 – L/S facet joint injection, single level
- 64476 - L/S facet joint injection, each additional level
- 76005 – Fluoroscopic guidance

Surgery Center

- 64475 – L/S facet joint injection, single level
- 64476-51 - L/S facet joint injection, each additional level

xvi. Bilateral lumbosacral facet joint injections (L3/4 and L4/5 joints)

Physician

- 64475-50 – L/S facet joint injection, single level (bilateral)
- 64476 – L/S facet joint injection, each additional level (right)
- 64476 – L/S facet joint injection, each additional level (left)
- 76005 – Fluoroscopic guidance

or

- 64475-50 – L/S facet joint nerve block, single level (bilateral)
- 64476-50 – L/S facet joint nerve block, each additional level (bilateral)
- 76005 – Fluoroscopic guidance
- For carriers who do not permit bilateral coding
- 64475– L/S facet joint nerve block, single level
- 64476 – 51 – (multiple units- 2 or 3) L/S facet joint nerve block, each additional level
- 76005 – Fluoroscopic guidance

Surgery Center

Medicare

- 64475-50 – L/S facet joint injection, single level (bilateral)
- 64476 – L/S facet joint injection, each additional level (right)
- 64476 – L/S facet joint injection, each additional level (left)

or

- 64475-50 – L/S facet joint injection, single level (bilateral)
- 64476-50 – L/S facet joint injection, each additional level (bilateral)

For carriers who do not permit bilateral coding

- 64475 – L/S facet joint injection, single level
- 64476-51 (two units) - L/S facet joint injection, each additional level

xvii. Lumbar facet joint nerve blocks, single level (L3/4

joint - L2 and L3 medial branch nerves or facet joint nerves)

Physician

- 64475 – L/S facet joint nerve block, single level
- 76005 – Fluoroscopic guidance

Surgery Center

- 64475 – L/S facet joint injection, single level

xviii. Multiple lumbar facet joint nerve blocks (L4/5 and L5/S1 joints – L3 and L4 medial branch nerves and L5 dorsal ramus)

Physician

- 64475 – L/S facet joint nerve block, single level
- 64476- (two units) – L/S facet joint nerve block, each additional level
- 76005 – Fluoroscopic guidance

Surgery Center

- 64475 – L/S facet joint nerve block, single level
- 64476-51 - L/S facet joint nerve block, each additional level

xix. Bilateral multiple lumbar facet joint nerve blocks (L3/4 through L5/S1 joints – L2 through L4 medial branch nerves and L5 dorsal ramus)

Physician

- 64475-50 – L/S facet joint nerve block, single level (bilateral)
- 64476 – L/S facet joint nerve block, each additional level (right)
- 64476 – L/S facet joint nerve block, each additional level (left)
- 76005 – Fluoroscopic guidance

or

- 64475-50 – L/S facet joint nerve block, single level (bilateral)
- 64476–50 – L/S facet joint nerve block, each additional level (bilateral)
- 76005 – Fluoroscopic guidance

For carriers who do not permit bilateral coding

- 64475 – L/S facet joint nerve block, single level
- 64476 – (multiple units – 2 or 3) – L/S facet joint nerve block, each additional level
- 76005 – Fluoroscopic guidance

Surgery Center

- 64475-50 – L/S facet joint nerve block, single level (bilateral)
- 64476-51 – L/S facet joint nerve block, each additional level (right)
- 64476-51 – L/S facet joint nerve block, each additional level (left)

or

- 64475-50 – L/S facet joint nerve block, single level (bilateral)
- 64476–50 – L/S facet joint nerve block, each additional level (bilateral)

For carriers who do not permit bilateral coding

- 64475 – L/S facet joint nerve block, single level
- 64476 – 51 (two units) – L/S facet joint nerve block, each additional level

xx. Cervical paravertebral facet joint nerve neurolysis – single level (C5/6 joint - C5 and C6 medial branch nerves)

Physician

- 64626 – C/T facet neurolysis, single level
- 76005 – Fluoroscopic guidance

Surgery Center

- 64626 – C/T facet neurolysis, single level

xxi. Multiple cervical paravertebral facet joint neurolysis (C4/5 through C6/7 joints - C4 through C7 medial branches)

Physician

- 64626 – C/T facet joint neurolysis, single level
- 64627- (two units) – C/T facet joint neurolysis, each additional level
- 76005 – Fluoroscopic guidance

Surgery Center

- 64626 – C/T facet joint neurolysis, single level
- 64627-51 (two units) – C/T facet joint neurolysis, each additional level

xxii. Bilateral thoracic facet joint nerve neurolysis (T4/5

through T6/7 joints – T4 through T7 medial branches)

Physician

- 64626-50 – C/T facet joint nerve neurolysis, single level (bilateral)
- 64627 – C/T facet joint nerve neurolysis, each additional level (right)
- 64627 – C/T facet joint nerve neurolysis, each additional level (left)
- 76005 – Fluoroscopic guidance

or

- 64626-50 – C/T facet joint nerve neurolysis, single level (bilateral)
- 64627–50 - C/T facet joint nerve neurolysis, each additional level (bilateral)
- 76005 – Fluoroscopic guidance

For carriers who do not permit bilateral coding

- 64626 – C/T facet joint nerve neurolysis, single level
- 64627 – (multiple units – 2 or 3) – C/T facet joint nerve neurolysis, each additional level
- 76005 – Fluoroscopic guidance

Surgery Center

- 64626-50 – C/T facet joint nerve neurolysis, single level (bilateral)
- 64627–50 - C/T facet joint nerve neurolysis, each additional level (bilateral)

For carriers who do not permit bilateral coding

- 64626 – C/T facet joint nerve neurolysis, single level
- 64627 – 51 (multiple units – 2 or 3) – C/T facet joint nerve neurolysis, each additional level

xxiii. Thoracic paravertebral facet joint nerve neurolysis – single level (T5/6 joint - T5 and T6 medial branch nerves)

Physician

- 64626 – C/T paravertebral facet joint neurolysis, single level
- 76005 – Fluoroscopic guidance

Surgery Center

- 64626 – C/T paravertebral facet joint neurolysis, single level

xxiv. Multiple thoracic paravertebral facet joint neurolysis (T4/5 through T6/7 joints - T4 through T7 medial branches)

Physician

- 64626 – C/T paravertebral facet joint neurolysis, single level
- 64627- (two units) – C/T paravertebral facet joint neurolysis, each additional level
- 76005 – Fluoroscopic guidance

Surgery Center

- 64626 – C/T paravertebral facet joint neurolysis, single level
- 64627-51 (two units) – C/T paravertebral facet joint neurolysis, each additional level

xxv. Lumbar paravertebral facet joint neurolysis – single level (L4/5 joint - L3 and L4 medial branch nerves)

Physician

- 64622 – L/S, paravertebral facet joint neurolysis, single level
- 76005 – Fluoroscopic guidance

Surgery Center

- 64622 – L/S, paravertebral facet joint neurolysis, single level

xxvi. Multiple lumbar paravertebral facet joint neurolysis (L3/4 through L5/S1 joints L2 through L4 medial branch nerves and L5 dorsal ramus)

Physician

- 64622 – L/S paravertebral facet joint neurolysis, single level
- 64623- (two units) – L/S paravertebral facet joint neurolysis, each additional level
- 76005 – Fluoroscopic guidance

Surgery Center

- 64622 – L/S paravertebral facet joint neurolysis, single level
- 64623-51 (two units) – L/S paravertebral facet joint neurolysis, each additional level

xxvii. Bilateral lumbar facet joint neurolysis (L3/4 through L5/S1 joints - L2 through L4 medial branch nerves and L5 dorsal ramus)

Physician

- 64622-50 – L/S paravertebral facet joint neurolysis, single level (bilateral)
- 64623 – L/S paravertebral facet joint neurolysis, each additional level (right)
- 64623 – L/S paravertebral facet joint neurolysis, each additional level (left)
- 76005 – Fluoroscopic guidance

or

- 64622-50 – L/S facet joint nerve neurolysis, single level (bilateral)
- 64623–50 – L/S facet joint nerve neurolysis, each additional level (bilateral)
- 76005 – Fluoroscopic guidance

For carriers who do not permit bilateral coding

- 64622 – L/S facet joint nerve neurolysis, single level
- 64476 – (multiple units – 2 or 3) – L/S facet joint nerve neurolysis, each additional level
- 76005 – Fluoroscopic guidance

Surgery Center

- 64622-50 – L/S paravertebral facet joint neurolysis, single level (bilateral)
- 64623-51 – L/S paravertebral facet joint neurolysis, each additional level (right)
- 64623-51 – L/S paravertebral facet joint neurolysis, each additional level (left)

or

- 64622-50 – L/S facet joint nerve neurolysis, single level (bilateral)
- 64623–50 – L/S facet joint nerve neurolysis, each additional level (bilateral)

For carriers who do not permit bilateral coding

- 64622 – L/S facet joint nerve neurolysis, single level
- 64476 – 51 (two units) – L/S facet joint nerve neurolysis, each additional level

EPIDURAL INJECTIONS

Procedure (CPT) 2002 Codes

- 62310 – Injection, single (not via indwelling catheter), not including neurolytic substances, with or without contrast (for either localization or epidurography), of diagnostic or therapeutic substance(s) (including anesthetic, antispasmodic, opioid, steroid, other solution), epidural or subarachnoid; cervical or thoracic
- 62311 - Injection, single (not via indwelling catheter), not including neurolytic substances, with or without contrast (for either localization or epidurography), of diagnostic or therapeutic substance(s) (including anesthetic, antispasmodic, opioid, steroid, other solution), epidural or subarachnoid; lumbar, sacral (caudal)
- 62318 - Injection, including catheter placement, continuous infusion or intermittent bolus, not including neurolytic substances, with or without contrast (for either localization or epidurography), of diagnostic or therapeutic substance(s) (including anesthetic, antispasmodic, opioid, steroid, other solution), epidural or subarachnoid; cervical or thoracic
- 62319 - Injection, including catheter placement, continuous infusion or intermittent bolus, not including neurolytic substances, with or without contrast (for either localization or epidurography), of diagnostic or therapeutic substance(s) (including anesthetic, antispasmodic, opioid, steroid, other solution), epidural or subarachnoid; lumbar, sacral (caudal)
- 64479 – Injection, anesthetic agent and/or steroid, transforaminal epidural; cervical or thoracic, single level
- 64480 - Injection, anesthetic agent and/or steroid, transforaminal epidural; cervical or thoracic, each additional level
- 64483 - Injection, anesthetic agent and/or steroid, transforaminal epidural; lumbar or sacral, single level
- 64484 - Injection, anesthetic agent and/or steroid, transforaminal epidural; lumbar or sacral, each additional level
- 72275 – Epidurography, radiological supervision and interpretation
- 76005 – Fluoroscopic guidance and localization or needle of catheter tip for spine or paraspinous diagnostic or therapeutic procedures

Examples

i. Cervical interlaminar epidural injection - without fluoroscopy

Physician

- 62310 – C/T epidural

Surgery Center

- 62310 – C/T epidural

ii. Cervical interlaminar epidural injection - with fluoroscopy

Physician

- 62310 – C/T epidural
- 76005 – Fluoroscopic guidance

Surgery Center

- 62310 – C/T epidural

iii. Thoracic interlaminar epidural injection - without fluoroscopy

Physician

- 62310 – C/T epidural

Surgery Center

- 62310 – C/T epidural

iv. Thoracic interlaminar epidural injection - with fluoroscopy

Physician

- 62310 – C/T epidural
- 76005 – Fluoroscopic guidance

Surgery Center

- 62310– C/T epidural

v. Lumbar interlaminar epidural injection - without fluoroscopy

Physician

- 62311 – L/S epidural

Surgery Center

- 62311– L/S epidural

vi. Lumbar interlaminar epidural - with fluoroscopy

Physician

- 62311 – L/S epidural
- 76005 – Fluoroscopic guidance

Surgery Center

- 62311– L/S epidural

vii. Caudal epidural injection - without fluoroscopy

Physician

- 62311 – L/S epidural
- 76005 – Fluoroscopic guidance

Surgery Center

- 62311– L/S epidural

viii. Caudal epidural injection – with fluoroscopy

Physician

- 62311 – L/S epidural
- 76005 – Fluoroscopic guidance

Surgery Center

- 62311– L/S epidural

ix. Cervical transforaminal epidural injection, single level (C5 spinal nerve, C4/5 foramen)

Physician

- 64479 – C/T transforaminal epidural, single level
- 76005 – Fluoroscopic guidance

Surgery Center

- 64479 – C/T transforaminal epidural, single level (C5)

x. Cervical transforaminal epidural injection, multiple levels (C6 and C7 spinal nerves)

Physician

- 64479 – C/T transforaminal epidural, single level
- 64480 – C/T transforaminal epidural, each additional level
- 76005 – Fluoroscopic guidance

Surgery Center

- 64479 – C/T transforaminal epidural, single level
- 64480-51– C/T transforaminal epidural, each additional level

xi. Thoracic transforaminal or selective epidural injection, single level (T5 spinal nerve, T4/5 foramen)

Physician

- 64479 – C/T, transforaminal epidural, single level
- 76005 – Fluoroscopic guidance

Surgery Center

- 64479 – C/T, transforaminal epidural, single level

xii. Thoracic transforaminal or selective epidural injection, multiple levels (T6 and T7 spinal nerves)

Physician

- 64479 – C/T, single level
- 64480 – C/T transforaminal epidural, each additional level
- 76005 – Fluoroscopic guidance

Surgery Center

- 64479 – C/T, single level
- 64480 – 51- C/T transforaminal epidural, each additional level

xiii. Bilateral thoracic transforaminal or selective epidural injections (T5, T6, and T7 spinal nerves)

Physician

- 64479-50 – CT transforaminal epidural, single level (bilateral)
- 64480 – C/T transforaminal epidural, each additional level (right)
- 64480 – C/T transforaminal epidural, each additional level (left)
- 76005 – Fluoroscopic guidance

or

- 64479-50 – C/T transforaminal epidural, single level (bi-lateral)
- 64480–50 - C/T transforaminal epidural, each additional level (bilateral)
- 76005 – Fluoroscopic guidance

For carriers who do not permit bilateral coding:

- 64479 – C/T transforaminal epidural, single level
- 64480 – 51 (multiple units – 2 or 3) – C/T transforaminal epidural, each additional level
- 76005 – Fluoroscopic guidance

Surgery Center

- 64479-50 – C/T transforaminal epidural, single level (bilateral)
- 64480–50 - C/T transforaminal epidural, each additional level (bilateral)

For carriers who do not permit bilateral coding:

- 64479 – C/T transforaminal epidural, single level
- 64480 – 51 (two units) – C/T transforaminal epidural, each additional level

xiv. Lumbar transforaminal or selective epidural injection (L5 spinal nerve)

Physician

- 64483 – L/S transforaminal epidural, single level
- 76005 – Fluoroscopic guidance

Surgery Center

- 64483 – L/S transforaminal epidural, single level

xv. Lumbar transforaminal or selective epidural injection, multiple levels (L4, L5, and S1 spinal nerves)

Physician

- 64483 – L/S transforaminal epidural, single level
- 64484- (two units) – L/S transforaminal epidural, each additional level
- 76005 – Fluoroscopic guidance

Surgery Center

- 64483 – L/S transforaminal epidural, single level
- 64484-51 (two units) – L/S transforaminal epidural, each additional level

xvi. Bilateral lumbar transforaminal or selective epidural injections (L5, S1)

Physician

- 64483-50 – L/S transforaminal epidural, single level (bilateral)
- 64484 – L/S transforaminal epidural, each additional level (right)
- 64484 – L/S transforaminal epidural, each additional level (left)
- 76005 – Fluoroscopic guidance

or

- 64483-50 – L/S transforaminal epidural, single level (bilateral)
- 64484-50 – L/S transforaminal epidural, each additional level (bilateral)
- 76005 – Fluoroscopic guidance

For carriers who do not permit bilateral coding:

- 64483 – L/S epidural, single level
- 64484 – (multiple units – 1 or 2) – L/S epidural, each additional level
- 76005 – Fluoroscopic guidance

Surgery Center

- 64483-50 – L/S transforaminal epidural, single level (bilateral)
- 64484-50 – L/S transforaminal epidural, each additional level (bilateral)

For carriers who do not permit bilateral coding:

- 64483 – L/S epidural, single level
- 64484 – 51 (two units) – L/S epidural, each additional level

PERCUTANEOUS LYSIS OF EPIDURAL ADHESIONS

Procedure (CPT) 2002 Codes

♦ 62263 - Percutaneous lysis of epidural adhesions using solution injection (eg, hypertonic saline, enzyme) or mechanical means including radiologic localization (includes contrast when administered).

Starting 1/1/2003, the definition will also include "Multiple adhesiolysis sessions; 2 or 3 days".

♦ 6226X – Percutaneous lysis of epidural adhesions using solution injection (eg, hypertonic saline, enzyme) or mechanical means including radiologic localization (includes contrast when administered) – 1- day

(To start from 1/1/2003)

♦ 62263-52 – Percutaneous lysis of epidural adhesions using solution injection (eg, hypertonic saline, enzyme) or mechanical means including radiologic localization (includes contrast when administered).

To be used from 1/1/2002 to 12/3/2002. New one day code will be implemented from 1/1/2003.

♦ 72275 - Epidurography, radiological supervision and interpretation

Example

Percutaneous lysis of adhesions utilizing a Racz catheter

Two or three day procedure

Physician

♦ 62263 - Percutaneous lysis of epidural adhesions using solution injection (eg, hypertonic saline, enzyme) or mechanical means including radiologic localization (includes contrast when administered).

♦ 72275 - Epidurography, radiological supervision and interpretation

Surgery Center

♦ 62263 - Percutaneous lysis of epidural adhesions using solution injection (eg, hypertonic saline, enzyme) or mechanical means including radiologic localization (includes contrast when administered).

Starting 1/1/2003, the definition will also include at the end "2 or 3 days"

One-day procedure

Physician

Until 12/31/2002

♦ 62263-52 - percutaneous lysis of epidural adhesions using solution injection (eg, hypertonic saline, enzyme) or mechanical means including radiologic localization (includes contrast when administered), multiple adhesiolysis sessions; 2 or more days

♦ 72275 – Epidurography, radiological supervision and interpretation

From 1/1/2003

♦ 6226X - percutaneous lysis of epidural adhesions using solution injection (eg, hypertonic saline, enzyme) or mechanical means including radiologic localization (includes contrast when administered), 1-day

♦ 72275 – Epidurography, radiological supervision and interpretation

Surgery center

Until 12/31/2002

♦ 62263 - Percutaneous lysis of epidural adhesions using solution injection (eg, hypertonic saline, enzyme) or mechanical means including radiologic localization (includes contrast when administered).

After 1/1/2003

♦ 6226X – Percutaneous lysis of epidural adhesions using solution injection (eg, hypertonic saline, enzyme) or mechanical means including radiologic localization (includes contrast when administered) – 1- day

SPINAL ENDOSCOPY

Procedure (CPT) Code 2002

♦ 0027T – Endoscopic lysis of epidural adhesions with direct visualization using mechanical means (eg, spinal endoscopic catheter system) or solution injection (eg, normal saline) including radiologic localization and epidurography.

This is a category III, CPT code, effective 1/1/2002.

Example:

Percutaneous endoscopic lysis of lumbar epidural adhesions.

Physician

- 0027T – Endoscopic lysis of epidural adhesions

Surgery Center

- 0027T – Endoscopic lysis of epidural adhesions

Medicare

Has not approved this procedure for ambulatory surgery centers.

Other Carriers

- 0027T – Endoscopic lysis of epidural adhesions

DISCOGRAPHY

Procedure (CPT) Codes 2002

- 62290 - Injection procedure for discography, each level; lumbar
- 62291 - Injection procedure for discography, each level; cervical or thoracic
- 72285 – Diskography, cervical or thoracic, radiological supervision and interpretation
- 72295 – Diskography, lumbar, radiological supervision and interpretation

Example(s)

i. Cervical discography – multiple levels (C4/5, C5/6)

Physician

- 62291 – C/T discography, each level
- 62291-51 – C/T discography, additional level
- 72285 – C/T discography, radiological supervision and interpretation

Surgery Center

Medicare

- Cervical discography procedures are not approved for surgery centers.

Other carriers

- 62291 – C/T discography, each level
- 62291-51 – C/T discography, additional level

ii. Thoracic discography – multiple levels (T4/5, T5/6)

Physician

- 62291 – C/T discography, each level
- 62291-51 – C/T discography, additional level
- 72285 – C/T discography, radiological supervision and interpretation

Surgery Center

Medicare

- Thoracic discography procedures are not approved for ASCs.

Other carriers

- 62291 – C/T discography, each level
- 62291-51 – C/T discography, additional level

iii. Lumbar discography – multiple levels (L3/4, L4/5, L5/S1)

Physician

- 62290 – Lumbar discography, each level
- 62290-51 – Lumbar discography, additional level
- 72295 – Lumbar discography, radiological supervision and interpretation

Surgery Center

Medicare

- Lumbar discography procedures are not approved

for ASCs.

Other carriers

- 62290 – Lumbar discography, each level
- 62290-51 – Lumbar discography, additional level

INTRADISCAL ELECTROTHERMAL ANNULOPLASTY

Intradiscal electrothermal annuloplasty has elicited significant controversy. The AMAs CPT Committee initially issued an opinion that CPT 62287 (aspiration or decompression procedure) was the appropriate code to utilize. However, in subsequent communications, AMA's CPT Committee advised to use an unlisted procedure code for the nervous system, either CPT 22899, or CPT 64999. None of the unlisted codes are approved by Medicare for surgery centers. The New Hospital Outpatient Rule also includes payment for an unlisted code, which will be insufficient to cover costs. Recently, the AMA's CPT Committee has been considering a request for a new code. Presently, all specialists performing these procedures are requested to obtain preapprovals with explicit understanding of the insurer of the procedure to be performed and the code to be utilized. In addition, providers should also obtain in writing the clarification of use of the insurers that they do indeed understand the nature of the procedure, ie, intradiscal electrothermal annuloplasty and the CPT code 62287, ie, aspiration or decompression procedure, percutaneous, of nucleus pulposus of intervertebral disk, any method; single or multiple levels are being used.

Physician

- 62287 - Aspiration or decompression procedure, percutaneous, of nucleus pulposus of intervertebral disk, any method, single or multiple levels; or
- 22899 – Unlisted, spine procedure; or
- 64999 – unlisted, spine procedure

Surgery Center

Medicare

- Intradiscal electrical thermal annuloplasty procedures; with present codes; are not approved to be performed in ASCs.

Other carriers

- 62287 - Aspiration or decompression procedure, percutaneous, of nucleus pulposus of intervertebral disk, any method, single or multiple levels; or
- 22899 – Unlisted, spine procedure; or
- 64999 – Unlisted, spine procedure

NUCLEOPLASTY

Procedure (CPT) Codes 2002

- 62287 – Aspiration or decompression procedure, percutaneous, of nucleus pulposus of intervertebral disk, any method, single or multiple levels, lumbar

Physician

- 62287 – Aspiration or decompression procedure, percutaneous, of nucleus pulposus of intervertebral disk, any method, single or multiple levels, lumbar

Surgery Center

Medicare

- 62287 - is not approved for ASCs.

Other Payors

- 62287 – Aspiration or decompression procedure, percutaneous, of nucleus pulposus of intervertebral disk, any method, single or multiple levels, lumbar

SYMPATHETIC NERVE BLOCKS

PROCEDURE (CPT) 2002 CODES

- 64505 – Injection, anesthetic agent; sphenopalatine ganglion
- 64510 - Injection, anesthetic agent; stellate ganglion
- 64520 - Injection, anesthetic agent; lumbar or thoracic
- 64530 – Injection, anesthetic agent; celiac plexus
- 64680 – Destruction by neurolytic agent; celiac plexus, with and without radiologic monitoring

Examples

i. Sphenopalatine ganglion block

Physician

- 64505 – Injection, anesthetic agent; sphenopalatine ganglion

Surgery Center

Medicare

Sphenopalatine ganglion block is not approved for ASCs

Other carriers

- 64505 – Injection, anesthetic agent; sphenopalatine ganglion

ii. Cervical sympathetic or stellate ganglion block

Physician

- 64510 - Injection, anesthetic agent; stellate ganglion

Surgery Center

- 64510 - Injection, anesthetic agent; stellate ganglion

iii. Thoracic or lumbar paravertebral sympathetic block, single level

Physician

- 64520 - Injection, anesthetic agent; lumbar or thoracic

Surgery Center

- 64520 - Injection, anesthetic agent; lumbar or thoracic

iv. Thoracic lumbar paravertebral sympathetic blocks (multiple levels, L2, L3)

Physician

- 64520 - Injection, anesthetic agent; lumbar or thoracic
- 64520 – 51- Injection, anesthetic agent; lumbar or thoracic

Surgery Center

- 64520 - Injection, anesthetic agent; lumbar or thoracic
- 64520 – 51- Injection, anesthetic agent; lumbar or thoracic

v. Celiac plexus block

Physician

- 64530 – Injection, anesthetic agent; celiac plexus

Surgery Center

- 64530 – Injection, anesthetic agent; celiac plexus

vi. Celiac plexus block (bilateral)

Physician

- 64530 – Injection, anesthetic agent; celiac plexus
- 64530-51 – Injection, anesthetic agent; celiac plexus

Surgery Center

- 64530 – Injection, anesthetic agent; celiac plexus
- 64530-51 – Injection, anesthetic agent; celiac plexus

vii. Neurolytic celiac plexus block

Physician

- 64680 – Destruction by neurolytic agent

Surgery Center

- 64680 – Destruction by neurolytic agent

viii. Neurolytic celiac plexus block (bilateral)

Physician

- 64680 – Destruction by neurolytic agent
- 64680-51 – Destruction by neurolytic agent

Surgery Center

- 64680 – Destruction by neurolytic agent
- 64680-51 – Destruction by neurolytic agent

SOMATIC NERVE BLOCKS

Procedure (CPT) Codes 2002

- 64400 – injection, anesthetic agent; trigeminal nerve
- 64405 – injection, anesthetic agent; greater occipital nerve
- 64420 - injection, intercostal nerve, single
- 64421 - injection, anesthetic agent; intercostal nerves, multiple, regional block
- 64415 - injection, brachial plexus
- 64417 - injection, axillary nerve
- 64418 - injection, suprascapular nerve
- 64425 - injection, iliohypogastric nerves
- 64450 - injection, other peripheral nerve or branch
- 64600 - destruction by neurolytic agent, trigeminal nerve; supraorbital, infraorbital, mental, or inferior alveolar branch
- 64610 - destruction by neurolytic agent, second and third division branches
- 64620 - destruction by neurolytic agent, intercostal nerve
- 64640 - destruction by neurolytic agent, other pe-

ripheral nerve or branch

Examples

iv. Intercostal nerve block (single)

Physician

- 64420 - injection, intercostal nerve, single

Surgery Center

- 64420 - injection, intercostal nerve, single

v. Multiple and/or bilateral intercostal nerve blocks

Physician

- 64421 - injection, anesthetic agent; intercostal nerves, multiple, regional block

Surgery Center

- 64421 - injection, anesthetic agent; intercostal nerves, multiple, regional block

i. Trigeminal nerve blocks

Physician

- 64400 – injection, anesthetic agent; trigeminal nerve, any division or branch

Surgery Center

Medicare

Nonapproved

Other Carriers

- 64400 – injection, anesthetic agent; trigeminal nerve

ii. Greater occipital nerve block (unilateral)

Physician

- 64405 – injection, anesthetic agent; greater occipital nerve

Surgery Center

Medicare

Nonapproved

Other Carriers

- 64405 – injection, anesthetic agent; greater occipital nerve

iii. Greater occipital nerve blocks (bilateral)

Physician

- 64405 – injection, anesthetic agent; greater occipital nerve
- 64405-51 – injection, anesthetic agent; greater occipital nerve

Surgery Center

Medicare

Nonapproved

Other Carriers

- 64405 – injection, anesthetic agent; greater occipital nerve

vi. Brachial plexus block

Physician

- 64415 - injection, brachial plexus

Surgery Center

- 64415 - injection, brachial plexus

vii. Suprascapular nerve block

Physician

- 64418 - injection, suprascapular nerve

Surgery Center

Medicare

Nonapproved

Other Carriers

- 64418 - injection, suprascapular nerve

viii. Axillary nerve block

Physician

- 64417 - injection, axillary nerve

Surgery Center

- 64417 - injection, axillary nerve

ix. Ilioinguinal, iliohypogastric nerve blocks

Physician

- 64425 - injection, iliohypogastric, ilioinguinal nerves

Surgery Center

Medicare

Nonapproved

Other carriers

- 64425 - injection, iliohypogastric, ilioinguinal nerves

x. Peripheral nerve block

Physician

- 64450 - injection, other peripheral nerve or branch

Surgery Center

Medicare

Nonapproved

Other Carriers

- 64450 - injection, other peripheral nerve or branch

xi. Trigeminal neurolysis, peripheral branches

Physician

- 64600 - destruction by neurolytic agent, trigeminal nerve; supraorbital, infraorbital, mental, or inferior alveolar branch

Surgery Center

- 64600 - destruction by neurolytic agent, trigeminal nerve; supraorbital, infraorbital, mental, or inferior alveolar branch

xii. Trigeminal neurolysis, second and third division

Physician

- 64610 - destruction by neurolytic agent, second and third division branches

Surgery Center

- 64610 - destruction by neurolytic agent, second and third division branches

xiii. Intercostal neurolysis

Physician

- 64620 - destruction by neurolytic agent, intercostal nerve

Surgery Center

- 64620 - destruction by neurolytic agent, intercostal nerve

xiv. peripheral nerve neurolysis

Physician

- 64640 - destruction by neurolytic agent, other peripheral nerve or branch

Surgery Center

Medicare

Nonapproved

Other Carriers

- 64640 - destruction by neurolytic agent, other peripheral nerve or branch

TRIGGER POINT AND INTRAARTICULAR INJECTIONS

Procedure (CPT) Codes 2002

- 20526 Injection, therapeutic (eg, local anesthetic; corticosteroid), carpel tunnel
- 20550 Injection; tendon sheath, ligament, ganglion cyst
- 20551 Injection; tendon origin insertion
- 20552 Injection; single or multiple trigger point(s), one or two muscle group(s)
- 20553 Injection; single or multiple trigger point(s), three or more muscle groups
- 20600 – Arthrocentesis, aspiration and/or injection; small joint, bursa or ganglion cyst (eg, fingers, toes)
- 20605 – Arthrocentesis, aspiration and/or injection; intermediate joint bursa or ganglion cyst (eg, temporomandibular, acromioclavicular, wrist, elbow or

ankle, olecranon bursa)

- 27093 – Injection procedure for hip arthrography; without anesthesia
- 27095 – Injection procedure for hip arthrography; with anesthesia
- 27096 – Injection procedure for sacroiliac joint, arthrography and/or anesthetic/steroid **(is to be used only with imaging confirmation of intra-articular positioning)**
  (Use Modifier -50 For Bilateral Procedures)
- 73542 – Radiological examination, sacroiliac joint arthrography, radiological supervision and interpretation

All procedures

Physician

Appropriate CPT code for the procedure(s)

Surgery Center

- None of the procedures are approved by Medicare for ASCs.
- Third party carriers may be billed using appropriate CPT code(s).

MULTIPLE REGIONS AND/OR COMBINATIONS

Due to various regulations in existence at the present time, interventional procedures performed in multiple regions and/or combinations can be utilized for the advantage of the physician in certain cases. It is common to perform blocks in multiple regions in interventional pain practices as it has been shown that involvement of multiple regions in chronic pain patients is more prevalent than assumed (14. It has also been shown that in patients suffering with chronic low back pain presenting to an interventional pain practice,33% of patients had three regions affected followed by 46% with two regions and the remaining 21% with pain in only one region. In addition, treating multiple regions at one time is not only beneficial to the patient, it is also cost and for the insurer, the facility, and time saving for physician and staff. The most common complication in including multiple regions into the treatment regimen at one time is steroid toxicity. However, this has been shown to be negligible when therapy was carried out with a low dose or no steroids (14) Creative billing will only create multiple problems for interventional pain practitioners across the country, as insurers universally blame interventional pain physicians across the board with examples of 24 charges on one patient, etc. These guidelines indicate a limitation of four procedures or line items for management of a single region and five for multiple regions. Thus, if a bilateral procedure is performed at two levels, that will constitute four procedures. Needle placement, epidurography, radiological interpretation and supervision, etc., are also considered a line item. Most Medicare carriers do not reimburse more than five line items, codes, or procedures at one time per patient. In addition, some insurers do not reimburse if a procedure code is repeated following the primary charge as an increase in the number of units. Considering the present situation with the proposed ASC ruling, higher reimbursement may be possible, within legal and ethical parameters, without using creative billing techniques, for procedures performed in a facility setting (the same as if they are performed in a nonfacility setting). It may be worthwhile for physicians to pay proper attention to billing and coding practices when multiple regions or combinations are utilized in managing these patients. Once again, these practices should be performed within the limits of the guidelines following the rules, regulations and ethical practices.

Examples

i Multiple cervical facet joint nerve blocks, (C3/4-C5/6 joints – C3-6 medial branch nerves) **and** multiple lumbar facet joint nerve blocks, (L3/4-L5/S1 joints L2-L4 medial branches and L5 dorsal- ramus)

Physician

- 64470 – C/T facet joint nerve block, single level
- 64472 - C/T facet joint nerve block, each additional level
- 64475-51- L/S facet joint nerve block, single level
- 64476 - L/S facet joint nerve blocks, each additional level
- 76005 - Fluoroscopic guidance

Surgery Center

- 64470 – C/T facet joint nerve block, single level
- 64472-51 - C/T facet joint nerve block, each additional level
- 64475-51 - L/S facet joint nerve block, single level
- 64476-51 – L/S facet joint nerve block, each additional level

ii. Caudal epidural **and** multiple cervical facet joint nerve blocks (C3/4-C5/6 joints – C3-6 medial branch nerves)

Physician

- 62311 – L/S epidural
- 64470-51 – CT facet joint nerve block, single level
- 64472 – C/T facet joint nerve block, each additional level
- 76005 – Fluoroscopic guidance (may or may not be used)

Surgery Center

- 62311 – L/S epidural
- 64470-51 – CT facet joint nerve block, single level
- 64472-51– C/T facet joint nerve block, each additional level

iii. Cervical epidural **and** multiple lumbar facet joint nerve blocks

Physician

- 62310 – Cervical epidural
- 64475-51 – L/S facet joint nerve block, single level
- 64476 – L/S facet joint nerve block, each additional level;
- 76005 – Fluoroscopic guidance

Surgery Center

- 62310 – Cervical epidural
- 64450-51 – L/S facet joint nerve block, single level
- 64462-51– L/S facet joint nerve block, each additional level

iv. Multiple cervical transforaminal epidurals **and** mul tiple lumbar facet joint nerve blocks

Physician

- 64479 – Cervical transforaminal, single level
- 64480– Cervical transforaminal, each additional level
- 64475-51 – L/S facet joint nerve block, single level
- 64476 – L/S facet joint nerve block, each additional level
- 76005 – Fluoroscopic guidance

Surgery Center

- 64479 – Cervical transforaminal, single level
- 64480-51 - Cervical transforaminal, each additional level
- 64475-51 – L/S facet joint nerve block, single level
- 64476-51 – L/S facet joint nerve block, each additional level

v. Multiple lumbar transforaminal epidurals **and** mul tiple cervical facet joint nerve blocks

Physician

- 64483 – L/S transforaminal epidural, single level
- 64484 – L/S transforaminal, each additional level
- 64470-51 – C/T facet joint nerve block, single level
- 64472 – C/T facet joint nerve blocks, each additional level
- 76005 – Fluoroscopic guidance

Surgery Center

- 64483 – L/S transforaminal epidural, single level
- 64484-51 – L/S transforaminal, each additional level
- 64470-51 – C/T facet joint nerve block, single level
- 64472-51 - C/T facet joint nerve blocks, each additional level

vi. One day percutaneous lysis of adhesions **and** mul tiple cervical facet joint nerve blocks

Physician

- 64470 - C/T facet joint nerve block, single level
- 62263–52 – Percutaneous lysis of epidural adhesions using solution injection (eg, hypertonic saline, enzyme) or mechanical means including radiologic localization (includes contrast when administered).
- 64472– C/T facet joint nerve block, each additional level
- 76005 Fluoroscopic guidance

Surgery Center

- 62263 – Percutaneous lysis of epidural adhesions using solution injection (eg, hypertonic saline, enzyme) or mechanical means including radiologic localization.
- 64470-51 C/T facet joint nerve block, single level
- 64472-51 – C/T facet joint nerve block, each additional level

Note: From 1/1/2003 a new code for 1-day adhesiolysis must be used

CONCLUSION

Interventional pain management coding is a dynamic process. The CPT descriptive terms and identification of codes currently are the only means of documenting medical necessity and serve a wide variety of important functions in the field of medical practice, including interventional pain management. Documentation of interventional pain procedures and subsequent billing and coding are of crucial importance not only for compliance with regulations, but also for good patient care, and, finally, last but not least, for survival of the practice itself. This review has provided generally accepted practice patterns performed in a safe manner. However, caution must be exercised in utilizing the issues and guidelines mentioned in this article in your own practices.

REFERENCES

1. Manchikanti L. Appropriate documentation, billing and coding of interventional pain procedures. *Pain Physician* 2000; 3:218-236.
2. Manchikanti L. Role of correct coding for interventional techniques.

Pain Physician 2001; 4:381-399.

3. Manchikanti L. CPT 2000. Interventional pain management coding in the new millennium. *Pain Physician* 2000; 3:73-85.
4. Current Procedural Terminology, CPT 2000, American Medical Association, Chicago, 1999.
5. Current Procedural Terminology, CPT 2001, American Medical Association, Chicago, 2000.
6. Current Procedural Terminology, CPT 2002, American Medical Association, Chicago, 2001.
7. Medicare Program; Revisions to Payment Policies Under the Physician Fee Schedule for Calender Year 2001 (HCFA-1120-P). Department of Health and Human Services. Centers for Medicare & Medicaid Services, 66 *Federal Register,* July 17, 2000.
8. Medicare Program; Revisions to Payment Policies and Five-Year Review of and Adjustments to the Relative Value Units Under the Physician Fee Schedule for Calender Year 2002. Department of Health and Human Services. Centers for Medicare & Medicaid Services, 66 *Federal Register,* 42 CFR Parts 405, 410, 411, 414 and 415, November 2, 2001.
9. Medicare Program; Prospective Payment System for Hospital Outpatient Services; Final Rule: Department of Health and Human Services. Centers for Medicare and Medicaid Services, 66 *Federal Register,* 42 CFR Parts 411 and 424, January 4, 2001.
10. Medicare Program; Prospective Payment System for Hospital Outpatient Services; Final Rule: Department of Health and Human Services. Health Care Financing Administration, 66 *Federal Register* 42 CFR, Final Rule, Parts 413, 419 and 489, November 30, 2001.
11. Manchikanti L. Correct coding in interventional pain management. *Pain Physician* 2000; 3:313-321.
12. Manchikanti L. The impact of National Correct Coding Policy on interventional pain management. *Pain Physician* 1999; 2:33-45.
13. National Correct Coding Primer with Correct Code Check 2002: United Communications Group, Rockville, 2002.
14. Manchikanti L, Singh V, Kloth D et al. Interventional techniques in the management of chronic pain. Part 2.0 *Pain Physician* 2001; 4:24-96.
15. Manchikanti L, Pampati V, Beyer C et al. The effect of neuraxial steroids on weight and bone mass density: A prospective evaluation. *Pain Physician* 2000; 3:(4): 357-366.

CORRECT CODING POLICIES FOR INTERVENTIONAL TECHNIQUES

Laxmaiah Manchikanti, MD

Interventional techniques are the centerpieces of interventional pain medicine, in conjunction with other services. Thus, interventional techniques and correct coding polices go hand in hand. Publication of National Correct Coding Manual, Versions 7.2, 7.3, and latest one 8.0 in 2002, included interventional pain medicine, with evolution of numerous component and mutually exclusive codes for almost all procedures. Thus, proper understanding of various pertinent correct coding policies, is not only crucial, but mandatory (1-11).

CCI 7.2, involved interventional pain medicine, with overall approximately 5000 new Correct Coding (CCI) Code-Pair edits which have gone into effect on July 1, 2001 (2, 9). Among the hardest hit by these changes were interventional pain physicians even though almost all of the specialties were affected.

Subsequent editions (10, 11) deleted some corrections while incorporating additional coding edits. Various commonly utilized interventional techniques in pain management are described here with comprehensive, component, and mutually exclusive codes. However, if there is a question about coding, its comprehensive nature, or mutual exclusion, physicians and other providers are urged to contact local Medicare carriers or third-party payors. Following are ten important aspects of interventional pain medicine coding, also illustrated in brief format in Table 1.

Watch component and mutually exclusive codes very carefully. (They are updated every 3 months).

Table 1. *Ten important aspects for correct coding for interventional techniques*

1. **Understand** comprehensive and mutually exclusive codes
2. **Do not** use component and mutually exclusive codes
3. **Watch** for exclusions of fluoroscopy codes:76000, 76001, 76003, 76005
4. **Do not** bill for combined epidural procedures in the same region (e.g., caudal and transforaminal epidural, lumbar)
5. **Do not** bill epidurals with discograms. Note: Discograms are non-covered procedures for ASC facility fees.
6. **Do not** bill for nerve blocks and neurolytic blocks in the same region
7. **Do not** bill CPT 20550 with somatic nerve blocks (CPT 64400-64445)
8. **Do not** bill CPT 20550 with intraarticular injections, facet joint nerve blocks, transforaminal epidural injections, myelography or discography interpretation and supervision
9. **Do not** bill medium and large joint injections with:
   - SI joint injection
   - All types of epidurals
   - Facet joint injections
10. **Do not** bill small joint injections with:
    - SI joint injection
    - Facet joint injections

Do not use fluoroscopy codes 76000-76003 with the following:

27096	62263	62270	62272	62273	62280
62281	62282	62284	62310	62311	62318
62319	64470	64475	64479	64483	64622
64626					

Do not use fluoroscopy code 76005 with the following:

62263	62284	62287	62290	62291

Do not combine epidural procedures in the same region.

- lysis of adhesions
- interlaminar / caudal
- transforaminal

Do not bill for epidurals with discograms.

Do not bill for nerve blocks and neurolytic blocks in the same region.

Do not combine CPT 20550 with the following somatic nerve blocks:

64400	64405	64413	64415	64417	64418
64420	64421	64425	64430	64445	

Do not bill CPT 20550 on the same day as facet joint injections and transforaminal epidural injections.

64470	64475	64479	64483

Do not bill intermediate and major joint injections (CPT 20605, 20610) with the following:

27096	62310	62311	62318	62319	64470
64475	64479	64483			

Do not bill small joint injection (CPT 20600) with the following:

27096	64470	64475

Table 2 illustrates most commonly used interventional techniques and correct coding policies (1, 2). Table 3 shows an easy cross-walk of comprehensive, component and mutually exclusive codes (1, 2).

COMPREHENSIVE, COMPONENT AND MUTUALLY EXCLUSIVE CODES

The CPT manual describes certain codes that include two or more component codes that should not be reported separately, as these are considered members of a code family and included in a more comprehensive code. As such, comprehensive codes include certain services that are separately identified by other component codes. Although, component codes as members of the comprehensive code family represent parts of the procedure, that should not be listed separately when the complete procedure is performed, the component codes are considered individually if the procedures they describe are performed independently of the complete procedure. If this is not the case, all services listed in the comprehensive codes will be considered to make up the total service. Mutually exclusive codes are codes for procedures that cannot be reasonably performed in the same section.

CPT 20550 injection; tendon sheath; a comprehensive code, includes the following component codes:

20500	29075	29105	29125	29130	29220
29260	29405	29425	29450	29515	29530
29540	29550	29580	29590	64550	64714
69990	72240	72265	72295	76000	87102
90780	90781	90782	95900		

Mutually exclusive code: 11010

CPT 20600 injection; small joint; a comprehensive code, includes the following component codes:

20500	20550	29065	29075	29085	29105
29125	29130	29260	29280	29365	29405
29425	29505	29515	29540	29550	29580
29590	64450	64704	64708	69990	72240
72265	76000	76003	90780	90782	95900
G0127					

Mutually exclusive code: 11010

CPT 20605 injection; intermediate joint; a comprehensive code, includes the following component codes:

20550	29065	29075	29085	29105	29125
29126	29240	29260	29405	29425	29445
29505	29515	29540	29580	29590	29705
64450	64550	64704	69990	76000	76003
90780	90782	95900			

Mutually exclusive code: 11010

CPT 20610 injection; major joint; a comprehensive code, includes the following component codes:

10060	10061	10140	10160	11900	12001
20500	20501	20550	29065	29075	29085
29105	29125	29130	29240	29260	29345
29355	29365	29405	29425	29505	29515
29530	29540	29580	64450	64550	64553
64718	69990	72255	72265	72295	76000
76003	76080	90780	90781	90782	95900
G0168					

Mutually exclusive code: 11010

Table 2. *Illustratation of most commonly used interventional techniques showing component and mutually exclusive codes*

Comprehensive Code	Component Codes	Mutually Exclusive Codes
20550 – tendonsheath, ligament injection	20500, 64550, 64714, 69990, 72240, 72265, 72295, 76000, 87102, 90780, 90781, 90782, 95900	11010
20600 – small joint injection	20500, 20550, 64450, 64704, 64708, 69990, 72240, 72265, 76000, 76003, 90780, 90782, 95900, G0127	11010
20605 –intermediate joint injection	20550, 64450, 64550, 64704, 69990, 76000, 76003, 90780, 90782, 95900	11010
20610 – major joint injection	20500, 20501, 20550, 64450, 64550, 64553, 64718, 69990, 72255, 72265, 72295, 76000, 76003, 76080, 90780, 90781, 90782, 95900, G0168	11010
27096 – sacroiliac joint injection	20600, 20605, 20610, 69990, 76000, 76001, 76003, 90782	NA
62263 – percutaneous adhesiolysis	62281, 62282, 62284, 62310, 62311, 62318, 62319, 64479, 64483, 64722, 69990, 76000, 76003, 76005	NA
62270 - spinal puncture, diagnostic	62273, 62311, 64483, 69990, 76000, 76001, 76003	NA
62272 – spinal puncture, therapeutic	62270, 62273, 62310, 62311, 64479, 64483, 69990, 76000, 76001, 76003	NA
62273 - epidural, blood patch	36000, 36140, 36410, 62310, 62311, 64479, 64483, 69990, 76000, 76001, 76003, G0001	NA
62280 - subarachnoid neurolytic injection	62270, 62272, 62273, 62284, 62310, 62311, 62318, 62319, 64479, 64483, 69990, 76000, 76001, 76003	NA
62281 - neurolytic epidural, C/T	62270, 62272, 62273, 62284, 62310, 62318, 64479, 69990, 76000, 76001, 76003	NA
62282 - neurolytic epidural, L/S	62270, 62272, 62273, 62311, 62319, 64483, 69990, 76000, 76001, 76003	NA
62287 – disc decompression	62290, 62310, 62311, 62318, 62319, 64479, 64483, 69990, 76000, 76001, 76005	22224, 22558, 63005, 63017, 63030,63042, 63056
62290 - lumbar discography	62311, 62319, 64483, 69990, 76005	NA
62291 - cervical discography	62310, 62318, 64479, 69990, 76005	NA
62310 - cervical epidural	20605, 20610, 36140, 62284, 69990, 76000, 76001, 76003	64479
62311 - lumbar epidural	20605, 20610, 36140, 62284, 69990, 76000, 76001, 76003	64483
62318 - epidural or subarachnoid, catheterization, C/T	01996, 20605, 20610, 36000, 36140, 36410, 62270, 62272, 62284, 62310, 69990, 76000, 76001, 76003	62273, 64479
62319 - catheterization, epidural, L/S	01996, 20605, 20610, 36000, 36140, 36410, 62270, 62272, 62284, 62311, 69990, 76000, 76001, 76003	62273, 64483
64420 - single intercostal nerve block	20550, 69990	NA
64421 - multiple intercostal nerve	20550, 64420, 69990	NA
64470 - C/T facet joint nerve block	20550, 20600, 20605, 20610, 36140, 76000, 76001, 76003	NA
64475 - lumbar facet joint nerve block	20550, 20600, 20605, 20610, 69990, 76000, 76001, 76003	NA
64479 - C/T transforaminal epidural	20550, 20605, 20610, 69990, 76000, 76001, 76003	NA
64483 - lumbar transforaminal epidural	20550, 20605, 20610, 36140, 76000, 76001, 76003	NA
64620 - intercostal neurolysis	64420, 64421, 69990	NA
64622 - lumbar facet neurolysis	64475, 69990, 76000, 76001, 76003	NA
64626 - cervical facet neurolysis	64470, 69990, 76000, 76001, 76003	NA
64640 - peripheral nerve neurolysis	64405, 64408, 64410, 64415, 64417, 64418, 64425, 64435, 64445, 64450, 69990	NA

Table 3. *Illustratation of most commonly used interventional techniques showing component and mutually exclusive codes*

Component Codes	Comprehensive Code										
	27096	62263	62281	62282	62287	62290	62291	62310	62311	62318	62319
20600	X										
20605	X							X	X	X	X
20610	X							X	X	X	X
36140								X	X	X	X
62270			X	X						X	X
62273			X	X						Y	Y
62284		X	X					X	X	X	X
62310		X	X		X		X			X	
62311		X		X	X	X					X
62318		X	X		X		X				
62319		X		X	X	X					
64479		X	X		X		X	Y		Y	
64483		X		X	X	X			Y		Y
69990	X	X	X	X	X	X	X	X	X	X	X
76000	X	X	X	X	X			X	X	X	X
76001	X		X	X	X			X	X	X	X
76003	X	X	X	X				X	X	X	X
76005		X			X	X	X				

X - Component Codes
Y – Mutually Exclusive Codes

20600-small joint injection; 20605-intermediate joint injection; 20610-major joint injection; 27096–sacroiliac joint injection; 36140-introduction of needle or intracatheter, extremity artery; 62270-spinal puncture, lumbar, diagnostic; 62273-injection, epidural, of blood or clot patch ; 62281-neurolytic epidural, cervical or thoracic; 62282-neurolytic epidural, lumbar, sacral (caudal); 62284-injection procedure for myelography; 62287–disc decompression procedure; 62290-lumbar discography, 62291-cervical discography; 62310–cervical epidural; 62311–lumbar epidural; 62318-catheter placement, continuous infusion or intermittent bolus; epidural or subarachnoid; cervical or thoracic; 62319-catheter placement, continuous infusion or intermittent bolus; epidural, lumbar, sacral (caudal); 64479 - cervical/thoracic transforaminal epidural ;64483 - lumbar transforaminal epidural; 69990 - use of operating microscope; 76000 - fluoroscopy codes; 76001 - fluoroscopy codes; 76003 - fluoroscopy codes, 76005 - fluoroscopy codes

Table 4. *Illustratation of most commonly used interventional techniques showing component and mutually exclusive codes*

Comprehensive Code	Components	Mutually Exclusive Codes
27096 – sacroiliac joint injection	20600, 20605, 20610, 69990, 76000, 76001, 76003, 90782	NA
62263 – adhesiolysis	62281, 62282, 62284, 62310, 62311, 62318, 62319, 64479, 64483, 64722, 69990, 76000, 76003, 76005	NA
62290 – lumbar discography	62311, 62319, 64483, 69990, 76005	NA
62291 – cervical discography	62310, 62318, 64479, 69990, 76005	NA
62310 – cervical epidural	20605, 20610, 36140, 62284, 69990, 76000, 76001, 76003	64479
62311 – lumbar epidural	20605, 20610, 36140, 62284, 69990, 76000, 76001, 76003	64483
64470 – C/T facet joint nerve block	20550, 20600, 20605, 20610, 36140, 76000, 76001, 76003	NA
64475 – lumbar facet joint nerve block	20550, 20600, 20605, 20610, 36140, 69990, 76000, 76001, 76003	NA
64479 – C/T transforaminal epidural	20550, 20605, 20610, 36140, 69990, 76000 to 76003	NA
64483 – lumbar transforaminal epidural	20550, 20605, 20610, 36140, 76000, 76001, 76003	NA
64620 – intercostal neurolysis	64420, 64421, 69990	NA
64622 – lumbar facet neurolysis	64475, 69990, 76000, 76001, 76003	NA
64626 – cervical facet neurolysis	64470, 69990, 76000, 76001, 76003	NA
64640 – peripheral nerve neurolysis	64405, 64408, 64410, 64412, 64413, 64415, 64417, 64418, 64425, 64435, 64445, 64450, 69990	NA

CPT 22520 percutaneous vertebroplasty; a comprehensive code, includes the following component codes:

36005 61795 72128 72129 72130 75872
76000 76001 76003 76005

Mutually exclusive codes: None

CPT 27096 (injection procedure for sacroiliac joint, arthrography); a comprehensive code, includes the following component codes:

20600 20605 20610 69990 76000 76001
76003 90782

Mutually exclusive codes: None

CPT 62263 percutaneous lysis of epidural adhesions; a comprehensive code, includes the following component codes:

62281 62282 62284 62310 62311 62318
62319 64479 64483 64722 69990 76000
76003 76005

Mutually exclusive codes: None

CPT 62270 spinal puncture, lumbar, diagnostic; a comprehensive code, includes the following component codes:

62273 62311 64483 69990 76000 76001
76003

Mutually exclusive codes: None

CPT 62272 spinal puncture, therapeutic, for drainage of spinal fluid (by needle or catheter); a comprehensive code,

includes the following component codes:

62270 62273 62310 62311 64479 64483
69990 76000 76001 76003

Mutually exclusive codes: None

CPT 62273 injection, epidural, of blood or clot patch; a comprehensive code, includes the following component codes:

36000 36140 36410 62310 62311 64479
64483 69990 76000 76001 76003 G0001

Mutually exclusive codes: None

CPT 62280 injection of neurolytic substance with or without other therapeutic substance (subarachnoid); a comprehensive code, includes the following component codes:

62270 62272 62273 62284 62310 62311
62318 62319 64479 64483 69990 76000
76001 76003

Mutually exclusive codes: None

CPT 62281 injection of neurolytic substance with or without other therapeutic substance (epidural, cervical or thoracic); a comprehensive code, includes the following component codes:

62270 62272 62273 62284 62310 62318
64479 69990 76000 76001 76003

Mutually exclusive codes: None

CPT 62282 injection of neurolytic substance with or without other therapeutic substance (epidural, lumbar, sacral (caudal)); a comprehensive code, includes the following component codes:

62270 62272 62273 62311 62319 64483
69990 76000 76001 76003

Mutually exclusive codes: None

CPT 62284 injection procedure for myelography and/or computerized axial tomography, spinal (other than C1-C2 and posterior fossa); a comprehensive code, includes the following component codes:

01906 01908 62270 62272 62273 62282
64479 64483 69990 76000 76001 76003
76005

Mutually exclusive codes: None

CPT 62287 aspiration or decompression procedure, percutaneous, of nucleus pulposus of intervertebral disk, any method, single or multiple levels, lumbar (eg, manual or automated percutaneous diskectomy, percutaneous laser diskectomy); a comprehensive code, includes the following component codes:

62290 62310 62311 62318 62319 64479
64483 69990 76000 76001 76005

Mutually exclusive codes are as follows:

22224 22558 63005 63017 63030 63042
63056

CPT 62290 injection procedure for diskography, each level (lumbar); a comprehensive code, includes the following component codes:

01912 62311 62319 64483 69990 76005

Mutually exclusive codes: None

CPT 62291 injection procedure for diskography, each level (cervical or thoracic); a comprehensive code, includes the following component codes:

01914 62310 62318 64479 69990 76005

Mutually exclusive codes: None

CPT 62310 cervical or thoracic epidural injection; a comprehensive code, includes the following component codes:

20605 20610 36140 62284 69990 76000
76001 76003

Mutually exclusive code: 64479

CPT 62311 lumbar (caudal epidural injection); a comprehensive code, includes the following component codes:

20605 20610 36140 62284 69990 76000
76001 76003

Mutually exclusive code: 64483

CPT 62318 continuous infusion with catheter placement (cervical or thoracic) a comprehensive code, includes the following component codes:

01996 20605 20610 36000 36140 36410
62270 62272 62284 62310 69990 76000
76001 76003

Mutually exclusive codes: 62273 64479

CPT 62319 injection, catheter placement, lumbar or caudal epidural space; a comprehensive code, includes the following component codes:

01996 20605 20610 36000 36140 36410
62270 62272 62284 62311 69990 76000

76001 76003

Mutually exclusive codes: 62273 64483

CPT 62350 implantation, revision or repositioning of tunneled intrathecal or epidural catheter, for long-term medication administration via an external pump or implantable reservoir/infusion pump (without laminectomy); a comprehensive code, includes the following component codes:

62270 62272 62273 62280 62281 62282
62310 62311 62318 62319 64479 64483
69990

Mutually exclusive codes: None

CPT 62351 implantation, revision or repositioning of tunneled intrathecal or epidural catheter, for long-term medication administration via an external pump or implantable reservoir/infusion pump (with laminectomy); a comprehensive code, includes the following component codes:

62280 62281 62282 62310 62311 62318
62319 62350 64479 64483 69990

Mutually exclusive codes: None

CPT 62355 removal of previously implanted intrathecal or epidural catheter; a comprehensive code, includes the following component codes:

62270 62272 62310 62311 62318 62319
64479 64483 69990

Mutually exclusive codes: 62350 62351

CPT 62360 implantation or replacement of device for intrathecal or epidural drug infusion (subcutaneous reservoir); a comprehensive code, includes the following component codes:

62270 62272 62273 62310 62311 62318
62319 62367 62368 64479 64483 69990

Mutually exclusive codes:

62280 62281 62282 62362

CPT 62361 implantation or replacement of device for intrathecal or epidural drug infusion (non-programmable pump); a comprehensive code, includes the following component codes:

62270 62272 62273 62310 62311 62318
62319 62367 62368 64479 64483 69990

Mutually exclusive codes:

62280 62281 62282 62360

CPT 62362 implantation or replacement of device for intrathecal or epidural drug infusion (programmable pump); a comprehensive code, a comprehensive code, includes the following component codes:

62270 62272 62273 62310 62311 62318
62319 62361 62367 62368 64479 64483
69990

Mutually exclusive codes:

62280 62281 62282

CPT 62365 removal of subcutaneous reservoir or pump, previously implanted for intrathecal or epidural infusion; a comprehensive code, a comprehensive code, includes the following component codes:

62310 62311 62318 62319 62367 62368
64479 64483 69990 96520

Mutually exclusive codes:

62360 62361 62362

CPT 64400 injection, anesthetic agent (trigeminal nerve, any division or branch); a comprehensive code, includes the following component codes:

20550 69990

Mutually exclusive codes: None

CPT 64405 injection, anesthetic agent (greater occipital nerve); a comprehensive code, includes the following component codes:

20550 69990

Mutually exclusive codes: None

CPT 64413 injection, anesthetic agent (trigeminal nerve, any division or branch); a comprehensive code, includes the following component codes:

20550 69990

Mutually exclusive codes: None

CPT 64415 injection, anesthetic agent (brachial plexus); a comprehensive code, includes the following component codes:

20550 69990

Mutually exclusive codes: None

CPT 64417 injection, anesthetic agent (axillary nerve); a comprehensive code, includes the following component codes:

20550 69990

Mutually exclusive codes: None

CPT 64418 injection, anesthetic agent (suprascapular nerve); a comprehensive code, includes the following component codes:

20550 69990

Mutually exclusive codes: None

CPT 64420 injection, anesthetic agent (intercostal nerve, single); a comprehensive code, includes the following component codes:

20550 69990

Mutually exclusive codes: None

CPT 64421 injection, anesthetic agent (intercostal nerves, multiple, regional block); a comprehensive code, includes the following component codes:

20550 64420 69990

Mutually exclusive codes: None

CPT 64425 injection, anesthetic agent (ilioinguinal, iliohypogastric nerves); a comprehensive code, includes the following component codes:

20550 69990

Mutually exclusive codes: None

CPT 64430 injection, anesthetic agent (pudendal nerve); a comprehensive code, includes the following component codes:

20550 69990

Mutually exclusive codes: None

CPT 64445 injection, anesthetic agent (sciatic nerve); a comprehensive code, includes the following component codes:

20550 69990

Mutually exclusive codes: None

CPT 64470 cervical/thoracic facet joint nerve block; a comprehensive code, includes the following component codes:

20550 20600 20605 20610 36140 76000
76001 76003

Mutually exclusive codes: None

CPT 64475 injection, lumbar facet joint nerve block; a comprehensive code, includes the following component codes:

20550 20600 20605 20610 36140
69990 76000 76001 76003

Mutually exclusive codes: None

CPT 64479 injection, cervical transforaminal epidural; a comprehensive code, includes the following component codes:

20550 20605 20610 36140 69990 76000
76001 76003

Mutually exclusive codes: None

CPT 64480 injection, anesthetic agent and/or steroid, transforaminal epidural (cervical or thoracic, each additional level); a comprehensive code, includes the following component codes:

69990

Mutually exclusive codes: None

CPT 64483 injection, anesthetic agent and/or steroid, transforaminal epidural (lumbar or sacral, single level); a comprehensive code, includes the following component codes:

20550 20605 20610 36140 76000 76001
76003

Mutually exclusive codes: None

CPT 64505 injection, anesthetic agent (sphenopalatine ganglion); a comprehensive code, includes the following component codes:

69990

Mutually exclusive codes: None

CPT 64510 injection, anesthetic agent (stellate ganglion (cervical sympathetic)); a comprehensive code, includes the following component codes:

69990

Mutually exclusive codes: None

CPT 64520 injection, anesthetic agent (lumbar or thoracic (paravertebral sympathetic)); a comprehensive code, includes the following component codes:

69990

Mutually exclusive codes: None

CPT 64530 injection, anesthetic agent (celiac plexus, with or without radiologic monitoring); a comprehensive code, includes the following component codes:

69990

Mutually exclusive codes: None

CPT 64600 destruction by neurolytic agent, trigeminal nerve (supraorbital, infraorbital, mental, or inferior alveolar branch); a comprehensive code, includes the following component codes:

64400 69990

Mutually exclusive codes: None

CPT 64605 destruction by neurolytic agent, trigeminal nerve (second and third division branches at foramen ovale); a comprehensive code, includes the following component codes:

69990

Mutually exclusive codes: None

CPT 64610 destruction by neurolytic agent, trigeminal nerve (second and third division branches at foramen ovale under radiologic monitoring); a comprehensive code, includes the following component codes:

64605 69990

Mutually exclusive codes: None

CPT 64612 chemodenervation of muscle(s) (muscle(s) innervated by facial nerve); a comprehensive code, includes the following component codes:

64402

Mutually exclusive codes: None

CPT 64613 chemodenervation of muscle(s) (cervical spine muscle(s)); a comprehensive code, includes the following component codes:

69990

Mutually exclusive codes: None

CPT 64620 destruction by neurolytic agent (intercostal nerve); a comprehensive code, includes the following component codes:

64420 64421 69990

Mutually exclusive codes: None

CPT 64622 destruction by neurolytic agent, paravertebral facet joint nerve (lumbar or sacral, single level); a comprehensive code, includes the following component codes:

64475 69990 76000 76001 76003

Mutually exclusive codes: None

CPT 64626 destruction by neurolytic agent, paravertebral facet joint nerve (cervical or thoracic, single level); a comprehensive code, includes the following component codes:

64470 69990 76000 76001 76003

Mutually exclusive codes: None

CPT 64630 destruction by neurolytic agent, pudendal nerve; a comprehensive code, includes the following component codes:

64430 69990

Mutually exclusive codes: None

CPT 64640 destruction by neurolytic agent, other peripheral nerve or branch; a comprehensive code, includes the following component codes:

64405 64408 64410 64412 64413 64415

64417 64418 64425 64435 64445 64450
69990

Mutually exclusive codes: None

CPT 64680 destruction by neurolytic agent, celiac plexus, with or without radiologic monitoring; a comprehensive code, includes the following component codes:

64530 69990

Mutually exclusive codes: None

CPT 72275 epidurography, radiological supervision and interpretation; a comprehensive code, includes the following component codes:

76000 76001 76003 76005

Mutually exclusive codes: None

CPT 72285 diskography, cervical or thoracic, radiological supervision and interpretation; a comprehensive code, includes the following component codes:

76005

Mutually exclusive codes: None

CPT 72295 diskography, lumbar, radiological supervision and interpretation; a comprehensive code, includes the following component codes:

76005

Mutually exclusive codes: None

REFERENCES

1. Manchikanti L. The impact of National Correct Coding Policy on interventional pain management. *Pain Physician* 1999; 2:33-45.
2. *National Correct Coding Manual 2001*: Medical Management Institute, Alpharetta; 2001.
3. CCI edits require expertise in the face of voluminous outpatient, coding changes. *HCPCS Report* 2000; 14:1-5.
4. *Current Procedural Terminology. CPT 1999*, American Medical Association, Chicago, 1998.
5. *Current Procedural Terminology. CPT 2000*, American Medical Association, Chicago,1999.
6. Manchikanti L. Appropriate documentation, billing and coding in interventional pain practice. *Pain Physician* 2000; 3:218-236.
7. Manchikanti L. CPT 2000: Interventional pain management coding in the new millennium. *Pain Physician* 2000; 3:73-85.
8. Manchikanti L. Role of correct coding for interventional techniques. *Pain Physician* 2001; 4:381-399.
9. National Correct Coding Primer 7.2: United Communications Group Publications, Rockville, 2001.
10. National Correct Coding Primer 7.3: United Communications Group Publications, Rockville, 2001.
11. National Correct Coding Primer 8.0: United Communications Group Publications, Rockville, 2002.

DEFINITIONS OF INTERVENTIONAL PROCEDURES

Laxmaiah Manchikanti, MD

Current procedural terminology (CPT), Fourth Edition, is a listing of descriptive terms and identifying codes for reporting medical services and procedures. The purpose of CPT is to provide a uniform language that accurately describes medical, surgical, and diagnostic services, and thereby serves as an effective means for reliable nationwide communication among physicians, patients, and third parties. Since the first publication of CPT in 1966, numerous CPT codes have been developed and incorporated into practices of interventional pain management. Major changes occurred in the year 2000 with revamping of interventional pain management codes. However, many of the codes were developed in early years and their descriptive terms vignettes, rationale, etc, are not available.

This chapter reviews various clinical examples included in CPT text for available codes which are presented to give practical situations for which these codes are appropriately reported. However, it is important to note that these vignettes do not limit the use of a code, but only represent the typical patient and service/procedure. They do not describe the universe of patients for whom the service/procedure would be appropriate. Third-party payer reporting practices may differ.

In the year 2000, multiple new or revised codes involved injections into the spine, along with new codes for radiological supervision and interpretation of epidurography and sacroiliac joint arthrography. Further, additional codes were also provided in 2001 and 2002 for some interventional procedures. Even though this description will not cover the entire gambit of interventional pain procedures it will cover a significant number of procedures. All the information provided here is obtained from CPT 2000 Changes and CPT 2002 Changes, An insider's view copyrighted publications of American Medical Association. The description of the code, rationale and vignette are described. For a limited number of codes with available descriptions from CPT 2000, CPT 2002 changes and proposed 2003 changes. The CPT codes for 2003 are listed with a X in the code. Consequently permanent numbers will be assigned in the 2003 CPT publication, which will be released in 2002.

BASIC CONCEPTS OF REVISION

A comprehensive revision of the spinal injection section of the CPT nervous system section in 2000 reflected the systematic organization of series of codes to differentiate the specific spinal anatomy (subarachnoid, epidural), specific levels (cervical, thoracic, lumbar, sacral), and types of substances injected (neurolytic, opioid, anesthetic, steroid, antispasmodic).

The comprehensive revision to the spine injection procedures in year 2000 includes the addition of four new codes, the revision of five codes, and the deletion of nine codes to differentiate multiple issues as follows:

1. Time and complexity between a single injection and a continuous infusion (or multiple injections through the same catheter).
2. Differences between subarachnoid and epidural routes of administration.
3. Time and complexity related to injections performed at the cervical, thoracic, lumbar, or sacral levels of the spine (eg, significant difference in complexity and time related to a cervical/thoracic injection as compared to a lumbar/sacral injection.
4. Time and complexity related to injections of difference substances (eg, opioid, steroid, neurolytic)

Substantial revisions also have been performed in 2001 which will be effective for spinal endoscopy code in 2002 and for 1-day adhesiolysis code in 2002, along with various codes for brachial plexus, femoral and sciatic nerve blocks, along with continuous infusion. In addition, there have also been multiple codes for providing anesthesia for interventional procedures.

FLUOROSCOPIC GUIDANCE VS CONTRAST STUDY

CPT 2000 and 2002 also clarified the issue of unilateral and bilateral procedures. All the injection procedure codes are considered unilateral procedures. Therefore, all the spinal injection procedures are considered unilateral procedures. Hence, these codes are reported once per level, per side (right or left) regardless of the number or types of injections performed on the right or left side at a specific spinal level. If bilateral injections are performed at a specific spinal level, then appropriate modifier –50 should be used.

Fluoroscopic guidance may or may not be required to visualize and identify specific spinal anatomy in the performance of either epidural or subarachnoid injection procedures. Injection of contrast even though not specifically described in the descriptor nomenclature is included in the injection procedures described by codes 62280 – 62282. Code 76005 identifies the fluoroscopy guidance to assist in accurately localizing specific spinal anatomy for placement of a needle or catheter tip for the spine or paraspinous diagnostic or therapeutic injection procedures (epidural, transforaminal epidural, subarachnoid, paravertebral facet joint or paravertebral facet joint nerve) including neurolytic agent destruction. Codes 62310 – 62319, 64470 – 64484, and 64622 – 64627 refer to injection of "contrast" in the descriptor nomenclature. Fluoroscopic guidance is required to perform paravertebral facet joint nerve destruction by neurolytic agent or sacroiliac joint injections (64470-64476, 64479-64484, 64622-64627, 27096). CPT 2000 clarified the corresponding use of radiology codes, namely, the fluoroscopic guidance and localization code 76005, epidurography code 72275, sacroiliac joint arthrography code 73542, and discography supervision and interpretation codes 72240, 72255, 72265, and 72270. Code 76005 should be reported in conjunction with codes 27096, 62270 – 62273, 62280 – 62282, 62310 – 62319, 64470 – 64474, 64479 – 64484, and 64622 – 64627, when fluoroscopic guidance is required in the performance of these injection procedures. Additionally, fluoroscopy is not bundled in the determination of relative value units for these procedures.

A word of caution. Code 76005 does not represent a formal contrast study. Examples of a formal contrast study are supervision and interpretation of epidurography, sacroiliac joint arthrography, and discography. These are separate and distinct services with proper documentation of medical necessity and separate report. Thus, fluoroscopy is considered an inclusive component of codes:

72240 Myelography, cervical, radiological supervision and interpretation

72255 Myelography, thoracic, radiological supervision and interpretation

72265 Myelography, lumbosacral, radiological supervision and interpretation

72270 Myelography, entire spinal canal, radiological su pervision and interpretation

72275 Epidurography, radiological supervision and inter pretation

73542 Radiological examination, sacroiliac joint arthrog raphy, radiological supervision and interpretation

SACROILIAC JOINT INJECTION

- 27096 Injection procedure for sacroiliac joint, arthrography and/or anesthetic/steroid

For radiological supervision and interpretation, code 73542 must be used. However, if formal arthrography is not performed, for fluoroscopic guidance CPT 76005 may be used.

CPT 2002 clarified that code 27096 was added for CPT 2000 to describe the injection of contrast for radiologic evaluation associated with sacroiliac joint arthrography and/or therapeutic injection of anesthetic or steroid to block the joint for immediate and potentially lasting pain relief. Thus, Code 27096, as with arthrography, represents a unilateral procedure. If bilateral SI joint arthrography is performed, 27096 should be coded with modifier -50.

CPT 2002 also made a modification/clarification of CPT 27096. It stated that since fluoroscopy is crucial to identify the optimal site for access to the joint, CPT 27096 should only be reported when imaging confirmation of intraarticular needle positioning has been performed. When a formal sacroiliac joint arthrography is performed, Code 73542 should be reported for the radiologic supervision and interpretation. It is important to note that fluoroscopic guidance and localization are inclusive of Code 73542 for radiological supervision and interpretation of sacroiliac joint arthrography; and would not be reported with Code 76005.

However, for sacroiliac joint injection (27096), if a formal arthrography (73542) is not performed and recorded and a formal radiologic report is not issued, then it is appropriate to report Code 76005 for the fluoroscopy guidance used to locate the specific anatomic site for needle insertion.

Rationale

Code 27096 describes the injection of contrast for radiologic evaluation associated with sacroiliac (SI) joint arthrography and/or therapeutic injection of an anesthetic/steroid to block the joint for immediate and potentially lasting pain relief. As with all arthrography, this code applies to a unilateral injection. If bilateral SI joint arthrograms are performed, 27096 should be reported using the '-50' modifier. Fluoroscopy is crucial to identify the optimal site for access to the joint. Once the specific anatomy is identified, the needle tip is placed in the caudal aspect of the joint and contrast material is injected. Contrast fills the joint to delineate integrity (or lack thereof) of articular cartilage, as well as morphologic features of the joint space and capsule. Films are then obtained in at least two projections. In many cases, local anesthetic is injected into the joint. Occasionally, local anesthetic is mixed with water-soluble steroid and injected into the joint for potentially lasting pain relief.

A new cross-reference has been added directing users to code 73542 for the radiologic supervision and interpretation associated with sacroiliac joint arthrography. The cross-reference also directs users to code 76005 when arthrography is not performed and recorded, and a formal radiologic report is not issued. In these instances, code 76005 should be used for fluoroscopic guidance and localization for insertion of the needle for sacroiliac joint injection(s). Fluoroscopic guidance and localization are included in code 73542. Therefore, it would not be appropriate to report both codes 73542 and 76005 for sacroiliac joint arthrography.

Vignette

27096----A 42-year-old man with a history of prior lumbosacral fusion presents with severe chronic low back, buttock, and groin pain. Imaging studies of the spine, pelvis, and sacroiliac joints are unremarkable, showing a solid lumbosacral fusion. The patient undergoes the diagnostic and therapeutic sacroiliac arthrogram, both to study intrinsic joint anatomy and to assess, by means of monitoring the joint blockade, whether the joint is the major source of his clinical pain.

PERCUTANEOUS LYSIS OF EPIDURAL ADHESIONS

- 62263 Percutaneous lysis of epidural adhesions using solution injection (eg, hypertonic saline, enzyme) or mechanical means (eg, spring-wound catheter) including radiologic localization (includes contrast when administered)

Rationale

Code 62263 was introduced in 2000, to describe a relatively new procedure not previously described by CPT. Code 62263 describes a percutaneous epidural catheter-based treatment involving targeted injection of various substances (including hypertonic saline, steroid, anesthetic, and mechanical adhesiolysis) coupled with epidural injection of contrast to define areas of scarring around nerve roots and/or spinal nerves as well as to define swollen nerves that might indicate moderate to severe inflammation in the nerves per se.

The treatment goal is a concerted effort to break down scar formation (adhesions), reduce edema, reduce inflammation, and block propagation of nociception (pain transmission) to the central nervous system. Since this treatment technique also involves several different injection treatments occurring during a several-day period, you may note that code 62263 should be reported once even though several injection treatments are performed over 1 or more days. As stated in the descriptor nomenclature, injection of contrast material is considered inclusive of 62263.

Because of the toxic nature of the neurolytic agent, radiographic verification of placement of the needle or catheter tip and flow characteristics of the injected space is very important. Percutaneous lysis of epidural adhesions requires epidural contrast injection for analysis of the epidural space prior to injection of the neurolytic agent to determine and confirm the exact level for injection to affect the desired nerve, nerve root, or level of spinal cord. Therefore, code 72275 should be additionally reported to describe the work involved in the radiologic supervision and interpretation associated with epidurography.

Vignette

62263-----A 35-year-old man has severe pain (rated 8/10) located in the right lower back and radiating down the outside of the right leg to the top of the foot and the big toe after multiple back operations during a 10-year period. Various systematic medications (oral narcotic and non-narcotic) and physical therapy have failed to provide significant long-term relief.

- 6226X Percutaneous lysis of epidural adhesions using solution injection (eg hypertonic saline, enzyme) or mechanical means (eg catheter) including radiologic localization (includes contrast when administered), multiple adhesiolysis sessions; 1-day

Rationale

Code 6226 approved in 2001 to be effective January 1, 2003, is a modification of Code 62263 which describes percutaneous epidural catheter based treatment involving targeted injection of various substances (including hypertonic saline, steroid, anesthetic and mechanical adhesiolysis) coupled with epidural injection of contrast to define areas of scarring around the nerve roots and/or spinal nerves, as well as to define nerve root edema that might indicate moderate to severe inflammation in the nerves, per se. The procedure differs from 62263 as it is performed with multiple injections on a single day. The treatment goal is a concerted effort to break down adhesions, reduce edema, reduce inflammation, and block propagation of nociception to the central nervous system. Since this treatment technique also involves several different injection treatments occurring on 1-day, you may note that Code 6226X should be reported only once, even though multiple injection treatments are performed. As stated in the descriptor nomenclature, injection of contrast material is considered inclusive of 6226X. However, a formal study with epidurography is not considered an inclusive component of 6226X.

Vignette

6226X ----- A 45-year-old white male with intermittent severe intractable low back pain with radiation into the right lower extremity associated with numbness, tingling and weakness for over 12 years which started following a work related injury. Subsequently, he underwent various modalities of treatments, initially conservative management with medication, subsequently physical therapy followed by lumbar laminectomy followed by lumbar fusion with hardware with intermittent conservative management with physical therapy and continuous medication management, but continued pain problems with significant deterioration of his physical and functional status leading to disability. At this time, he is on significant amounts of narcotics, anxiolytics, as well as other drugs with interrelated depression, generalized anxiety disorder and significant functional limitations.

Following his presentation to a multidisciplinary pain management program, he was diagnosed to be negative for facet joint mediated pain. Subsequently, an epidurogram showed significant filling defects. His MRI also showed significant scar tissue on the right side occupying L5 and S1 nerve roots. He failed to respond significantly to transforaminal epidural steroid injections even though diagnosis was confirmed by blocking right L5 and S1 nerve roots and also failed to respond to high volume caudal epidural steroid injection. A one-day percutaneous lysis of adhesions is scheduled.

EPIDURAL BLOOD PATCH

- ♦ 62273 Injection, epidural, of blood or clot patch

Rationale

Code 62273 has been revised by deleting the specific reference to the lumbar region of the spine, because an ongoing cerebrospinal fluid leak can occur at any level of the spinal column. CSF leak, for example, may occur in post-lumbar puncture headache, cerebrospinal fluid hygroma, posttraumatic cerebrospinal fluid leakage, and actual cerebrospinal fluid leakage outside the skin. Therefore, this revision clarifies that the epidural injection of blood or blood clot is not limited to the lumbar region.

Vignette

62273 ----- A 39-year-old woman has recently undergone an intrathecal injection of some substance. Since the injection, the patient has experienced severe headaches that are worse upon sitting or standing. The headaches have not resolved after 1 week despite bedrest, oral hydration, and oral caffeine. There are no changes or fluid accumulation at the injection site.

NEUROLYTIC SUBARACHNOID INJECTIONS

- ♦ 62280 Injection/infusion of neurolytic substance (eg, alcohol, phenol, iced saline solutions), with or without other therapeutic substance; subarachnoid
- ♦ 6228 Injection/infusion of neurolytic substance (eg, alcohol, phenol, iced saline solutions), with or without other therapeutic substance; epidural, cervical or thoracic
- ♦ 62282 Injection/infusion of neurolytic substance (eg, alcohol, phenol, iced saline solutions), with or without other therapeutic substance; epidural, lumbar, sacral (epidural)

Rationale

Codes 62280-62282 describe neurolytic injections performed when ablation of a nerve, nerve root, or portion of the spinal cord is desired. This clinical indication often occurs because of intractable pain from malignancy, tumor radiation therapy effects, and/or surgical scarring. Neurolytic injections can also be performed where ablation of a primarily sensory nerve root, nerve, or a specific spinal cord dermatome level is desired without causing significant functional impairment to the patient (eg, elimination of motor function from the target site because of prior trauma).

Because the site of the pain could be at the cervical, thoracic, lumbar, or caudal vertebral level, codes 62280-62282 specify either the subarachnoid or epidural spaces of the spinal column; and codes 62281 and 62282 differentiate upper and lower spinal epidural regions. From a procedural standpoint, the same procedure is performed. The difference is that, after the needle is initially placed but before the neurolytic injection, contrast injection is performed to confirm needle position. Again, as with other neurolytic injections, it is important to determine and confirm the exact level and space for the injection to affect the desired nerve root.

Vignette

62280 ----- A 45-year-old man with extensive rectal carcinoma involving the left lumbosacral plexus has intractable left perirectal pain but has lost much of his control of both bladder and bowel function. Various systematic medications (oral narcotic and nonnarcotic), physical therapy, radiation therapy, and chemotherapy have all failed to provide significant long-term pain relief. There is no further operative resection possible for the tumor.

This patient is a good candidate for a neurolytic injection because of the severity of the pain and the diminished control of bladder and bowel function. A neurolytic injection to ablate the left S2-4 nerve roots is recommended.

62282 ----- A 45-year-old man with extensive rectal carcinoma involving the left lumbosacral plexus has intractable left perirectal pain but has last much of his control of both bladder and bowel function. Various systemic medications (oral narcotic and nonnarcotic), physical therapy, radiation therapy, and chemotherapy have all failed to provide significant long-term pain relief. There is no further operative resection possible for the tumor.

This patient is a good candidate for a neurolytic injection because of the severity of the pain and the diminished control of bladder and bowel function. A neurolytic injection to ablate the left S2-4 nerve roots is recommended.

PERCUTANEOUS DISC DECOMPRESSION OR DISCECTOMY

- 62287 Aspiration or decompression procedure, percutaneous, of nucleus pulposus of intervertebral disc, any method, single or multiple levels, lumbar (eg, manual or automated percutaneous discectomy, percutaneous laser discectomy).

For fluoroscopy guidance, CPT 2000 says 76003 may be used. However, correct coding initiative considers fluoroscopy codes from 76000-76005, component codes of 62287.

Rationale

Code 62287 was revised to describe percutaneous methods for decompressing a lumbar intervertebral disc by including examples for each method to clarify appropriate application of this code. Further clarification has been added indicate the use of code 62287 for percutaneous aspiration or decompression of an intervertebral disc using a laser. A cross-reference has been added to direct users to the fluoroscopic localization code 76003 (for fine needle biopsy or aspiration).

Codes 62288, 62289, and 62298 have been deleted to eliminate overlapping procedures, accommodate placement of new combinations of procedures and substances (eg, injection of local anesthetic and steroid), and designate types of administration, and specific spinal anatomy.

Vignette

62287 ----- A 25-year-old male athlete has had 5 weeks of low back pain with sciatica, an absent ankle reflex, and weakness of the posterior calf muscle. He has not responded to anti-inflammatory treatment and restricted activities. He has a history of a previous similar episode that cleared in 3 weeks. An MRI exam shows a diffuse bulging annulus and disc at L5-S1.

DISCOGRAPHY

- 62290 Injection procedure for discography, each level; lumbar
- 62291 Injection procedure for discography, each level; cervical or thoracic
  (For radiological supervision and interpretation codes 72285 or 72295 may be used)

Rationale

Code 62291 has been revised to include thoracic discography, a minimally invasive procedure used to evaluate and localize the etiology of back pain in order to plan therapy (surgical or nonsurgical) for patients with long-standing thoracic-level back pain. There are existing codes for cervical and lumbar discography; and similarly, thoracic discography involves insertion of a spinal needle into the disc using fluoroscopic guidance. Injection of contrast material and assessment of the patient's response provides information regarding the status of the disc.

Imaging of the patient after a contrast injection provides additional information regarding the morphology of the disc. Therefore, the radiologic supervision and interpretation code 72285 has also been revised to include the thoracic spinal region. Codes 72285 and 72295 include the fluoroscopic guidance, and thus 76005 should not be additionally reported.

Vignette

62291 ----- A 33-year-old man with known scoliosis has severe right-sided pain. Correlation is made with a previous MR imaging study of the thoracic spine. Preliminary AP and lateral radiograph scout views reveal 13 ribs with five subjacent lumbar segments. There is scoliosis of the upper thoracic spine to the left with a moderate rotational lower thoracic and upper lumbar curve to the right. There is moderate rotational midlumbar curvature to the left.

EPIDURAL INJECTIONS

- 62310 Injection, single (not via indwelling catheter), not including neurolytic substances, with or without contrast (for either localization or epidurography), of diagnostic or therapeutic substance(s) (including anesthetic, antispasmodic, opioid, steroid, other solution), epidural or subarachnoid; cervical or thoracic

- ♦ 62311 Injection, single (not via indwelling catheter), not including neurolytic substances, with or without contrast (for either localization or epidurography), of diagnostic or therapeutic substance(s) (including anesthetic, antispasmodic, opioid, steroid, other solution), epidural or subarachnoid; lumbar, sacral (caudal)
- ♦ 62318 Injection, including catheter placement, continuous infusion or intermittent bolus, not including neurolytic substances, with or without contrast (for either localization or epidurography), of diagnostic or therapeutic substance(s) (including anesthetic, antispasmodic, opioid, steroid, other solution), epidural or subarachnoid; cervical or thoracic
- ♦ 62319 Injection, including catheter placement, continuous infusion or intermittent bolus, not including neurolytic substances, with or without contrast (for either localization or epidurography), of diagnostic or therapeutic substance(s) (including anesthetic, antispasmodic, opioid, steroid, other solution), epidural or subarachnoid; lumbar, sacral (caudal)

Rationale

Codes 62310-62311 and 62318-62319 represent essentially a reordering of the previous subarachnoidal injection codes and the epidural narcotic injection codes as part of a larger, more logical format.

Code 62310 is a combination of deleted codes 62274, 62275, 62288, and 62298. Code 62274 described subarachnoid injection of opioids, antispasmodic, and anesthetic substances; 62275 described epidural injection of opioids, antispasmodic, and anesthetic substances; 62275 described epidural injection of opioids, antispasmodic, and anesthetic substances; 62288 described, in essence, those other nonneurolytic substances, primarily steroids or even opioids, depending upon the interpretation of its use.

Codes 62275 and 62298 have been combined to allay confusion in the reporting of these procedures, and to distinctly delineate that code 62310 should be reported to describe cervical or thoracic epidural or subarachnoid injection of substances other than neurolytics. Similar, but yet distinct, code 62311 is also a combination of deleted codes 62274, 62278, 62288, and 62289 for lumbar or caudal epidural or subarachnoid injection of nonneurolytic substances.

Code 62318 represents the cervical/thoracic counterpart to the lumbar continuous epidural infusion of nonneurolytic substances (code 62319) and deleted codes 62276 and 62279. Although it is uncommon to place a cervical or thoracic catheter for epidural opioid infusion, this procedure was not previously described by *CPT.* This technique involves greater risk related to possible damage to the spinal cord at the cervical or thoracic levels, and delayed respiratory side effects from a cervical/thoracic opioid infusion as compared to a similar infusion in the lumbar region.

For codes 62318 and 62319, use 01996 for subsequent daily management of epidural or subarachnoid catheter drug administration.

Vignettes

62310 ----- A 45-year-old man has severe pain (rated at 8/10) involving both arms and the neck after multiple neck operations during a 10-year period. Various systematic medications (oral narcotic and nonnarcotic) and physical therapy have failed to provide significant long-term pain relief.

62311 ----- A 45-year-old man has severe pain (rated at 8/10) involving both legs and the lower back after multiple back operations during a 10-year period. Various systematic medication (oral narcotic and non-narcotic) and physical therapy have failed to provide significant long-term pain relief.

62318 ----- A 45-year-old man has severe pain (rated at 8/10) involving both arms and the neck after multiple neck operations during a 10-year period. Various systematic medications (oral narcotic and nonnarcotic) and physical therapy have failed to provide significant long-term pain relief.

62319 ----- A 45-year-old man has severe pain (rated at 8/10) involving both legs and the lower back after multiple neck operations during a 10-year period. Various systematic medications (oral narcotic and nonnarcotic) and physical therapy have failed to provide significant long-term pain relief.

CATHETER IMPLANTATION

- ♦ 62350 Implantation, revision or repositioning of tunneled intrathecal or epidural catheter, for long-term pain management via an external pump or implantable reservoir/infusion pump; without laminectomy
- ♦ 62351 Implantation, revision or repositioning of tunneled intrathecal or epidural catheter, for long-term pain management via an external pump or implantable reservoir/infusion pump; with laminectomy

Rationale

The cross-reference following this subsection heading has been revised to reflect the new or renumbered spine injection codes.

Code 62350 has been revised to clarify its use when the intrathecal or epidural catheter is connected to either an external pump, an implantable reservoir, or an implantable infusion pump with catheter placement requiring (62351) or not requiring (62350) laminectomy.

Another cross-reference has been added directing users to code 96530 to describe the services for refilling and maintenance of an implantable reservoir or infusion pump. The refilling and maintenance of an external pump is not reportable by *CPT.*

Vignette

62350 ----- A 73-year-old man is referred for complaints of pain in the lumbar region and right lower extremity. The patient has a history of lung carcinoma which was first diagnosed 2 years ago. He underwent a left lung resection. One year later he was found to have a mass in the right chest or lung. X-ray therapy was performed as his severe COPD precluded further lung resection.

He was doing well until 2 months ago, when he developed pain in the lumbar region. Work-up at that time revealed metastasis at the L-5 vertebral body. Pain has persisted after radiation therapy. Oral narcotic medications resulted in constipation or severe CNS side effects. His oncologist has requested a trial of spinal narcotics and provides a 2-month life expectancy.

FACET JOINT INJECTIONS

- ♦ 64470 Injection, anesthetic agent and/or steroid, paravertebral facet joint or facet joint nerve; cervical or thoracic, single level
- ♦ 64472 Injection, anesthetic agent and/or steroid, paravertebral facet joint or facet joint nerve; cervical or thoracic, each additional level
  (Code 64472 is always used in conjunction with code 64470).
- ♦ 64475 Injection, anesthetic agent and/or steroid, paravertebral facet joint or facet joint nerve; lumbar or sacral, single level
- ♦ 64476 Injection, anesthetic agent and/or steroid, paravertebral facet joint or facet joint nerve; lumbar or sacral, each additional level
  (Code 64476 is always used in conjunction with code 64475).

Rationale

The 64400-64484 series of spine injection procedures has been updated to reflect current clinical practice. Descriptors now include spinal anatomy not previously identified, for example, the cervical and thoracic regions of the spine. The paravertebral facet joint or facet joint nerve codes are intended to clarify the spinal anatomy, the substances injected, and the spinal level(s) involved. Certain codes (64440-64443) have been deleted to allow sequential numbering of the new paravertebral facet injection codes 64470-64476.

Codes 64472 and 64476 represent add-on codes for each additional spinal level injected.

Codes 64470-64476 are considered *unilateral* procedures. When injections are performed at both the right *and* left paravertebral facet joints or paravertebral facet joint nerves, append the bilateral procedure modifier '-50' to the appropriate code.

Codes 64470-64472 were added to describe the procedural differences when a spinal needle is placed at the medial branch nerve of a cervical or thoracic facet joint, which is much smaller than a lumbar facet joint, resulting in a technically more difficult injection. The cervical and thoracic facets are located in closer proximity to more delicate neural and vascular structures, making it a higher-risk procedure than when performed at the lumbar facet joint(s).

The paravertebral facet joint or paravertebral facet joint nerve injections (64470-64476) are performed under fluoroscopic guidance for precise anatomic localization to avoid potential injury to the vertebral artery or damage to the spinal cord or surrounding nerve roots.

Code 76005 for fluoroscopic guidance and localization is not an included component of codes 64470-64476 and should be additionally reported.

Vignettes

64470 ----- A 67-year-old woman presents with a long history of cervical spine pain in her neck and radiating down to her shoulders. She has a no pain into her fingertips, has no weakness in her arms, and denies any bowel or bladder symptoms. She has failed to obtain relief by using various oral medications and physical therapy. A recent x-ray showed cervical spondylosis between C5-6.

64472 ----- A 67-year-old woman presents with a long history of cervical spine pain in her neck and radiating down to her shoulders. She has no pain into her fingertips, has no weakness in her arms, and denies any bowel or bladder symptoms. She has failed to obtain relief by using various oral medications and physical therapy. A recent x-ray showed cervical spondylosis between C5-6 and C6-7.

64475 ----- A 67-year-old female presents with a long history of neck pain that radiates down to her shoulders. She has no pain into her fingertips. She has no weakness in her arms. She denies any bowel or bladder symptoms. The patient had an x-ray that showed cervical spondylosis between C5-6 and C6-7 bilaterally.

The patient has undergone physical therapy and has had a trial of nonsteroidal anti-inflammatories, as well as opiate therapy. Despite all of these treatments, the patient has had no improvements. She then had an MRI, which showed facet arthropathy at C5-6 and C6-7 with small disc bulges at both levels. An electromyogram was negative. Because of failure of conservative care, diagnostic testing with cervical facet blocks at C5-6 and C6-7 levels bilaterally is indicated.

64476 ----- A 67-year-old woman presents with a long history of neck pain that radiates down to her shoulders. She has no pain into her fingertips. She has no weakness in her arms. She denies any bowel or bladder symptoms. The patient had an x-ray that showed cervical spondylosis between C5-6 and C6-7 bilaterally.

The patient has undergone physical therapy and has had a trial of nonsteroidal anti-inflammatories, as well as opiate therapy. Despite all of these treatments, the patient has had no improvements. She then had an MRI, which showed facet arthropathy at C5-6 and C6-7 with small disc bulges at both levels. An electromyogram was negative. Because of failure of conservative care, diagnostic testing with cervical facet blocks at C5-6 and C6-7 levels bilaterally indicated.

TRANSFORAMINAL EPIDURAL INJECTIONS

- ♦ 64479 Injection, anesthetic agent and/or steroid, transforaminal epidural; cervical or thoracic, single level
- ♦ 64480 Injection, anesthetic agent and/or steroid, transforaminal epidural; cervical or thoracic, each additional level
  (Code 64480 is always used in conjunction with code 64479).
- ♦ 64483 Injection, anesthetic agent and/or steroid, transforaminal epidural; lumbar or sacral, single level
- ♦ 64484 Injection, anesthetic agent and/or steroid, transforaminal epidural; lumbar or sacral, each additional level
  (Code 64484 is always used in conjunction with code 64483).

Rationale

Four new codes (64479-64484) have been added to describe a procedurally more difficult nerve root injection technique that requires entry into the epidural space through the nerve root foramen. Transforaminal epidural spinal injection technique is a technically different approach from translaminar injection (62310-62319). Because the vertebral artery as well as the spinal cord is in proximity to the nerve root, this procedural technique is more difficult than a translaminar injection. The code descriptors again identify the spinal anatomy, the substances injected, and the spinal level or levels involved. This technique was previously reported by either code 62284 or 62298.

Codes 64480 and 64484 represent add-on codes for each additional spinal level injected.

Codes 64479-64484 are considered *unilateral* procedures. When both a right and a left transforaminal epidural injection is performed, append the bilateral procedure modifier '-50' to the appropriate code.

Code 64479 describes both diagnostic and therapeutic nerve root injections that enter the epidural space through the *nerve root foramen*. This is important when treating patients with foraminal stenosis from a variety of disorders including foraminal spinal stenosis and disc herniations are treated.

Code 64480 represents the add-on code for each additional cervical or thoracic level injected by means of transforaminal epidural technique. Because certain spinal pathology occurs at multiple levels (eg, cervical spondylosis), it is necessary to separately inject multiple levels. Each level injected is reported separately. However, code 64480 is reported once regardless of the number of injections performed at a particular spinal level.

Code 64483 was added to separate lumbar or sacral transforaminal injections from the cervical or thoracic levels. This code represents nerve root injections performed, for example, for lumbar spinal stenosis, unilateral radicular pain, postoperative back and leg pain, and herniated discs in the far lateral or neuroforaminal position.

Code 64484 represents the add-on code for each additional lumbar or sacral level injected, using transforaminal epidural technique. There can be multiple levels of pathology, which may require more than one injection site for diagnostic and therapeutic reasons. Each level injected is reported separately. However, code 64484 is reported once regardless of the number of injections performed at a particular spinal level.

Transforaminal epidural spinal injections (64479-64484) are performed under fluoroscopic guidance for precise anatomic localization to avoid potential injury to the vertebral artery or damage to the spinal cord or surrounding nerve roots.

Code 76005 for fluoroscopic guidance and localization is not an included component of codes 64479-64484 and should be additionally reported.

Vignettes

64479 -----A 55-year-old man with coronary artery disease and moderate heart failure presents with constant moderately severe right arm pain that limits all activity. The patient's history includes a previous laminectomy at C5-6. An MRI with gadolinium shows a small bony spur at the right C5-6 foramen compressing the C-6 nerve root, and neurodiagnostic studies are compatible with an acute C-6 radiculopathy. He has failed to obtain relief with various oral medications, physical therapy, and traction.

64480 ----- A 55-year-old man with coronary artery disease and moderate heart failure presents with constant moderately severe right arm pain that limits all activity. The patient's history includes a previous laminectomy at C5-6 and C6-7. An MRI with gadolinium, shows small bony spurs at the right C5-6 and C6-7 foramen compressing the C-6 nerve root; and neurodiagnostic studies are compatible with an acute C-6 radiculopathy. He has failed to obtain relief with various oral medications, physical therapy, and traction.

64483 ----- A 71-year-old male with coronary artery disease and moderate heart failure presents with recurrent right leg pain, the ability to stand for only 10 minutes and walk less than one block, and minimal problems sitting. The patient's history includes a previous laminectomy at L4-5; an MRI with gadolinium, showing a small recurrent herniation between L4-5 with scar tissue; and neurodiagnostic studies compatible with an acute L-5 radiculopathy. He has failed to obtain relief with various oral medications, physical therapy, and traction.

64484 ----- A 71-year-old man with coronary artery disease and moderate heart failure presents with recurrent right leg pain, the ability to stand for only 10 minutes and walk less than one block, and minimal problems sitting. The patient's history includes previous laminectomy at L3-4 and L4-5; an MRI with gadolinium, showing a small recurrent herniation between L4-5 with scar tissue; and neurodiagnostic studies compatible with an acute L-4 and L-5 radiculopathy. He has failed to obtain relief with various oral medications, physical therapy, and traction.

FACET JOINT NEUROLYSIS

- 64622 Destruction by neurolytic agent, paravertebral facet joint nerve; lumbar or sacral, single level
- 64623 Destruction by neurolytic agent, paravertebral facet joint nerve; lumbar or sacral, each additional level
  (CPT 64623 should always be used with 64622).
- 64626 Destruction by neurolytic agent, paravertebral facet joint nerve; cervical or thoracic, single level.
- 64627 Destruction by neurolytic agent, paravertebral facet joint nerve; cervical or thoracic, each additional level
  (CPT 64627 should always be used with 64626).

Rationale

This series of neurolytic "destruction" techniques was revised (64622, 64623) and two new codes were established (64626, 64627) to delineate paravertebral facet joint nerve destruction by a neurolytic agent (eg, phenol injection, radiofrequency) at the cervical/thoracic, lumbar or sacral regions of the spine. Because the level of work performed in the cervical/thoracic levels is more intense, codes 64626 and 64627 were added to distinguish this work from the lumbar regions (64622, 64623).

Codes 64623 and 64627 are add-on codes delineating the neurolytic destruction technique performed at each additional single spinal level.

Codes 64622-64627 are considered *unilateral* procedures. When these procedures are performed on both the right and left sides, append the bilateral procedure modifier '-50' to the appropriate code.

Fluoroscopic guidance and localization are performed to assist in accurately localizing specific spinal anatomy for placement of a needle or catheter tip for spinal or paraspinous diagnostic or therapeutic injection procedures.

Code 76005 for fluoroscopic guidance and localization is not an included component of codes 64622-64627 and should be additionally reported.

Vignettes

64622 ----- A 65-year-old woman received a flexion-extension injury in an automobile accident. She was tread and on imaging studies was found to have minimal degenerative disc disease at C4-5 and C5-6 with no facet arthropathy. The patient has undergone 6 weeks of extensive physical therapy, nonsteroidal anti-inflammatory drugs, and trigger point injections with poor results. She then underwent two series of cervical medial branch blocks with 1% PF Xylocaine that gave her 2 hours of 100% relief of her neck pain. The pain then returned. Because of the success of two separate trials with medial branch blocks, the patient is an ideal candidate for radiofrequency rhizotomy of the C-4 and C-5 medial branch nerves. Because of problems only on the right side, this would be performed on the right at C-4 and C-5 medial branch nerves. Because of problems only on the right side, this would be performed on the right at C-4 and C-5. Physical therapy and medication therapy have failed. On two separate occasions medial branch blocks significantly decreased the pain for the duration of the anesthetic, confirming that simpler, less invasive treatments have been unsuccessfully tried and are not applicable for this patient.

64623 ----- A 65-year-old woman received a flexion-extension injury in an automobile accident. She was treated and on imaging studies was found to have minimal degenerative disc disease at C4-5 and C5-6 with no facet arthropathy. The patient has undergone 6 weeks of extensive physical therapy, nonsteroidal anti-inflammatory drugs, and trigger point injections with poor results. She then underwent two series of cervical medial branch blocks with 1% PF Xylocaine that gave her two hours of 100% relief of her neck pain. the pain then returned. Because of the success of two separate trials with medial branch blocks, the patient is an ideal candidate for radiofrequency rhizotomy of the C-4 and C-5 medial branch nerves. Because of problems only on the right side, this would be performed on the right at C-4 and C-5. Physical therapy and medication therapy have failed. On two separate occasions medial branch blocks significantly decreased the pain for the duration of the anesthetic, confirming that simpler, less invasive treatments have been unsuccessfully tried and are not applicable for this patient.

64626 ----- A 65-year-old woman with flexion-extension injury from an automobile accident presents with constant neck pain. The patient's history includes imaging studies that found minimal degenerative disc disease at C4-5 with no facet arthropathy and no relief with physical therapy, nonsteroidal anti-inflammatory drugs, or trigger point injection. Previously, two trials of cervical medial branch block gave her 2 hours of 100% relief of her neck pain. She undergoes radiofrequency rhizotomy of the right C-4 medial branch nerves.

64627 ----- A 65-year-old woman with flexion extension injury from an automobile accident presents with constant neck pain. The patient's history includes imaging studies that found minimal degenerative diseases at C4-5 and C5-6 with no facet arthropathy and no relief with physical therapy, nonsteroidal anti-inflammatory drugs, or trigger point injections. Previously two trials of cervical medial branch blocks gave her 2 hours of 100% relief of her neck pain. She undergoes radiofrequency rhizotomy of the right C-4 and C-5 medial branch nerves.

TRIGGER POINT INJECTIONS

- 20526 Injection, therapeutic (eg, local anesthetic, corticosteroid), carpal tunnel
- 20550 Injection; tendon sheath, ligament, ganglioncyst
- 20551 Injection; tendon origin/insertion
- 20552 Injection; single or multiple trigger point(s), one or two muscle group(s)
- 20553 Injection; single or multiple trigger point(s), three or more muscle group(s)

Rationale

Code 20526 has been established to describe the procedural technique required to perform a therapeutic injection into the carpal tunnel (an anatomic space).

Prior to CPT 2002, code 20550 described injection of various anatomic sites (ie, tendon sheath, ligament, ganglion, trigger point). To differentiate the techniques associated with multiple muscle group injections for trigger points, codes 20552 and 20553 were established since this procedure, and its protocol for injection varies from specialty to specialty. Code 20550 has been revised to describe only injections of a tendon sheath, ligament, or ganglion cyst.

Code 20551 was established to describe therapeutic injection of a tendon at its origin/insertion.

Vignettes

20526 ----- A 31-year old secretary with complaints of numbness involving the 3 radial digits of the right upper extremity. Physical examination reveals a positive Tinel's sign of the median nerve at the right wrist and decreased sensation of the radial 3 digits in a median nerve distribution. Electrodiagnostic studies reveal a median nerve sensory mononeuropathy at the right wrist consistent with the clinical findings and diagnosis for carpal tunnel syndrome. The patient has failed physical therapy and bracing, as well as job modification. She presents now for right carpal canal injection to be followed by physical therapy and post-injection splinting.

20550 ----- A 25-year old construction worker with complaints of right sided neck and posterior shoulder pain for past five weeks. Examination reveals a strained/inflamed acromioclavicular ligament. Progress has been slow in physical therapy. Patient now presents for injection.

20551 ----- A 41-year old right-handed librarian with complaints of pain at base of right radial wrist aggravated with stacking books. Examination reveals positive Finkelstein's test and tenderness over the abductor pollicis brevis and extensor pollicis longus tendons. She has failed conservative care including physical therapy. She presents today for local tendon injections.

20526 ----- A 60-year old female with a three-month history of pain in the left low back above the left posterior iliac crest with radiation of pain into the left buttock. Muscle relaxants, nonsteroidal anti-inflammatory drugs and physical therapy have been ineffective in relieving her pain. Physical examination reveals no evidence of neurological dysfunction, but does reveal a distinct trigger point in the multifidus muscle left of the L5 spinous process. She now presents for injection of the trigger point.

20553 ----- A 40-year old male presents with chronic left neck and right upper back pain resulting from cervical degenerative disc disease and myofascial pain syndrome. The patient has already completed a trial of physical therapy and nonsteroidal anti-inflammatory drug therapy without relief of his pain. Physical examination reveals no evidence of neurological dysfunction, but does reveal three distinct trigger points in the left multifidus muscle, the left trapezius muscle and the right levator scapular muscle. He presents for injection of the trigger points.

SCIATIC NERVE BLOCK

- 64445 Injection, anesthetic agent; sciatic nerve, single
- 6444X3 Injection, anesthetic agent, sciatic nerve, continuous infusion by catheter (including catheter placement) including daily management for anesthetic agent administration

The code was approved in 2001, which will be effective in January 1, 2003.

Vignettes

64445 ----- A 55-year old male sustains a tri-malleolar fracture of his left ankle while rock climbing. He undergoes surgical repair of his left ankle under general anesthesia. In order to provide post-operative pain control, a sciatic nerve block is performed at the end of surgery. This block will decrease post-op pain, allow earlier ambulation, and lessen the amount of post-op analgesic medication required.

6444X3 ----- A 30-year old male smashes his left foot in an automobile accident. He undergoes major reconstruction of his left foot and ankle under general anesthesia. In order to provide post-operative pain control, a continuous sciatic nerve block is performed at the end of surgery. This block will decrease post-op pain, allow earlier ambulation, and lessen the amount of post-op analgesic medication required.

BRACHIAL PLEXUS BLOCK

- 64415 Injection, anesthetic agent; brachial plexus, single
- 6441X Injection, anesthetic agent, brachial plexus, continuous infusion by catheter (including catheter placement) including daily management for anesthetic agent administration

The code was approved in 2001, which will be effective in January 1, 2003.

Vignettes

64415 ----- A 36-year old male suffered a crush injury of his thumb and forefinger on the right hand in an auto accident. He has developed marked immobility of these digits and symptoms of reflex sympathetic dystrophy (complex regional pain syndrome). He is to receive a series of axillary blocks to both treat the reflex sympathetic dystrophy and to allow analgesia for physical therapy to his hand.

6441X ----- A 36-year old male suffered traumatic amputation of his thumb and forefinger on the right hand in an auto accident. He has had these digits replanted under a general anesthetic and five hours of surgery. The digits are ischemic in appearance and cold with poor capillary filling despite a good surgical repair and anastomoses of the digital arteries. A continuous brachial plexus block using a catheter placed in the brachial plexus at the axilla and the infusion of local anesthetic is planned to provide relief and to provide vasodilatation of the arterial supply to the hand and digits in an effort to improve survival of the re-implanted digits.

FEMORAL NERVE INJECTION

- 6444X1 Injection, anesthetic agent; femoral nerve, single level
- 6444X2 Injection, anesthetic agent, femoral nerve, continuous infusion by catheter (including catheter placement) including daily management for anesthetic agent administration

These codes have been approved in 2001. They will be effective January 1, 2003.

Vignettes

6444X1 ----- A 30-year old male undergoes a right anterior cruciate ligament repair under general anesthesia. In order to provide post-operative pain control and increase mobility in his knee, a femoral nerve block is performed. This block will allow earlier discharge from the recovery room, decreased post-op pain and earlier ambulation.

6444X2 ----- A 65-year old male undergoes a right total knee replacement (CPT Code 27447) under general anesthesia. In order to provide post-operative pain control and increased mobility in his knee, a continuous femoral nerve block is performed. This block will allow earlier discharge from the recovery room, decreased post-op pain, earlier ambulation, improved range of motion of the knee and enhanced rehabilitation.

SPINAL ENDOSCOPY

- CPT 0027T endoscopic lysis of epidural adhesions with direct visualization using mechanical means (example: spinal endoscopic catheter system) or solution injection (example: normal saline) including radiologic localization and epidurography

This is a category III code, effective January 1, 2002.

Vignette

A 45-year-old white male with intermittent severe intractable low back pain with radiation into the right lower extremity associated with numbness, tingling and weakness for over 12 years which started following a work related injury. Subsequently, he underwent various modalities of treatments, initially conservative management with medication, subse quently physical therapy followed by lumbar laminectomy followed by lumbar fusion with hardware with intermittent conservative management with physical therapy and continuous medication management, but continued pain problems with significant deterioration of his physical and functional status leading to disability. At this time, he is on significant amounts of narcotics, anxiolytics, as well as other drugs with interrelated depression, generalized anxiety disorder and significant functional limitations.

Following his presentation to a multidisciplinary pain management program, he was diagnosed to be negative for facet joint mediated pain. Subsequently, an epidurogram showed significant filling defects. His MRI also showed significant scar tissue on the right side occupying L5 and S1 nerve roots. He failed to respond significantly to transforaminal epidural steroid injections even though diagnosis was confirmed by blocking right L5 and S1 nerve roots and also failed to respond to high volume caudal epidural steroid injection, as well as percutaneous lysis of adhesions utilizing a catheter.

FLUOROSCOPIC GUIDANCE

- 76005 Fluoroscopic guidance and localization of needle or catheter tip for spine or paraspinous diagnostic or therapeutic injection procedures (epidural, transforaminal epidural, subarachnoid, paravertebral facet joint, paravertebral facet joint nerve or sacroiliac joint), including neurolytic agent destruction

Rationale

Code 76005 identifies the fluoroscopic "guidance" to assist in accurately localizing specific spinal anatomy for placement of a needle or catheter tip for spine or paraspinous diagnostic or therapeutic injection procedures (epidural, transforaminal epidural, subarachnoid, paravertebral facet joint, paravertebral facet joint nerve, or sacroiliac joint) including neurolytic agent destruction.

Code 76005 should be reported in conjunction with codes 62270-62273, 62280-62282, and 62310-62319, when fluoroscopic guidance is required in the performance of these injection procedures. Since fluoroscopic guidance is required to perform paravertebral facet joint and facet joint nerve injections, paravertebral facet joint nerve destruction by neurolytic agent, transforaminal epidural and sacroiliac joint injections, code 76005 should be additionally reported in conjunction with codes 27096, 64470-64476, 64479-64484, and 64622-64627.

Code 76005 does not represent a formal contrast study. Examples of a formal contrast study are myelography, epidurography, and sacroiliac joint arthrography. These codes include the use of fluoroscopy. Therefore, code 76005 is considered an included component of codes 72240, 72255, 72265, 72270, 72275, and 73542.

Vignette

76005 ----- A 45-year-old man has severe pain (rated at 8 on a scale of 0-10, where 10 is the worst pain imaginable) involving both legs and the lower back after multiple back operations during a 10-year period. Various systemic medications (oral narcotic and nonnarcotic) and physical therapy have all failed to provide significant long-term pain relief. There are no further operations on his spine that are felt likely to provide further relief.

EPIDUROGRAPHY

- 72275 Epidurography, radiological supervision and interpretation

Rationale

As part of the comprehensive revisions to the spinal injection section of *CPT 2000*, new code 72275 was added to describe the work involved in the radiologic supervision and interpretation services associated with epidurography. Epidurography includes a diagnostic imaging evaluation following an injection of contrast material into the epidural space under direct fluoroscopic visualization. This allows for evaluation of the epidural space under direct fluoroscopic visualization. This allows for evaluation of the epidural space around the target nerve roots or spinal nerves. Visualization of the free flow (of lack thereof) of contrast material in the epidural space assists in identifying focal scarring, areas of moderate to severe narrowing in the diameter of the nerve/ nerve root, moderate to severe swelling of other parts of the nerve/nerve root, and the shape and size of the target nerves. Based on the epidurographic findings, potential treatment options can be evaluated.

Code 72275 differs from code 76005 in that it represents a formal recorded and reported contrast study that includes fluoroscopy. Code 72275 includes the use of fluoroscopy. Therefore, it is not appropriate to report code 76005 in addition to code 72275. Other examples of formal contrast studies are myelography and/or arthrography. Neither code 72275 nor 76005 includes injection of contrast material or other substances, which are coded separately.

Vignette

72275 ----- A 45-year-old man with extensive rectal carcinoma involving the left lumbosacral plexus has intractable left perirectal pain but has lost much of his control of both bladder and bowel function. Various systemic medications (oral narcotic and nonnarcotic), physical therapy, radiation therapy, and chemotherapy have all failed to provide significant long-term pain relief. There is no further operative resection possible for the tumor. This patient is a good candidate for a neurolytic injection because of the severity of the pain and the diminished control of bladder and bowel function. A neurolytic injection to ablate the left S2-4 nerve roots is recommended.

IMAGING OF DISCOGRAPHY

- 72285 Discography, cervical or thoracic, radiological supervision and interpretation

Rationale

Reference to the thoracic spine has been added to code 72285 to expand its use to include thoracic discography procedures. It is appropriate to report the radiologic supervision and interpretation codes for cervical or thoracic (72285) and lumbar (72295-59) discography for each region evaluated.

Vignette

72285 ----- A 33-year-old man with known scoliosis has severe right-sided pain. Correlation is made with a previous MR imaging study of the thoracic spine. Preliminary AP and lateral radiograph scout views reveal 13 ribs with 5 subjacent lumbar segments. There is scoliosis of the upper thoracic spine to the left with a moderate rotational lower thoracic and upper lumbar curve to the right. There is moderate rotational midlumbar curvature to the left.

IMAGING OF SACROILIAC JOINT

- 73542 Radiological examination, sacroiliac joint arthrography, radiological supervision and interpretation.

Rationale

Code 73542 describes the radiologic supervision and interpretation of sacroiliac joint arthrography. Fluoroscopy is crucial to identify the optimal site for access to the joint. Code 73542 does not include injection of contrast material for formal arthrography. Therefore, code 27096 for sacroiliac (SI) joint injection should be additionally reported.

A new cross-reference has been added to direct users to a new code 27096 for the injection procedure. The cross-reference also directs users to code 76005 when an arthrography is not performed and recorded, and a formal radiologic report is not issued. In these instances, code 76005 should be used for fluoroscopic guidance and localization for insertion of the needle for sacroiliac joint injection. Fluoroscopic guidance and localization are included in code 73542. Therefore, it would not be appropriate to report both codes 73542 and 76005 for sacroiliac joint arthrography. Code 73542 applies to a unilateral SI joint arthrogram. If bilateral arthrograms are performed, 73542 should be ported with the '-50' modifier.

Vignette

73542 ----- A 42-year-old man with history of lumbosacral fusion presents with severe chronic low back, buttock, and groin pain. Imaging studies of the spine, pelvis, and sacroiliac joints are unremarkable, showing a solid lumbosacral fusion. The patient undergoes diagnostic and therapeutic sacroiliac arthrography, both to study intrinsic joint anatomy and to assess, by means of monitoring the joint blockade, whether the joint is the major source of his clinical pain.

ANESTHESIA FOR INTERVENTIONAL PROCEDURES

- 01905 Anesthesia for myelography, discography, vertebroplasty
- 019X1 Anesthesia (general) for diagnostic or therapeutic nerve blocks and injections (when block or injection is performed by a different provider); other than the prone position
- 019X2 Anesthesia (general) for diagnostic or therapeutic nerve blocks and injections (when block or injection is performed by a different provider); prone position
- 0064X Anesthesia for manipulation of the spine or for closed procedures on the cervical, thoracic or lumbar spine

The codes 019X1, 019X2 and 0064X were approved in 2001, which will be effective in January 1, 2003.

Rationale

Code 01905 also describes the anesthesia services associated with the percutaneous vertebroplasty procedures 22520-22522. Vertebroplasty codes were added for CPT 2001 and describe percutaneous, minimally invasive, radiologically guided vertebral augmentation to repair vertebral fractures commonly associated with osteoporosis.

Vignettes

019X1 ----- A 47-year old woman presents to the pain clinic with chronic pain in the left buttock and leg. She has had three previous lumbar spine procedures including microdiscectomy, decompressive lumbar laminectomy and posterior lumbar interbody arthrodesis and pedicle screw fixation. Her buttock and leg pain persisted and she failed a dorsal column stimulator trial. She also suffers from an anxiety disorder. The pain physician determines that the patient has neuropathic pain and a trial of epidural opioids and/or alpha-2 agonists via indwelling lumbar epidural catheter (CPT 62319) is indicated. If successful, the physician will recommend implantation of a subarachnoid drug delivery system. The patient had a very unpleasant experience with the dorsal column stimulator and insists upon general anesthesia for the epidural catheter placement. General anesthesia in the lateral position is planned.

019X2 ----- A 47-year old woman presents to the pain clinic with chronic pain in the left buttock and leg. She has had three previous lumbar spine procedures including microdiscectomy, decompressive lumbar laminectomy and posterior lumbar interbody arthrodesis and pedicle screw fixation. Her buttock and leg pain persisted and she failed a dorsal column stimulator trial. She also suffers from an anxiety disorder. The pain physician determines that the patient has neuropathic pain and a trial of epidural opioids and/or alpha-2 agonists via indwelling lumbar epidural catheter (CPT 62319) is indicated. If successful, the physician will recommend implantation of a subarachnoid drug delivery system. The patient had a very unpleasant experience with the dorsal column stimulator and insists upon general anesthesia for the epidural catheter placement. General anesthesia in the prone position is planned.

0064X ----- The typical patient is a middle-aged, moderately obese male with lumbar back pain secondary to a workplace injury. The patient has been treated by multiple practitioners, including a chiropractor, whose office manipulations of the lumbar spine have failed to relieve the pain syndrome. The patient is unable to work, his activities are restricted and he resists further office therapy because of the pain involved. He is receiving multiple medications, including an oral opioid and an antihypertensive, with only moderate pain relief. He is scheduled for manipulation of his lumbar spine under general anesthesia. He does not have any medical allergies and does not smoke.

CONCLUSION

Multiple interventional pain procedures vary in their descriptions, rationale and vignettes. These are available only for some procedures, which either have been modified recently or revised recently. However, for the old procedures, which have been archived, the rationales and vignettes are not available. This chapter is designed to serve as a reference guide to understanding the changes contained in the *Current Procedural Terminology* of CPT 2000 and CPT 2002, along with proposed codes. However, it is not intended to replace the CPT book. Even though these descriptors have been provided along with rationale and vignettes where available, insurers may interpret them differently.

INTERVENTIONAL PAIN MANAGEMENT PRACTICE POLICIES

Laxmaiah Manchikanti, MD
Vijay Singh, MD
David Kloth, MD

Interventional pain management practice policies are statements developed to assist physician and patient decisions about appropriate health care related to chronic pain. These policies are professionally derived recommendations for practices in the diagnosis and treatment of chronic or persistent pain. They were developed utilizing a combination of evidence- and consensus-based techniques to increase patient access to treatment, improve outcomes and appropriateness of care, and optimize cost effectiveness. These policies include a discussion and the pathophysiologic basis for intervention.

These practice policies do not constitute inflexible treatment recommendations. It is recommended that a provider establish a plan of care on a case-by-case basis, taking into account an individual patient's medical condition, and the physician's experience. Based on an individual patient's needs, treatment different from that outlined here may be warranted.

PURPOSES

The purposes of these policies are to:

1. Improve quality of care,
2. Improve patient access,
3. Improve patient outcomes,
4. Improve appropriateness of care,
5. Improve efficiency and effectiveness, and
6. Achieve cost containment by improving the cost-benefit ratio.

The most compelling single reason for the development of these practice policies is to improve the quality of care and life for patients suffering from painful disorders. Available evidence documents a wide degree of variance in the practice of interventional pain management and pain medicine for even the most commonly performed procedures and treated condition(s). These policies also address the issue of systematic evaluation and ongoing care of chronic or persistent pain and provide information about the scientific basis of the procedures, thus potentially increasing compliance; dispelling misconceptions among providers and patients; managing patient expectations reasonably; and forming the basis of a therapeutic partnership among the patient, the provider, and the payer.

SCOPE OF THE PROBLEM OF CHRONIC PAIN

In spite of the best efforts of the public, providers and the government, pain continues to be a problem of epidemic proportions. In addition, inadequate treatment of pain also continues to be a public health problem that is also reaching epidemic proportions in the United States and around the world. The knowledge and understanding of this complex entity, including diagnosis and treatment, are in their infancy, in spite of modern developments in medicine. Providers, patients, and the government all understand the devastating nature of chronic pain which destroys the quality of life by eroding the will to live, disturbing sleep and appetite, creating fatigue, and impairing recovery from illness or injury. In elderly patients it may make the difference between life and death by resulting in vocational, social, and family discord.

Among the chronic pain problems, spinal pain, which includes pain emanating from cervical, thoracic and lumbosacral regions, constitutes the majority of the problems. It is estimated that episodes of low back pain that are frequent or persistent have been reported in 15% of the US population, with a lifetime prevalence of 65% to 80%. The prevalence of neck pain, though not as common as that of low back pain, is estimated at 35% to 40%, of which 30% of patients will develop chronic symptoms. In contrast, the epidemiological data in relation to thoracic pain support the view that the thoracic spine is less commonly involved. The prevalence of spinal pain has been estimated in the general population at 66%, with only 15% of those reporting thoracic pain; in comparison to 56% to 44% for the lumbar and cervical regions, respectively. The study of the prevalence of chronic low back pain and its impact on general health in the Canadian population showed an 84% lifetime prevalence, with 47% of the patients reporting grade I pain (low pain intensity and low disability), 12% grade II pain (high pain intensity and low disability), 13% grade III (high pain intensity/moderate disability) and grade IV (high pain intensity/severe disability). They also reported that grade I low back pain was more common in the younger population, while older age groups reported higher incidence of grade III/IV pain. Thus, a total 13% of the population suffers with high pain intensity with moderate or severe disability, whereas an additional 12% suffer with high pain intensity but with low disability. A similar study evaluating neck pain and its related disability reported that, overall, 39% of the sample experienced grade I neck pain; whereas 9% experienced grade II neck pain, and 5% had grade III and IV neck pain. Almost 16% of the respondents reported having previously injured the neck in a motor vehicle collision.

Duration of back pain and its chronicity have been a topic of controversy. It is believed that most of these episodes will be short-lived, with 80% to 90% of attacks resolving in about 6 weeks irrespective of the administration or type of treatment; and 5% to 10% of patients developing persistent back pain. However, this concept has been questioned, as the condition tends to relapse, so most patients will experience multiple episodes. Prevalence of low back pain has ranged from 35% to 79% at 3 months and 35% to 75% at 12 months in recent studies. The studies evaluating the chronicity of low back pain estimated the average of age-related prevalence of persistent low back pain as 12% in children and adolescents, 15% in adults, and 27% in the elderly.

EVALUATION

Appropriate history, physical examination, and medical decision making comprise the initial evaluation of a patient's presenting symptoms. A patient's evaluation should not only meet all the required medical criteria but also meet the regulatory requirements. The guidelines of the Centers for Medicare and Medicaid, formerly the Health Care Financing Administration provide various criteria for five levels of services. The three crucial components of evaluation and management services are: history, physical examination, and medical decision making. Other components include: counseling, coordination of care, nature of presenting problem, and time.

HISTORY

The history includes:

- Chief complaint;
- History of present illness;
- Review of systems; and
- Past, family, and/or social history.

Chief Complaint

The chief complaint is a concise statement describing the symptom, problem, condition, diagnosis, or other factor that is the reason for the encounter, usually stated in the patient's words.

History of Present Illness

The history of present illness is a chronological description of the development of the patient's present illness from the first sign and/or symptom. It includes the following elements:

- Location,
- Quality,
- Severity,
- Duration,
- Timing,
- Context,
- Modifying factors, and
- Associated signs and symptoms.

Review of Systems

The review of systems is an inventory of body systems obtained through a series of questions seeking to identify signs and/or symptoms that the patient may be experiencing or has experienced.

Past, Family, and/or Social History

The past, family, and/or social history consists of a review of the past history of the patient including past experiences, illnesses, operations, injuries, and treatment; family history, including a review of medical events in the patient's family, hereditary diseases, and other factors; and social history appropriate for age reflecting past and current activities.

Past history in interventional pain medicine includes history of past pain problems and motor vehicle, occupational, or nonoccupational injuries; history of headache, neck pain, upper-extremity pain, pain in the upper or mid back or chest wall, pain in the lower back or lower extremities, and pain in joints; and disorders such as arthritis, fibromyalgia, or systemic lupus erythematosus.

Family history includes history of pain problems in the

family, degenerative disorders, familial disorders, drug dependency, alcoholism, or drug abuse; and psychological disorders such as depression, anxiety, schizophrenia, and suicidal tendencies, etc. Family history of medical problems is also important.

Social history includes environmental information, education, marital status, children, habits, hobbies, and occupational history, whenever available.

Physical Examination

Physical examination in interventional pain medicine involves general, musculoskeletal, and neurological examination.

Examination of other systems, specifically cardiovascular, lymphatic, skin, eyes, and cranial nerves is recommended, based on the presenting symptomatology.

Medical Decision Making

Medical decision making refers to the complexity of establishing a diagnosis and/or selecting a management option as measured by three components, including;

1. Diagnosis/management options with a number of possible diagnoses and/or the number of management options;
2. Review of records/investigations, with number and/or complexity of medical records, diagnostic tests, and other information that must be obtained, reviewed, and analyzed; and
3. Risk(s) of significant complications, morbidity and mortality, as well as comorbidities associated with the patient's presenting problem(s), the diagnostic procedure(s), and/or the possible management options.

Psychological evaluation, laboratory evaluation, imaging techniques, electromyography and nerve conduction and somatosensory evoked potentials are also an extension of the evaluation process. It is beyond the scope of these guidelines to discuss these techniques of assessment.

Appropriate history and physical examination with the assistance of other evaluations should direct a physician to formulate a provisional diagnosis. A suggested algorithm for comprehensive evaluation and management of chronic pain is illustrated in Fig. 1.

In summary, the following criteria should be considered carefully in performing interventional techniques:

1. Complete initial evaluation, including history and physical examination;
2. Physiological and functional assessment, as necessary and feasible;
3. Definition of indications and medical necessity, as follows:
   - Suspected organic problem;
   - Nonresponsiveness to less invasive modalities of treatment except in acute situations such as acute disc herniation, herpes zoster and postherpetic neuralgia, reflex sympathetic dystrophy, and intractable pain secondary to carcinoma;
   - Pain and disability of moderate-to-severe degree;
   - No evidence of contraindications such as severe spinal stenosis resulting in intraspinal obstruction, infection, or predominantly psychogenic pain;
   - Responsiveness to prior interventions with improvement in physical and functional status for repeat blocks or other interventions;
   - Repeating interventions only upon return of pain and deterioration in functional status.

INTERVENTIONAL TECHNIQUES

The overall benefit of various types of injection techniques includes pain relief outlasting by days, weeks, or months the relatively short duration of pharmacologic action of the local anesthetics and other agents used. Clear-cut explanations for these benefits are not currently available. It is believed that neural blockade alters or interrupts nociceptive input, reflex mechanisms of the afferent limb, self-sustaining activity of the neuron pools and neuraxis, and the pattern of central neuronal activities. The explanations are based in part on the pharmacological and physical actions of local anesthetics, corticosteroids, and other agents. It is also believed that local anesthetics interrupt the pain-spasm cycle and reverberating nociceptor transmission, whereas corticosteroids reduce inflammation either by inhibiting the synthesis or release of a number of pro-inflammatory substances. Various modes of action of corticosteroids include membrane stabilization; inhibition of neural peptide synthesis or action; blockade of phospholipase A_2 activity; prolonged suppression of ongoing neuronal discharge; suppression of sensitization of dorsal horn neurons; and reversible local anesthetic effect. In addition, local anesthetics have been shown to produce prolonged dampening of C-fiber activity. Physical effects include clearing adhesions or inflammatory exudates from the vicinity of the nerve root sleeve. The scientific basis of some of these concepts, at least in part, is proven for spinal pain management with epidural injections of betamethasone, and intravenous (IV) methylprednisolone.

DIAGNOSTIC INTERVENTIONAL TECHNIQUES

Diagnostic blockade of a structure with a nerve supply which can generate pain can be performed to test the hypothesis that the target structure is a source of the patient's pain. Testing the hypothesis by provoking pain in any structure is an unreliable criterion except in provocative discography. Although neurodiagnostics of the involved nerve pathways have proven valuable, the relief of pain is the essential criterion in almost all structures, including analgesic discography in the cervical spine, the only deviation being lumbar discs. If the pain is not relieved, the source may be in another structural component of the spine similar to the one tested such as a different facet joint or a different nerve root or some other structure. Thus, precision diagnostic injections directed towards specific spinal pathology are potentially powerful tools for diagnosis of chronic spinal pain, but often technically challenging. Identifying the specific pathology responsible for pain is often difficult, leading to frustrated patients and clinicians. Nevertheless, these injections may be safely performed by properly trained anesthesiologists, physiatrists, neurologists, radiologists, spine surgeons and physicians from other related specialties who take the time to learn the basis for and perfect the application of these techniques.

When the source of pain is more than one structure or multiple levels, it is not expected that all the pain will be relieved. For example, there may be painful facet joints bilaterally at a given segmental level, in which case anesthetizing the left joint should relieve the left side, but not the right side; there may be pain from two consecutive joints on one side, in which case anesthetizing the lower joint alone may relieve only the lower half of the pain; or there may be more than one structure involved, such as pain contributed by discs and facet joints or facet joints and nerves.

True positive responses are secured by performing controlled blocks. Ideally, this should be in the form of placebo injections of normal saline; but logistical and/or ethical considerations prohibit the use of normal saline in conventional practice.

Rationale

The rationale for diagnostic neural blockade in the management of spinal pain stems from the fact that clinical features and imaging or neurophysiologic studies do not permit the accurate diagnosis of the causation of spinal pain in the majority of patients in the absence of disc herniation and neurological deficit. Further rationale is based on the recurring facts showing the overall rate of inaccurate or incomplete diagnosis in patients referred to pain treatment centers as ranging from 40% to 67%, the incidence of psychogenic pain

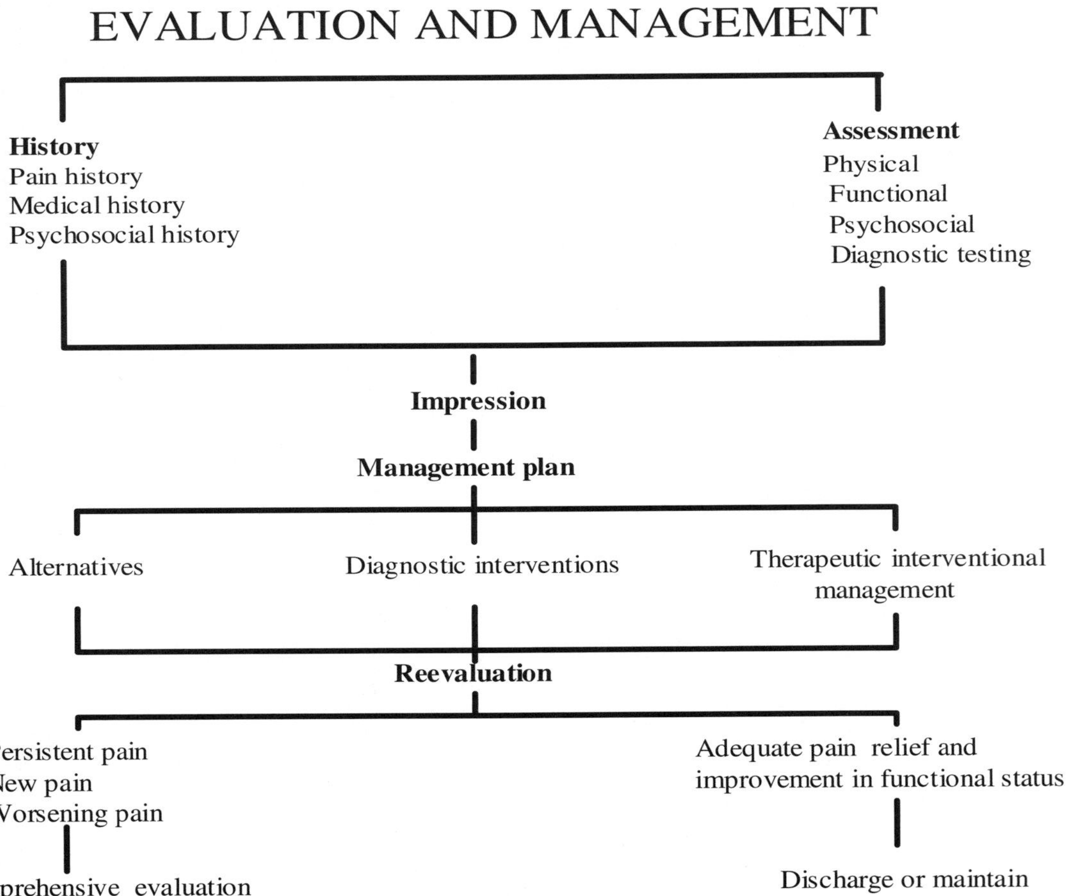

Fig 1. *Suggested algorithm for comprehensive evaluation and management of chronic pain*

to be only 1 in 3,000 patients, and the presence of organic origin of the pain mistakenly branded as psychosomatic in 98% of cases. Finally, chronic low back pain is a diagnostic dilemma in 85% of patients, even in experienced hands with all the available technology. It has been determined that utilizing alternative means of diagnosis including precision diagnostic blocks in cases where there is a lack of definitive diagnostic radiologic or electrophysiologic criteria can enable an examiner to identify the source of pain in the majority of patients, thus reducing the proportion of patients who cannot be given a definite diagnosis from 85% to 30% or even as low as 15%.

Fig 2A. *A suggested algorithm for application of interventional techniques in conservative care of radicular pain*

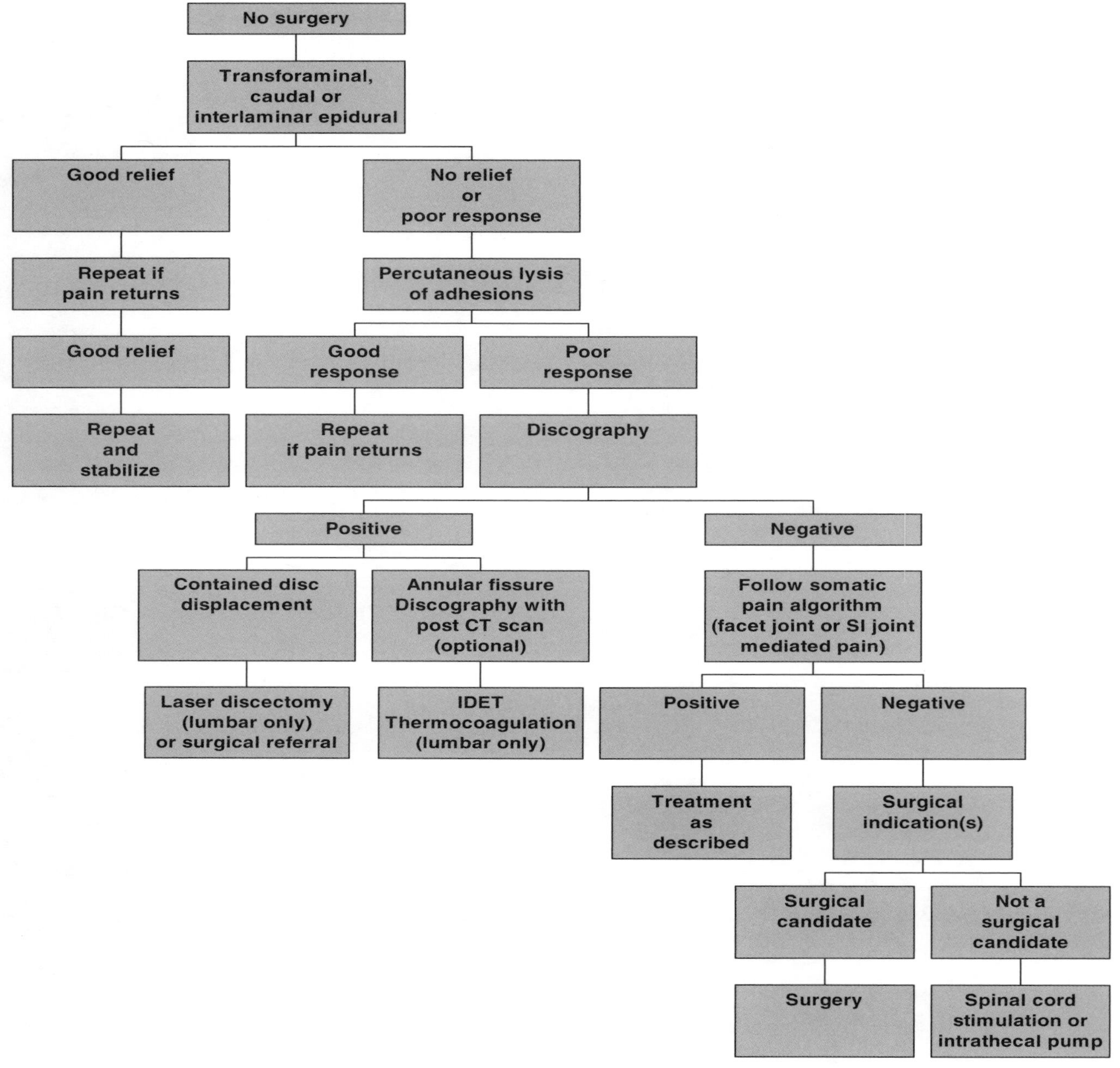

Fig 2B. *A suggested algorithm for application of interventional techniques in conservative care of radicular pain*

Algorithm for Somatic Pain I

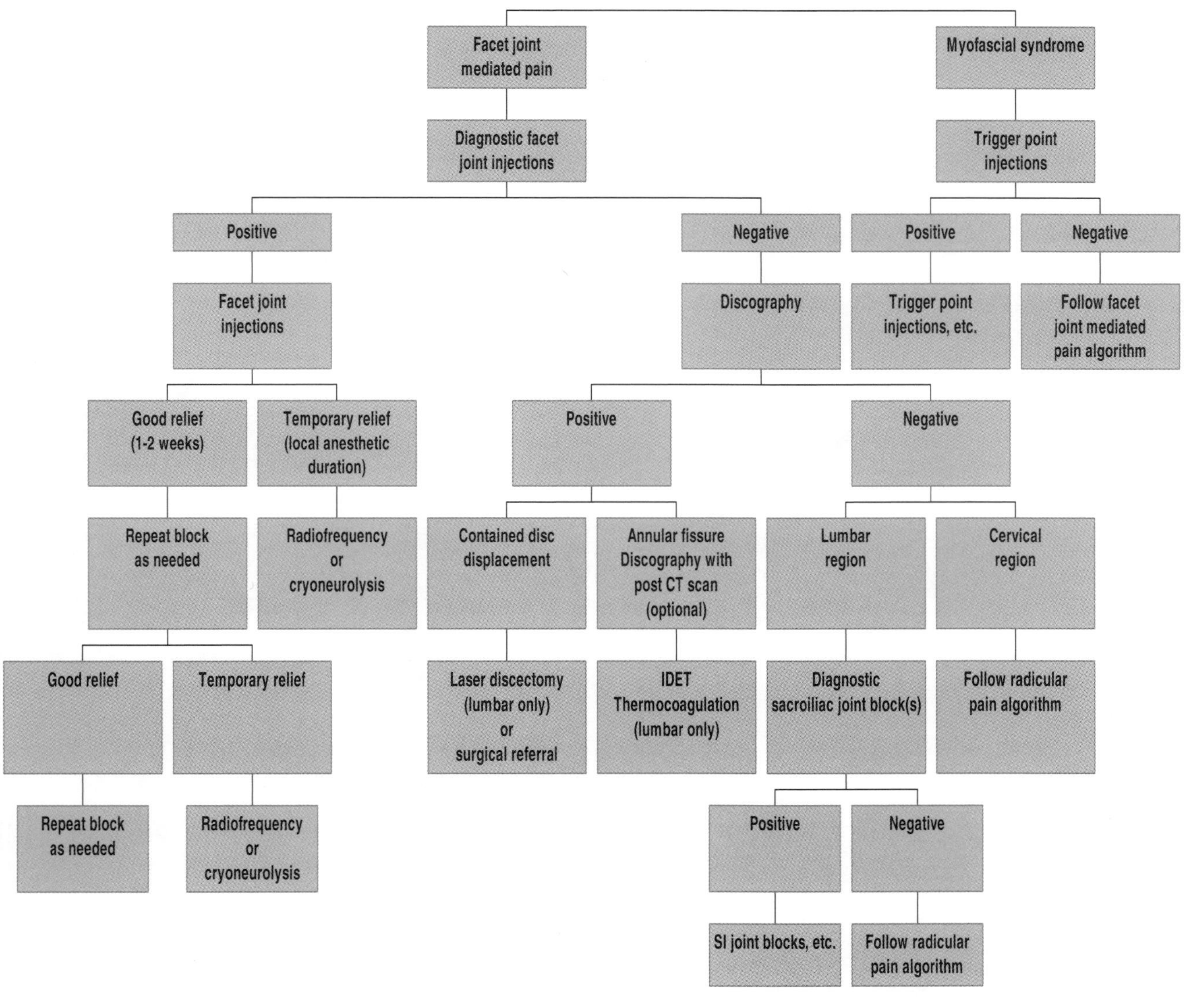

Fig 3A. *A suggested algorithm for application of interventional techniques in conservative care of chronic spinal pain: a patient with somatic pain*

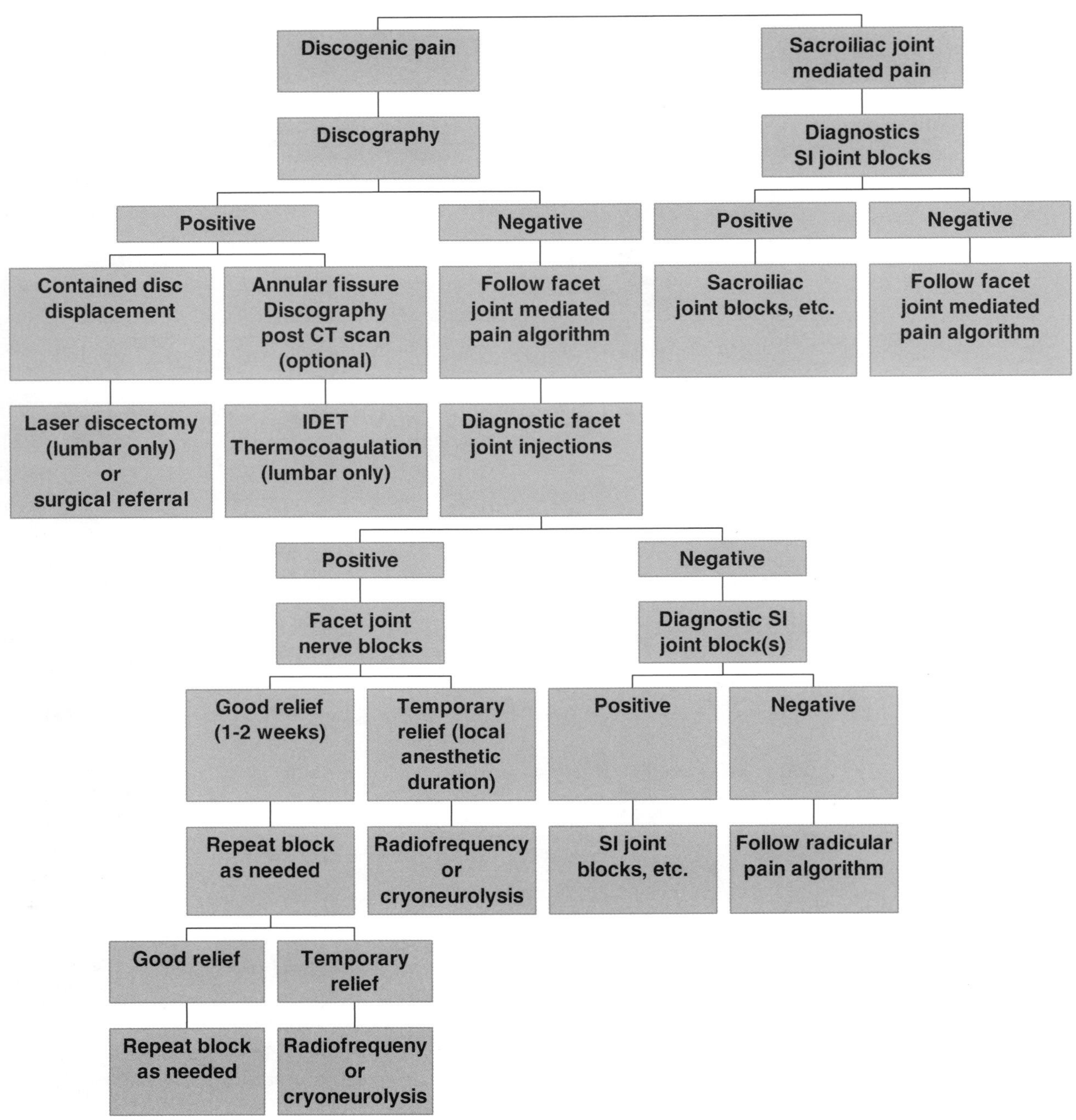

Fig 3B. *A suggested algorithm for application of interventional techniques in conservative care of chronic spinal pain: a patient with somatic pain*

THERAPEUTIC INTERVENTIONAL TECHNIQUES

Rationale

The rationale for therapeutic interventional techniques in the spine is based upon several considerations: the cardinal source of chronic spinal pain, namely discs and joints, is accessible to neural blockade; removal or correction of structural abnormalities of the spine may fail to cure and may even worsen painful conditions; degenerative processes of the spine and the origin of spinal pain are complex; and the effectiveness of a large variety of therapeutic interventions in managing chronic spinal pain has not been demonstrated conclusively. It has been shown that there is no conclusive evidence supporting the effectiveness of numerous conservative modalities used in managing chronic low back pain, including drug therapy, manipulation, back schools, electromyographic biofeedback therapy, exercise therapy, traction and orthoses, behavioral/cognitive/relaxation therapy, and transcutaneous electrical nerve stimulation. There are a multitude of interventional techniques in the management of chronic pain, including not only neural blockade but also minimally invasive surgical procedures such as peripheral nerve blocks, trigger-point injections, epidural injections, facet joint injections, sympathetic blocks, neuroablation techniques, intradiscal thermal therapy, disc decompression, morphine pump implantation, and spinal cord stimulation.

AN ALGORITHMIC APPROACH

Two suggested algorithms for the application of interventional techniques in conservative care of chronic spinal pain describe steps for diagnosis and management, as shown in Figs. 2A to 3B. These are only suggested algorithms and are limited to the management of chronic spinal pain. Further clinical evaluation, in spite of drawbacks, is extremely important, as is the documentation of indications for interventional techniques.

The clinical algorithms presented on the following pages show an effort to blend conscientious, explicit, and judicious use of the current best evidence in making decisions about the care of individual patients. When this is combined with the clinician's experience and judgment, and patient preferences, it should result in improved outcomes and significantly improved quality of care. These policies are intended to establish a boundary of reasonable care giving latitude to the individual physician.

EPIDURAL INJECTIONS

Description

Spinal pain generates from multiple structures in the spine with a nerve supply capable of causing pain similar to that seen in clinically normal volunteers, and which are susceptible to diseases or injuries that are known to be painful. Certain conditions may not be detectable using currently available technology or biochemical studies. However, for a structure to be implicated, it should have been shown to be a source of pain in patients, using diagnostic techniques of known reliability and validity. The structures responsible for pain in the spine include the intervertebral discs, spinal cord, nerve roots, facet joints, ligaments, muscles, atlanto-occipital joints, atlanto-axial joints, and sacroiliac joints.

One of the most common structures responsible for pain in the spine is the intervertebral disc. Even though disc herniation is seen only in a small number of patients, degeneration of the disc resulting in primary discogenic pain is seen much more commonly. In contrast to a ruptured disc with pain arising from the nerve root, in discogenic pain a disc with or without internal disruption is implicated rather than the nerve root.

Postlaminectomy syndrome or pain following operative procedures of the spine, sometimes known as failed management syndrome, is becoming a common entity in modern medicine. It is estimated that 20% to 30% of spinal surgeries, occasionally up to as high as 60%, may not be successful as a result of either the surgery being inadequate, incorrect, or unnecessary; but also it may result following a well-indicated and well-performed surgical procedure. Even in cases of successful surgery, pain and subsequent disability have returned after variable periods of 6 months to 20 years. However, surgical results are extremely poor in patients after a failed surgical procedure. Other spinal conditions include various degenerative disorders such as spinal stenosis, spondylolysis, spondylolisthesis, degenerative scoliosis, idiopathic vertebrogenic sclerosis, diffuse idiopathic spinal hyperostosis, and segmental instability. Degenerative conditions other than disc disruption and facet arthritis may contribute to approximately 5% to 10% of spinal pain.

CPT Code(s)

- 62310 – Injection, single, not including neurolytic substances, with or without contrast of diagnostic or therapeutic substance(s), epidural or subarachnoid; cervical or thoracic
- 62311 – Injection, single, not including neurolytic substances, with or without contrast of diagnostic or therapeutic substance(s), epidural or subarachnoid; lumbar, sacral (caudal)
- 62318 – catheter placement, continuous infusion for intermittent bolus; epidural or subarachnoid; cervical or thoracic
- 62319 - catheter placement, continuous infusion for intermittent bolus; epidural, lumbar, sacral (caudal)
- 64479 – cervical/thoracic transforaminal epidural, single level

- 64480 - cervical/thoracic transforaminal epidural, each additional level
- 64483 – transforaminal epidural; lumbar or sacral, single level
- 64484 - transforaminal epidural; lumbar or sacral, each additional level
- 72275 - Epidurography, radiological supervision and interpretation
- 76005 – fluoroscopic guidance and needle localization

Indications and Medical Necessity

The following criteria should be considered carefully in performing epidural injections:

1. Complete initial evaluation including history and physical examination;
2. Physiological and functional assessment, as necessary and feasible;
3. Definition of indications and medical necessity, as follows:

- Suspected organic problem;
- Nonresponsiveness to conservative modalities of treatment except in acute situations such as acute disc herniation, herpes zoster and postherpetic neuralgia, reflex sympathetic dystrophy, and intractable pain secondary to carcinoma;
- Pain and disability of moderate-to-severe degree;
- No evidence of contraindications such as severe spinal stenosis resulting in intraspinal obstruction, infection, or predominantly psychogenic pain;
- Responsiveness to prior interventions with improvement in physical and functional status for repeat blocks or other interventions;
- Repeating interventions only upon return of pain and deterioration in functional status.

Approaches to Epidural Space

Approaches available to access the epidural space are the interlaminar (cervical, thoracic, and lumbar), transforaminal (cervical, thoracic, lumbar, and sacral), and caudal. The perceived advantages of each of the three approaches include:

1. The interlaminar entry is directed more closely to the assumed site of pathology, facilitating delivery of the injectate directly to its target and requiring less volume.
2. The caudal entry is relatively easily achieved, with minimal risk of inadvertent dural puncture.
3. The transforaminal approach is target specific in fulfilling the aim of reaching the primary site of pathology.

The disadvantages of each of the three approaches include:

1. With caudal entry:
   - The necessity of injection of a substantial volume of fluid;
   - Unrecognized placement of the needle outside the epidural space in a substantial number of cases;
2. With interlaminar entry, at the cervical, thoracic, or lumbar levels:
   - Extradural placement of the needle that may go unrecognized without fluoroscopic guidance;
   - The possibility of erroneously missing the targeted interspace by one or two levels without fluoroscopic guidance, specifically in the thoracic and lumbar regions;
   - The necessity of positioning the needle one level below the site of suspected pathology due to preferential cranial flow of solutions in the epidural space;
   - The potential for deviation of the needle toward the nondependent side, and difficulty that may be encountered with placement of injectate below L5 for S1 nerve root involvement;
   - The trauma of the needle to the spinal cord is becoming a major issue in the cervical, thoracic, and upper lumbar regions;
   - Potential risk of dural puncture, and postdural puncture headache, as well as total spinal block;
3. With transforaminal entry:
   - Potential risk of intraneural injection and neural trauma.

ICD-9 Codes That Support Medical Necessity

1. Postlaminectomy syndrome
   - 722.81 cervical, 722.82 thoracic, 722.83, lumbosacral
2. Disc displacement without myelopathy (disc herniation, radiculitis, disc extrusion, disc protrusion, disc prolapse, discogenic syndrome).
   - 722.0 cervical, 722.11 thoracic, 722.10 lumbosacral
3. Disc displacement with myelopathy
   - 722.71 cervical, 722.72 thoracic, 722.73 lumbosacral
4. Degeneration of intervertebral disc (includes narrowing of disc space)
   - 722.4 cervical, 722.51 thoracic, 722.52 lumbosacral
5. Radiculitis
   - 723.4 cervical, 724.4 thoracic, 724.4 lumbosacral
6. Spinal stenosis
   - 723.0 cervical, 724.04 thoracic, 724.02 lumbosacral
7. Spondylosis with myelopathy
   - 721.1 cervical, 721.41 thoracic, 721.42 lumbosacral
8. Closed fracture of spine
   - 805.0 cervical, 805.2 thoracic, 805.4 lumbar, 805.6 sacral
9. Congenital spondylolysis
   - 756.11 cervical, 756.11 thoracic, 756.11 lumbosacral
10. Acquired/degenerative spondylolysis or acquired spondylolisthesis
    - 738.4 cervical, 738.4 thoracic, 738.4 lumbosacral
11. Congenital spondylolisthesis

- 756.12 cervical, 756.12 thoracic, 756.12 lumbosacral

12. Coccygodynia 724.79
13. Sciatica 724.3
14. Complex regional pain syndrome (Type I or reflex sympathetic dystrophy)
    - 337.20 reflex sympathetic dystrophy unspecified, 337.21 reflex sympathetic dystrophy upper limb, 337.22 reflex sympathetic dystrophy lower limb, 337.29 reflex sympathetic dystrophy other unspecified site
15. Complex regional pain syndrome (Type II or causalgia)
    - 355.9 causalgia, 354.4 causalgia upper limb, 355.71 causalgia lower limb
16. Peripheral neuropathy
    - 356.4 idiopathic, 356.0 hereditary, 357.2 diabetic, 357.5 alcoholic, 357.6 due to drug
17. Limb pain
    - 353.6 phantom limb pain, 997.60 stump pain, 997.61 neuroma of amputation stump, 342.0 hemiplegia – flaccid, 342.1 hemiplegia – spastic
18. Postherpetic neuralgia
    - 053.10 with unspecified nerve system complication
    - 053.13 postherpetic polyneuropathy
19. Pain syndromes secondary to neoplasm 141.0 - 239.9
20. Vascular ischemic pain 440.22

Frequency and Number of Injections or Interventions

- In the diagnostic or stabilization phase, a patient may receive injections at intervals of no sooner than 1 week or preferably, 2 weeks, except for blockade in cancer pain or when a continuous administration of local anesthetic is employed for reflex sympathetic dystrophy.
- In the treatment or therapeutic phase (after the diagnostic phase is completed), the frequency of interventional techniques should be 2 months or longer between each injection, provided that at least >50% relief is obtained for 6 to 8 weeks. However, if the neural blockade is applied for different regions, it can be performed at intervals of no sooner than 1 week and preferably 2 weeks for most type of blocks. The therapeutic frequency must remain at least 2 months for each region. It is further suggested that all regions be treated at the same time, provided all procedures are performed safely.
- In the diagnostic or stabilization phase, the number of injections should be limited to no more than four times except for reflex sympathetic dystrophy, in which case six times should be reasonable.
- In the treatment or therapeutic phase, the interventional procedures should be repeated only as necessary judging by the medical necessity criteria, and these should be limited to a maximum of six times.
- Under unusual circumstances with a recurrent injury, carcinoma, or reflex sympathetic dystrophy, blocks may be repeated at intervals of 6 weeks after diagnosis/stabilization in the treatment phase.

Combinations of Blocks/Interventions

It may be essential to combine, in certain circumstances, more than one block. This may include an epidural for the cervical region and facet-joint blocks for the lumbar region; or epidural and facet-joint blocks for the same region in the case of identification of pain generators from both sources.

Number Per Setting

It is recommended that a physician should consider a patient in totality and treat multiple regions of the patient in the same setting, as long as it is safe and feasible. Attempts to treat one particular organ at a different time are not an absolute necessity.

However, no more than five procedures (different procedures and/or multiples of different procedures - or total line items or procedures) may be billed in one setting when the procedures are performed in multiple regions. For treatment of a single region with only epidurals eg, only lumbosacral spine or cervical spine, a maximum of two procedures should be billed. If combined with others with medical necessity, a maximum of four procedures may be billed for one region. Procedure billing excludes CPT 76005, which may be added in addition to the above.

Documentation Requirements

The patient's medical record must contain documentation that fully supports the medical necessity for epidural injections.

Documentation must also support the frequency and the appropriateness of this procedure, as opposed to alternate forms of therapy.

Comprehensive, Component and Mutually Exclusive Codes

CPT 62310 - cervical or thoracic epidural injection; a comprehensive code, includes the following component codes:

- 20605 injection, intermediate joint, bursa or ganglion
- 20610 injection, major joint or bursa
- 36140 introduction of needle or intracatheter, extremity artery
- 62284 injection procedure for myelography
- 69990 use of operating microscope
- 76000-76003 fluoroscopy codes

Mutually exclusive code:

- 64479 cervical or thoracic transforaminal epidural, single level

CPT 62311 - lumbar (caudal epidural injection); a comprehensive code, includes the following component codes:

- 20605 injection, intermediate joint, bursa or ganglion
- 20610 injection, major joint or bursa
- 36140 introduction of needle or intracatheter, extremity artery
- 62284 injection procedure for myelography
- 69990 use of operating microscope
- 76000, 76001, 76003 fluoroscopy codes

Mutually exclusive code:

- 64483 lumbar or sacral, transforaminal epidural, single level

CPT 62318 - continuous infusion with catheter placement (cervical or thoracic) a comprehensive code, includes the following component code:

- 01996 daily management of epidural or subarachnoid drug administration
- 20605 injection, intermediate joint, bursa or ganglion
- 20610 injection, major joint or bursa
- 36000 introduction of needle or intracatheter, vein
- 36140 introduction of needle or intracatheter, extremity artery
- 36410 venipuncture, child over age 3 years or adult, necessitating physician's skill
- 62270 spinal puncture, lumbar, diagnostic
- 62272 spinal puncture, therapeutic, for drainage of spinal fluid
- 62284 injection procedure for myelography
- 62310 injection, single, epidural or subarachnoid; cervical or thoracic
- 69990 use of operating microscope
- 76000, 76001, 76003 fluoroscopy codes

Mutually exclusive codes:

- 62273 epidural blood patch
- 64479 cervical transforaminal epidural, single level

CPT 62319 - injection, catheter placement, lumbar or caudal epidural space; a comprehensive code, includes the following component codes:

- 01996 daily management of epidural or subarachnoid drug administration
- 20605 injection, intermediate joint, bursa or ganglion
- 20610 injection, major joint or bursa
- 36000 introduction of needle or intracatheter, vein
- 36140 introduction of needle or intracatheter, extremity artery
- 36410 venipuncture, child over age 3 years or adult, necessitating physician's skill
- 62270 spinal puncture, lumbar, diagnostic
- 62272 spinal puncture, therapeutic, for drainage of spinal fluid
- 62284 injection procedure for myelography
- 62311 injection, single; epidural, lumbar sacral (caudal)
- 69990 use of operating microscope
- 76000, 76001, 76003 fluoroscopy codes

Mutually exclusive codes:

- 62273 epidural blood patch
- 64483 cervical transforaminal epidural, single level

CPT 64479 - injection, cervical transforaminal epidural; a comprehensive code, includes the following component codes:

- 20550 injection, tendon sheath, ligament, trigger points or ganglion cyst
- 20605 injection, intermediate joint, bursa or ganglion
- 20610 injection, major joint or bursa
- 36140 introduction of needle or intracatheter, extremity artery
- 69990 use of operating microscope
- 76000, 76001, 76003 fluoroscopy codes

Mutually exclusive codes: None

CPT 64480 - injection, anesthetic agent and/or steroid, transforaminal epidural (cervical or thoracic, each additional level); a comprehensive code, includes the following component codes:

- 69990 use of operating microscope

Mutually exclusive codes: None

CPT 64483 - injection, anesthetic agent and/or steroid, transforaminal epidural (lumbar or sacral, single level); a comprehensive code, includes the following component codes:

- 20550 injection, tendon sheath, ligament, trigger points or ganglion cyst
- 20605 injection, intermediate joint, bursa or ganglion
- 20610 injection, major joint or bursa
- 36140 introduction of needle or intracatheter, extremity artery
- 76000, 76001, 76003 fluoroscopy codes

Mutually exclusive codes: None

CPT 72275 - epidurography, radiological supervision and interpretation; a comprehensive code, includes the following component codes:

- 76000 fluoroscopy (separate procedure), up to 1

hour of physician time, other than 71023 or 71034

- 76001 fluoroscopy, physician time more than 1 hour, assisting a nonradiologic physician
- 76003 fluoroscopic guidance for needle placement
- 76005 fluoroscopic guidance and localization of needle or catheter tip for spine or paraspinous diagnostic or therapeutic injection procedures

Mutually exclusive codes: None

Sources of Information

1. Manchikanti L, Singh V, Kloth D et al. Interventional techniques in the management of chronic pain: Part 2.0. *Pain Physician* 2001; 4:24-96.
2. Koes BW, Scholten R, Mens JMA et al. Epidural steroid injections for low back pain and sciatica. An updated systematic review of randomized clinical trials. *Pain Digest* 1999; 9:241-247.
3. Benzon HT. Epidural steroid injections for low back pain and lumbosacral radiculography. *Pain* 1986; 24:277.
4. Watts RW, Silagy CA. A meta-analysis on the efficacy of epidural corticosteroids in the treatment of sciatica. *Anaesth Intens Care* 1995; 23:564-569.
5. Bogduk N, Christophidis N, Cherry D et al. Epidural use of steroids in the management of back pain. Report of working party on epidural use of steroids in the management of back pain. National Health and Medical Research Council. Canberra, Commonwealth of Australia, 1994, pp 1-76.
6. Breivik H, Hesla PE, Molnar I et al. Treatment of chronic low back pain and sciatica. Comparison of caudal epidural injections of bupivacaine and methylprednisolone with bupivacaine followed by saline. In Bonica JJ, Albe-Fesard D (eds). *Advances in Pain Research and Therapy.* Raven Press, New York, 1976, Vol. 1, pp 927-932.
7. Bush K, Hillier S. A controlled study of caudal epidural injections of triamcinolone plus procaine for the management of intractable sciatica. *Spine* 1991; 16:572-575.
8. Yates DW. A comparison of the types of epidural injection commonly used in the treatment of low back pain and sciatica. *Rheum Rehab* 1978; 17:181-186.
9. Matthews JA, Mills SB, Jenkins VM et al. Back pain and sciatica: Controlled trials of manipulation, traction, sclerosant and epidural injections. *Brit J Rheumatol* 1987; 26:416-423.
10. Czarski Z. Leczenie rwy kulszowej wstrzykiwaniem hydrokortyzonu inowokainy do rozworu kryzowego. *Przeglad Kekarski* 1965; 21:511-513.
11. Beliveau P. A comparison between epidural anesthesia with and without corticosteroids in the treatment of sciatica. *Rheum Phys Med* 1971; 11:40-43.
12. Waldman SD. The caudal epidural administration of steroids in combination with local anesthetics in the palliation of pain secondary to radiographically documented lumbar herniated disc: A prospective outcome study with 6-months follow-up. *Pain Clinic* 1998; 11:43-49.
13. Meadeb J, Rozenberg S, Duquesnoy B et al. Forceful sacrococcygeal injections in the treatment of postdiscectomy sciatica. A controlled study versus glucocorticoid injections. *Joint Bone Spine* 2001; 68:43-49.
14. Revel M, Auleley GR, Alaoui S et al. Forceful epidural injections for the treatment of lumbosciatic pain with postoperative lumbar spinal fibrosis. *Rev Rhum Engl Ed* 1996; 63:270-277.
15. Manchikanti L, Pampati VS, Rivera J et al. Caudal epidural injections with Sarapin or steroids in chronic low back pain. *Pain Physician* 2001; 4:322-335.
16. Manchikanti L, Singh V, Rivera J et al. Effectiveness of caudal epidural injections in discogram positive and negative chronic low back pain. *Pain Physician* 2002; 5:18-29
17. Cuckler JM, Bernini PA, Wiesel SW et al. The use of epidural steroid in the treatment of radicular pain. *J Bone Joint Surg* 1985; 67:63-66.
18. Ridley MG, Kingsley GH, Gibson T et al. Outpatient lumbar epidural corticosteroid injection in the management of sciatica. *Br J Rheumatol* 1988; 27:295-299
19. Helliwell M, Robertson JC, Ellia RM. Outpatient treatment of low back pain and sciatica by a single extradural corticosteroid injection. *Br J Clin Pract* 1985; 39:228-231.
20. Stav A, Ovadia L, Sternberg A et al. Cervical epidural steroid injection for cervicobrachialgia. *Acta Anaesthesiol Scand* 1993; 37:562-566.
21. Castagnera L, Maurette P, Pointillart V et al. Long-term results of cervical epidural steroid injection with and without morphine in chronic cervical radicular pain. *Pain* 1994; 58:239-243.
22. Serrao JM, Marks RL, Morley SJ et al. Intrathecal midazolam for the treatment of chronic mechanical low back pain: A controlled comparison with epidural steroid in a pilot study. *Pain* 1992; 48:5-12.
23. Klenerman L, Greenwood R, Davenport HT et al. Lumbar epidural injections in the treatment of sciatica. *Br J Rheumatol* 1984; 23:35-38.
24. Rogers P, Nash T, Schiller D et al. Epidural steroids for sciatica. *The Pain Clinic* 1992; 5:67-72.
25. Rocco AG, Frank E, Kaul AF et al. Epidural steroids, epidural morphine and epidural steroids combined with morphine in the treatment of post-laminectomy syndrome. *Pain* 1989; 36:297-303.
26. Snoek W, Weber H, Jorgensen B. Double-blind evaluation of extradural methylprednisolone for herniated lumbar disc. *Acta Orthop Scand* 1977; 48:635-641.
27. Carette S, Lecaire R, Marcoux S et al. Epidural corticosteroid injections for sciatica due to herniated nucleus pulposus. *N Engl J Med* 1997; 336:1634-1640.
28. Bush K, Hillier S. Outcome of cervical radiculopathy treated with periradicular/epidural corticosteroid injections: A prospective study with independent clinical review. *Eur Spine J* 1996; 5:319-325.
29. Ciocon JO, Galindo-Clocon D, Amarnath L et al. Caudal epidural blocks for elderly patients with lumbar canal stenosis. *J Am Geriatr Soc* 1994; 42:593-596.
30. Manchikanti L, Pakanati RR, Pampati V. Comparison of three routes of epidural steroid injections in low back pain. *Pain Digest* 1999; 9:277-285.
31. Riew KD, Yin Y, Gilula L, et al. Can nerve root injections obviate the need for operative treatment of lumbar radicular pain? A prospective, randomized, controlled, double-blind study. *J Bone Joint Surg* 2000, 82A:1589-1593.
32. Kraemer J, Ludwig J, Bickert U et al. Lumbar epidural perineural injection: A new technique. *Eur Spine J* 1997; 6:357-361.
33. Vad V, Bhat A, Lutz G et al. Transforaminal epidural steroid injections in lumbosacral radiculopathy; A prospective randomized study. *Spine* 2002; 27:11-16.
34. Lutz GE, Vad VB, Wisneski RJ. Fluoroscopic transforaminal lumbar epidural steroids: An outcome study. *Arch Phys Med Rehabil* 1998; 79:1362-1366.
35. Kikuchi S, Hasue M, Nishiyama K. Anatomic and clinical studies of radicular symptoms. *Spine* 1984; 9:23-30.
36. Devulder J. Transforaminal nerve root sleeve injection with corticosteroids, hyaluronidase, and local anesthetic in the failed back surgery syndrome. *J Spinal Disord* 1998; 11:151-154.
37. Slipman CW, Lipetz JS, Jackson HB et al. Therapeutic selective nerve root block in the nonsurgical treatment of atraumatic cervical spondylotic radicular pain: A retrospective analysis with independent clinical review. *Arch Phys Med Rehabil* 2000; 81:741-746.
38. Weiner BK, Fraser RD. Foraminal injection for lateral lumbar disc herniation. *J Bone Joint Surg* 1997; 79-B:804-807.
39. Karppinen J, Malmivaara A, Kurunlahti M et al. Periradicular infiltration for sciatica. A randomized controlled trial. *Spine* 2001; 26:1059-1067.
40. Karppinen J, Ohinmaa A, Malmivaara A et al. Cost Effectiveness of Periradicular Infiltration for Sciatica: Subgroup Analysis of a Randomized Controlled Trial. *Spine* 2001; 26:2587-2595.
41. Manchikanti L, Jasper J, Singh V. Cochrane review is mixing apples and oranges. *Spine* 2001; 26:2641-2642.
42. Manchikanti L, Singh V. Periradicular infiltration for sciatica. Is it an interlaminar epidural or a transforaminal epidural? *Spine* 2002; 27:335-336

FACET JOINT BLOCKS

Description

Spinal pain generates from multiple structures in the spine with a nerve supply capable of causing pain similar to that seen in clinically normal volunteers, and which are susceptible to diseases or injuries that are known to be painful. Certain conditions may not be detectable using currently available technology or biochemical studies. However, for a structure to be implicated, it should have been shown to be a source of pain in patients, using diagnostic techniques of known reliability and validity. The structures responsible for pain in the spine include the intervertebral discs, spinal cord, nerve roots, facet joints, ligaments, and muscles.

Even though disc herniation, strained muscles, and torn ligaments have been attributed in the past to be the cause of most spinal pain either in the neck and upper extremities, upper and mid back, or low back and lower extremities; disorders of the spinal joints, which include facet joints, have been implicated more commonly than disc herniation, attributing some 50% of spinal pain to these joints. Facet joints were described as a potential source of low back pain as early as 1911, 20 years earlier than ruptured discs. The existence of lumbar facet joint pain is supported by a preponderance of scientific evidence, even though a few detractors have disputed this. The prevalence of facet joint pain in patients with chronic spinal pain has been established as 15% to 50% in low back pain, and 54% to 60% in neck pain, utilizing controlled diagnostic blocks, based on type of setting and population studied.

Postlaminectomy syndrome or pain following operative procedures of the spine is estimated to occur following 20% to 30% of spinal surgeries and occasionally up to as high as 40%. Surgery may not be successful as a result of either the surgery being inadequate, incorrect, or unnecessary; but also it may be unsuccessful following a well-indicated and well-performed surgical procedure. Even in cases of successful surgery, pain and subsequent disability have returned after variable periods of from 6 months to 20 years. In these cases, destabilization of the spinal joints, scar tissue development, and recurrent or repeat disc herniation may be responsible for continued pain problems. However, surgical results are extremely poor in patients after a failed surgical procedure. Facet joints are involved in approximately 30% of the patients in this phase.

In managing low back pain, local anesthetic injection into the facet joints or interruption of the nerve supply to the facet joints has been accepted as the standard for diagnosis of facet joint pain. Since a single joint is innervated by at least two medial branches, two adjacent levels should always be blocked.

If the pain is relieved, the joint may be considered to be the source of pain. However, false-positive responses must be ruled out, which may be seen in almost 47% of the patients.

- All the patient's pain need not be relieved, for it is possible that a patient may have several sources of pain.
- Comparative local anesthetic blocks, should be administered so that the same joint is anesthetized on two separate occasions, but using local anesthetics with different durations of action or placebo blocks.
- A true positive response confirms that the joint is the source of the pain, with a confidence of 85%.

It is recognized that it may be necessary to provide additional blocks such as selective nerve root or selective epidural blocks and disc injections in conjunction with facet-joint blocks. It is also recognized that multiple levels of facet-joint blocks may be performed in one setting, either in the same region or in multiple regions, more commonly than not.

Therapeutic facet joint blocks are based on the outcome of a diagnostic facet-joint block, with the patient obtaining sufficient relief for a meaningful period of time; but when pain recurs, a repeat block utilizing a small dose of local anesthetic and steroid provides longer-lasting relief (4 to 8 weeks).

If facet joint pain is present in conjunction with radiculopathy, both ailments should be managed.

CPT Code(s)

- 64470 – Cervical paravertebral facet joint nerve block, single level
- 64472 – Injection, cervical facet joint nerve block, each additional level
- 64475 - Injection, lumbar facet joint nerve block, single level
- 64476 - Injection, lumbar facet joint nerve block, each additional level
- 76005 – Fluoroscopic guidance and needle localization

Indications and Medical Necessity

The following criteria should be considered carefully in performing facet blocks:

1 Complete initial evaluation, including history and physical examination;
2 Physiological and functional assessment, as necessary and feasible;
3 Definition of indications and medical necessity, as follows:
  - Suspected organic problem;
  - Nonresponsiveness to conservative modalities of treatments;
  - Pain and disability of moderate-to-severe degree;
  - No evidence of contraindications such as severe

spinal stenosis resulting in intraspinal obstruction, infection, or predominantly psychogenic pain;
- Responsiveness to prior interventions with improvement in physical and functional status for repeat blocks or other interventions;
- Repeating interventions only upon return of pain and deterioration in functional status.

ICD-9 Codes That Support Medical Necessity

1. Spondylosis without myelopathy, dorsal arthritis, osteoarthritis, and spondyloarthritis (facet-joint arthropathy)
   - 721.0 cervical, 721.2 thoracic, 721.3 lumbar, and 721.7 traumatic spondylopathy
2. Postlaminectomy syndrome
   - 722.81 cervical; 722.82 thoracic; 722.83 lumbar
3. Spondylolysis
   - 756.11 congenital, 738.4 acquired
4. Spondylolisthesis
   - 756.12 congenital, 738.4 acquired

It is the responsibility of the provider to code to the highest level specified in the ICD-9-CM eg, to the fourth or fifth digit. The service must be reasonable and necessary in the specific case and must meet criteria specified in the policy.

Noncovered ICD-9 Codes

Any code not listed in the "ICD-9 Codes That Support Medical Necessity" section of this policy may not be covered, unless specific additional information is provided.

Frequency and Number of Injections or Interventions

- In the diagnostic or stabilization phase, a patient may receive injections at intervals of no sooner than 1 week or, preferably, 2 weeks.
- In the treatment or therapeutic phase (after the stabilization is completed), the frequency should be 2 months or longer between each injection, provided that at least > 50% relief is obtained for 6 weeks. However, if the neural blockade is applied for different regions, it can be performed at intervals of no sooner than 1 week or preferably 2 weeks for most type of blocks. The therapeutic frequency must remain at 2 months for each region. It is further suggested that all regions be treated at the same time, provided all procedures are performed safely. Administar Federal of Kentucky and Indiana limits to a total of six blocks per year, per region.
- In the diagnostic or stabilization phase, the number of injections should be limited to no more than four times per year.
- In the treatment or therapeutic phase, the interventional procedures should be repeated only as necessary judging by the medical necessity criteria, and these should be limited to a maximum of six times for local anesthetic and steroid blocks for a period of 1 year.
- Under unusual circumstances with a recurrent injury or cervicogenic headache, blocks may be repeated at intervals of 6 weeks after stabilization in the treatment phase.

Number Per Setting

It is recommended that a physician should consider a patient in totality and treat multiple regions of the patient in the same setting, as long as it is safe and feasible. Attempts to treat one particular organ at a different time are not an absolute necessity.

However, no more than five procedures (different procedures and/or multiples of one procedure – or total line items or procedures) must be billed in one setting for any of the following: the procedures are performed in different regions or a combination of procedures in multiple regions. For treatment of a single region, eg, only lumbosacral spine or cervical spine, a maximum of four procedures (different procedures and/or multiple of one procedure – or total line items or procedures) should be billed. Procedure billing excludes CPT 76005, which may be added in addition to the above.

Documentation Requirements

The patient's medical record must contain documentation that fully supports the medical necessity for facet joint injections and neurolytic blocks as it is covered by Medicare as described above.

Documentation must also support the frequency and the appropriateness of this procedure, as opposed to alternate forms of therapy.

Comprehensive, Component and Mutually Exclusive Codes

CPT 64470 - cervical/thoracic facet joint nerve block; a comprehensive code, includes the following component codes:

- 20550 injection, tendon sheath, ligament, trigger points or ganglion cyst
- 20600 injection; small joint, bursa or ganglion
- 20605 injection, intermediate joint, bursa or ganglion
- 20610 injection, major joint or bursa
- 36140 introduction of needle or intracatheter, extremity artery
- 76000, 76001, 76003 fluoroscopy codes

Mutually exclusive codes: None

CPT 64475 - injection, lumbar facet joint nerve block; a comprehensive code, includes the following component codes:

- 20550 injection, tendon sheath, ligament, trigger points or ganglion cyst
- 20600 injection; small joint, bursa or ganglion
- 20605 injection, intermediate joint, bursa or ganglion
- 20610 injection, major joint or bursa
- 36140 introduction of needle or intracatheter, extremity artery
- 69990 use of operating microscope
- 76000, 76001, 76003 fluoroscopy codes

Mutually exclusive codes: None

Sources of Information

1. Manchikanti L, Singh V, Kloth D et al. Interventional techniques in the management of chronic pain: Part 2.0. *Pain Physician* 2001; 4:24-96.
2. Bogduk N. International Spinal Injection Society guidelines for the performance of spinal injection procedures. Part 1: Zygapophyseal joint blocks. *Clin J Pain* 1997; 13:285-302.
3. Mooney V, Robertson J. The facet syndrome. *Clin Orthop* 1976; 115:149-156.
4. McCall IW, Park WM, O'Brien JP. Induced pain referral from posterior elements in normal subjects. *Spine* 1979; 4:441-446.
5. Marks R. Distribution of pain provoked from lumbar facet joints and related structures during diagnostic spinal infiltration. *Pain* 1989; 39:37-40.
6. Fukui S, Ohseto K, Shiotani M et al. Distribution of referral pain from the lumbar zygapophyseal joints and dorsal rami. *Clin J Pain* 1997; 13:303-307.
7. Fukui S, Ohseto K, Shiotani M et al. Referred pain distribution of the cervical zygapophyseal joints and cervical dorsal rami. *Pain* 1996; 68:79-83.
8. Dwyer A, Aprill C, Bogduk N. Cervical zygapophyseal joint pain patterns: A study in normal volunteers. *Spine* 1990; 6:453-457.
9. Aprill C, Dwyer A, Bogduk N. The prevalence of cervical zygapophyseal joint pain patterns II: A clinical evaluation. *Spine* 1990; 6:458-461.
10. Bogduk N, Marsland A. The cervical zygapophyseal joints as a source of neck pain. *Spine* 1988; 13:610-617.
11. Bogduk N, Aprill C. On the nature of neck pain, discography, and cervical zygapophyseal joint blocks. *Pain* 1993; 54:213-217.
12. Bogduk N. Musculoskeletal pain: Toward precision diagnosis. Progress in pain research and management. In Jensen TS, Turner JA, Wiesenfeld-Hallin Z (eds). *Proceedings of the 8th World Congress on Pain.* IASP Press, Seattle, 1997, pp 507-525.
13. Bogduk N, Simons DG. Neck pain: Joint pain or trigger points. In: H Vaeroy and J Merskey (eds). *Progress in Fibromyalgia and Myofascial Pain.* Elsevier, Amsterdam, 1993, pp 267-273.
14. Slipman CW, Plastaras CT, Palmitier RA et al. Symptom provocation of fluoroscopically guided cervical nerve root stimulation: Are dynatomal maps identical to dermatomal maps? *Spine* 1998; 23:2235-2242.
15. Dreyfuss P, Tibiletti C, Dreyer SJ. Thoracic zygapophyseal joint pain patterns: A study in normal volunteers. *Spine* 1994; 19:807-811.
16. Dreyfuss P, Michaelsen M, Fletcher D. Atlanto-occipital and lateral atlanto-axial joint pain patterns. *Spine* 1994; 19:1125-1131.
17. Barnsley L, Lord S, Bogduk N. Whiplash injury. *Pain* 1994; 58:283-307.
18. Schwarzer AC, Derby R, Aprill CN et al. The value of the provocation response in lumbar zygapophysial joint injections. *Clin J Pain* 1994; 10:309-313.
19. Schwarzer AC, Wang S, Laurent R et al. The role of the zygapophysial joint in chronic low back pain. *Aust N Z J Med* 1992; 22:185.
20. Schwarzer AC, Derby R, Aprill CN et al. Pain from the lumbar zygapophysial joints: A test of two models. *J Spinal Disord* 1994; 7:331-336.
21. Schwarzer AC, Aprill CN, Derby R et al. Clinical features of patients with pain stemming from the lumbar zygapophysial joints. Is the lumbar facet syndrome a clinical entity? *Spine* 1994; 19:1132-1137.
22. Schwarzer AC, Wang S, Bogduk N et al. Prevalence and clinical features of lumbar zygapophysial joint pain: A study in an Australian population with chronic low back pain. *Am Rheum Dis* 1995; 54:100-106.
23. Schwarzer AC, Aprill CN, Derby R et al. The relative contributions of the disc and zygapophyseal joint in chronic low back pain. *Spine* 1994; 19:801-806.
24. Manchikanti L, Pampati VS, Fellows B et al. Prevalence of lumbar facet joint pain in chronic low back pain. *Pain Physician* 1999; 2:59-64.
25. Manchikanti L, Pampati VS, Bakhit CE et al. The diagnostic validity and therapeutic value of lumbar facet joint nerve blocks with or without adjuvant agents. *Cur Rev Pain* 2000; 4:337-344.
26. Manchikanti L, Pampati V, Fellows B et al. The inability of the clinical picture to characterize pain from facet joints. *Pain Physician* 2000; 3:158-166.
27. Barnsley L, Lord SM, Wallis BJ et al. The prevalence of chronic cervical zygapophyseal joint pain after whiplash. *Spine* 1995; 20:20-26.
28. Lord SM, Barnsley L, Wallis BJ et al. Chronic cervical zygapophysial joint pain with whiplash: A placebo-controlled prevalence study. *Spine* 1996; 21:1737-1745.
29. Manchikanti L. Facet joint pain and the role of neural blockade in its management. *Cur Rev Pain* 1999; 3:348-358.
30. Manchikanti L, Pampati VS, Bakhit C et al. Effectiveness of lumbar facet joint nerve blocks in chronic low back pain: A randomized clinical trial. *Pain Physician* 2001; 4:101-117.
31. Manchikanti L, Pampati VS, Baha A et al. Contribution of facet joints to chronic low back pain in postlumbar laminectomy syndrome: A controlled comparative prevalence evaluation. *Pain Physician* 2001; 4:175-180.
32. Manchikanti L, Pampati VS, Rivera J et al. Role of facet joints in chronic low back pain in the elderly: A controlled comparative prevalence study. *Pain Practice* 2001; 1:332-337.
33. Manchikanti L, Pampati VS, Singh V et al. Evaluation of the role of facet joints in persistent low back pain in obesity: A controlled, prospective, comparative evaluation. *Pain Physician* 2001; 4:266-272.
34. Manchikanti L, Pampati VS, Fellows B et al. Influence of psychological factors on the ability to diagnose chronic low back pain of facet joint origin. *Pain Physician* 2001: 4:349-357.
35. Manchikanti L, Singh V, Fellows B et al. Evaluation of influence of gender, occupational injury, and smoking on chronic low back pain of facet joint origin: A subgroup analysis. *Pain Physician* 2002; 5:30-35.
36. Manchikanti L Fellows B, Pampati V et al. Evaluation of the relative contributions of various structures in chronic low back pain. *Pain Physician* 2001; 4:308-316.
37. Carette S, Marcoux S, Truchon R et al. A controlled trial of corticosteroid injections into facet joints for chronic low back pain. *N Engl J Med* 1991; 325:1002-1007.
38. Barnsley L, Lord SM, Wallis BJ et al. Lack of effect of intra-articular corticosteroids for chronic pain in the cervical zygapophyseal joints. *N Engl J Med* 1994; 330:1047-1050.
39. Lynch MC, Taylor JF. Facet joint injection for low back pain. A clinical study. *J Bone Joint Surg* (Br) 1986; 68:138-141.
40. Lilius G, Laasonen EM, Myllynen P et al. Lumbar facet joint syndrome. A randomized clinical trial. *J Bone Joint Surg* (Br) 1989; 71:681-684.
41. Nash TP. Facet joints. Intra-articular steroids or nerve blocks? *Pain Clinic* 1990; 3:77-82.
42. Marks RC, Houston T, Thulbourne T. Facet joint injection and facet nerve block. A randomized comparison in 86 patients with chronic low back pain. *Pain* 1992; 49:325-328.
43. Manchikanti L, Singh V. Review of chronic low back pain of facet joint origin. *Pain Physician* 2002; 5:83-101.

FACET JOINT NEUROLYTIC BLOCKS

Description

Spinal pain generates from multiple structures in the spine with a nerve supply capable of causing pain similar to that seen in clinically normal volunteers, and which are susceptible to diseases or injuries that are known to be painful. Certain conditions may not be detectable using currently available technology or biochemical studies. However, for a structure to be implicated, it should have been shown to be a source of pain in patients, using diagnostic techniques of known reliability and validity. The structures responsible for pain in the spine include the intervertebral discs, spinal cord, nerve roots, facet joints, ligaments, and muscles.

Even though disc herniation, strained muscles, and torn ligaments have been attributed in the past to be the cause of most spinal pain either in the neck and upper extremities, upper and mid back, or low back and lower extremities; disorders of the spinal joints, which include facet joints, have been implicated more commonly than disc herniation, attributing some 50% of spinal pain to these joints. Facet joints were described as a potential source of low back pain as early as 1911, 20 years earlier than ruptured discs. The existence of lumbar facet joint pain is supported by a preponderance of scientific evidence, even though a few detractors have disputed this. The prevalence of facet joint pain in patients with chronic spinal pain has been established as 15% to 45% in low back pain, and 54% to 60% in neck pain utilizing controlled diagnostic blocks.

Facet joint denervation is based on the outcome of a diagnostic facet-joint block, with the patient obtaining sufficient relief for a meaningful period of time; but, when pain recurs, a repeat block utilizing a small dose of local anesthetic and steroid does not provide longer-lasting relief. This is performed either by injecting neurolytic substance or by denervation utilizing radiofrequency thermoneurolysis or cryoneurolysis.

If facet joint pain is present in conjunction with radiculopathy, both ailments should be managed.

CPT Code(s)

- 64626 – destruction by neurolytic agent, paravertebral facet joint nerve; cervical or thoracic, single level
- 64627 - destruction by neurolytic agent, paravertebral facet joint nerve; cervical or thoracic, each additional level
- 64622 - destruction by neurolytic agent, paravertebral facet joint nerve; lumbar or sacral, single level
- 64623 – destruction by neurolytic agent, paravertebral facet joint nerve; lumbar or sacral, each additional level
- 76005 – fluoroscopy code

Indications and Medical Necessity

The following criteria should be considered carefully in performing facet neurolytic blocks:

1. Complete initial evaluation including history and physical examination;
2. Physiological and functional assessment, as necessary and feasible;
3. Definition of indications and medical necessity, as follows:
   - Suspected organic problem;
   - Nonresponsiveness to conservative modalities of treatments;
   - Pain and disability of moderate-to-severe degree;
   - No evidence of contraindications such as severe spinal stenosis resulting in intraspinal obstruction, infection, or predominantly psychogenic pain;
   - Responsiveness to prior interventions with improvement in physical and functional status for repeat blocks or other interventions.
   - Repeating interventions only upon return of pain and deterioration in functional status.

4. Confirmation of facet joint pain with double diagnostic blocks.

ICD-9 Codes That Support Medical Necessity

1. Spondylosis without myelopathy, dorsal arthritis, osteoarthritis, and spondyloarthritis (facet-joint arthropathy)
   - 721.0 cervical, 721.2 thoracic, 721.3 lumbar, and 721.7 traumatic spondylopathy
2. Postlaminectomy syndrome
   - 722.81 cervical; 722.82 thoracic; 722.83 lumbar
3. Spondylolysis
   - 756.11 congenital, 738.4 acquired
4. Spondylolisthesis
   - 756.12 congenital, 738.4 acquired

It is the responsibility of the provider to code to the highest level specified in the ICD-9-CM, eg, to the fourth or fifth digit. The service must be reasonable and necessary in the specific case and must meet criteria specified in the policy.

Noncovered ICD-9 Codes

Any code not listed in the "ICD-9 Codes That Support Medical Necessity" section of this policy may not be covered, unless specific additional information is provided.

Frequency and Number of Injections or Interventions

- The frequency should be 3 months or longer between each neurolytic procedure, provided that at least > 50% relief is obtained for 10 to 12 weeks. However, if the neural blockade is applied for different regions, it can be performed at intervals of no sooner than 1 week or, preferably, 2 weeks for most type of blocks. The therapeutic frequency for neurolytic blocks must remain at least at 3 months for each region. It is further suggested that all regions be treated at the same time, provided all procedures are performed safely.
- Under unusual circumstances with a recurrent injury or cervicogenic headache, blocks may be repeated at intervals of 2 months after stabilization in the treatment phase.

Number Per Setting

It is recommended that a physician should consider a patient in totality and treat multiple regions of the patient in the same setting, as long as it is safe and feasible. Attempts to treat one particular organ at a different time are not an absolute necessity.

However, no more than five procedures (different procedures and/or multiples of one procedure – or total line items or procedures) must be billed in one setting for any of the following: the procedures are performed in different regions or a combination of procedures is performed in multiple regions. For treatment of a single region, eg, only lumbosacral spine or cervical spine, a maximum of four procedures (different procedures and/or multiple of one procedure – or total line items or procedures) should be billed. Procedure billing excludes CPT 76005, which may be added in addition to the above.

Documentation Requirements

The patient's medical record must contain documentation that fully supports the medical necessity for facet joint injections and neurolytic blocks.

Documentation must also support the frequency and the appropriateness of this procedure, as opposed to alternate forms of therapy.

Comprehensive, Component And Mutually Exclusive Codes

CPT 64622 - destruction by neurolytic agent, paravertebral facet joint nerve (lumbar or sacral, single level); a comprehensive code, includes the following component codes:

- 64475 lumbar facet joint nerve block
- 69990 use of operating microscope
- 76000, 76001, 76003 fluoroscopy codes

Mutually exclusive codes: None

CPT 64626 - destruction by neurolytic agent, paravertebral facet joint nerve (cervical or thoracic, single level); a comprehensive code, includes the following component codes:

- 64470 cervical paravertebral facet joint nerve block
- 69990 use of operating microscope
- 76000, 76001, 76003 fluoroscopy codes

Mutually exclusive codes: None

Sources of Information

1. Manchikanti L, Singh V, Kloth D et al. Interventional techniques in the management of chronic pain: Part 2.0. *Pain Physician* 2001; 4:24-96.
2. Lord SM, Barnsley L, Wallis BJ et al. Percutaneous radio-frequency neurotomy for chronic cervical zygapophyseal-joint pain. *N Eng J Med* 1996; 335:1721-1726.
3. Vervest ACM, Stolker RJ. The treatment of cervical pain syndromes with radiofrequency procedures. *Pain Clinic* 1991; 4:103-112.
4. Van Kleef AR, Spaans F, Digemavs W et al. Effects and side effects of percutaneous thermal lesions of the dorsal root ganglion in patients with cervical pain syndromes. *Pain* 1993; 52:49-53.
5. Gallagher J, Vadi PLP, Wesley JR. Radiofrequency facet joint denervation in the treatment of low back pain - A prospective controlled double-blind study to assess efficacy. *Pain Clinic* 1994; 7:193-198.
6. Leclaire R, Fortin L, Lambert R et al. Radiofrequency facet joint denervation in the treatment of low back pain. *Spine* 2001; 26:1411-1417.
7. Sapir DA, Gorup JM. Radiofrequency medial branch neurotomy in litigant and nonlitigant patients with cervical whiplash: A prospective study. *Spine* 2001; 26:E268-273.
8. Geurts JW, van Wijk RM, Stolker RJ et al. Efficacy of radiofrequency procedures for the treatment of spinal pain: A systematic review of randomized clinical trials. *Reg Anesth Pain Med* 2001; 26:394-400.
9. Manchikanti L, Singh V. Review of chronic low back pain of facet joint origin. *Pain Physician* 2002; 5:83-101.
10. North RB, Han M, Zahurak M et al. Radiofrequency lumbar facet denervation: Analysis of prognostic factors. *Pain* 1994; 57:77-83.
11. Sluijter ME. The use of radiofrequency lesions of the communicating ramus in the treatment of low back pain. In Racz GB (ed). *Techniques of Neurolysis.* Kluwer Academic Publishers, Boston, 1989, pp 145-160.
12. Ogsbury JS, Simon RH, Lehman RAW. Facet "denervation" in the treatment of low back syndrome. *Pain* 1977; 3:257-263.
13. Wertheim HM, Rovenstine EA. Suprascapular nerve block. *Anesthesiology* 1941; 2:541.
14. Schaerer JP. Treatment of prolonged neck pain by radiofrequency facet rhizotomy. *J Neurol Orthop Med Surg* 1988; 9:74-76.
15. Bogduk N, Macintosh J, Marsland A. Technical limitations to the efficacy of radiofrequency neurotomy for spinal pain. *Neurosurgery* 1987; 20:529-535.
16. Van Kleef M, Liem L, Lousberg R et al. Radiofrequency lesions adjacent to the dorsal root ganglion for cervicobrachial pain. A prospective double blind randomized study. *Neurosurgery* 1996; 38(6): 1131-2

PERCUTANEOUS LYSIS OF EPIDURAL ADHESIONS

Description

Postlaminectomy syndrome or pain following operative procedures of the spine, sometimes known as failed management syndrome, is becoming a common entity in modern medicine. It is estimated that 20% to 30% of spinal surgeries, occasionally up to as high as 40%, may not be successful as a result of either the surgery being inadequate, incorrect, or unnecessary; but also it may result following a well-indicated and well-performed surgical procedure. Even in cases of successful surgery, pain and subsequent disability have returned after variable periods of from 6 months to 20 years. In these cases, scar tissue development, destabilization of the spinal joints, and recurrent or repeat disc herniation may be responsible for continued pain problems. However, surgical results are extremely poor in patients after a failed surgical procedure. Other spinal conditions producing chronic low back pain include disc displacement, internal disc disruption, facet arthropathy, and various other degenerative disorders such as spinal stenosis, spondylolysis, spondylolisthesis, degenerative scoliosis, idiopathic vertebrogenic sclerosis, diffuse idiopathic spinal hyperostosis, segmental instability; and multiple myofascial syndromes with involvement of muscles and ligaments.

Percutaneous nonendoscopic adhesiolysis and injection of hypertonic saline in the lumbar spine, its utilization and its studies have been reasonable and acceptable. This modality of treatment appears to be reasonable in the management of refractory low back pain secondary to failed back surgery, disc disruption, and multilevel degenerative arthritis, even though there are a few detractors.

Percutaneous epidural adhesiolysis is also indicated for patients suffering with refractory low back pain secondary to a multitude of causes, including postlumbar laminectomy syndrome, lumbar epidural fibrosis, and multilevel disc disruption, or multilevel degenerative arthritis. However, this should only be used after the failure of the conservative modalities of treatment, including caudal and transforaminal epidural injections.

CPT Code(s)

- 62263 – Percutaneous lysis of epidural adhesions using solution injection, eg, hypertonic saline, enzyme, or mechanical means including radiologic localization (includes contrast when administered), <u>multiple adhesiolysis sessions; 2 or more days</u>
- 6226X – Percutaneous lysis of epidural adhesions using solution injection, eg, hypertonic saline, enzyme, or mechanical means including radiologic localization (includes contrast when administered), <u>1 day</u>.
- 72275 - epidurography, radiological supervision and interpretation

Indications and Medical Necessity

The following criteria should be considered carefully in performing lysis of epidural adhesions:

1. Complete initial evaluation including history and physical examination;
2. Physiological and functional assessment, as necessary and feasible;
3. Definition of indications and medical necessity, as follows:
   - Suspected organic problem;
   - Nonresponsiveness to conservative modalities of treatment and other invasive modalities, including fluoroscopically directed epidural steroid injections;
   - Pain and disability of moderate-to-severe degree;
   - No evidence of contraindications such as severe spinal stenosis resulting in intraspinal obstruction, infection, or predominantly psychogenic pain;
   - Responsiveness to prior interventions with improvement in physical and functional status for repeat blocks or other interventions;
   - Repeating interventions only upon return of pain and deterioration in functional status.

ICD-9 Codes That Support Medical Necessity

1. Postlaminectomy syndrome
   - 722.81 cervical, 722.82 thoracic, 722.83 lumbosacral
2. Epidural fibrosis 349.2
3. Disc displacement with myelopathy
   - 722.71 cervical, 722.72 thoracic, 722.73 lumbosacral
4. Disc displacement without myelopathy (disc herniation, radiculitis, disc extrusion, disc protrusion, disc prolapse, discogenic syndrome).
   - 722.0 cervical, 722.11 thoracic, 722.10, lumbosacral
5. Degeneration of intervertebral disc (includes narrowing of disc space)
   - 722.4 cervical, 722.51 thoracic, 722.52 lumbosacral

It is the responsibility of the provider to code to the highest level specified in the *ICD-9-CM* eg, to the fourth or fifth digit. The service must be reasonable and necessary in the specific case and must meet the criteria specified in the policy.

Noncovered ICD-9 Codes

Any code not listed in the "ICD-9 Codes That Support Medical Necessity" section of this policy may not be covered, unless specific additional information is provided.

Frequency and Number of Injections or Interventions

- In the diagnostic or stabilization phase, a patient may receive injections at intervals of no sooner than 4 weeks.
- In the treatment or therapeutic phase, the number of injections should be limited to:
- With a 3-day protocol, two to three interventions per year,
- With a 1-day protocol, a maximum of six times per year.

Documentation Requirements

The patient's medical record must contain documentation that fully supports the medical necessity for lysis of epidural adhesions.

Documentation must also support the frequency and the appropriateness of this procedure, as opposed to alternate forms of therapy.

Comprehensive, Component and Mutually Exclusive Codes

CPT 62263 - percutaneous lysis of epidural adhesions; a comprehensive code, includes the following component codes:

- 62281 injection/infusion of neurolytic substance; (epidural, cervical or thoracic)
- 62282 injection/infusion of neurolytic substance; epidural lumbar, sacral (caudal).
- 62284 injection procedure for myelography
- 62310 injection, single, epidural or subarachnoid; cervical or thoracic
- 62311 injection, single; epidural, lumbar sacral (caudal)
- 62318 catheter placement, continuous infusion or intermittent bolus; epidural, lumbar, sacral (caudal)
- 62319 injection, including catheter placement, continuous infusion or intermittent bolus; epidural, lumbar, sacral (caudal)
- 64479 transforaminal epidural; cervical or thoracic, single level
- 64483 transforaminal epidural; lumbar or sacral, single level
- 64722 decompression; unspecified nerve(s)
- 69990 use of operating microscope
- 76000, 76003, 76005 fluoroscopy codes

Mutually exclusive codes: None

CPT 72275 - epidurography, radiological supervision and interpretation; a comprehensive code, includes the following component codes:

- 76000 fluoroscopy (separate procedure), up to 1 hour of physician time, other than 71023 or 71034
- 76001 fluoroscopy, physician time more than 1 hour, assisting a nonradiologic physician
- 76003 fluoroscopic guidance for needle placement
- 76005 fluoroscopic guidance and localization of needle or catheter tip for spine or paraspinous diagnostic or therapeutic injection procedures

Mutually exclusive codes: None

Sources of Information

1. Manchikanti L, Singh V, Kloth D et al. Interventional techniques in the management of chronic pain: Part 2.0. *Pain Physician* 2001; 4:24-96.
2. Lou L, Racz GB, Heavner JE. Percutaneous epidural neuroplasty. In Waldman SD (ed). *Interventional Pain Management.* WB Saunders, Philadelphia, 2001; pp 434-445.
3. Racz GB, Holubec JT. Lysis of adhesions in the epidural space. In Racz GB (ed). *Techniques of Neurolysis.* Kluwer Academic Publishers, Boston, 1989; pp 57-72.
4. Manchikanti L, Pakanati RR, Bakhit CE et al. Role of adhesiolysis and hypertonic saline neurolysis in management of low back pain. Evaluation of Modification of Racz Protocol. *Pain Digest* 1999; 9:91-96.
5. Racz GB, Heavner JE, Raj PP. Percutaneous epidural neuroplasty. Prospective one-year follow up. *Pain Digest* 1999; 9:97-102.
6. Heavner JE, Racz GB, Raj P. Percutaneous epidural neuroplasty. Prospective evaluation of 0.9% NaCl versus 10% NaCl with or without hyaluronidase. *Reg Anesth Pain Med* 1999; 24:202-207.
7. Manchikanti L, Pakanati RR, Bakhit CE et al. Non-endoscopic and endoscopic adhesiolysis in post lumbar laminectomy syndrome. A one-year outcome study and cost effectiveness analysis. *Pain Physician* 1999; 2:52-58.
8. Manchikanti L, Bakhit CE. Percutaneous epidural adhesiolysis. *Pain Physician* 2000; 3:46-64.
9. Manchikanti L, Pakanati RR, Pampati V. The value and safety of epidural endoscopic adhesiolysis. *Amer J Anesthesiol* 2000; 27:275-279.
10. Anderson SR, Racz GB, Heavner J. Evolution of epidural lysis of adhesions. *Pain Physician* 2000; 3:262-270.
11. Manchikanti L, Pampati VS, Fellows B et al. Role of one day epidural adhesiolysis in management of chronic low back pain: A randomized clinical trial. *Pain Physician* 2001; 4:153-166.
13. Manchikanti L, Pampati V, Rivera JJ et al. Effectiveness of percutaneous adhesiolysis and hypertonic saline neurolysis in refractory spinal stenosis. *Pain Physician* 2001; 4:366-373.
14. Hammer M, Doleys D, Chung O. Transforaminal ventral epidural adhesiolysis. *Pain Physician* 2001; 4: 273-279.

SPINAL ENDOSCOPY

Description

Spinal endoscopy with epidural adhesiolysis is an invasive but important treatment modality in managing chronic low back pain that is nonresponsive to other modalities of treatment, including percutaneous spring guided adhesiolysis and transforaminal epidural injection.

Low back pain is the most common ailment in the modern era, burdening approximately 15% to 39% of the population with serious financial and social consequences, and ranking first among musculoskeletal disorders. Multiple investigators have shown that as many as 79% of patients continue to suffer with chronic or recurrent low back pain 1 year after its onset. Among various causes of low back pain, postlumbar laminectomy syndrome is increasingly recognized as a cause. It is estimated that 5% to 40% of lumbar surgeries result in failed back surgery syndrome, with some statistics showing failure rates reaching as high as 68%. Postlumbar laminectomy syndrome may result from surgery that may have been inadequate, incorrect, or unnecessary; but it may also result following a well-indicated and well-performed surgical intervention. Endoscopic adhesiolysis is based on the premise that the three-dimensional visualization of the contents of the epidural space provides the operator with the ability to steer the catheter toward structures of interest, allowing the examination of a specific nerve root and its pathology, lysis of adhesions, and target-specific injection of a drug(s).

The purpose of spinal or epidural endoscopy is to directly visualize the contents of the epidural space, lyse the adhesions, and directly apply drugs, thus assuring delivery of high concentrations of injected drugs to the target areas. Thus, spinal endoscopy with lysis of adhesions incorporates multiple therapeutic goals into one treatment, similar to percutaneous lysis of adhesions with a spring guided catheter, with added advantages of direct visualization of the epidural space and its contents, a three-dimensional view, and increased steerability of endoscopic equipment with a fiberoptic catheter. Nomenclature used to describe this procedure includes *spinal canal endoscopy, spinal epiduroscopy, myeloscopy, spinal or lumbar epiduroscopy,* and *endoscopic adhesiolysis*.

Percutaneous epidural endoscopic adhesiolysis is also indicated for patients suffering with refractory low back pain secondary to a multitude of causes, including postlumbar laminectomy syndrome, lumbar epidural fibrosis, and multilevel disc disruption, or multilevel degenerative arthritis. However, this should only be used after the failure of the conservative modalities of treatments, as well as other interventional procedures, including caudal and transforaminal epidural steroid injections and percutaneous lysis of adhesions.

CPT Code(s)

- 0027T – Endoscopic lysis of epidural adhesions with direct visualization using mechanical means, eg, spinal endoscopic catheter system, or solution injection, eg, normal saline, including radiologic localization and epidurography, which retained its approval even though EBI opposed the code.

Indications and Medical Necessity

The following criteria should be considered carefully in performing lysis of epidural adhesions:

1. Complete initial evaluation, including history and physical examination;
2. Physiological and functional assessment, as necessary and feasible;
3. Definition of indications and medical necessity:
   - Suspected organic problem;
   - Nonresponsiveness to conservative modalities of treatment and other invasive modalities, including fluoroscopically directed epidural steroid injections and percutaneous lysis of epidural adhesions;
   - Pain and disability of moderate-to-severe degree;
   - No evidence of contraindications such as severe spinal stenosis resulting in intraspinal obstruction, infection, or predominantly psychogenic pain;
   - Responsiveness to prior interventions with improvement in physical and functional status for repeat blocks or other interventions;
   - Repeating interventions only upon return of pain and deterioration in functional status.
4. Responsiveness to prior spinal endoscopy and epidural adhesiolysis with improvement in physical and functional status;
5. Repeating the procedure only upon return of pain and deterioration and functional status; however, no sooner than 6 months after the prior endoscopic procedure.

ICD-9 Codes That Support Medical Necessity

1. Postlaminectomy syndrome
   - 722.81 cervical, 722.82 thoracic, 722.83 lumbosacral
2. Epidural fibrosis 349.2
3. Disc displacement with myelopathy
   - 722.71 cervical, 722.72 thoracic, 722.73 lumbosacral
4. Disc displacement without myelopathy (disc herniation, radiculitis, disc extrusion, disc protrusion, disc prolapse, discogenic syndrome).
   - 722.0 cervical, 722.11 thoracic, 722.10, lumbosacral
5. Degeneration of intervertebral disc (includes narrowing of disc space)
   - 722.4 cervical, 722.51 thoracic, 722.52 lumbosacral

It is the responsibility of the provider to code to the highest level specified in the *ICD-9-CM* eg, to the fourth or fifth digit. The service must be reasonable and necessary in the specific case and must meet the criteria specified in the policy.

Noncovered ICD-9 Codes

Any code not listed in the "ICD-9 Codes That Support Medical Necessity" section of this policy may not be covered, unless specific additional information is provided.

Frequency and Number of Injections or Interventions

- Spinal endoscopy with adhesiolysis may not be repeated within 6 months after the procedure.

Documentation Requirements

The patient's medical record must contain documentation that fully supports the medical necessity for lysis of epidural adhesions.

Documentation must also support the frequency and the appropriateness of this procedure, as opposed to alternate forms of therapy.

Comprehensive, Component and Mutually Exclusive Codes

CPT 0027T – endoscopic lysis of epidural adhesions with direct visualization using mechanical means, eg, spinal endoscopic catheter system, or solution injection, eg, normal saline, including radiologic localization and epidurography, which retained its approval even though EBI opposed the code.

- 72275 - epidurography, radiological supervision and interpretation
- 76005 – fluoroscopy code

Mutually exclusive codes:

- 62263 – Percutaneous lysis of epidural adhesions using solution injection, eg, hypertonic saline, enzyme or mechanical means including radiologic localization (includes contrast when administered), multiple adhesiolysis sessions; 2 or more days
- 6226X – Percutaneous lysis of epidural adhesions using solution injection eg, hypertonic saline, enzyme or mechanical means including radiologic localization (includes contrast when administered), 1-day.

Sources of Information

1. Manchikanti L, Singh V, Kloth D et al. Interventional techniques in the management of chronic pain: Part 2.0. *Pain Physician* 2001; 4:24-96.
2. Manchikanti L, Saini B, Singh V. Spinal endoscopy and lysis of epidural adhesions in the management of chronic low back pain. *Pain Physician* 2001; 4:240-265.
3. Wilkinson HA. Introduction: Etiology, diagnosis, and therapy. In *The Failed Back Syndrome. Etiology and Therapy*, ed 2. Springer-Verlag, New York, 1992, pp 1-3.
4. Wilkinson HA. The role of improper surgery in the etiology of the failed back syndrome. In *The Failed Back Syndrome. Etiology and Therapy,* ed 2. Springer-Verlag, New York, 1992, pp 4-12.
5. Nachemson AL. Failed back surgery syndrome is syndrome of failed back surgeons. *The Pain Clinic* 1999; 11:271-284.
6. Waddell G, Kummel EG, Lotto WN et al. Failed lumbar disc surgery and repeat surgery following industrial injury. *J Bone Joint Surg* (Am) 1979; 61:201-207.
7. Fritsch EW, Heisel J, Rupp S. The failed back surgery syndrome. Reasons, intraoperative findings, and long-term results: A report of 182 operative treatments. *Spine* 1996; 21:626-633.
8. Anderson S. A rationale for the treatment algorithm of failed back surgery syndrome. *Curr Rev Pain* 2000; 4:395-406.
9. Ross JS, Robertson JT, Frederickson RCA et al. Association between peridural scar and recurrent radicular pain after lumbar discectomy: Magnetic resonance evaluation. *Neurosurgery* 1996; 38:855-863.
10. Kuslich SD, Ulstrom CL, Michael CJ. The tissue origin of low back pain and sciatica. *Orthop Clin North Am* 1991; 22:181-187.
11. Richardson J, McGurgan P, Cheema S et al. Spinal endoscopy in chronic low back pain with radiculopathy: A prospective case series. *Anaesthesia* 2001; 56:454-460.
12. Saberski L. A retrospective analysis of spinal canal endoscopy and laminectomy outcomes data. *Pain Physician* 2000; 3:193-196.
13. Manchikanti L, Pampati V, Bakhit CE et al. Non-endoscopic and endoscopic adhesiolysis in post lumbar laminectomy syndrome: A one-year outcome study and cost effective analysis. *Pain Physician* 1999; 2:52-58.
14. Manchikanti L. The value and safety of epidural endoscopic adhesiolysis. *Amer J Anesthsiol* 2000; 275-278.
15. Krasuski P, Poniecka AW, Gal E et al. Epiduroscopy: Review of techniques and results. *The Pain Clinic* 2001; 13:71-76.
16. Saberski L, Kitahata L. Direct visualization of the lumbosacral epidural space through the sacral hiatus. *Anesth Analg* 1995; 80:839-840.
17. Saberski L, Kitahata L. Review of the clinical basis and protocol for epidural endoscopy. *Connecticut Medicine* 1996; 60:71-73.
18. Saberski L, Kitahata L. Persistent radiculopathy diagnosed and treated with epidural endoscopy. *J Anesth* 1996; 10:292-295.

DISCOGRAPHY

Description

Disc herniation, strained muscles, and torn ligaments have been attributed in the past to be the cause of most spinal pain, either in the neck and upper extremities, upper and mid back, or low back and lower extremities. However, disc herniation is seen only in a small number of patients; whereas degeneration of the disc resulting in primary discogenic pain is seen much more commonly. In contrast to a ruptured disc having pain arising from the nerve root, in discogenic pain a disc with or without internal disruption is implicated rather than the nerve root.

Even though riddled with controversy, disc stimulation is used quite frequently for diagnosis of discogenic syndrome, as well as a precursor to surgical intervention such as fusion. Stringent standards of practice have been established to ensure that the results of discography are not polluted by false-positive responses.

CPT Code(s)

- 62290 - injection procedure for discography, each level; lumbar
- 62291 - injection procedure for discography, each level; cervical or thoracic
- 72285 – diskography, cervical or thoracic, radiological supervision and interpretation
- 72295 – diskography, lumbar, radiological supervision and interpretation

Indications and Medical Necessity

The following criteria should be considered carefully in performing disc interventions:

1. Complete initial evaluation, including history and physical examination;
2. Physiological and functional assessment, as necessary and feasible;
3. Definition of indications and medical necessity as follows:
   - ·Suspected organic problem;
   - Nonresponsiveness to conservative modalities of treatments;
   - Pain and disability of moderate-to-severe degree;
   - No evidence of contraindications such as severe spinal stenosis resulting in intraspinal obstruction, infection, or predominantly psychogenic pain
4. Candidacy for discography

According to the position statement on discography by the Executive Committee of the North American Spine Society,

> Discography is indicated in the evaluation of patients with unremitting spinal pain, with or without extremity pain, of greater than 4 months' duration, when the pain has been unresponsive to all appropriate methods of conservative therapy. Before discography, the patients should have undergone investigation with other modalities which have failed to explain the source of pain; such modalities should include, but not be limited to, either computed tomography (CT) scanning, MRI scanning and/or myelography. In these circumstances, discography, especially when followed by CT scanning, may be the only study capable of providing a diagnosis or permitting a precise description of the internal anatomy of the disc and the detailed determination of the integrity of the disc substructures. Additionally, the anatomic observations may be complicated by the critical physiological induction of pain, which is recognized by the patient as similar to or identical with his/her complaint. By including multiple levels in the study, the patient acts as his/her own control for evaluation of the reliability of the pain response.

Other indications for discography include: (1) ruling out secondary internal disc disruption or recurrent herniation in the postoperative patient; (2) exploring pseudarthrosis; (3) determining the number of levels to include in a spine fusion; and (4) identifying the primary symptom-producing level when annular denervation (via thermocoagulation with an intradiscal catheter or a radiofrequency probe) is contemplated.

ICD-9 Codes That Support Medical Necessity

1. Disc displacement without myelopathy (disc herniation, radiculitis, extrusion, protrusion, prolapse, discogenic syndrome)
   - 722.0 cervical, 722.11 thoracic, 722.10 lumbosacral
2. Degeneration of intervertebral disc including narrowing of disc space
   - 722.4 cervical, 722.51, thoracic, 722.52 lumbosacral

It is the responsibility of the provider to code to the highest level specified in the *ICD-9-CM* eg, to the fourth or fifth digit. The service must be reasonable and necessary in the specific case and must meet the criteria specified in the policy.

Noncovered ICD-9 Codes

Any code not listed in the "ICD-9 Codes That Support Medical Necessity" section of this policy may not be covered, unless specific additional information is provided.

Comprehensive, Component and Mutually Exclusive Codes

CPT 62290 - injection procedure for diskography, each level (lumbar); a comprehensive code, includes

the following component codes:

- 62311 injection, single; epidural, lumbar sacral (caudal)
- 62319 catheter placement, continuous infusion or intermittent bolus; epidural, lumbar, sacral (caudal)
- 64483 transforaminal epidural; lumbar or sacral, single level
- 69990 use of operating microscope
- 76005 fluoroscopy codes

Mutually exclusive codes: None

CPT 62291 - injection procedure for diskography, each level (cervical or thoracic); a comprehensive code, includes the following component codes:

- 62310 injection, single, epidural or subarachnoid; cervical or thoracic
- 62318 catheter placement, continuous infusion or intermittent bolus; epidural or subarachnoid; cervical or thoracic
- 64479 transforaminal epidural; cervical or thoracic, single level
- 69990 use of operating microscope
- 76005 fluoroscopy codes

Mutually exclusive codes: None

Sources of Information

1. Manchikanti L, Singh V, Kloth D et al. Interventional techniques in the management of chronic pain: Part 2.0. *Pain Physician* 2001; 4:24-96.
2. Bogduk N. The argument for discography. *Neurosurgery Quarterly* 1996; 6:152-153.
3. Moneta GB, Videman T, Kaivanto K et al. Reported pain during lumbar discography as a function of annular ruptures and disc degenerations: A re-analysis of 833 discograms. *Spine* 1994; 17:1968-1974.
4. The Executive Committee of the North American Spine Society. Position statement on discography. *Spine* 1988; 13:1343.
5. Guarino AH. Discography. A review. *Cur Rev Pain* 1999; 3:473-480.
6. Fortin JD. Precision diagnostic disc injections. *Pain Physician* 2000; 3:271-288.
7. Manchikanti L, Singh V, Pampati V et al. Evaluation of the relative contributions of various structures in chronic low back pain. *Pain Physician* 2001; 4:308-316.
8. Carragee EJ, Tanner CM, Yang B et al. False-positive findings on lumbar discography. *Spine* 1999; 24:2542-2547.
9. Carragee E, Tanner C, Khurana S et al. The rates of false-positive lumbar discography in select patients without low back symptoms. *Spine* 2000; 25:1373-1381.
10. Walsh TR, Weinstein JN, Spratt KP et al. Lumbar discography in normal subjects. *J Bone Joint Surg* 1990; 72A:1081-1088.
11. Schwarzer AC, Aprill CN, Derby R et al. The prevalence and clinical features of internal disc disruption in patients with chronic low back pain. *Spine* 1995; 20:1878-1883.
12. Guyer RD, Ohnmeiss DD. Contemporary concepts in spine care. Lumbar discography. Position statement from the North American Spine Society and Therapeutic Committee. *Spine* 1995; 18:2048-2059.
13. Merskey H, Bogduk N (eds). Classification of chronic pain. In *Descriptions of Chronic Pain Syndromes and Definitions of Pain Terms,* ed 2. IASP Press, Seattle, 1994.
14. Manchikanti L, Singh V, Pampati VS et al. Provocative discography in low back pain patients with or without somatization disorder: A randomized, prospective evaluation. *Pain Physician* 2001; 4:227-239.

INTRADISCAL THERMAL ANNULOPLASTY

Description

The structures responsible for pain in the low back include the vertebrae, intervertebral discs, nerve roots, facet joints, ligaments, and muscles. Although, disc disorders are common, disc herniation is seen in a very small number of patients, ranging from 2% to 6%. In contrast to the disc herniation, the degeneration of the disc resulting in primary discogenic pain is seen commonly with or without internal disc disruption in 26% to 39% of patients.

Intradiscal electrothermal annuloplasty is a minimally invasive treatment for chronic discogenic low back pain that is an alternative to interbody fusion surgery. Application of thermal energy to the disc alters collagen structure and may perform a functional deafferentation on the disc. The technique of Intradiscal electrothermal annuloplasty utilizes this principle to treat patients with intractable low back pain.

CPT Codes

- 62287 - Aspiration or decompression procedure, percutaneous, of nucleus pulposus of intervertebral disc, any method, single or multiple levels; or
- 22899 – Unlisted, spine procedure; or
- 64999 – unlisted, spine procedure

Indications and Medical Necessity

The following criteria should be considered carefully in performing intradiscal electrothermal annuloplasty: complete initial evaluation, and physiologic function when feasible; suspected organic problem; abnormalities noted on MRI responding to clinical symptomatology or provocative discography with low volume and low pressure generally limited to one or two levels and with a negative control disc; nonresponsiveness to conservative modalities of treatments and other invasive modalities, including fluoroscopically directed epidural steroid injections; facet joint and sacroiliac joint pain, ruling out evidence of contraindication such as severe spinal stenosis spondylolysis, spondylolisthesis, on severely degenerated disc.

ICD-9 Codes That Support Medical Necessity

1. Disc displacement without myelopathy (disc herniation, radiculitis, extrusion, protrusion, prolapse, discogenic syndrome)
   - 722.0 cervical, 722.11 thoracic, 722.10 lumbosacral
2. Degeneration of intervertebral disc, including narrowing of disc space
   - 722.4 cervical, 722.51, thoracic, 722.52 lumbosacral

It is the responsibility of the provider to code to the highest level specified in the *ICD-9-CM* eg, to the fourth or fifth digit. The service must be reasonable and necessary in the specific case and must meet the criteria specified in the policy.

Noncovered ICD-9 Codes

Any code not listed in the "ICD-9 Codes That Support Medical Necessity" section of this policy may not be covered, unless specific additional information is provided.

Comprehensive, Component and Mutually Exclusive Codes

CPT 62287 - aspiration or decompression procedure, percutaneous, of nucleus pulposus of intervertebral disk, any method, single or multiple levels, lumbar, eg, manual or automated percutaneous diskectomy, percutaneous laser diskectomy; a comprehensive code, includes the following component codes:

- 62290 injection procedure for diskography, each level; lumbar
- 62310 injection, single, epidural or subarachnoid; cervical or thoracic
- 62311 injection, single; epidural, lumbar sacral (caudal)
- 62318 catheter placement, continuous infusion or intermittent bolus; epidural or subarachnoid; cervical or thoracic
- 62319 catheter placement, continuous infusion or intermittent bolus; epidural, lumbar, sacral (caudal)
- 64479 transforaminal epidural; cervical or thoracic, single level
- 64483 transforaminal epidural; lumbar or sacral, single level
- 69990 use of operating microscope
- 76000, 76001, 76005 fluoroscopy codes

Mutually exclusive codes

- 22224 osteotomy of spine, including diskectomy, anterior approach, single vertebral segment (lumbar)
- 22558 arthrodesis, anterior interbody technique, including minimal diskectomy to prepare interspace (other than for decompression, (lumbar))
- 63005 laminectomy with exploration and/or decompression of spinal cord and/or cauda equina, without facetectomy, foraminotomy or diskectomy, one or two vertebral segments (lumbar, except for spondylolisthesis)
- 63017 laminectomy with exploration and/or decompression of spinal cord and/or cauda equina, without facetectomy, foraminotomy or diskectomy, more than two vertebral segments (lumbar)
- 63030 laminotomy (hemilaminectomy), with decom-

pression of nerve root(s), including partial facetectomy, foraminotomy and/or excision of herniated intervertebral disk; one interspace (lumbar)

- 63042 laminotomy (hemilaminectomy), with decompression of nerve root(s), including partial facetectomy, foraminotomy and/or excision of herniated intervertebral disk, re-exploration, single interspace (lumbar)
- 63056 transpedicular approach with decompression of spinal cord, equina and/or nerve root(s), single segment (lumbar)

Sources of Information

1. Manchikanti L, Singh V, Kloth D et al. Interventional techniques in the management of chronic pain: Part 2.0. *Pain Physician* 2001; 4:24-96.
2. Bogduk N. The argument for discography. *Neurosurgery Quarterly* 1996; 6:152-153.
3. Moneta GB, Videman T, Kaivanto K et al. Reported pain during lumbar discography as a function of anular ruptures and disc degenerations: A re-analysis of 833 discograms. *Spine* 1994; 17:1968-1974.
4. The Executive Committee of the North American Spine Society. Position statement on discography. *Spine* 1988; 13:1343.
5. Guarino AH. Discography. A review. *Cur Rev Pain* 1999; 3:473-480.
6. Fortin JD. Precision diagnostic disc injections. *Pain Physician* 2000; 3:271-288.
7. Manchikanti L, Singh V, Pampati V et al. Evaluation of the relative contributions of various structures in chronic low back pain. *Pain Physician* 2001; 4:308-316.
8. Carragee EJ, Tanner CM, Yang B et al. False-positive findings on lumbar discography. *Spine* 1999; 24:2542-2547.
9. Carragee E, Tanner C, Khurana S et al. The rates of false-positive lumbar discography in select patients without low back symptoms. *Spine* 2000; 25:1373-1381.
10. Walsh TR, Weinstein JN, Spratt KP et al. Lumbar discography in normal subjects. *J Bone Joint Surg* 1990; 72A:1081-1088.
11. Schwarzer AC, Aprill CN, Derby R et al. The prevalence and clinical features of internal disc disruption in patients with chronic low back pain. *Spine* 1995; 20:1878-1883.
12. Guyer RD, Ohnmeiss DD. Contemporary concepts in spine care. Lumbar discography. Position statement from the North American Spine Society and Therapeutic Committee. *Spine* 1995; 18:2048-2059.
13. Merskey H, Bogduk N. Classification of chronic pain. In *Descriptions of Chronic Pain Syndromes and Definitions of Pain Terms,* ed 2, IASP Press, Seattle, 1994.
14. Manchikanti L, Singh V, Pampati VS et al. Provocative discography in low back pain patients with or without somatization disorder: A randomized, prospective evaluation. *Pain Physician* 2001; 4:227-239.
15. Saal JS, Saal JA. Management of chronic discogenic low back pain with a thermal intradiscal catheter: A preliminary study. *Spine* 2000; 25:382-388.
16. Van Kleef M, Barendse GA. Percutaneous intradiscal radiofrequency thermocoagulation in chronic non-specific low back pain. *Pain Clinic* 1996; 3:259-268.
17. Derby R, Eek B, Chen Y et al. Intradiscal electrothermal annuloplasty (IDET): A novel approach for treating chronic discogenic back pain. *Neuromodulation*, 2000; 3(2):82-88.
18. Saal JA, Saal JS. Intradiscal electrothermal treatment for chronic discogenic low back pain. *Spine* 2000; 25:2622-2627.
19. Singh V. Intradiscal electrothermal therapy: A preliminary report. *Pain Physician* 2000; 3:367-373.
20. Karasek M, Bogduk N. Twelve-month follow-up of a controlled trial of intradiscal thermal annuloplasty for back pain due to internal disc disruption. *Spine* 2000; 25:2601-2607.
21. Wetzel FT, Andersson G, Pezola JH et al. Intradiscal electrothermal annuloplasty (IDET) to treat discogenic low back pain: Preliminary results of a multi-center. Cohort study. In *Proceedings of North American Spine Society*, 15th Annual Meeting, New Orleans, 2000, pp 195-197.
22. Derby R, O'Neill CW. The reported effects on referred leg pain post intradiscal electrothermal therapy. In *Proceedings of International Spinal Injection Society*, San Francisco, September 8-10, 2000.
23. Liu B, Manos R, Criscitiello A et al. Clinical factors associated with favorable outcomes using intradiscal electrothermal modulation (IDET). In *Proceedings of Spine Across the Sea*, Hawaii, July 23-27, 2000.
24. Maurer P, Schlemback D, Brown M. Lumbar intradiscal electrothermal annuloplasty (IDEA) for discogenic low back pain. In *Proceedings of International Intradiscal Therapy Society,* Annual Meeting, Williamsburg, June 8-10, 2000.
25. Saal JA, Saal JS. Intradiscal electrothermal treatment (IDET) for chronic discogenic low back pain with two year follow-up. In *Proceedings of North American Spine Society*, 15th Annual Meeting, New Orleans, 2000, pp 5-7.
26. Crock HV. Isolated lumbar disc resorption as a cause of nerve root canal stenosis. *Clin Orthop* 1976; 115:109-115.
27. Crock HV. A reappraisal of intervertebral disc lesions. *Med J Aust* 1970; 1:983-989.
28. Sehgal N, Fortin JD. Internal disc disruption and low back pain. *Pain Physician* 2000; 3:143-157.

PERCUTANEOUS DISC DECOMPRESSION

Percutaneous disc decompression or nucleoplasty is a minimally invasive treatment for chronic discogenic low back pain that is an alternative to intradiscal electrothermal annuloplasty and also in a few cases laser diskectomy. Coblation-assisted nucleoplasty delivers radiofrequency energy to molecularly disintegrate tissue there by debulking a pressure-sensitive disc. Bipolar radiofrequency coagulation further denatures proteoglycans, altering the internal milieu of the affected nucleus. This technique purports to treat axial and radicular pain (contained lumbar discs) and is currently undergoing clinical trials.

Percutaneous disc decompression or nucleoplasty must be performed only in patients with discogenic low back pain existing for 6 months or longer who have failed an exhaustive, conservative treatment regimen including fluoroscopically directed injection therapy. The ideal candidates for this procedure are patients with any segmental disease or a single affected disc level as determined by MRI or provocative discography with low volume, low pressure with a normal control disc.

CPT Code

- CPT 62287 aspiration or decompression procedure, percutaneous, of nucleus pulposus of intervertebral disc, any method, single or multiple levels, lumbar, eg, manual or automated percutaneous diskectomy, percutaneous laser diskectomy

Indications and Medical Necessity

The following criteria should be considered carefully when performing intradiscal electrothermal annuloplasty: complete initial evaluation, physiologic function when feasible; suspected organic problem; abnormalities noted on MRI responding to clinical symptomatology or provocative discography with low volume and low pressure, generally limited to one or two levels and with a negative control disc; nonresponsiveness to conservative modalities of treatment and other invasive modalities, including fluoroscopically directed epidural steroid injections; and facet joint and sacroiliac joint pain, ruling out evidence of contraindication such as severe spinal stenosis spondylolysis, spondylolisthesis, and severely degenerated disc.

ICD-9 Codes That Support Medical Necessity

1. Disc displacement without myelopathy (disc herniation, radiculitis, extrusion, protrusion, prolapse, discogenic syndrome)
   - 722.0 cervical, 722.11 thoracic, 722.10 lumbosacral
2. Degeneration of intervertebral disc, including narrowing of disc space
   - 722.4 cervical, 722.51, thoracic, 722.52 lumbosacral

It is the responsibility of the provider to code to the highest level specified in the *ICD-9-CM* eg, to the fourth or fifth digit. The service must be reasonable and necessary in the specific case and must meet the criteria specified in the policy.

Noncovered ICD-9 Codes

Any code not listed in the "ICD-9 Codes That Support Medical Necessity" section of this policy may not be covered, unless specific additional information is provided.

Comprehensive, Component and Mutually Exclusive Codes

CPT 62287 - aspiration or decompression procedure, percutaneous, of nucleus pulposus of intervertebral disc, any method, single or multiple levels, lumbar, eg, manual or automated percutaneous diskectomy, percutaneous laser diskectomy; a comprehensive code, includes the following component codes:

- 62290 injection procedure for diskography, each level; lumbar
- 62310 injection, single, epidural or subarachnoid; cervical or thoracic
- 62311 injection, single; epidural, lumbar sacral (caudal)
- 62318 catheter placement, continuous infusion or intermittent bolus; epidural or subarachnoid; cervical or thoracic
- 62319 catheter placement, continuous infusion or intermittent bolus; epidural, lumbar, sacral (caudal)
- 64479 transforaminal epidural; cervical or thoracic, single level
- 64483 transforaminal epidural; lumbar or sacral, single level
- 69990 use of operating microscope
- 76000, 76001, 76005 fluoroscopy codes

Mutually exclusive codes are as follows:

- 22224 osteotomy of spine, including diskectomy, anterior approach, single vertebral segment (lumbar)
- 22558 arthrodesis, anterior interbody technique, including minimal diskectomy to prepare interspace (other than for decompression, (lumbar))
- 63005 laminectomy with exploration and/or decompression of spinal cord and/or cauda equina, without facetectomy, foraminotomy or diskectomy, one or two vertebral segments (lumbar, except for spondylolisthesis)
- 63017 laminectomy with exploration and/or decompression of spinal cord and/or cauda equina, without facetectomy, foraminotomy or diskectomy, more than two vertebral segments (lumbar)
- 63030 laminotomy (hemilaminectomy), with decom-

pression of nerve root(s), including partial facetectomy, foraminotomy and/or excision of herniated intervertebral disk; one interspace (lumbar)

- 63042 laminotomy (hemilaminectomy), with decompression of nerve root(s), including partial facetectomy, foraminotomy and/or excision of herniated intervertebral disc, re-exploration, single interspace (lumbar)
- 63056 transpedicular approach with decompression of spinal cord, equina and/or nerve root(s), single segment (lumbar)

Source of Information

1. Manchikanti L, Singh V, Kloth D et al. Interventional techniques in the management of chronic pain: Part 2.0. *Pain Physician* 2001; 4:24-96.
2. Bogduk N. The argument for discography. *Neurosurgery Quarterly* 1996; 6:152-153.
3. Moneta GB, Videman T, Kaivanto K et al. Reported pain during lumbar discography as a function of annular ruptures and disc degenerations: A re-analysis of 833 discograms. *Spine* 1994; 17:1968-1974.
4. The Executive Committee of the North American Spine Society. Position statement on discography. *Spine* 1988; 13:1343.
5. Guarino AH. Discography. A review. *Cur Rev Pain* 1999; 3:473-480.
6. Fortin JD. Precision diagnostic disc injections. *Pain Physician* 2000; 3:271-288.
7. Manchikanti L, Singh V, Pampati V et al. Evaluation of the relative contributions of various structures in chronic low back pain. *Pain Physician* 2001; 4:308-316.
8. Carragee EJ, Tanner CM, Yang B et al. False-positive findings on lumbar discography. *Spine* 1999; 24:2542-2547.
9. Carragee E, Tanner C, Khurana S et al. The rates of false-positive lumbar discography in select patients without low back symptoms. *Spine* 2000; 25:1373-1381.
10. Walsh TR, Weinstein JN, Spratt KP et al. Lumbar discography in normal subjects. *J Bone Joint Surg* 1990; 72A:1081-1088.
11. Schwarzer AC, Aprill CN, Derby R et al. The prevalence and clinical features of internal disc disruption in patients with chronic low back pain. *Spine* 1995; 20:1878-1883.
12. Guyer RD, Ohnmeiss DD. Contemporary concepts in spine care. Lumbar discography. Position statement from the North American Spine Society and Therapeutic Committee. *Spine* 1995; 18:2048-2059.
13. Merskey H, Bogduk N. Classification of chronic pain. In *Descriptions of Chronic Pain Syndromes and Definitions of Pain Terms,* ed 2. IASP Press, Seattle, 1994.
14. Manchikanti L, Singh V, Pampati VS et al. Provocative discography in low back pain patients with or without somatization disorder: A randomized, prospective evaluation. *Pain Physician* 2001; 4:227-239.
15. Crock HV. Isolated lumbar disc resorption as a cause of nerve root canal stenosis. *Clin Orthop* 1976; 115:109-115.
16. Crock HV. A reappraisal of intervertebral disc lesions. *Med J Aust* 1970; 1:983-989.
17. Sehgal N, Fortin JD. Internal disc disruption and low back pain. *Pain Physician* 2000; 3:143-157.

SYMPATHETIC BLOCKS

Description

The evolution of the nomenclature, conceptual understanding, and management of complex regional pain syndrome, formerly known as reflex sympathetic dystrophy and causalgia, has been dynamic. *Reflex sympathetic dystrophy, causalgia, sympathetically maintained pain, sympathetically independent pain*, and *complex regional pain syndrome* encompass some of the commonly utilized nomenclature. As per the International Association for the Study of Pain Committee on Taxonomy, to satisfy the diagnosis of complex regional pain syndrome Type I (reflex sympathetic dystrophy), the clinical findings include regional pain, sensory changes, eg, allodynia, abnormalities of temperature, abnormal pseudomotor activity, edema, and an abnormal skin color that occurs after a noxious event. Complex regional pain syndrome Type II, or causalgia, includes all of the above-described features, in addition to a peripheral nerve lesion. However, the pathophysiology of these syndromes is poorly understood.

Sympathetically maintained pain, by definition, is eliminated by an anesthetic blockade of the sympathetic efferents that serve the painful area. Similarly, neuropathic pain which is similar to reflex sympathetic dystrophy, however, represents various heterogenous conditions, which neither can be explained by one single etiology, nor by a particular anatomical lesion.

Visceral pain also may be caused by sympathetic overactivity. Temporary relief of abdominal visceral pain can therefore be obtained by blockade of the celiac plexus or lumbar or thoracic sympathetic chain.

In addition to the above conditions, sympathetic blockade may also be used for treatment of other painful conditions, including vascular ischemic pain, phantom limb pain, herpes zoster, postherpetic neuralgia, facial pain of unknown origin, neuropathic pain, pain secondary to carcinoma, headache, and other painful conditions which may not be differentiated.

Numerous modalities of treatments include sympathetic ganglion blocks, intervenous regional blocks, physical therapy, administration of a host of pharmacological agents, behavioral interventions, and surgical interventions with either sympathetectomy or radiofrequency neurotomy.

CPT Code(s)

A. Local anesthetic blocks

- 64505 sphenopalatine ganglion block
- 64510 injection, anesthetic agent; stellate ganglion (cervical sympathetic)
- 64520 injection, anesthetic agent; lumbar or thoracic (paravertebral sympathetic)
- 64530 injection, anesthetic agent; celiac plexus, with or without radiological monitoring

B. Neurolytic blocks

- 64680 celiac plexus neurolytic block
- A physician may use modifier 22 for:
- Sphenopalatine ganglion
- Stellate ganglion
- Thoracic or lumbar paravertebral sympathetic

Indications and Medical Necessity

Sympathetic blocks are indicated and are considered appropriate to confirm the diagnosis of sympathetically maintained pain. The following criteria should be considered carefully in performing sympathetic blocks:

1. Complete initial evaluation, including history and physical examination;
2. Physiological and functional assessment, as necessary and feasible;
3. Definition of indications and medical necessity as follows:
   - Suspected organic problem;
   - Nonresponsiveness to conservative modalities of treatment. However, in certain cases with intractable pain in complex regional pain syndrome I, complex regional pain syndrome II, herpes zoster, postherpetic neuralgia, and neuropathic pain secondary to carcinoma; sympathetic blocks may be initiated in conjunction with conservative treatment with drugs and physical therapy;
   - Pain and disability of moderate-to-severe degree;
   - No evidence of contraindications such as infection or predominant pain of psychogenic origin;
   - Responsiveness to prior interventions, with improvement in physical and functional status for repeat blocks or other interventions;
   - Repeating interventions only upon return of pain and deterioration in functional status.

Frequency and Number of Injections or Interventions

- In the diagnostic or stabilization phase, a patient may receive injections at intervals of no sooner than 1 week or, preferably, 2 weeks except for cancer pain or when a continuous administration of local anesthetic for sympathetic block is employed. However, the total number of injections in the stabilization phase should be limited to four to six per year.
- In the treatment or therapeutic phase, that is, after the stabilization phase, the frequency of sympathetic

blocks should be limited to 6 weeks or longer between each injection, provided that at least >50% relief is obtained for 4 to 6 weeks.

ICD-9 CODES THAT SUPPORT MEDICAL NECESSITY

1. Complex regional pain syndrome Type I reflex sympathetic dystrophy, Type II (causalgia)
   - 337.20 reflex sympathetic dystrophy unspecified, 337.21 RSD upper limb, 337.22 reflex sympathetic dystrophy lower limb, 337.29 reflex sympathetic dystrophy other unspecified site
   - 355.9 causalgia, 354.4 causalgia upper limb, 355.71 causalgia lower limb
2. Peripheral neuropathy
   - 356.4 idiopathic, 356.0 hereditary, 357.2 diabetic, 357.5 alcoholic, 357.6 due to drug
3. Limb pain
   - 353.6 phantom limb pain, 997.60 stump pain, 997.61 neuroma of amputation stump, 342.0 hemiplegia - flaccid, 342.1 hemiplegia - spastic
4. Plexus lesions
   - 353.0 thoracic outlet syndrome, 353.1 lumbar plexus lesions
5. Postherpetic neuralgia
   - 053.10 with unspecified nerve system complication, 053.11 geniculate herpes zoster, 053.12 postherpetic trigeminal neuralgia, 053.13 postherpetic polyneuropathy, 053.19 other, 053.12 herpes zoster dermatitis of upper eyelid, 053.21 herpes zoster keratoconjunctivitis, 053.22 herpes zoster iridocyclitis, 053.29 other ophthalmic complications
6. Pain syndromes secondary to neoplasm 141.0 - 239.9
7. Vascular ischemic pain
8. Headache
   - 346.01 intractable migraine with aura, 346.11 intractable migraine without aura, 346.21 intractable cluster, 346.20 nonintractable cluster, 346.9 unspecified migraine

It is the responsibility of the provider to code to the highest level specified in the *ICD-9-CM* eg, to the fourth or fifth digit. The service must be reasonable and necessary in the specific case and must meet the criteria specified in the policy.

Noncovered ICD-9 Codes

Any code not listed in the "ICD-9 Codes That Support Medical Necessity" section of this policy may not be covered, unless specific additional information is provided.

Documentation Requirements

The patient's medical record must contain documentation that fully supports the medical necessity for sympathetic blocks. Documentation must also support the frequency and the appropriateness of this procedure, as opposed to alternate forms of therapy.

Comprehensive, Component And Mutually Exclusive Codes

CPT 64505 - injection, anesthetic agent (sphenopalatine ganglion); a comprehensive code, includes the following component codes:

- 69990 use of operating microscope

Mutually exclusive codes: None

CPT 64510 - injection, anesthetic agent (stellate ganglion) cervical sympathetic; a comprehensive code, includes the following component codes:

- 69990 use of operating microscope

Mutually exclusive codes: None

CPT 64520 - injection, anesthetic agent (lumbar or thoracic) paravertebral sympathetic; a comprehensive code, includes the following component codes:

- 69990 use of operating microscope

Mutually exclusive codes: None

CPT 64530 - injection, anesthetic agent (celiac plexus, with or without radiologic monitoring); a comprehensive code, includes the following component codes:

- 69990 use of operating microscope

Mutually exclusive codes: None

CPT 64680 - destruction by neurolytic agent, celiac plexus, with or without radiologic monitoring; a comprehensive code, includes the following component codes:

- 64530 celiac plexus block
- 69990 use of operating microscope

Mutually exclusive codes: None

Sources of Information

1. Manchikanti L, Singh V, Kloth D et al. Interventional techniques in the management of chronic pain: Part 2.0. *Pain Physician* 2001; 4:24-96.
2. Stanton-Hicks M, Baron R, Boas et al. Complex regional pain syndromes: Guidelines for therapy. *Clin J Pain* 1988; 14:155-166.
3. International Association for the Study of Pain Subcomittee on Taxonomy (Merskey H et (eds). Classification of chronic pain: Description of

chronic pain syndromes and definitions of pain terms. Prepared by the subcommittee on taxonomy. *Pain* 1986 (Supplement), 3:S29-S30.

4. Raj PP. Complex regional pain syndrome-reflex sympathetic dystrophy and causalgia. *Cur Rev Pain* 1998; 2:242-253.
5. Rocco AG. Radiofrequency lumbar sympatholysis. The evolution of a technique for managing sympathetically maintained pain. *Reg Anesth* 1995; 20:3-12.
6. Elias M. Cervical sympathetic and stellate ganglion blocks. *Pain Physician* 2000; 3:294-304.
7. Manchikanti L. The role of radiofrequency in managing complex regional pain syndrome. *Cur Rev Pain* 2000 4:437-444.
8. Rauck RL. Stellate ganglion block. *Tech Reg Anesth Pain Manage* 2001; 5:88-93.
9. Stanton-Hicks M. Thoracic sympathetic block: A new approach. *Tech Reg Anesth Pain Manage* 2001; 5:94-98.
10. Raj P. Celical plexus/ splanchnic nerve blocks. *Tech Reg Anesth Pain Manage* 2001; 5:102-115.
11. Haynsworth RF, Noe CE. Percutaneous lumbar sympathectomy: A comparison of radiofrequency denervation versus phenol neurolysis. *Anesthesiology* 1991; 74:459-463.
12. Kantha KS. Radiofrequency percutaneous lumbar sympathectomy: Technique and review of indications. In Racz (ed). *Techniques of Neurolysis.* Academic Publishers, Kluwer, Boston, 1989:pp 71-183.

TRIGEMINAL NERVE BLOCKS

Description

Trigeminal nerve block with local anesthetic and steroid is utilized in managing pain of trigeminal neuralgia or cancer pain when pharmacological measures fail.

CPT Code(s)

- 64400 - injection, anesthetic agent; trigeminal nerve, any division or branch.
- 64600 - destruction by neurolytic agent, trigeminal nerve; supraorbital, infraorbital, mental, or inferior alveolar branch
- 64605 - destruction by neurolytic agent, trigeminal nerve; second and third branches at foramen ovale
- 64610 - destruction by neurolytic agent, trigeminal nerve; second and third division branches at foramen ovale under radiological monitoring

Frequency and Number of Injections or Interventions

- In the diagnostic or stabilization phase, a patient may receive injections at intervals of no sooner than 1 week or, preferably, 2 weeks.
- In the treatment or therapeutic phase (after the stabilization is completed), the frequency should be 2 months or longer between each injection, provided that at least >50% relief is obtained for 6 to 8 weeks. However, if the neural blockade is applied for different regions, it can be performed at intervals of no sooner than 1 week or, preferably, 2 weeks for most type of blocks. The therapeutic frequency must remain at 2 months for each region. It is further suggested that all regions be treated at the same time, provided all procedures are performed safely.
- In the diagnostic or stabilization phase, the number of injections should be limited to no more than four times per year.
- In the treatment or therapeutic phase, the interventional procedures should be repeated only as necessary judging by the medical necessity criteria, and these should be limited to a maximum of six times for local anesthetic and steroid blocks and four times for interventions such as radiofrequency thermoneurolysis, and cryoneurolysis for a period of 1 year.

ICD-9 Codes That Support Medical Necessity

1. Trigeminal neuralgia - 350.1
2. Atypical facial pain - 350.2
3. Trigeminal neuralgia, specified - 350.8
4. Trigeminal neuralgia, unspecified - 350.9
5. Postherpetic trigeminal neuralgia - 053.12

It is the responsibility of the provider to code to the highest level specified in the *ICD-9-CM* eg, to the fourth or fifth digit. The service must be reasonable and necessary in the specific case and must meet the criteria specified in the policy.

Noncovered ICD-9 Codes

Any code not listed in the "ICD-9 Codes That Support Medical Necessity" section of this policy may not be covered, unless specific additional information is provided.

Documentation Requirements

The patient's medical record must contain documentation that fully supports the medical necessity for trigeminal nerve blocks and neurolytic procedures.

Documentation must also support the frequency and the appropriateness of this procedure, as opposed to alternate forms of therapy.

Comprehensive, Component and Mutually Exclusive Codes

CPT 64400 - injection, anesthetic agent (trigeminal nerve, any division or branch); a comprehensive code, includes the following component codes:

- 20550 injection, tendon sheath, ligament, trigger points or ganglion cyst
- 69990 use of operating microscope

Mutually exclusive codes: None

CPT 64600 - destruction by neurolytic agent, trigeminal nerve (supraorbital, infraorbital, mental, or inferior alveolar branch); a comprehensive code, includes the following component codes:

- 64400 injection, anesthetic agent (trigeminal nerve, any division or branch)
- 69990 use of operating microscope

Mutually exclusive codes: None

CPT 64605 - destruction by neurolytic agent, trigeminal nerve (second and third division branches at foramen ovale); a comprehensive code, includes the following component codes:

- 69990 use of operating microscope

Mutually exclusive codes: None

CPT 64610 - destruction by neurolytic agent, trigeminal nerve (second and third division branches at foramen ovale

under radiologic monitoring); a comprehensive code, includes the following component codes:

- 64605 destruction by neurolytic agent, trigeminal nerve; second and third division branches at foramen ovale
- 69990 use of operating microscope

Mutually exclusive codes: None

Sources of Information

1. Manchikanti L, Singh V, Kloth D et al. Interventional techniques in the management of chronic pain: Part 2.0. *Pain Physician* 2001; 4:24-96.
2. Waldman SD. Blockade of the gasserian ganglion and the distal trigeminal nerve In Waldman SD (ed) – *Interventional pain management.* Edition 2. WB Sanders Company, Philadelphia 2001, pp316-320.
3. Taha JM, Tew JM. Comparison of surgical treatments for trigeminal neuralgia: Reevaluation of radiofrequency rhizotomy. *Neurosurgery* 1996; 38:865-871.
4. Taha JM, Tew JM. Treatment of trigeminal neuralgia by percutaneous radiofrequency rhizotomy. *Neurosurg Clin North AM* 1997; 8:31-39.
5. Oturai AB, Jensen K, Eriksen J. Neurosurgery for trigeminal neuralgia: Comparison of alcohol block, neurectomy and radiofrequency coagulation. *Clin J Pain* 1996; 12:311-315.
6. Taha JM, Tew JM, Buncher CR. A prospective 15-year follow up of 154 consecutive patients with trigeminal neuralgia treated by percutaneous stereotactic radiofrequency thermal rhizotomy. *J Neurosurg* 1995; 83:989-993.
7. Scrivani SJ, Keith DA, Mathews ES et al. Percutaneous stereotactic differential radiofrequency thermal rhizotomy for the treatment of trigeminal neuralgia. *J Oral Maxillofacial Surg* 1999; 57:104-111.

INTERCOSTAL NERVE BLOCKS AND NEUROLYSIS

Description

Intercostal/chest wall pain usually results from irritation or inflammation of the intercostal nerve, which may result from, but is not limited to: trauma, rib fracture, cancer, injury from a thoracotomy incision, osteoarthritis or degenerative arthritis of the thoracic spine, herpes zoster or postherpetic neuralgia, compression fracture of vertebrae, sternal fracture, injury to the nerve trunk, compression of nerves, or nerve-root lesions. This type of pain can be managed with either an intercostal nerve block or neurolysis (via radiofrequency ablation, cryoablation, or injection of a neurolytic agent such as phenol).

CPT Code(s)

- 64420 - injection, anesthetic agent; intercostal nerve, single
- 64421 -.intercostal nerves, multiple, regional block
- 64620 -.destruction by neurolytic agent; intercostal nerve

Indications and Medical Necessity

The following criteria should be considered carefully when performing either intercostal nerve blocks or intercostal neurolysis:

1. Complete initial evaluation including history and physical examination;
2. Physiological and functional assessment, as necessary and feasible;
3. Definition of indications and medical necessity as follows:
   - Suspected organic problem;
   - Nonresponsiveness to conservative modalities of treatments;
   - Pain and disability of moderate-to-severe degree;
   - No evidence of contraindications such as infection or pain of predominantly psychogenic origin;
   - Responsiveness to prior interventions, with improvement in physical and functional status for repeat blocks or other interventions;
   - Repeating interventions only upon return of pain and deterioration in functional status.

ICD-9 Codes That Support Medical Necessity

1. Herpes zoster, with unspecified nervous system complication - 053.10
2. Postherpetic polyneuropathy - 053.13
3. Pain syndromes secondary to neuroplasm - 114.02 – 239.9
4. Malignant neoplasm of ribs, sternum, and clavicle - 170.3
5. Secondary malignant neoplasm of other specified sites, bone and bone marrow - 198.5
6. Benign neoplasm of ribs, sternum, and clavicle - 213.3
7. Thoracic root lesions, not elsewhere classified (intercostal neuritis) - 353.3
8. Other nerve root and plexus disorders - 353.8
9. Unspecified nerve root and plexus disorder - 353.9
10. Pathologic fracture of other specified site - 733.19
11. Fracture of rib(s) closed - 807.00
12. Or rib(s) open - 807.1
13. Of sternum, closed - 807.2
14. Of sternum, open - 807.3
15. Flail chest - 807.4
16. Injury to other nerve(s) of trunk, excluding shoulder and pelvis girdles, other specified nerve(s) of trunk - 954.8

It is the responsibility of the provider to code to the highest level specified in the ICD-9-CM eg, to the fourth or fifth digit. The service must be reasonable and necessary in the specific case and must meet the criteria specified in the policy.

Frequency and Number of Injections or Interventions

- In the diagnostic or stabilization phase, a patient may receive injections at intervals of no sooner than 1 week or, preferably, 2 weeks.
- In the treatment or therapeutic phase (after the stabilization is completed), the frequency should be 2 months or longer between each injection, provided that at least >50% relief is obtained for 6 weeks. However, if the neural blockade is applied for different regions, it can be performed at intervals of no sooner than 1 week or, preferably, 2 weeks for most type of blocks. The therapeutic frequency must remain at 2 months for each region. It is further suggested that all regions be treated at the same time, provided all procedures are performed safely.
- In the diagnostic or stabilization phase, the number of injections should be limited to no more than four times per year.
- In the treatment or therapeutic phase, the interventional procedures should be repeated only as necessary judging by the medical necessity criteria, and these should be limited to a maximum of six times for local anesthetic and steroid blocks and four times for interventions such as radiofrequency thermoneurolysis, and cryoneurolysis for a period of 1 year.

Noncovered ICD-9 Codes

Any code not listed in the "ICD-9 Codes That Support Medical Necessity" section of this policy may not be covered, unless specific additional information is provided.

Coding Guidelines

For multiple levels of neurolytic blocks for additional levels, CPT 64620-51 may be used.

Documentation Requirements

The patient's medical record must contain documentation that fully supports the medical necessity for intercostal nerve blocks and neurolysis.

Documentation must also support the frequency and the appropriateness of this procedure, as opposed to alternate forms of therapy.

Comprehensive, Component and Mutually Exclusive Codes

CPT 64420 - injection, anesthetic agent (intercostal nerve, single); a comprehensive code, includes the following component codes:

- 20550 injection, tendon sheath, ligament, trigger points or ganglion cyst
- 69990 use of operating microscope

Mutually exclusive codes: None

CPT 64421 - injection, anesthetic agent (intercostal nerves, multiple, regional block); a comprehensive code, includes the following component codes:

- 20550 injection, tendon sheath, ligament, trigger points or ganglion cyst
- 64420 injection, anesthetic agent (intercostal nerve, single)
- 69990 use of operating microscope

Mutually exclusive codes: None

CPT 64620 - destruction by neurolytic agent (intercostal nerve); a comprehensive code, includes the following component codes:

- 64420 injection, anesthetic agent (intercostal nerve, single)
- 64421 injection, anesthetic agent (intercostal nerves, multiple, regional block)
- 69990 use of operating microscope

Mutually exclusive codes: None

Sources of Information

1. Manchikanti L, Singh V, Kloth D et al. Interventional techniques in the management of chronic pain: Part 2.0. *Pain Physician* 2001; 4:24-96.
2 Thompson GE. Intercostal nerve block In: Waldman SD, Winnie A (eds) – *Interventional Pain Management.* WB Sanders Company, Philadelphia, 1996, pp 311-318.

SUPRASCAPULAR NERVE BLOCKS

Description

Pain secondary to irritation or inflammation of the suprascapular nerve may be caused by multiple variants such as soft tissue trauma, arthritis, cysts or lesions. The irritation of the suprascapular nerve is manifested with pain in the distribution of the shoulder and shoulder - girdle area. This may be associated with weakness of the supraspinatus and infraspinatus muscles. Weakness of these muscles may be diagnosed by weakness of abduction of the shoulder, as well as lateral rotation.

A suprascapular nerve block, which results in relief of pain, can confirm the diagnosis of suprascapular neuritis. This may be followed by injection of depo-steroids.

CPT Code(s)

- 64418 – Suprascapular nerve block

Indications and Medical Necessity

The following criteria should be considered carefully in performing either intercostal nerve blocks or intercostal neurolysis:

1. Complete initial evaluation, including history and physical examination;
2. Physiological and functional assessment, as necessary and feasible;
3. Definition of indications and medical necessity; as follows:
   - Suspected organic problem;
   - Nonresponsiveness to conservative modalities of treatments;
   - Pain and disability of moderate-to-severe degree;
   - No evidence of contraindications such as infection or pain of predominantly psychogenic origin;
   - Responsiveness to prior interventions, with improvement in physical and functional status for repeat blocks or other interventions;
   - Repeating interventions only upon return of pain and deterioration in functional status.

ICD-9 Codes That Support Medical Necessity

1. Brachial neuritis or radiculitis - 723.4
2. Degeneration of cervical intervertebral disc, including narrowing of disc space - 722.4
3. Cervical disc displacement without myelopathy (disc herniation, radiculitis, disc extrusion, disc protrusion, disc prolapse, discogenic syndrome) - 722.0
4. Frozen shoulder - 726.0

It is the responsibility of the provider to code to the highest level specified in the *ICD-9-CM* eg, to the fourth or fifth digit. The service must be reasonable and necessary in the specific case and must meet the criteria specified in the policy.

Frequency and Number of Injections or Interventions

- In the diagnostic or stabilization phase, a patient may receive injections at intervals of no sooner than 1 week or, preferably, 2 weeks.
- In the treatment or therapeutic phase (after the stabilization is completed), the frequency should be 2 months or longer between each injection, provided that at least >50% relief is obtained for 6 weeks. However, if the neural blockade is applied for different regions, it can be performed at intervals of no sooner than 1 week or, preferably, 2 weeks for most type of blocks. The therapeutic frequency must remain at 2 months for each region. It is further suggested that all regions be treated at the same time provided all procedures are performed safely.
- In the diagnostic or stabilization phase, the number of injections should be limited to no more than four times per year.
- In the treatment or therapeutic phase, the interventional procedures should be repeated only as necessary judging by the medical necessity criteria, and these should be limited to a maximum of six times for local anesthetic and steroid blocks and four times for interventions such as radiofrequency thermoneurolysis, and cryoneurolysis for a period of 1 year.

Noncovered ICD-9 Codes

Any code not listed in the "ICD-9 Codes That Support Medical Necessity" section of this policy may not be covered, unless specific additional information is provided.

Documentation Requirements

The patient's medical record must contain documentation that fully supports the medical necessity for suprascapular nerve block.

Documentation must also support the frequency and the appropriateness of this procedure, as opposed to alternate forms of therapy.

Comprehensive, Component and Mutually Exclusive Codes

CPT 64418 - injection, anesthetic agent (suprascapular nerve); a comprehensive code, includes the following com-

ponent codes:

- 20550 injection, tendon sheath, ligament, trigger points or ganglion cyst
- 69990 use of operating microscope

Mutually exclusive codes: None

Sources of Information

1. Manchikanti L, Singh V, Kloth D et al. Interventional techniques in the management of chronic pain: Part 2.0. *Pain Physician* 2001; 4:24-96.
2. Waldman SD. Suprascapular nerve block. In Waldman SD (ed), *Interventional Pain Management*, Edition 2. WB Saunders Company, Philadelphia, 2001; pp388-389.

GREATER OCCIPITAL NERVE BLOCKS

Description

Cervicogenic headache may result from either cervical facet joint syndrome, cervical spinal disease, or occipital neuritis. Cervicogenic headache may be caused either by arthritis of the facet joints or whiplash syndrome causing facet joint mediated pain or irritation of the greater occipital nerve. Rarely, the greater occipital nerve may be entrapped, however, more commonly it is inflamed.

A diagnostic block or greater occipital nerve can confirm the clinical impression of occipital neuralgia. Headaches secondary to occipital neuralgia are either unilateral or bilateral. They may be constant, or intermittent. Headaches may be radiating behind the ear or to the face. Therapeutically, injection of local anesthetic with or without steroids along the greater occipital nerve in its course also may provide relief which may be long-lasting in some cases, particularly, if chronic muscle spasm is present and in conjunction with other modalities of treatments, including physical therapy and an exercise program.

CPT Code(s)

- ♦ 64405 – Greater occipital nerve block

Indications and Medical Necessity

The following criteria should be considered carefully in performing either intercostal nerve blocks or intercostal neurolysis:

1. Complete initial evaluation, including history and physical examination;
2. Physiological and functional assessment, as necessary and feasible;
3. Definition of indications and medical necessity; as follows:
   - Suspected organic problem;
   - Nonresponsiveness to conservative modalities of treatments;
   - Pain and disability of moderate-to-severe degree;
   - No evidence of contraindications such as infection or pain of predominantly psychogenic origin;
   - Responsiveness to prior interventions, with improvement in physical and functional status for repeat blocks or other interventions;
   - Repeating interventions only upon return of pain and deterioration in functional status.

ICD-9 Codes That Support Medical Necessity

1. Occipital neuritis - 729.2
2. Cervical spondylosis or cervical facet joint arthropathy - 721.0
3. Cervical intervertebral disc disease - 722.4

It is the responsibility of the provider to code to the highest level specified in the *ICD-9-CM* eg, to the fourth or fifth digit. The service must be reasonable and necessary in the specific case and must meet the criteria specified in the policy.

Frequency and Number of Injections or Interventions

- ♦ In the diagnostic or stabilization phase, a patient may receive injections at intervals of no sooner than 1 week on, preferably, 2 weeks.
- ♦ In the treatment or therapeutic phase (after the stabilization is completed), the frequency should be 2 months or longer between each injection, provided that at least >50% relief is obtained for 6 weeks. However, if the neural blockade is applied for different regions, it can be performed at intervals of no sooner than 1 week or, preferably, 2 weeks for most type of blocks. The therapeutic frequency must remain at 2 months for each region. It is further suggested that all regions be treated at the same time, provided all procedures are performed safely.
- ♦ In the diagnostic or stabilization phase, the number of injections should be limited to no more than four times per year.
- ♦ In the treatment or therapeutic phase, the interventional procedures should be repeated only as necessary judging by the medical necessity criteria and these should be limited to a maximum of six times for local anesthetic and steroid blocks and four times for interventions such as radiofrequency thermoneurolysis, and cryoneurolysis for a period of 1 year.
- ♦ Under unusual circumstances with a recurrent injury or cervicogenic headache, blocks may be repeated at intervals of 6 weeks after stabilization in the treatment phase.

Noncovered ICD-9 Codes

Any code not listed in the "ICD-9 Codes That Support Medical Necessity" section of this policy may not be covered, unless specific additional information is provided.

Documentation Requirements

The patient's medical record must contain documentation that fully supports the medical necessity for occipital nerve blocks.

Documentation must also support the frequency and the appropriateness of this procedure, as opposed to alternate forms of therapy.

Comprehensive, Component and Mutually Exclusive Codes

CPT 64405 - injection, anesthetic agent (greater occipital nerve); a comprehensive code, includes the following component codes:

- 20550 injection, tendon sheath, ligament, trigger points or ganglion cyst
- 69990 use of operating microscope

Mutually exclusive codes: None

Sources of Information

1. Manchikanti L, Singh V, Kloth D et al. Interventional techniques in the management of chronic pain: Part 2.0. *Pain Physician* 2001; 4:24-96.
2. Brown DL, Wong, GY. Occipital nerve block In Waldman SD (ed) – *Interventional Pain Management*, Edition 2. WB Saunders Company, Philadelphia, 2001, pp312-315.

PERIPHERAL NERVE BLOCKS

Description

Peripheral nerve blocks may be performed to manage pain emanating from irritation or inflammation of peripheral nerve(s). If response to a peripheral nerve block with local anesthetic is significant and predictable, a peripheral neurolytic block may be performed, either by injection of neurolytic agent or cryoablation.

CPT Code(s)

- 64450-Peripheral nerve block
- 64640-Peripheral neurolytic block

Indications and Medical Necessity

The following criteria should be considered carefully in performing either intercostal nerve blocks or intercostal neurolysis:

1. Complete initial evaluation including history and physical examination;
2. Physiological and functional assessment, as necessary and feasible;
3. Definition of indications and medical necessity as follows:
   - Suspected organic problem;
   - Nonresponsiveness to conservative modalities of treatments;
   - Pain and disability of moderate-to-severe degree;
   - No evidence of contraindications such as infection or pain of predominantly psychogenic origin;
   - Responsiveness to prior interventions with improvement in physical and functional status for repeat blocks or other interventions;
   - Repeating interventions only upon return of pain and deterioration in functional status;

ICD-9 Codes That Support Medical Necessity

Codes describing peripheral neuritis will be considered to support medical necessity.

It is the responsibility of the provider to code to the highest level specified in the *ICD-9-CM* eg, to the fourth or fifth digit. The service must be reasonable and necessary in the specific case and must meet the criteria specified in the policy.

Noncovered ICD-9 Codes

Any code not listed in the "ICD-9 Codes That Support Medical Necessity" section of this policy may not be covered, unless specific additional information is provided.

Documentation Requirements

The patient's medical record must contain documentation that fully supports the medical necessity for peripheral nerve blocks or neurolysis as it is covered by Medicare as described above.

Documentation must also support the frequency and the appropriateness of this procedure, as opposed to alternate forms of therapy.

Frequency and Number of Injections or Interventions

- In the diagnostic or stabilization phase, a patient may receive injections at intervals of no sooner than 1 week or, preferably, 2 weeks.
- In the treatment or therapeutic phase (after the stabilization is completed), the frequency should be 2 months or longer between each injection, provided that at least >50% relief is obtained for 6 weeks. However, if the neural blockade is applied for different regions, it can be performed at intervals of no sooner than 1 week or, preferably, 2 weeks for most type of blocks. The therapeutic frequency must remain at 2 months for each region. It is further suggested to that all regions be treated at the same time, provided all procedures are performed safely.
- In the diagnostic or stabilization phase, the number of injections should be limited to no more than four times per year.
- In the treatment or therapeutic phase, the interventional procedures should be repeated only as necessary judging by the medical necessity criteria, and these should be limited to a maximum of six times for local anesthetic and steroid blocks and four times for neurolytic blocks for a period of 1 year.

Comprehensive, Component and Mutually Exclusive Codes

CPT 64450 – injection, anesthetic agent; other peripheral nerve or branch; a comprehensive code, includes the following component codes:

- 20550 Injection, tendon sheath, ligament, trigger points or ganglion cyst
- 69990 use of operating microscope

Mutually exclusive codes: None

CPT 64640 - destruction by neurolytic agent, other peripheral nerve or branch; a comprehensive code, includes the following component codes:

- 64405 injection, anesthetic agent (greater occipital nerve)
- 64408 injection, anesthetic agent (vagus nerve)
- 64410 injection, anesthetic agent (phrenic nerve)
- 64412 injection, anesthetic agent (spinal accessory nerve)
- 64413 injection, anesthetic agent (cervical plexus)
- 64415 injection, anesthetic agent (brachial plexus)
- 64417 injection, anesthetic agent (axillary nerve)
- 64418 injection, anesthetic agent (suprascapular nerve)
- 64425 injection, anesthetic agent (ilioinguinal, ilio-hypogastric nerve)
- 64435 injection, anesthetic agent (paracervical [uterine] nerve)
- 64445 injection, anesthetic agent (sciatic nerve)
- 64450 injection, anesthetic agent (other peripheral nerve or branch)
- 69990 use of operating microscope

Mutually exclusive codes: None

Sources of Information

1. Manchikanti L, Singh V, Kloth D et al. Interventional techniques in the management of chronic pain: Part 2.0. *Pain Physician* 2001; 4:24-96.
2. Raj PP, Anderson SR. Peripheral neurolysis in the management of pain. In Waldman SD (ed). *Interventional Pain Management.* Edition 2. WB Saunders Company, Philadelphia 2001, pp 541-553.

SACROILIAC JOINT INJECTIONS

Description

The sacroiliac joint is a joint with a joint capsule, synovial fluid, and hyaline cartilage on the sacral side and fibrocartilage on the iliac side. The sacroiliac joint possesses widespread neural innervation, anatomic variability, and unique biomechanical properties. Now there is evidence that the sacroiliac joint is a source of mechanical low back and lower extremity pain. Provocative injections and arthrography have described sacroiliac joint pain referral patterns in asymptomatic volunteers, predicted symptomatic sacroiliac joints in patients with suspected lumbar discogenic or facet joint pain, described morphologic futures of sacroiliac joint capsule, and defined contrast extravasation patterns on sacroiliac joint arthrography and post-arthrography – CT in subjects with low back or groin pain.

Sacroiliac joint block may be diagnostic or therapeutic. In the diagnostic sacroiliac joint block, anesthetic agent is introduced into the sacroiliac joint under fluoroscopic guidance. At least 75% resolution of the patient's pain over the ipsilateral SI joint is considered diagnostic of pain emanating from the sacroiliac joint. Incidence of sacroiliac joint pain has been highly variable.

CPT Code(s)

- 27096 – Injection procedure for sacroiliac joint, arthrography, and/or anesthetic/steroid
- 73542 – Radiologic examination, sacroiliac joint arthrography, radiological supervision and interpretation
- 76005 – fluoroscopy code

Indications and Medical Necessity

The following criteria should be considered carefully in performing SI joint blocks:

1. Complete initial evaluation including history and physical examination;
2. Physiological and functional assessment, as necessary and feasible;
3. Definition of indications and medical necessity as follows:
   - Suspected organic problem;
   - Nonresponsiveness to conservative modalities of treatments;
   - Pain and disability of moderate-to-severe degree;
   - No evidence of contraindications such as infection, or predominantly psychogenic pain;
   - Responsiveness to prior interventions with improvement in physical and functional status for repeat blocks or other interventions;
   - Repeating interventions only upon return of pain and deterioration in functional status;

ICD-9 CODES THAT SUPPORT MEDICAL NECESSITY

- Sacroiliitis - 720.2

It is the responsibility of the provider to code to the highest level specified in the *ICD-9-CM*, eg, to the fourth or fifth digit. The service must be reasonable and necessary in the specific case and must meet criteria specified in the policy.

- Noncovered ICD-9 Codes

Any code not listed in the "ICD-9 Codes That Support Medical Necessity" section of this policy may not be covered, unless specific additional information is provided.

Frequency and Number of Injections or Interventions:

- In the diagnostic or stabilization phase, a patient may receive injections at intervals of no sooner than 1 week or, preferably, 2 weeks.
- In the treatment or therapeutic phase (after the stabilization is completed), the frequency should be 2 months or longer between each injection, provided that at least > 50% relief is obtained for 6 weeks. However, if the neural blockade is applied for different regions, it can be performed at intervals of no sooner than 1 week or, preferably, 2 weeks for most type of blocks. The therapeutic frequency must remain at 2 months for each region. It is further suggested that all regions be treated at the same time, provided all procedures are performed safely.
- In the diagnostic or stabilization phase, the number of injections should be limited to no more than four times per year.
- In the treatment or therapeutic phase, the interventional procedures should be repeated only as necessary judging by the medical necessity criteria, and these should be limited to a maximum of six times for local anesthetic and steroid blocks for a period of 1 year.

Number Per Setting

It is recommended that a physician should consider a patient in totality and treat multiple regions of the patient in the same setting, as long as it is safe and feasible. Attempts to treat one particular organ at a different time are not an absolute necessity.

However, no more than five procedures (different procedures and/or multiples of one procedure – or total line items or procedures) must be billed in one setting for any of the following: the procedures are performed in different regions or a combination of procedures is performed in multiple regions. For treatment of a single region, eg, only lumbosacral spine or cervical spine, a maximum of four procedures (different procedures and/or multiple of one procedure – or total line items or procedures) should be billed. Procedure billing excludes CPT 76005, which may be added in addition to the above.

Documentation Requirements

The patient's medical record must contain documentation that fully supports the medical necessity for sacroiliac joint injections.

Documentation must also support the frequency and the appropriateness of this procedure, as opposed to alternate forms of therapy.

Comprehensive, Component and Mutually Exclusive Codes

CPT 27096 - injection procedure for sacroiliac joint, arthrography; a comprehensive code includes several component codes as follows:

- 20600 injection; small joint, bursa or ganglion
- 20605 injection, intermediate joint, bursa or ganglion
- 20610 injection, major joint or bursa
- 69990 operating microscope
- 76000, 76001, 76003 fluoroscopy codes, and
- 90782 administration of therapeutic substance

Mutually exclusive codes: None

CPT 73542- radiologic examination, sacroiliac joint arthrography, radiologic supervision and interpretation; a comprehensive code includes several component codes as follows:

- 76000, 76001, 76005 fluoroscopy codes

Mutually exclusive codes: None

Sources of Information

1. Manchikanti L, Singh V, Kloth D et al. Interventional techniques in the management of chronic pain: Part 2.0. *Pain Physician* 2001; 4:24-96.
2. Fortin JD. The sacroiliac joint: A new perspective. *J Back Musculoskeletal Rehabil* 1993; 3:31-43.
3. Fortin JD, Dwyer A, West S et al. Sacroiliac joint pain referral patterns upon application of a new injection/arthrography technique. Part I: Asymptomatic volunteers. *Spine* 1994; 19:1475-1482.
4. Fortin JD, Dwyer A, Aprill C et al. Sacroiliac joint pain referral patterns. Part II: Clinical evaluation. *Spine* 1994; 19:1483-1489.
5. Dreyfuss P, Dreyer S, Griffin J et al. Positive sacroiliac screening tests in asymptomatic adults. *Spine* 1994; 19:1138-1143.
6. Dreyfuss P, Michaelsen M, Pauza K et al. The value of medical history and physical examination in diagnosing sacroiliac joint pain. *Spine* 1996; 21:2594-2602.
7. Maigne JY, Aivaliklis A, Pfefer F. Results of sacroiliac joint double block and value of sacroiliac pain provocation tests in 54 patients with low back pain. *Spine* 1996; 21:1889-1892.
8. Vogler JB, III, Brown WH, Helms CA et al. The normal sacroiliac joint: A CT study of asymptomatic patients. *Radiol* 1984; 151:433-437.
9. Norman GF, May A. Sacroiliac conditions simulating intervertebral disc syndrome. *West J Surg* 1956; 64:461-462.
10. Slipman CW, Plastaras CT, Yang ST et al. Outcomes of therapeutic fluoroscopically guided sacroiliac joint injections for definitive SIJS. *Arch Phys Med Rehabil* 1996; 77:937.
11. Slipman CW, Whyte WS, Chow DW et al. Sacroiliac joint syndromes. *Pain Physician* 2001; 4:143-152.

TRIGGER POINT INJECTIONS

Description

Myofascial pain syndrome, which is a regional muscle pain disorder accompanied by trigger points, appears to be a common phenomenon in multiple regions, specifically in the cervical spine. In the head and neck region, it is believed that myofascial pain syndrome can manifest not only with mechanical symptoms in the neck, but as a headache, tinnitus, shoulder pain, temporomandibular joint pain, eye symptoms, and torticollis. However, there is absolutely no epidemiologic data on the prevalence of myofascial pain in the neck. The authors exploring the role of trigger points and myofascial pain in whiplash injuries believe that the theory of trigger points lacks demonstrated internal validity. Formal studies also have shown that myofascial experts have difficulty in agreeing on the presence of a trigger point, which is the cardinal feature of regional myofascial pain syndrome. In addition to this, it has been shown that, topographically, trigger points of the neck overlay the cervical facet joints; and it has been reported that pain patterns of cervical trigger points are identical to those of referred pain from the facet joints.

Similar to the cervical spine, the most common diagnosis for low back pain is acute or chronic lumbosacral strain or sprain; however, the scientific evidence for low back pain of muscle origin is not overwhelming.

Myofascial trigger points are self-sustaining, hyper-irritative foci that may occur in any skeletal muscle in response to strain produced by acute or chronic overload. Classically these trigger points produce a referred-pain pattern characteristic for that individual muscle. Thus, each pattern becomes part of a single muscle myofascial pain syndrome. To successfully treat chronic myofascial pain syndrome, each single muscle syndrome needs to be identified, along with every perpetuating factor.

Since there is no laboratory or imaging test available for establishing or confirming the diagnosis of trigger points, it mainly depends upon detailed history and specific musculoskeletal examination. Some of the cardinal features of trigger points are as follows:

1. Distribution pattern of the pain consistent with the referral pattern of trigger points that are described in the literature;
2. The presence of trigger points with focal tenderness with a specific referral pattern of pain;
3. A palpable taut band of muscle in which the trigger point is located;
4. Reproduction of referred-pain pattern upon stimulation of the trigger point.

CPT Code(s)

- 20550 Injection, tendon sheath, ligament, trigger points or ganglion cyst
- 20552 Injection, single or multiple trigger point(s), one or two muscle groups
- 20553 Injection, single or multiple trigger point(s), three or more muscle groups

Indications and Medical Necessity

The following criteria should be considered carefully in performing trigger point injections:

1. Complete initial evaluation, including history and physical examination;
2. Physiological and functional assessment, as necessary and feasible;
3. Definition of indications and medical necessity as follows:
   - Suspected organic problem;
   - Nonresponsiveness to conservative modalities of treatments;
   - Pain and disability of moderate-to-severe degree;
   - No evidence of contraindications such as infection or pain of predominantly psychogenic origin;
   - Responsiveness to prior interventions with improvement in physical and functional status for repeat blocks or other interventions;
   - Repeating interventions only upon return of pain and deterioration in functional status.

ICD-9 Codes That Support Medical Necessity

1. Myalgia and myositis, unspecified - 729.1
2. Rheumatism, unspecified and fibrositis - 729.0

It is the responsibility of the provider to code to the highest level specified in the *ICD-9-CM* eg, to the fourth or fifth digit. The service must be reasonable and necessary in the specific case and must meet the criteria specified in the policy.

Frequency and Number of Injections or Interventions

- In the diagnostic or stabilization phase, a patient may receive injections at intervals of no sooner than 1 week or, preferably, 2 weeks.
- In the treatment or therapeutic phase (after the stabilization is completed), the frequency should be 2 months or longer between each injection, provided that at least >50% relief is obtained for 6 weeks. However, if the neural blockade and/or injections are applied for different regions, it/they can be performed at intervals of no sooner than 1 week or, preferably, 2 weeks for most type of blocks. The

therapeutic frequency must remain at 2 months for each region. It is further suggested that all regions be treated at the same time provided all procedures are performed safely.

- In the diagnostic or stabilization phase, the number of trigger point injections should be limited to no more than four times per year.
- In the treatment or therapeutic phase, the trigger point injections should be repeated only as necessary judging by the medical necessity criteria, and these should be limited to a maximum of six times for local anesthetic and steroid blocks.

Noncovered ICD-9 Codes

Any code not listed in the "ICD-9 Codes That Support Medical Necessity" section of this policy.

Documentation Requirements

The patient's medical record must contain documentation that fully supports the medical necessity for trigger point injections.

Documentation must also support the frequency and the appropriateness of this procedure, as opposed to alternate forms of therapy.

Comprehensive, Component and Mutually Exclusive Codes

CPT - 20550 injection, tendon sheath, ligament, trigger points or ganglion cyst; a comprehensive code which also includes several component codes as follows:

- 10160 puncture aspiration of abscess, hematoma or cyst
- 11900 injection, intralesional; up to and including seven lesions
- 11901 injection, intralesional; more than seven lesions
- 12032 layer closure of wounds of scalp, axillae, trunk, and/or extremities; 2.6 cm to 7.5 cm
- 12042 layer closure of wounds of neck, hands, feet, and/or external genitalia; 2.6 cm to 7.5 cm
- 20500 injection of sinus tract; therapeutic (separate procedure)
- 29075 application of halo-type body cast; elbow to finger (short arm)
- 29105 application of long arm splint (shoulder to hand)
- 29125 application of short arm splint (forearm to hand); static
- 29130 application of finger splint; static
- 29220 strapping; low back
- 29260 strapping; elbow or wrist
- 29405 application of short leg cast (below knee to toes)
- 29425 application of short leg cast (below knee to toes); walking or ambulatory type
- 29450 application of clubfoot cast with molding or manipulation, long or short leg
- 29515 application of short leg splint (calf to foot)
- 29530 strapping; knee
- 29540 strapping; ankle
- 29550 strapping; toes
- 29580 strapping; Unna boot
- 29590 Denis-Browne splint strapping
- 64550 application of surface (transcutaneous) neurostimulator
- 64714 neuroplasty, major peripheral nerve, arm or leg; lumbar plexus
- 69990 operating microscope
- 72240 myelography, cervical radiological supervision and interpretation
- 72265 myelography, lumbosacral, radiological supervision and interpretation
- 72295 diskography, lumbar, radiological supervision and interpretation
- 76000-76003 fluoroscopy codes
- 87102 culture, fungi (mold or yeast) isolation, with presumptive identification of isolates; other source (except blood)
- 90780 IV infusion for therapy
- 90781 IV infusion for therapy
- 90782 subcutaneous or intramuscular IM injection
- 95900 nerve conduction, amplitude and latency/velocity study, each nerve; motor, without F-wave study

Mutually exclusive code:

- 11010 debridement and removal of foreign material associated with open fractures; skin and subcutaneous tissues.

Sources of Information

1. Manchikanti L, Singh V, Kloth D et al. Interventional techniques in the management of chronic pain: Part 2.0. *Pain Physician* 2001; 4:24-96.
2. Manchikanti, L. Neural blockade in cervical pain syndromes. *Pain Physician* 1999; 2:65-84.
3. Travell J. Myofascial trigger points. Clinical view. In Advances in Pain Research and Therapy. New York , Bonica JJ, Able-Fessardi D (eds). Raven Press, 1976, Vol. 1 pp 919-926.
4. Skootsky SA, Jaeger B, Oye RK. Prevalence of myofascial pain in general internal medicine practice. *West J Med* 1989; 151:157-160.
5. Han SC, Harrison P. Myofascial pain syndrome and trigger point management. *Reg Anesth* 1997; 22:89-101.
6. Barnsley L, Lord S, Bogduk N. Whiplash injury. *Pain* 1994; 58:283-307.
7. Wole F, Simons DG, Fricton J et al. The fibromyalgia and myofascial pain syndromes. A preliminary study of tender point and trigger points in persons with fibromyalgia pain and no disease. *J Rheumatol* 1992; 19:944-951.
8. Bogduk N, Simons DG. Neck pain: Joint pain or trigger points. In Vaeroy H and Merskey J (eds). Progress in Fibromyalgia and Myofascial Pain, Elsevier, Amsterdam, 1993; pp 267-273.
9. Gerwin RD. Myofascial pain syndromes from trigger points. *Pain* 1999; 3:153-159.
10. Rauck RL. Myofascial pain syndrome and fibromyalgia. *Pain* 1996; 41-53.
11. Harden RN, Bruehl SP, Gass S et al. Signs and symptoms of the myofascial pain syndrome: A national survey of pain management providers. *Clin J Pain* 2000; 16:64-72.

SPINAL CORD STIMULATORS

Description

Spinal cord or epidural stimulation involves an electric field, and a specified waveform, pulse width, and rate, and is reported to diminish pain intensity in select cases of chronic neurogenic pain. In spinal cord stimulation used to treat chronic neurogenic pain, most typically, the dorsal or sensory fibers of the spinal cord are stimulated. Spinal cord stimulation is indicated for the treatment of a number of conditions that are intractable and nonresponsive to many of the other modalities of treatments. The neurostimulator electrodes used for this purpose are implanted percutaneously in the epidural space through a special needle. Some patients may need an open procedure requiring a laminectomy to place the electrodes.

Prior to placement of the permanent electrodes, trial electrodes are placed and stimulation is carried out with an external stimulator. The trial period may be extended up to 4 weeks if necessary. If during the trial period, it is determined that the spinal cord stimulation is not effective or is not acceptable to the patient, the electrodes may be removed. However, if the trial has been successful, a spinal neurostimulator and pulse generator are inserted subcutaneously and connected to the electrodes already in place or to new electrodes.

In some cases, neurostimulator electrodes migrate or move from the area which needed to be stimulated, in which case these electrodes require realignment. Additionally, in very few cases, electrodes may need to be removed. If the patient cannot tolerate the electrodes, the spinal cord stimulation becomes ineffective after a period of time, and the leads and/or the impulse generator become infected.

CPT Code(s)

- ♦ 63650 - Percutaneous implantation of neurostimulator electrodes; epidural
- ♦ 63655 - Laminectomy for implantation of neurostimulator electrodes; epidural
- ♦ 63685 - Incision and subcutaneous placement of spinal neurostimulator pulse generator or receiver, direct or inductive coupling.
- ♦ 63660 - Revision or removal of spinal neurostimulator electrodes
- ♦ 63688 -Revision or removal of implanted spinal neurostimulator pulse generator or receiver

Indications and Medical Necessity

The following criteria should be considered carefully in performing spinal cord simulation procedures:

1. Complete initial evaluation, including history and physical examination;
2. Physiological and functional assessment, as necessary and feasible;
3. Psychological evaluation as necessary;
4. Definition of indications and medical necessity as follows:

   - Suspected organic problem;
   - Nonresponsiveness to almost all conservative modalities of treatments, including fluoroscopically directed epidural injections;
   - Pain and disability of severe degree;
   - No evidence of contraindications such as severe spinal stenosis resulting in intraspinal obstruction, infection, or predominantly psychogenic pain;

5. Implantation of the spinal cord stimulator used only as a choice of last resort and after other treatment modalities including medical management and, where applicable, other invasive procedures like appropriate nerve blocks, including fluoroscopically directed epidural injections, have been tried and did not prove to be satisfactory, or these have been judged to be unsuitable or contraindicated for the given patient.
6. In addition to the physical, functional and psychological assessment, which is basic, careful screening and evaluation by a multidisciplinary team prior to implantation, which should include physical and functional as well as psychological evaluation.
7. Prior to implantation of the permanent electrodes, demonstrated relief of pain with a temporarily implanted electrode, without any deleterious effects.

ICD-9 Codes That Support Medical Necessity

1. Postlaminectomy syndrome

   - 722.81 cervical, 722.82 thoracic, 722.83, lumbosacral

2. Disc displacement without myelopathy (disc herniation, radiculitis, disc extrusion, disc protrusion, disc prolapse, discogenic syndrome).

   - 722.0 cervical, 722.11 thoracic, 722.10 lumbosacral

3. Disc displacement with myelopathy

   - 722.71 cervical, 722.72 thoracic, 722.73 lumbosacral

4. Epidural fibrosis

   - 349.2 cervical, 349.2 thoracic, 349.2 lumbosacral

5. Complex regional pain syndrome (Type I or reflex sympathetic dystrophy)

- 337.20 reflex sympathetic dystrophy unspecified, 337.21 reflex sympathetic dystrophy upper limb, 337.22 reflex sympathetic dystrophy lower limb, 337.29 reflex sympathetic dystrophy other unspecified site

6. Complex regional pain syndrome (Type II or causalgia)

- 355.9 causalgia, 354.4 causalgia upper limb, 355.71 causalgia lower limb

7. Limb pain

- 353.6 phantom limb pain, 997.60 stump pain, 997.61 neuroma of amputation stump, 342.0 hemiplegia – flaccid, 342.1 hemiplegia – spastic

8. Postherpetic neuralgia

- 053.10 with unspecified nerve system complication

- 053.13 postherpetic polyneuropathy

9. Cauda equina injury 952.4
10. Chronic arachnoiditis 322.2
11. Arthrosclerosis of extremities with wrist pain 440.22
12. Mechanical complications of nervous system device implanted graft 996.2 (to be used to indicate intolerance of the device by the patient or failure of equipment/loss of effectiveness).
13. Infection and inflammatory reaction due to internal prosthetic device, implant and graft; due to nervous system device, implant and graft 996.63

It is the responsibility of the provider to code to the highest level specified in the *ICD-9-CM* (eg, to the fourth or fifth digit. The service must be reasonable and necessary in the specific case and must meet the criteria specified in the policy.

Non Covered ICD-9 Code(s)

All ICD-9-CM codes not listed as covered in this policy may not be covered. Individual consideration can be given when the claim is submitted with a special report detailing the reason for performing the procedure for any other condition.

Sources of Information

1. Manchikanti L, Singh V, Kloth D et al. Interventional techniques in the management of chronic pain: Part 2.0. *Pain Physician* 2001; 4:24-96.
2. Wetzel FT, Hassenbusch S, Oakley JC et al. Treatment of chronic pain in failed back surgery patients with spinal cord stimulation: A review of current literature and proposal for future investigation. *Neuromodulation* 2000;3:59-74
3. May RJ, Volker S. Chronic pain management and spinal cord stimulation: Patient-screening guidelines to improve treatment outcome. *Pain Digest* 1999; 9:353-363.
4. Neilson KD, Adams Je, Hosobuchi Y. Experience with dorsal column stimulation for relief of chronic intractable pain:1968-1973. *Surg Neurol* 1975;4:148-152.
5. Pineda A. Dorsal column stimulation and its prospects. *SurgNeurol* 1975;4:157-63
6. Richardson RR, Siqueira EB, Cerullo LJ. Spinal epidural neurostimulation for treatment of acute and chronic intractable pain: Initial and long term results. *Neurosurgery* 1979; 5:344-348.
7. Kumar K, Nath R, Wyant GM. Treatment of chronic pain by epidural spinal cord stimulation.: A 10-year experience. *J Neurosurg* 1991; 75:402-407.
8. North RB, Ewend MG, Lawton MT et al. Failed back surgery syndrome: 5-year follow- up after spinal cord stimulator implantation. *Neurosurgery* 1991; 28:692-699.
9. North RB, Ewend MG, Lawton MT et al. Spinal cord stimulation for chronic, intractable pain: Superiority of "multi-channel" devices. *Pain* 1991; 44:119-130.
10. LeDoux MS, Langford KH. Spinal cord stimulation for the failed back syndrome. *Spine* 1993;18:191-194.
11. North RB, Kidd DH, Zahurak M et al. Spinal cord stimulation for chronic intractable pain: Experience over two decades. *Neurosurgery* 1993; 32:384-395.
12. Barolat G, Ketcik B, He J. Long-term outcome of spinal cord stimulation for chronic pain management. *Neuromodulation* 1998;1:19-29.
13. Deer TR. Current and future trends in spinal cord stimulation for chronic pain. *Curr Pain and Headache Reports* 2001; 5:503-509.
14. Burchiel KJ, Anderson VC, Brown FD et al. Prospective, multicenter study of spinal cord stimulation for relief of chronic back and extremity pain. *Spine* 1996; 21:2786-2794.
15. de la Porte C Van de Kelft E. Spinal cord stimulation in failed back surgery syndrome. *Pain* 1993; 52:55-61.
16. Kumar K, Nath R. Spinal cord stimulation for chronic pain in peripheral neuropathy. *Surg Neurol* 1996; 46:363-364.
17. Turner J, Loeser J, Bell K. Spinal cord stimulation for chronic low back pain: A systematic literature synthesis. *Neurosurgery* 1995; 37:1088-1096.
18. Segal R Stacey BR, Rudy TE et al. Spinal cord stimulation revisited. *Neurol Res* 1998; 20:391-396.
19. Kemler MA. Spinal cord stimulation in patients with chronic reflex sympathetic dystrophy. *N Engl J Med* 2000; 343:618-624.
20. Kumar K, Nath R, Toth C. Spinal cord stimulation is effective in the management of reflex sympathetic dystrophy. *Neurosurgery* 1997; 3:503-508.
21. North R, Kidd D, Lee M et al. A prospective randomized study of spinal cord stimulation versus reoperation for failed back surgery syndrome: Initial results. *Stereotact Funct Neurosurg* 1994; 267-272.
22. Devulder J, De Colvenaer L, Rolly G et al. Spinal cod stimulation in chronic pain therapy. *Clin J Pain* 1990; 6:51-56.
23. Burchiel KJ, Anderson VC, Wilson BJ et al. Prognostic factors of spinal cord stimulation for chronic back pain. *Neurosurgery* 1995; 36:1101-1110.
24. de la Porte C, Siegfried J. Lumbosacral spinal fibrosis (spinal arachnoiditis). Its diagnosis and treatment by spinal cord stimulation. *Spine* 1983; 8:593-603.
25. Ohnmeiss DD, Rashbaum RF, Bogdanffy GM. Prospective outcome evaluation of spinal cord stimulation in patients with intractable leg pain. *Spine* 1996; 21:1344-1350.
26. Ohnmeiss DD, Rashbaum RF. Patient satisfaction with spinal cord stimulation for predominant complaints of chronic, intractable low back pain. *The Spine J* 2001; 1:358-363.

INTRATHECAL PUMPS

Description

Chronic opioid therapy in the treatment of persistent pain of noncancer origin has gained broad acceptance. The multiple routes of administration available to the practitioner are the oral, transdermal, epidural, and intrathecal. This policy will address intrathecal administration of opioids and other drugs. Opioid agonists produce analgesia at the spinal cord level when administered in the intrathecal or epidural space. This technique may be used for the management of chronic intractable pain when it is not controlled by less invasive techniques, as well as oral narcotics. Intrathecal baclofen is used for the treatment of intractable spasticity of the spine or brain etiology. For intrathecal administration of drugs, a reservoir is inserted subcutaneously; and it is attached to the proximal portion of the catheter, which is tunneled beneath the skin.

With the epidural catheterization, preservative-free morphine sulfate, hydromorphone hydrochloride (Dilaudid®), Fentanyl or baclofen can be administered every 8 to 12 hours in the epidural space through an indwelling catheter, which can be placed percutaneously.

CPT Code(s)

- 62350 Implantation, revision or repositioning of intrathecal or epidural catheter, for implantable reservoir or implantable infusion pump, without laminectomy
- 62351 with laminectomy
- 62355 Removal of previously implanted intrathecal or epidural catheter
- 62360 Implantation or replacement of device for intrathecal or epidural drug infusion; subcutaneous reservoir
- 62361 Nonprogrammable pump
- 62362 Programmable pump, including preparation or pump, with or without programming
- 62365 Removal of subcutaneous reservoir or pump previously implanted for intrathecal or epidural infusion
- 62367 Electronic analysis of programmable, implanted pump for intrathecal or epidural drug infusion (includes evaluation of reservoir status, alarm status, drug prescription status); without reprogramming.
- 62368 With reprogramming
- 62310 Injection, single, epidural or subarachnoid; cervical or thoracic
- 62311 Lumbar, sacral (caudal)
- 62318 Catheter placement, continuous infusion or intermittent bolus; epidural or subarachnoid; cervical or thoracic
- 62319 Lumbar, sacral (caudal)
- 96530 Refilling or maintenance of implantable pump or reservoir

Indications and Medical Necessity

The following criteria should be considered carefully in performing intrathecal pump placements:

1. Complete initial evaluation, including history and physical examination;
2. Physiological and functional assessment, as necessary and feasible;
3. Psychological evaluation as necessary;
4. Definition of indications and medical necessity as follows:

   - Suspected organic problem;
   - Nonresponsiveness to almost all conservative modalities of treatments, including fluoroscopically directed epidural injections;
   - Pain and disability of severe degree;
   - No evidence of contraindications such as severe spinal stenosis resulting in intraspinal obstruction, infection, or predominantly psychogenic pain.

5. Implantation of the morphine pump or epidural catheterization for long-term purposes used only as a choice of last resort and after other treatment modalities including medical management and, where applicable, other invasive procedures like appropriate nerve blocks, including fluoroscopically directed epidural injections, have been tried and did not prove to be satisfactory; or these have been judged to be unsuitable or contraindicated for the given patient.
6. In addition to the physical, functional and psychological assessment, which is basic, careful screening and evaluation by a multidisciplinary team prior to implantation, which should include physical and functional, as well as psychological, evaluation.
7. Prior to implantation of the pump, demonstrated relief of pain with subarachnoid or epidural injections of morphine reliably on at least two occasions, without any deleterious effects.
8. A patient with the diagnosis of cancer with a likely life expectancy of at least 3 months and unresponsiveness to less invasive medical therapy or that may no longer be the choice of therapy.

ICD-9 Codes That Support Medical Necessity

For implantation of catheter/pump services:

1. Postherpetic trigeminal neuralgia - 053.12
2. Postherpetic polyneuropathy - 053.13
3. Carcinomas - 141.0-239.9
4. Chronic arachnoiditis - 322.2

5. Reflex Sympathetic Dystrophy - 337.20-337.29
6. Unspecified disease of spinal cord - 336.9
(To be used only for the diagnosis of myelopathy)
7. Phantom limb pain - 353.6
8. Causalgia of upper limb - 354.4
9. Causalgia of lower limb - 355.71
10. Postlaminectomy syndrome, cervical region - 722.81
11. Postlaminectomy syndrome, thoracic region - 722.82
12. Postlaminectomy syndrome, lumbar region - 722.83

For removal/revision of catheter/pump services:

1. Other complications of internal (biological) (synthetic) 996.70 due to unspecified device, implant, and graft

It is the responsibility of the provider to code to the highest level specified in the *ICD-9-CM* eg, to the fourth or fifth digit. The service must be reasonable and necessary in the specific case and must meet the criteria specified in the policy.

Noncovered ICD-9 Codes

Any code not listed in the "ICD-9 Codes That Support Medical Necessity" section of this policy may not be covered, unless specific additional information is provided.

Documentation Requirements

The patient's medical record must contain documentation that fully supports the medical necessity for pump implantation and administration of drugs.

Documentation must also support the frequency and the appropriateness of this procedure, as opposed to alternate forms of therapy.

Comprehensive Codes

CPT 62310 - cervical or thoracic epidural injection; a comprehensive code, includes the following component codes:

- 20605 injection, intermediate joint, bursa or ganglion
- 20610 injection, major joint or bursa
- 36140 introduction of needle or intracatheter, extremity artery
- 62284 injection procedure for myelography
- 69990 use of operating microscope
- 76000, 76001, 76003 fluoroscopy codes

Mutually exclusive code:

- 64479 cervical or thoracic transforaminal epidural, single level

CPT 62311 - lumbar (caudal epidural injection); a comprehensive code, includes the following component codes:

- 20605 injection, intermediate joint, bursa or ganglion
- 20610 injection, major joint or bursa
- 36140 introduction of needle or intracatheter, extremity artery
- 62284 injection procedure for myelography
- 69990 use of operating microscope
- 76000, 76001, 76003 fluoroscopy codes

Mutually exclusive code:

- 64483 lumbar or sacral, transforaminal epidural, single level

CPT 62318 - continuous infusion with catheter placement (cervical or thoracic) a comprehensive code, includes the following component code:

- 01996 - daily management of epidural or subarachnoid drug administration
- 20605 - injection, intermediate joint, bursa or ganglion
- 20610 - injection, major joint or bursa
- 36000 - introduction of needle or intracatheter, vein
- 36140 - introduction of needle or intracatheter, extremity artery
- 36410 - venipuncture, child over age 3 years or adult, necessitating physician's skill
- 62270 - spinal puncture, lumbar, diagnostic
- 62272 - spinal puncture, therapeutic, for drainage of spinal fluid
- 62284 - injection procedure for myelography
- 62310 - injection, single, epidural or subarachnoid; cervical or thoracic
- 69990 - use of operating microscope
- 76000, 76001, 76003 - fluoroscopy codes

Mutually exclusive codes:

- 62273 - epidural blood patch
- 64479 - cervical transforaminal epidural, single level

CPT 62319 - injection, catheter placement, lumbar or caudal epidural space; a comprehensive code, includes the following component codes:

- 01996 - daily management of epidural or subarachnoid drug administration
- 20605 - injection, intermediate joint, bursa or ganglion
- 20610 - injection, major joint or bursa
- 36000 - introduction of needle or intracatheter, vein
- 36140 - introduction of needle or intracatheter, extremity artery
- 36410 - venipuncture, child over age 3 years or adult, necessitating physician's skill

- 62270 - spinal puncture, lumbar, diagnostic
- 62272 - spinal puncture, therapeutic, for drainage of spinal fluid
- 62284 - injection procedure for myelography
- 62311 - injection, single; epidural, lumbar sacral (caudal)
- 69990 - use of operating microscope
- 76000, 76001, 76003 - fluoroscopy codes

Mutually exclusive codes:

- 62273 - epidural blood patch
- 64483 - cervical transforaminal epidural, single level

CPT 62350 - implantation, revision or repositioning of tunneled intrathecal or epidural catheter, for long-term medication administration via an external pump or implantable reservoir/infusion pump (without laminectomy); a comprehensive code, includes the following component codes:

- 62270 spinal puncture, lumbar, diagnostic
- 62272 spinal puncture, therapeutic, for drainage of spinal fluid
- 62273 injection, epidural, of blood or clot patch
- 62280 injection/infusion of neurolytic substance (subarachnoid)
- 62281 injection/infusion of neurolytic substance (epidural, cervical or thoracic)
- 62282 injection/infusion of neurolytic substance; epidural lumbar, sacral (caudal).
- 62310 injection, single, epidural or subarachnoid; cervical or thoracic
- 62311 injection, single; epidural, lumbar sacral (caudal)
- 62318 catheter placement, continuous infusion or intermittent bolus; epidural or subarachnoid; cervical or thoracic
- 62319 catheter placement, continuous infusion or intermittent bolus; epidural, lumbar, sacral (caudal)
- 64479 transforaminal epidural; cervical or thoracic, single level
- 64483 transforaminal epidural; lumbar or sacral, single level
- 69990 use of operating microscope

Mutually exclusive codes: None

CPT 62351 - implantation, revision or repositioning of tunneled intrathecal or epidural catheter, for long-term medication administration via an external pump or implantable reservoir/infusion pump (with laminectomy); a comprehensive code, includes the following component codes:

- 62280 injection/infusion of neurolytic substance (subarachnoid)
- 62281 injection/infusion of neurolytic substance (epidural, cervical or thoracic)
- 62282 injection/infusion of neurolytic substance; epidural lumbar, sacral (caudal).
- 62310 injection, single, epidural or subarachnoid; cervical or thoracic
- 62311 injection, single; epidural, lumbar sacral (caudal)
- 62318 catheter placement, continuous infusion or intermittent bolus; epidural or subarachnoid; cervical or thoracic
- 62319 catheter placement, continuous infusion or intermittent bolus; epidural, lumbar, sacral (caudal)
- 62350 implantation, revision or repositioning of tunneled intrathecal or epidural catheter, for long-term medication administration via an external pump or implantable reservoir/infusion pump (without laminectomy)
- 64479 transforaminal epidural; cervical or thoracic, single level
- 64483 transforaminal epidural; lumbar or sacral, single level
- 69990 use of operating microscope

Mutually exclusive codes: None

CPT 62355 - removal of previously implanted intrathecal or epidural catheter; a comprehensive code, includes the following component codes:

- 62270 spinal puncture, lumbar, diagnostic
- 62272 spinal puncture, therapeutic, for drainage of spinal fluid
- 62310 injection, single, epidural or subarachnoid; cervical or thoracic
- 62311 injection, single; epidural, lumbar sacral (caudal)
- 62318 catheter placement, continuous infusion or intermittent bolus; epidural or subarachnoid; cervical or thoracic
- 62319 catheter placement, continuous infusion or intermittent bolus; epidural, lumbar, sacral (caudal)
- 64479 transforaminal epidural; cervical or thoracic, single level
- 64483 transforaminal epidural; lumbar or sacral, single level
- 69990 use of operating microscope

Mutually exclusive codes:

- 62350 implantation, revision or repositioning of tunneled intrathecal or epidural catheter, for long-term medication administration via an external pump or implantable reservoir/infusion pump (without laminectomy)
- 62351 implantation, revision or repositioning of tunneled intrathecal or epidural catheter, for long-term medication administration via an external pump or implantable reservoir/infusion pump (with laminectomy)

CPT 62360 - implantation or replacement of device for intrathecal or epidural drug infusion (subcutaneous reser-

voir); a comprehensive code, includes the following component codes:

- 62270 spinal puncture, lumbar, diagnostic
- 62272 spinal puncture, therapeutic, for drainage of spinal fluid
- 62273 injection, epidural, of blood or clot patch
- 62310 injection, single, epidural or subarachnoid; cervical or thoracic
- 62311 injection, single; epidural, lumbar sacral (caudal)
- 62318 catheter placement, continuous infusion or intermittent bolus; epidural or subarachnoid; cervical or thoracic
- 62319 catheter placement, continuous infusion or intermittent bolus; epidural, lumbar, sacral (caudal)
- 62367 electronic analysis of programmable, implanted pump for intrathecal or epidural drug infusion (without programming)
- 62368 electronic analysis of programmable, implanted pump for intrathecal or epidural drug infusion (with reprogramming)
- 64479 transforaminal epidural; cervical or thoracic, single level
- 64483 transforaminal epidural; lumbar or sacral, single level
- 69990 use of operating microscope

Mutually exclusive codes:

- 62280 injection/infusion of neurolytic substance (subarachnoid)
- 62281 injection/infusion of neurolytic substance (epidural, cervical or thoracic)
- 62282 injection/infusion of neurolytic substance; epidural lumbar, sacral (caudal).
- 62362 implantation of replacement of device for intrathecal or epidural drug infusion; programmable pump, including preparation of pump, with or without programming

CPT 62361 - implantation or replacement of device for intrathecal or epidural drug infusion (nonprogrammable pump); a comprehensive code, includes the following component codes:

- 62270 spinal puncture, lumbar, diagnostic
- 62272 spinal puncture, therapeutic, for drainage of spinal fluid
- 62273 injection, epidural, of blood or clot patch
- 62310 injection, single; epidural or subarachnoid; cervical or thoracic
- 62311 injection, single; epidural, lumbar, sacral (caudal)
- 62318 catheter placement, continuous infusion or intermittent bolus; epidural or subarachnoid; cervical or thoracic
- 62319 catheter placement, continuous infusion or intermittent bolus; epidural, lumbar, sacral (caudal)
- 62367 electronic analysis of programmable, implanted pump for intrathecal or epidural drug infusion (without programming)
- 62368 electronic analysis of programmable, implanted pump for intrathecal or epidural drug infusion (with reprogramming)
- 64479 transforaminal epidural; cervical or thoracic, single level
- 64483 transforaminal epidural; lumbar or sacral, single level
- 69990 use of operating microscope

Mutually exclusive codes:

- 62280 injection/infusion of neurolytic substance (subarachnoid)
- 62281 injection/infusion of neurolytic substance (epidural, cervical or thoracic)
- 62282 injection/infusion of neurolytic substance; epidural lumbar, sacral (caudal).
- 62360 implantation or replacement of device for intrathecal or epidural drug infusion; subcutaneous reservoir

CPT 62362 implantation or replacement of device for intrathecal or epidural drug infusion (programmable pump); a comprehensive code, a comprehensive code, includes the following component codes:

- 62270 spinal puncture, lumbar, diagnostic
- 62272 spinal puncture, therapeutic
- 62273 injection, epidural, of blood or clot patch
- 62310 cervical epidural
- 62311 lumbar epidural
- 62318 catheter placement, continuous infusion or intermittent bolus; epidural or subarachnoid; cervical or thoracic
- 62319 catheter placement, continuous infusion or intermittent bolus; epidural, lumbar, sacral (caudal)
- 62361 implantation or replacement of device for intrathecal or epidural drug infusion (nonprogrammable pump)
- 62367 electronic analysis of programmable, implanted pump for intrathecal or epidural drug infusion (without programming)
- 62368 electronic analysis of programmable, implanted pump for intrathecal or epidural drug infusion (with reprogramming)
- 64479 injection, cervical transforaminal epidural
- 64483 injection, anesthetic agent and/or steroid, transforaminal epidural (lumbar or sacral, single level)
- 69990 use of operating microscope

Mutually exclusive codes:

- 62280 injection/infusion of neurolytic substance (subarachnoid)
- 62281 injection/infusion of neurolytic substance (epidural, cervical or thoracic)
- 62282 injection/infusion of neurolytic substance; epidural lumbar, sacral (caudal)

CPT 62365 removal of subcutaneous reservoir or pump, previously implanted for intrathecal or epidural infusion; a comprehensive code, includes the following component codes:

- 62310 cervical epidural
- 62311 lumbar epidural
- 62318 catheter placement, continuous infusion or intermittent bolus; epidural or subarachnoid; cervical or thoracic
- 62319 catheter placement, continuous infusion or intermittent bolus; epidural, lumbar, sacral (caudal)
- 62367 electronic analysis of programmable, implanted pump for intrathecal or epidural drug infusion (without programming)
- 62368 electronic analysis of programmable, implanted pump for intrathecal or epidural drug infusion (with reprogramming)
- 64479 injection, cervical transforaminal epidural
- 64483 injection, anesthetic agent and/or steroid, transforaminal epidural (lumbar or sacral, single level)
- 69990 use of operating microscope
- 96520 refilling and maintenance of portable pump

Mutually exclusive codes:

- 62360 implantation or replacement of device for intrathecal or epidural drug infusion; subcutaneous reservoir
- 62361 implantation or replacement of device for intrathecal or epidural drug infusion (nonprogrammable pump)
- 62362 implantation or replacement of device for intrathecal or epidural drug infusion; (programmable pump, including preparation of pump, with or without programming)

Sources of Information

1. Manchikanti L, Singh V, Kloth D et al. Interventional techniques in the management of chronic pain: Part 2.0. *Pain Physician* 2001; 4:24-96.
2. Willis KD, Doleys DM. The effects of long-term intraspinal infusion therapy with noncancer pain patients; Evaluation of patient, significant-other, and clinical staff appraisals. *Neuromodulation* 1999; 2:241-253.
3. Avellino AM, Loeser JD. Intrathecal Baclofen for the treatment of intractable spasticity of spine or brain etiology. *Neuromodulation* 2000; 3:75-81.
4. Dougherty PM, Staats PS. Intrathecal drug therapy for chronic pain. *Anesthesiology* 1999; 91:1891-1918.
5. Maron J, Loeser JD. Spinal opioid infusion in treatment of chronic pain of non-malignant origin. *Clin J Pain* 1996; 12:174-179.
6. Krames ES, Schuchard M. Implantable intraspinal infusion analgesia: Management guidelines. *Pain Rev* 1995;2:243-267.
7. Schuchard M, Lanning R, North R et al. Neurologic sequelae of intraspinal drug delivery systems: Results of a survey of American implanters of implantable drug delivery systems. *Neuromodulation* 1998; 1:137-148.
8. Doleys DM, Coleton M, Tutak U. Use of intraspinal infusion therapy with non-cancer pain patients: Follow up and comparison of worker's compensation versus non-worker's compensation patients. *Neuromodulation* 1998;1:149-159.
9. Hassenbusch SJ, Stanton-Hicks M, Covington EC et al. Long-term intraspinal infusion of opiates in the treatment of neuropathic pain. *J Pain Symptom Manage* 1995; 10:527-543.
10. Grabow TS, Derdzinski D, Staats PS. Spinal drug delivery. *Curr Pain and Headache Reports* 2001; 5:510-516.
11. Onofrio BM, Yaksh TL, Arnold PG. Continuous low-dose intrathecal morphine administration in the treatment of chronic pain of malignant origin. *Mayo Clin Proc* 1981; 56:516-520.
12. Anderson VC, Burchiel KJ. A prospective study of long-term intrathecal morphine in the management of chronic nonmalignant pain. *Neurosurgery* 1999; 44:289-300.
13. Goodman RR, Brisman R. Treatment of lower extremity reflex sympathetic dystrophy with continuous intrathecal morphine infusion. *Appl Neurophysiol* 1987; 50:425-426.
14. Coombs DW, Saunders RL, Fratkin JD et al. Continuous intrathecal hydromorphone and clonidine for intractable cancer pain. *J Neurosurg* 1986; 64:890-894.
15. Harvey SC, O'Neil MG, Pope CA et al. Continuous intrathecal meperidine via an implantable infusion pump for chronic nonmalignant pain. *Ann Pharmacother* 1997; 31:1306-1308.
16. Max MB, Inturrisi CE, Kaiko RF et al. Epidural and intrathecal opiates: Cerebrospinal fluid and plasma profiles in patients with chronic cancer pain. *Clin Pharmacol Ther* 1985; 38:631-641.
17. Meignier M, Ganansia MF, Lejus C et al. Intrathecal morphine therapy in children with cancer. *Cah Anesthesiol* 1992; 40:487-490.
18. Devulder J. Hyperalgesia induced by high-dose intrathecal sufentanil in neuropathic pain. *J Neurosurg Anesthesiol* 1997; 9:146-148.
19. Oyama T, Jin T, Yamaya R et al. Profound analgesic effects of beta-endorphin in man. *Lancet* 1980; 1:122-124.
20. Moulin DE, Max MB, Kaiko RF et al. The analgesic efficacy of intrathecal D-Ala2-D-Leu5-enkephalin in cancer patients with chronic pain. *Pain* 1985; 23:213-221.
21. Wen HL, Mehal ZD, Ong BH et al. Treatment of pain in cancer patients by intrathecal administration of dynorphin. *Peptides* 1987; 8:191-193.
22. Schoeffler P, Auroy P, Bazin JE et al. Subarachnoid midazolam: Histologic study in rats and report of its effect on chronic pain in humans. *Reg Anesth* 1991; 16:329-332.
23. Borg PA, Krijnen HJ. Long-term intrathecal administration of midazolam and clonidine. *Clin J Pain* 1996; 12:63-68.
24. Zuniga RE, Schlicht CR, Abram SE. Intrathecal baclofen is analgesic in patients with chronic pain. *Anesthesiology* 2000; 92:876-880.
25. Tumber PS, Fitzgibbon DR. The control of severe cancer pain by continuous intrathecal infusion and patient controlled intrathecal analgesia with morphine, bupivacaine and clonidine. *Pain* 1998; 78:217-220.
26. Mironer YE, Tollison CD. Methadone in the intrathecal treatment of chronic nonmalignant pain resistant to other neuroaxial agents: The first experience. *Neuromodulatiion* 2001; 4:25-31.
27. Siddall PJ, Gray M, Rutkowski S et al. Intrathecal morphine and clonidine in the management of spinal cord injury pain: A case report. *Pain* 1994; 59:147-148.
28. Eisenach JC, Hood DD, Curry R. Intrathecal, but not intravenous, clonidine reduces experimental thermal or capsaicin-induced pain and hyperalgesia in normal volunteers. *Anesth Analg* 1998; 87:591-596.
29. Sjoberg M, Appelgren L, Einarsson S et al. Long-term intrathecal morphine and bupivacaine in "refractory" cancer pain. I. Results from the first series of 52 patients. *Acta Anaesthesiol Scand* 1991; 35:30-43.
30. Nitescu P, Dahm P, Appelgren L et al. Continuous infusion of opioid and bupivacaine by externalized intrathecal catheters in long-term treatment of "refractory" nonmalignant pain. *Clin J Pain* 1998; 14:17-28.
31. Penn RD, Paice JA Adverse effects associated with the intrathecal administration of ziconotide. *Pain* 2000; 85:291-296.
32. Brose WG, Gutlove DP, Luther RR et al. Use of intrathecal SNX-111, a

novel, N-type, voltage-sensitive, calcium channel blocker, in the management of intractable brachial plexus avulsion pain. *Clin J Pain* 1997; 13:256-259.

33. Staats PS, Luthardt F, Shipley J et al. Long-term intrathecal ziconotide therapy: A case study and discussion. *Neuromodulation* 2001; 4:121-126.
34. Yang CY, Wong CS, Chang JY et al. Intrathecal ketamine reduces morphine requirements in patients with terminal cancer pain. *Can J Anaesth* 1996; 43:379-383.
35. Kristensen JD, Svensson B, Gordh T Jr. The NMDA-receptor antagonist CPP abolishes neurogenic "wind-up pain" after intrathecal administration in humans. *Pain* 1992; 51:249-253.
36. Penn RD, Paice JA, Kroin JS. Octreotide: A potent new non-opiate analgesic of intrathecal infusion. *Pain* 1992; 49:13-19.
37. Paice JA, Penn RD Kroin JS. Intrathecal octreotide for relief of intractable nonmalignant pain: 5-year experience with two cases. *Neurosurgery* 1996; 38:203-207.
38. Karlesten R, Gordh T Jr. An A1-selective adenosine agonist abolishes allodynia elicited by vibration and touch after intrathecal injection. *Anesth Analg* 1995; 80:844-847.
39. Klamt JG, Garcia LV, Prado WA. Analgesic and adverse effects of a low dose of intrathecally administered hyperbaric neostigmine alone or combined with morphine in patients submitted to spinal anaesthesia: Pilot studies. *Anaesthesia* 1999; 54:27-31.
41. Devoghel JC. Small intrathecal doses of lysine-acetylsalicylate relieve intractable pain in man. *J Int Med Res* 1983; 11:90-91.
42. Pellerin M, Hardy F, Abergel A et al. Chronic refractory pain in cancer patients. Value of the spinal injection of lysine acetylsalicylate 60 cases. *Presse Med* 1987; 16:1465-1468.

CODING FOR THE PROCEDURES AND SUPPLIES IN THE OFFICE

Jo Anne E. Burkhardt
Amy G. Mowles

BILLING AS OFFICE

To qualify as an office, the space must be rented or leased at a fair market value, there must be a written agreement for the rental or lease and the agreement must be for at least one year in duration. The staff must be an expense to the practice and can be either employed or leased. If hospital space is rented or leased for an office, this space must be separate and distinct space, not included in the hospital's cost-reporting space.

"INCIDENT TO" SERVICES

If a location qualifies as an office, the physician may bill Medicare for the services provided "incident to" his/her professional services provided these services are commonly provided in physician offices and are either commonly rendered with or without charge or included in the physician's bills. "Incident to" services include drugs, supplies and personnel employed by the physician including non-physician practitioners, clinical social workers and nursing staff.

Physician Assistants, Nurse Practitioners and Clinical Nurse Specialists may be assigned a provider number by Medicare and bill independently for their services. They are reimbursed at 85% of the physician's fee schedule. This allows billing for their services when a physician is not present. If the physician is present and participates in the treatment planning, the services of these providers may be billed to Medicare under the physician's provider number and payment is made at 100% of the physician's fee schedule. For the services to be considered "incident to" they must be furnished in the course of treatment where a physician performs an initial service and subsequent services of a frequency that reflects the physician's active participation in, and management of a course of treatment.

Other third party payors may or may not allow "incident to" billing. This should be verified at contract time and if allowed, there should be a clear understanding of how the payor wants the billing for these services handled.

FLUOROSCOPY

If a physician purchases or leases a C-arm for the office, the physician may bill globally for the services that require fluoroscopic guidance. Global billing means that the physician is billing for both the technical and professional components of the service. The pain management physician owns the equipment, pays for the technician to operate the equipment, supervises the technician and performs the fluoroscopic guidance. The fluoroscopy CPT code that the physician bills will depend on the service rendered. The most common fluoroscopy CPT codes for services rendered by the pain management physician are:

76003 This code is used for codes 64400-64450,64505-64530, 64600-64620 and 64630-64680.

76005 This code is used for spinal injection codes 62272-62282, 62310-62319, 64470-64484 and 64622-64627.

When a pain management physician renders the service in a setting where the facility and not the pain management physician own the C-arm, the fluoroscopy is billed with a -26 modifier, indicating the professional component only.

For discussion of radiological reports performed under fluoroscopic guidance see the RADIOLOGICAL SECTION of the CPT manual.

DRUGS

Medicare does reimburse for injectible drugs based on the lower of the billed charge or 95 percent of the average wholesale price of the drug. Drugs that cannot be self-administered are reimbursed.

Drugs are billed to Medicare using HCPCS codes that begin with the letter J. A drug may or may not have a specific J code established for it. Each J code also includes a specific dosage by which the J code is measured. A drug is billed in units and each unit represents the dosage specified by the code. To determine the number of units to bill, calculate as follows:

$$\frac{\text{(Fill Volume) x (Concentration of drug)}}{\text{Dosage of J code}}$$

= # units to place in box 24G of the HCFA1500 claim form

Code J3490 is the unlisted drug code and is used for any drug that does not have a specific J code established for it. Certain medications injected via implantable pumps are actually powdered form reconstituted by a compounding pharmacist or even in the office. The cost of this the powder is significantly lower than that of commercially prepared medication. These powdered reconstituted powders must not be billed with the J codes for the commercially prepared medications. These drugs should be billed with the unlisted drug code, specify the dosage and attach a copy of the medication invoice. Medicare does not pay for drugs that are considered experimental or not proven effective. Medicare publishes the drug fee schedule on a quarterly basis and the approved drugs are listed. The approved fee listed in the fee schedule represents a per unit fee based on the dosage specified for each J code.

Other third party payors may or may not reimburse the office for drugs separately from the service rendered. This should be clarified at contract negotiation time. Third party payors may want drugs submitted using the miscellaneous expense code of 99070 or may bundle the drugs into the fee for the service. When 99070 is used it is important to specify the drug name, dosage and concentration. This is an important item to negotiate with a payor. It is not unusual for a payor to reimburse separately for the drugs and it is important to clarify the basis by which they calculate their reimbursement. If they bundle drugs, be sure to identify the more expensive drugs and "carve out" these drugs so they are not bundled.

SUPPLIES

Medicare does not reimburse separately for the majority of the office supplies. They consider supplies to be bundled into the fee for the service rendered. Separate payment may be made for some surgical trays based on the procedure.

Other third party payors do reimburse for supplies using the 99070 code. At contract negotiation time it should be clarified as to what supplies are reimbursed separately and how to bill these supplies.

PROCEDURES

When billing for procedures done in the office setting, it is important for the office staff to understand the payment rules of the different payors. The following are some important items to clarify with the payors because they often impact reimbursement significantly:

I. Insurance Coverage Verification

- What co-pays or co-insurance pertain to the services?
- What is an effective date of coverage?
- Are there any special rules for surgical services?
- Are there procedures that may not be done in the office?

II. Pre-Certification

- Does the payor require preauthorization for any of the procedures performed in the office?
- If so, what must be done to obtain pre-certification?
- What must be included when the claim is filed?

III. Medical Review Policies

- Does the payor have any policies based on the frequency of treatment, the number of injections, special conditions supporting medical necessity; or any other special rules?
- If so, are you required to use an Advanced Beneficiary Notice (or any other notice) and any modifier at time of claim filing?
- Are you permitted to bill the patient for these balances?

IV. Bilateral Procedures

- How does the payor handle bilateral services? Are you to use the 50 modifier on one line of the HCFA 1500 or with the 50 modifier and use two lines, or are you to use RT/LT?
- Are there any procedures that when done bilaterally are not reimbursed at all?
- Are the bilateral services subject to a multiple procedure reduction?

V. Multiple Levels

- How does the payor reimburse for services rendered

at multiple levels on the same day?

- Will these services be subject to the multiple procedure reduction?
- Will they be bundled if done with other certain services?

VI. Correct Coding Initiative

- Does the payor follow CCI (Correct Coding Initiative) rules or do they have their own rules?
- If they have their own, what are the rules?
- Can you bill the patient for any of the bundled services if patient is notified in advance or are you prohibited from billing the patient?

VII. Modifiers

- What modifiers does the payor recognize and how do these modifiers affect payment? Under what circumstances should modifiers be used?

VIII. Global Surgery Rules

- Does the payor have global surgery rules for any of the services rendered in the office? If so, what are they and what services are considered to be part of the global surgical package?

Once the office staff has a clear understanding of the rules for each of the primary payors of the practice, it is important to establish office policies to address the various situations that are likely to arise. These policies should identify:

a) When to use the Advanced Beneficiary Notice
b) What may be billed to the patient and what are the collection rules at time of service?
c) What is the self-pay payment rule for patients without insurance?
d) Will the practice accept payment plans and if so what is the minimum payment and maximum repayment direction that is acceptable?
e) When will the patient be dismissed from the practice for non- payment?

Pain management physicians do some procedures in the office where they would bill with a site of service of 11. They may also perform services in the ambulatory surgery center and the site of service would be 24, in the outpatient hospital setting and the site if service is 22, and inpatient the site of service is 21. Some commercial payors use one digit site of service codes and this should be verified with the payor which code they use. Since fees may vary by site of service it is important that the proper site of service is used on the claim.

The following table lists the services usually done by the pain management physician in all locations and the CPT code that describes the service:

Trigger Points

20526	Injection, therapeutic (eg, local anesthetic; corticos teroid), carpal tunnel
20550	Injection, tendon sheath, ligament, ganglion cyst
20551	Tendon origin/insertion
20552	Single or multiple trigger point(s), one or two muscle group(s)
20553	Single or multiple trigger point(s), three or more muscle groups

Injections

11900	Scar injection
20600	Small joint injection (fingers, toes)
20605	Intermediate joint injection (leg, wrist, elbow, ankle, etc.)
20610	Major joint or bursa (shoulder, knee, hip)
27096	SI joint injection under fluoroscopy
62263	Adhesiolysis - 3 days
62263	Adhesiolysis - 1 day until 12/31/2002
6226X	(Final code will be released later) Adhesiolysis - 1 day after 1/1/03
62272	Spinal puncture, therapeutic, for drainage of cere brospinal fluid (by needle or catheter)
62273	Epidural, of blood or clot patch
62280	Injection of neurolytic substance (alcohol, phenol, etc) with or w/o other therapeutic substance; sub arachnoid
62281	Injection of neurolytic substance (alcohol, phenol, etc) with or w/o other therapeutic substance; epi dural, cervical/thoracic
62282	Injection of neurolytic substance (alcohol, phenol, etc) with or w/o other therapeutic substance; epi dural, lumbar/sacral (caudal)
62284	Myelography
62310	Epidural injection, single; cervical, thoracic
62311	Epidural injection, single; lumbar, sacral
62318	Continuous epidural; cervical, thoracic
62319	Continuous epidural; lumbar, sacral

Blocks

64400	Trigeminal nerve, any division or branch
64402	Facial nerve
64405	Greater occipital nerve
64408	Vegus nerve
64410	Phrenic nerve
64412	Spinal accessory nerve
64413	Cervical Plexus (occipitalis major/minor)
64415	Brachial plexus
64417	Axillary nerve

64418 Suprascapular nerve
64420 Intercostal nerve, single
64421 Intercostal nerves, multiple
64425 Ilioinguinal, iliohypogastric nerves
64430 Pudendal nerve
64435 Paracervical (uterine) nerve
64445 Sciatic nerve
64470 Paravertebral facet joint or joint nerve; cervical/tho racic, single
64472 Cervical/thoracic each additional level
64445 Sciatic nerve
64450 Peripheral nerve or branch
64470 Paravertebral facet joint or joint nerve; cervical/tho racic, single
64472 Paravertebral facet joint or joint nerve; cervical/tho racic, each additional level
64475 Paravertebral facet joint or joint nerve; lumbar, sac ral, single
64476 Paravertebral facet joint or joint nerve; lumbar/sac ral each additional level
64479 Transforaminal epidural; cervical, thoracic, single level
64480 Transforaminal cervical, thoracic, each additional level
64483 Transforaminal epidural; lumbar, sacral, single level
64484 Transforaminal lumbar, sacral each additional level

Sympathetic Blocks

64505 Sphenopalatine Injection
64508 Carotid sinus
64510 Stellate ganglion block
64520 Lumbar sympathetic block, ganglion impar, supe rior hypogastric
64530 Celiac plexus block

Neurolytic Blocks

62280 Injection/infusion of neurolytic substance, subcu taneous
62281 Epidural, cervical thoracic
62282 Epidural, lumbar, sacral (caudal)
64600 Destruction by neurolytic agent, trigeminal nerve
64605 Second and third division branches at foramen ovale
64610 Neurolysis of second and third division branches at foramen ovale

Note: 64610 is not approved by medicare to be performed in office setting.

64612 Chemodenervation of muscle(s); innervated by fa cial nerve
64613 Chemodenervation of cervical spinal muscle(s)
64614 Chemodenervation of extremity(s) and/or trunk muscles
64620 Destruction by neurolytic agent, intercostals nerve
64622 Facet joint, neurolytic, lumbar/sacral, single
64623 Facet joint, neurolytic lumbar/sacral, each addt'l level
64626 Facet joint, neurolytic, cervical/thoracic, single
64627 Facet joint, neurolytic, cervical/thoracic, each addt'l level
64630 Destruction by neurolytic agent; pudendal nerve
64640 Neurolytic peripheral block
64680 Celiac plexus neurolysis

Pumps, Stimulators, Catheters

62350 Implantation, revision of intrathecal or epidural cath eter, for implantable reservoir or implantable infu sion pump (tunneled)
62355 Removal of implanted intrathecal or epidural cath eter
62360 Implantation or replacement of intrathecal or epidu ral subcutaneous reservoir
62362 Implantation of pump, includes programming
62365 Removal of reservoir/pump
62367 Analysis of programmable pump without reprogram ming
62368 Analysis of pump with reprogramming
63650 Stimulator electrode
63655 Laminectomy for implantation of neurostimulator electrodes, plate/paddle, epidural
63660 Revision/remove percutaneous trial electrode
63685 Implant generator
63688 Revision/remove generator

Note: 62350 - 63688 are not approved by medicare to be performed in office setting.

95970 Analysis of generator without reprogramming
95971 Analysis of generator w/ reprogramming, 1st hour
96530 Refilling reservoir
A4220 Pump Refill Kit (Not for Medicare)
64550 Transcutaneous neurostimulator placement
64555 Percutaneous implant of neurostimulator electrodes; peripheral nerve
64575 Incision for implantation of neurostimulator elec trodes; peripheral nerve(excludes sacral nerve)
64585 Revision/removal of peripheral nerve stimulator
64590 Incision and subcutaneous placement of peripheral neurosimulator pulse generator or receiver, direct or inductive coupling
64595 Revision or removal of peripheral neurostimulator generator or receiver

Diagnostic

76000 Fluoroscopy, < one hour
76003 Fluoroscopy, needle placement

76005 Fluoroscopy guidance localization of needle for spinal/paraspinal
76012 Fluoroscopy, vertebroplasty, per vertebral body
76013 CT guidance, vertebroplasty
73542 Arthrogram
62290 Diskography procedure, each level, lumbar
62291 Diskography procedure, each level, cervical
72141 MRI, spinal canal and contents, cervical; w/o con trast
72158 MRI, spinal canal and contents, lumbar; w/o con trast
72275 Epidurogram
72285 Diskography, cervical radiologic interpretation
72295 Diskography, lumbar radiologic interpretation
73542 Sacroiliac joint arthrography

NOTE: The 26 modifier is used when the office does not own or lease the fluoroscopy equipment. If the office owns the equipment, no modifier is necessary and the global is billed. Technical component may be billed by the owner of the equipment.

Medications

J3302 Aristocort, per 5 mg
J0475 Baclofen, 10 mg
J0585 Botox A, per unit
J0587 Botox B per 100 units
J0704 Celestone Phosphate, per 4 mg
S0020 Bupivicaine, 30mL
J0706 Caffeine, Injection citrate 5mg.
J1020 Depomedrol (methylprednisolone acetate) 20mg
J1030 Depomedrol 40 mg
J1040 Depomedrol 80 mg
J1050 Depromedrol 100 mg
J3010 Fentanyl, up to .1mg
J3301 Kenalog, 10mg
J1885 Ketorolac, per 15 mg.
J2000 Lidocaine HCI, 50 cc
J3490** Marcaine
J2175 Meperidene Hydrochloride per 100 mg
J2930 Methylprednisone, up to 125 mg
J2920 Methylprednisone, up to 40 mg.
J2275 Morphine sulfate, up to 10 mg
S0093 Morphine sulfate, up to 500 mg.
J7042 Normal saline solution (500 ml)
J1885 Toradol (Ketorolac) per 15 mg
J3301 Triamcinolene, Acetonide (Kenalog), per 10mg.
J3302 Triamcinolene, Diaceate (Aristocort), per 5 mg
J2250 Versed, per 1 mg
J3490** Misc. Drugs (Unlisted Drugs that do not have a specified code)

** Unlisted Drug Code-must specify name and dosage of drug

Visit During a Global Period

99024 Visit during a global period
99025 Visit when * procedure represents major service

Select the name of the procedure or service that accurately identifies the service performed. Do not select a CPT code that merely approximates the service provided. If no such procedure or service exists, then report the service using the appropriate unlisted procedure or service code (CPT changes 2001: An Insider's View, page 5).

The following are the Version 8.0 CCI edits that impact pain procedures:

COMPREHENSIVE CODES

CODE	DESCRIPTION	PROCEDURES INCLUDED IN CODE	
22520	**Percutaneous vertebroplasty**	36005	Contrast venography
		72128	CAT, thoracic spine w/o contrast
		72129	CAT, thoracic spine with contrast
		72130	CAT, thoracic spine w/o followed by contrast material and further sections
		75872	Venography, epidural S&I
		76000	Fluoroscopy, up to 1 hr
		76001	Fluoroscopy, more than 1 hr
		76003 76005	Fluoroscopic guidance for needle placement Fluoroscopic guidance and localization of needle or catheter tip for spine or paraspinous diagnostic or therapeutic injection procedures
27096	**SI joint, arthrography and/or anesthetic/steroid with flouroscopy**	20600	Small joint injection
		20605	Intermediate joint injection
		20610	Major joint injection

CODE	DESCRIPTION	PROCEDURES INCLUDED IN CODE	
		69990	Operating microscope
		76000	Fluoroscopy, up to 1 hr
		76001	Fluoroscopy, more than 1 hr
		76003	Fluoroscopic guidance for needle placement
		90782	Administration of therapeutic substance
62263	**Percutaneous lysis of adhesions**	62281	Neurolytic injection/infusion; epidural, cervical/thoracic
		62282	Neurolytic injection/infusion; epidural, lumbar/sacral
		62284	Myelography
		62310	Epidural injection, single; cervical/thoracic
		62311	Epidural injection, single; lumbar/sacral
		62318	Catheter placement, continuous infusion or intermittent bolus; epidural, cervical/thoracic
		62319	Catheter placement, continuous infusion or intermittent bolus; epidural, lumbar/sacral
		64479	Transforaminal; cervical/thoracic, single level
		64483	Transforaminal; lumbar/sacral, single level
		64722	Decompression, unspecified nerve
		69990	Operating microscope
		76000	Fluoroscopy, up to 1 hr
		76003	Fluoroscopic guidance for needle placement
		76005	Fluoroscopic guidance and localization of needle or catheter tip for spine or paraspinous diagnostic or therapeutic injection procedures
62270	**Spinal puncture, lumbar, diagnostic**	62273	Blood clot or patch
		62311	Epidural injection, single; lumbar/sacral
		64483	Transforaminal; cervical/thoracic, single level
		69990	Operating microscope
		76000	Fluoroscopy, up to 1 hr
		76001	Fluoroscopy, more than 1 hr
		76003	Fluoroscopic guidance for needle placement
62272	**Spinal puncture; therapeutic for drainage of cerebrospinal fluid**	62270	Spinal puncture, lumbar, diagnostic
		62273	Blood clot or patch
		62310	Epidural injection, single; cervical/thoracic
		62311	Epidural injection, single; lumbar/sacral
		64479	Transforaminal; cervical/thoracic, single level
		64483	Transforaminal; cervical/thoracic, single level
		69990	Operating microscope
		76000	Fluoroscopy, up to 1 hr
		76001	Fluoroscopy, more than 1 hr
		76003	Fluoroscopic guidance for needle placement
62273	**Injection, epidural of blood or clot patch**	36000	Introduction of needle or intracatheter, vein
		36140	Introduction of needle or intracatheter, extremity artery
		36410	Venipuncture, child >3yr or adult
		62310	Epidural injection, single; cervical/thoracic
		62311	Epidural injection, single; lumbar/sacral
		64479	Transforaminal; cervical/thoracic, single level
		64483	Transforaminal; cervical/thoracic, single level
		69990	Operating microscope
		76000	Fluoroscopy, up to 1 hr
		76001	Fluoroscopy, more than 1 hr
		76003	Fluoroscopic guidance for needle placement
		G0001	Routine venipuncture for specimen collection

CODE	DESCRIPTION	PROCEDURES INCLUDED IN CODE	
62280	**Injection/infusion of neurolytic substance, with or w/o other therapeutic substance; subarachnoid**	62270	Spinal puncture, lumbar, diagnostic
		62272	Spinal puncture; therapeutic for drainage of cerebrospinal fluid
		62273	Injection, epidural of blood or clot patch
		62284	Myelography
		62310	Epidural injection, single; cervical/thoracic
		62311	Epidural injection, single; lumbar/sacral
		62318	Catheter placement, continuous infusion or intermittent bolus; epidural, cervical/thoracic
		62319	Catheter placement, continuous infusion or intermittent bolus; epidural, lumbar/sacral
		64479	Transforaminal; cervical/thoracic, single level
		64483	Transforaminal; cervical/thoracic, single level
		69990	Operating microscope
		76000	Fluoroscopy, up to 1 hr
		76001	Fluoroscopy, more than 1 hr
		76003	Fluoroscopic guidance for needle placement
62281	**Injection of Neurolytic substance, epidural; cervical/thoracic**	62270	Spinal puncture, lumbar, diagnostic
		62272	Spinal puncture; therapeutic for drainage of cerebrospinal fluid
		62273	Injection, epidural of blood or clot patch
		62284	Myelography
		62310	Epidural injection, single; cervical/thoracic
		62318	Catheter placement, continuous infusion or intermittent bolus; epidural, cervical/thoracic
		64479	Transforaminal; cervical/thoracic, single level
		69990	Operating microscope
		76000	Fluoroscopy, up to 1 hr
		76001	Fluoroscopy, more than 1 hr
		76003	Fluoroscopic guidance for needle placement
62282	**Injection of Neurolytic substance, epidural; lumbar/sacral**	62270	Spinal puncture, lumbar, diagnostic
		62272	Spinal puncture; therapeutic for drainage of cerebrospinal fluid
		62273	Injection, epidural of blood or clot patch
		62311	Epidural injection, single; lumbar/sacral
		62319	Catheter placement, continuous infusion or intermittent bolus; epidural, lumbar/sacral
		64483	Transforaminal; cervical/thoracic, single level
		69990	Operating microscope
		76000	Fluoroscopy, up to 1 hr
		76001	Fluoroscopy, more than 1 hr
		76003	Fluoroscopic guidance for needle placement
62284	**Myleography**	01905	Anesthesia for myleography
		62270	Spinal puncture, lumbar, diagnostic
		62272	Spinal puncture; therapeutic for drainage of cerebrospinal fluid
		62273	Injection, epidural of blood or clot patch
		62282	Injection of Neurolytic substance, epidural; lumbar/sacral
		64479	Transforaminal; cervical/thoracic, single level

CODE	DESCRIPTION	PROCEDURES INCLUDED IN CODE	
		64483	Transforaminal; cervical/thoracic, single level
		69990	Operating microscope
		76000	Fluoroscopy, up to 1 hr
		76001	Fluoroscopy, more than 1 hr
		76003	Fluoroscopic guidance for needle placement
		76005	Fluoroscopic guidance and localization of needle or catheter tip for spine or paraspinous diagnostic or therapeutic injection procedures
62287	**Aspiration or decompression, percutaneous of nucleous pulposus of intervetebral disk, any method, single or multiple levels, lumbar**	62290	Diskography, each level; lumbar
		62310	Epidural injection, single; cervical/thoracic
		62311	Epidural injection, single; lumbar/sacral
		62318	Catheter placement, continuous infusion or intermittent bolus; epidural, cervical/thoracic
		62319	Catheter placement, continuous infusion or intermittent bolus; epidural, lumbar/sacral
		64479	Transforaminal; cervical/thoracic, single level
		64483	Transforaminal; cervical/thoracic, single level
		69990	Operating microscope
		76000	Fluoroscopy, up to 1 hr
		76001	Fluoroscopy, more than 1 hr
		76005	Fluoroscopic guidance and localization of needle or catheter tip for spine or paraspinous diagnostic or therapeutic injection procedures
62290	**Diskography, each level; lumbar**	01912	Anesthesia for diskography
		62311	Epidural injection, single; lumbar/sacral
		62319	Catheter placement, continuous infusion or intermittent bolus; epidural, lumbar/sacral
		64483	Transforaminal; cervical/thoracic, single level
		69990	Operating microscope
		76005	Fluoroscopic guidance and localization of needle or catheter tip for spine or paraspinous diagnostic or therapeutic injection procedures
62291	**Diskography, each level; cervical/thoracic**	01914	Anesthesia for diskography
		62310	Epidural injection, single; cervical/thoracic
		62318	Catheter placement, continuous infusion or intermittent bolus; epidural, cervical/thoracic
		64479	Transforaminal; cervical/thoracic, single level
		69990	Operating microscope
		76005	Fluoroscopic guidance and localization of needle or catheter tip for spine or paraspinous diagnostic or therapeutic injection procedures
62310	**Epidural injection, single, cervical/thoracic**	20605	Intermediate joint injection
		20610	Major joint injection
		36140	Introduction of needle or intracatheter, extremity artery
		62284	Myleography
		69990	Operating microscope
		76000	Fluoroscopy, up to 1 hr
		76001	Fluoroscopy, more than 1 hr
		76003	Fluoroscopic guidance for needle placement

CODE	DESCRIPTION	PROCEDURES INCLUDED IN CODE	
62311	**Epidural injection, single; lumbar/sacral**	20605	Intermediate joint injection
		20610	Major joint injection
		36140	Introduction of needle or intracatheter, extremity artery
		62284	Myleography
		69990	Operating microscope
		76000	Fluoroscopy, up to 1 hr
		76001	Fluoroscopy, more than 1 hr
		76003	Fluoroscopic guidance for needle placement
62318	**Catheter placement, continuous infusion or intermittent bolus; epidural, cervical/thoracic**	01996	Daily management of epidural or subarachnoid drug administration
		20605	Intermediate joint injection
		20610	Major joint injection
		36000	Introduction of needle or intracatheter, vein
		36140	Introduction of needle or intracatheter, extremity artery
		36410	Venipuncture, child >3yr or adult
		62270	Spinal puncture, lumbar, diagnostic
		62272	Spinal puncture; therapeutic for drainage of cerebrospinal fluid
		62284	Myleography
		62310	Epidural injection, single; cervical/thoracic
		69990	Operating microscope
		76000	Fluoroscopy, up to 1 hr
		76001	Fluoroscopy, more than 1 hr
		76003	Fluoroscopic guidance for needle placement
62319	**Catheter placement, continuous infusion or intermittent bolus; epidural, lumbar/sacral**	01996	Daily management of epidural or subarachnoid drug administration
		20605	Intermediate joint injection
		20610	Major joint injection
		36000	Introduction of needle or intracatheter, vein
		36140	Introduction of needle or intracatheter, extremity artery
		36410	Venipuncture, child >3yr or adult
		62270	Spinal puncture, lumbar, diagnostic
		62272	Spinal puncture; therapeutic for drainage of cerebrospinal fluid
		62284	Myleography
		62311	Epidural injection, single; cervical/thoracic
		69990	Operating microscope
		76000	Fluoroscopy, up to 1 hr
		76001	Fluoroscopy, more than 1 hr
		76003	Fluoroscopic guidance for needle placement
62350	**Tunneled intrathecal or epidural catheter for long-term medication administration via an external pump or implantable reservoir; w/o laminectomy**	62270	Spinal puncture, lumbar, diagnostic
		62272	Spinal puncture; therapeutic for drainage of cerebrospinal fluid
		62273	Injection, epidural of blood or clot patch
		62280	Injection/infusion of neurolytic substance, with or w/o other therapeutic substance; subarachnoid
		62281	Injection of Neurolytic substance, epidural; cervical/thoracic

CODE	DESCRIPTION	PROCEDURES INCLUDED IN CODE	
		62282	Injection of Neurolytic substance, epidural; lumbar/sacral
		62310	Epidural injection, single; cervical/thoracic
		62311	Epidural injection, single; lumbar/sacral
		62318	Catheter placement, continuous infusion or intermittent bolus; epidural, cervical/thoracic
		62319	Catheter placement, continuous infusion or intermittent bolus; epidural, lumbar/sacral
		64479	Transforaminal; cervical/thoracic, single level
		64483	Transforaminal; cervical/thoracic, single level
		69990	Operating microscope
62351	**Tunneled intrathecal or epidural catheter for long-term medication administration via an external pump or implantable reservoir; with laminectomy**	62280	Injection/infusion of neurolytic substance, with or w/o other therapeutic substance; subarachnoid
		62281	Injection of Neurolytic substance, epidural; cervical/thoracic
		62282	Injection of Neurolytic substance, epidural; lumbar/sacral
		62310	Epidural injection, single; cervical/thoracic
		62311	Epidural injection, single; lumbar/sacral
		62318	Catheter placement, continuous infusion or intermittent bolus; epidural, cervical/thoracic
		62319	Catheter placement, continuous infusion or intermittent bolus; epidural, lumbar/sacral
		62350	Tunneled intrathecal or epidural catheter for long-term medication administration via an external pump or implantable reservoir; w/o laminectomy
		64479	Transforaminal; cervical/thoracic, single level
		64483	Transforaminal; cervical/thoracic, single level
		69990	Operating microscope
62355	**Removal or previously implanted intrathecal or epidural catheter**	62270	Spinal puncture, lumbar, diagnostic
		62272	Spinal puncture; therapeutic for drainage of cerebrospinal fluid
		62310	Epidural injection, single; cervical/thoracic
		62311	Epidural injection, single; lumbar/sacral
		62318	Catheter placement, continuous infusion or intermittent bolus; epidural, cervical/thoracic
		62319	Catheter placement, continuous infusion or intermittent bolus; epidural, lumbar/sacral
		64479	Transforaminal; cervical/thoracic, single level
		64483	Transforaminal; cervical/thoracic, single level
		69990	Operating microscope
62360	**Implant or replacement of device for intrathecal or epidural drug infusion; subcutaneous reservoir**	62270	Spinal puncture, lumbar, diagnostic
		62272	Spinal puncture; therapeutic for drainage of cerebrospinal fluid
		62273	Injection, epidural of blood or clot patch
		62310	Epidural injection, single; cervical/thoracic
		62311	Epidural injection, single; lumbar/sacral
		62318	Catheter placement, continuous infusion or intermittent bolus; epidural, cervical/thoracic

CODE	DESCRIPTION	PROCEDURES INCLUDED IN CODE	
		62319	Catheter placement, continuous infusion or intermittent bolus; epidural, lumbar/sacral
		62367	Electronic analysis of programmable implanted pump; w/o programming
		62368	Electronic analysis of programmable implanted pump; with programming
		64479	Transforaminal; cervical/thoracic, single level
		64483	Transforaminal; cervical/thoracic, single level
		69990	Operating microscope
62361	**Implantation or replacement of device for epidural drug infusion; non-programmable pump**	62270	Spinal puncture, lumbar, diagnostic
		62272	Spinal puncture; therapeutic for drainage of cerebrospinal fluid
		62273	Injection, epidural of blood or clot patch
		62310	Epidural injection, single; cervical/thoracic
		62311	Epidural injection, single; lumbar/sacral
		62318	Catheter placement, continuous infusion or intermittent bolus; epidural, cervical/thoracic
		62319	Catheter placement, continuous infusion or intermittent bolus; epidural, lumbar/sacral
		62367	Electronic analysis of programmable implanted pump; w/o programming
		62368	Electronic analysis of programmable implanted pump; with programming
		64479	Transforaminal; cervical/thoracic, single level
		64483	Transforaminal; cervical/thoracic, single level
		69990	Operating microscope
64400	**Injection, anesthetic agent; Trigeminal nerve, any division or branch**	20550	Injection, tendon sheath, ligament, trigger points or ganglion cyst
		69990	Operating microscope
64402	**Facial nerve**	20550	Injection, tendon sheath, ligament, trigger points or ganglion cyst
		69990	Operating microscope
64405	**Greater occipital nerve**	20550	Injection, tendon sheath, ligament, trigger points or ganglion cyst
		69990	Operating microscope
64408	**Vagus nerve**	69990	Operating microscope
64410	**Phrenic nerve**	69990	Operating microscope
64412	**Spinal accessory nerve**	20550	Injection, tendon sheath, ligament, trigger points or ganglion cyst
		69990	Operating microscope
64413	**Cervical plexus**	20550	Injection, tendon sheath, ligament, trigger points or ganglion cyst
		69990	Operating microscope
64415	**Brachial plexus**	20550	Injection, tendon sheath, ligament, trigger points or ganglion cyst
		69990	Operating microscope
64417	**Axillary nerve**	20550	Injection, tendon sheath, ligament, trigger points or ganglion cyst
		69990	Operating microscope
64418	**Suprascapular nerve**	20550	Injection, tendon sheath, ligament, trigger points or ganglion cyst
		69990	Operating microscope

CODE	DESCRIPTION	PROCEDURES INCLUDED IN CODE	
64420	**Intercostal, single**	20550	Injection, tendon sheath, ligament, trigger points or ganglion cyst
		69990	Operating microscope
64421	**Intercostal, multiple, regional block**	20550	Injection, tendon sheath, ligament, trigger points or ganglion cyst
		64420	Intercostal, single
		69990	Operating microscope
64425	**Ilioinguinal, Iliohypogastric**	20550	Injection, tendon sheath, ligament, trigger points or ganglion cyst
		69990	Operating microscope
64430	**Pudendal nerve**	20550	Injection, tendon sheath, ligament, trigger points or ganglion cyst
		69990	Operating microscope
64435	**Paracervical nerve**	69990	Operating microscope
64445	**Sciatic nerve**	20550	Injection, tendon sheath, ligament, trigger points or ganglion cyst
		69990	Operating microscope
64450	**Other peripheral nerve or branch**	20550	Injection, tendon sheath, ligament, trigger points or ganglion cyst
		69990	Operating microscope
64470	**Paravertebral facet joint or facet joint nerve; cervical/thoracic, single level**	20550	Injection, tendon sheath, ligament, trigger points or ganglion cyst
		20600	Small joint injection
		20605	Intermediate joint injection
		20610	Major joint injection
		36140	Introduction of needle or intracatheter, extremity artery
		76000	Fluoroscopy, up to 1 hr
		76001	Fluoroscopy, more than 1 hr
		76003	Fluoroscopic guidance for needle placement
64475	**Paravertebral facet joint or facet joint nerve; lumbar/sacral, single**	20550	Injection, tendon sheath, ligament, trigger points or ganglion cyst
		20600	Small joint injection
		20605	Intermediate joint injection
		20610	Major joint injection
		36140	Introduction of needle or intracatheter, extremity artery
		69990	Operating microscope
		76000	Fluoroscopy, up to 1 hr
		76001	Fluoroscopy, more than 1 hr
		76003	Fluoroscopic guidance for needle placement
64479	**Transforaminal epidural;cervical/thoracic, single level**	20550	Injection, tendon sheath, ligament, trigger points or ganglion cyst
		20605	Intermediate joint injection
		20610	Major joint injection
		36140	Introduction of needle or intracatheter, extremity artery
		69990	Operating microscope
		76000	Fluoroscopy, up to 1 hr
		76001	Fluoroscopy, more than 1 hr
		76003	Fluoroscopic guidance for needle placement
64480	**Transforaminal epidural; cervical/thoracic, each addt'l level**	69990	Operating microscope

CODE	DESCRIPTION	PROCEDURES INCLUDED IN CODE	
64483	**Transforaminal epidural; lumbar/sacral, single level**	20550	Injection, tendon sheath, ligament, trigger points or ganglion cyst
		20605	Intermediate joint injection
		20610	Major joint injection
		36140	Introduction of needle or intracatheter, extremity artery
		76000	Fluoroscopy, up to 1 hr
		76001	Fluoroscopy, more than 1 hr
		76003	Fluoroscopic guidance for needle placement
64505	**Sphenopalatine Ganglion**	69990	Operating microscope
64510	**Stellate Ganglion(Cervical Sympathetic)**	69990	Operating microscope
64520	**Lumbar Paravertebral sympathetic**	69990	Operating microscope
64530	**Celiac Plexus**	69990	Operating microscope
64600	**Trigeminal, Neurolytic**	64400	Trigeminal nerve
		69990	Operating microscope
64605	**Trigeminal(second and third division), neurolytic**	69990	Operating microscope
64610	**Trigeminal(second and third division), neurolytic under radiologic monitoring**	64605	Trigeminal(second and third division), neurolytic
		69990	Operating microscope
64612	**Chemodenervation of facial nerve muscles**	64402	Facial nerve
64613	**Chemodenervation of cervical spinal muscles**	69990	Operating microscope
64622	**Lumbar paravertebral facet, single, neurolytic**	64475	Paravertebral facet joint or facet joint nerve; lumbar/sacral, single
		69990	Operating microscope
		76000	Fluoroscopy
		76001	Fluoroscopy
		76003	Fluoroscopy
64626	**Cervical/thoracic paravertebral facet, single, neurolytic**	64470	Paravertebral facet joint or facet joint nerve; cervical/thoracic, single level
		69990	Operating microscope
		76000	Fluoroscopy
		76001	Fluoroscopy
		76003	Fluoroscopy
64630	**Pudendal, neurolytic**	64430	Pudendal nerve
		69990	Operating microscope
64640	**Other peripheral nerve, neurolytic**	64405	Greater occipital nerve
		64408	Vagus nerve
		64410	Phrenic nerve
		64412	Spinal accessory nerve
		64413	Cervical plexus
		64415	Brachial Plexus
		64417	Axillary nerve
		64418	Suprascapular
		64425	ilioinguinal/iliohypogastric
		64450	Other peripheral
		69990	Operating microscope
64680	**Celiac Plexus, neurolytic**	64530	Celiac plexus
		69990	Operating microscope

MUTUALLY EXCLUSIVE

CODE	DESCRIPTION	PROCEDURES INCLUDED IN CODE	
62287	**Percutaneous decompression or aspiration of nucleous pulposus**	22224	Osteotomy of spine
		22558	Arthrodesis, anterior interbody technique
		63005	Laminectomy with exploration and/or decompression of spinal cord
		63017	Laminectomy with exploration and/or decompression of spinal cord, more than 2 vertebral segments
		63030	Laminotomy with decompression intervertebral disk, single interspace
		63042	Laminotomy with decompression intervertebral disk, re-exploration, single interspace
		63056	Transpedicular approach with decompression
62310	**Epidural injection, single, cervical/thoracic**	64479	Transforaminal epidural; cervical/thoracic, single level
62311	**Epidural injection, single; lumbar/sacral**	64483	Transforaminal epidural; lumbar/sacral, single level
62318	**Catheter placement, continuous infusion or intermittent bolus; epidural, cervical/thoracic**	62273	Injection, epidural of blood or clot patch
		64479	Transforaminal epidural; cervical/thoracic, single level
62319	**Catheter placement, continuous infusion or intermittent bolus; epidural, lumbar/sacral**	62273	Injection, epidural of blood or clot patch
		64483	Transforaminal epidural; lumbar/sacral, single level
62355		62350	Tunneled intrathecal or epidural catheter for long-term medication administration via an external pump or implantable reservoir; w/o laminectomy
		62351	Tunneled intrathecal or epidural catheter for long-term medication administration via an external pump or implantable reservoir; with laminectomy
62360	**Implant or replacement of device for intrathecal or epidural drug infusion; subcutaneous reservoir**	62280	Injection/infusion of neurolytic substance, with or w/o other therapeutic substance; subarachnoid
		62281	Injection of Neurolytic substance, epidural; cervical/thoracic
		62282	Injection of Neurolytic substance, epidural; lumbar/sacral
		62362	Implant programmable pump
62361	**Implant non-programmable pump**	62280	Injection/infusion of neurolytic substance, with or w/o other therapeutic substance; subarachnoid
		62281	Injection of Neurolytic substance, epidural; cervical/thoracic
		62282	Injection of Neurolytic substance, epidural; lumbar/sacral
		62360	Implant/replace device for intrathecal or epidural drug infusion
62362	**Implant programmable pump**	62280	Injection/infusion of neurolytic substance, with or w/o other therapeutic substance; subarachnoid
		62281	Injection of Neurolytic substance, epidural; cervical/thoracic
		62282	Injection of Neurolytic substance, epidural; lumbar/sacral
62365		62360	Implant/replace device for intrathecal or epidural drug infusion
		62361	Implant non-programmable pump
		62362	Implant programmable pump

Diagnosis

Assignment of a proper diagnosis is a key element for reimbursement because this is what determines medical necessity.

Each visit or service should fully document the patient's chief complaint and the physician must document his/her assessment of the patient's condition. This assessment justifies the medical necessity for the service rendered.

The diagnosis (es) billed for the services rendered should only be for conditions addressed at the time the service is rendered, Historical conditions should only be billed if they influence or impact the treatment of the patient.

The diagnosis code selected should always be specific. Some ICD-9 codes require additional digits to further clarify the condition. It is important that the physician be as specific as possible.

If for any reason the patient presents with additional problems, other than the original reason for the service, it is important that the physician specify the diagnosis for each of the services rendered and link the appropriate diagnosis to the appropriate services.

FACILITY FEES IN SURGERY CENTERS

Amy G. Mowles
Jo Anne E. Burkhardt

To participate in the Federal ASC program and receive facility fees from governmental payors, the ASC must meet Medicare criteria and approval.

General conditions for coverage include:

- A distinct entity that operates exclusively to furnish outpatient surgical services.
- Either an independent freestanding facility, or under the common ownership, licensure or control of a hospital.
- Surveyed and approved by Medicare for functional compliance with the standard conditions of coverage and Fire and Life Safety Code.

Specific conditions for coverage for coverage can be found on the Federal Register, CFR 416.

Each state department of health is there own authority having jurisdiction over the program. Forty-three states require a state licensure for ASCs. These states specify the criteria that ASCs must meet for licensure prior to Certification.

Some states require a Certificate of Need to establish a new ASC. It may be possible to obtain an exemption in some states for single specialty ASC's.

Physical environment specifics used by the individual state can be from the Centers for Medicare and Medicaid Services (CMS, formerly, HCFA), the National Fire Protection Association and/or from the American Institute of Architects. It is critical to determine the state regulations prior to any construction as the source and year version of the requirements holds different requirements. These may include specifics on: number and size of operating rooms, the amount of recovery stations, parking spaces, etc.

In addition to state and federal inspections, many surgery centers choose to go through voluntary accreditation processes conducted by their peers. This accreditation is sometimes referred to a "third party survey" and may be mandatory in some states or with some payors. ASC's can seek accreditation from one of three accrediting bodies (AAAHC, JCAHO, and AAAASF). All accredited ASCs must meet specific standards that are evaluated during on-site inspections

Once an ASC is approved for Medicare participation, the ASC can only be reimbursed for procedures that are on a list of procedures that Medicare will reimburse to an ASC. Procedures on the list fall into one of 8 groupings with a payment rate assigned to each group. Non-covered services provided in an ASC paid by Medicare at the higher site of service differential in lieu of a facility fee.

Pain Management procedures fall into groups one or two. The payment group is determined by the CPT procedure rendered.

Medicare facility fees include:

- Use of the facility
- Nursing and technician services
- Drugs
- Biologicals
- Surgical dressings
- Materials for anesthesia
- Splints, casts and equipment directly related to the provision of the procedure
- Administrative, record-keeping and housekeeping items and services

In addition to facility fees in the ASC setting, the following are paid separately:

- Physician services
- Laboratory expenses
- X-Rays
- Diagnostic procedures other than those directly related to the surgical procedure
- Prosthetic devices
- Leg, arm, back and neck braces
- Artificial limbs
- DME for use in the patients home

In order to contract with other third party payors, Certification by Medicare as a supplier of surgical services is mandatory. Many also require accreditation before the facility can contract with them. Typically, there are fee schedules for each CPT code that represent the approved fees. These fee schedules generally are subject to change based on the contract with the payor. It is critical at contract negotiation time to identify the current fee schedule and how often the payor can change these fees and what notification timeframe is required when a change is made.

A supplier number is applied for by the ASC and issued by the Medicare carrier. This supplier number is applied for under the ASC Tax ID. Once approval is received, facility fees are billed to Medicare on the standard HCFA 1500 form using the CPT code with the modifier –SG. Site of service is 24 (ASC)

Some third party payors require the UB92 form for filing the ASC facility fee. This should be clarified at contract negotiation time. Most payors that require the use of a UB92 form will accept the CPT and the applicable revenue code. It is important to be aware of incidentals that can be billed separately; all exclusions, special rules for bundling, handling of multiple services, multiple levels and bilateral services

Some states use coding schedules for Worker's Comp facility fees. In states that do not have a set facility fee payment schedule, the facility fee reimbursement is based on their assumption of customary rates and paid at fee for service. Commercial payors and Workers Comp fee for service are typically billed as follows:

UB92 •Type of Bill: 831
Always use –SG modifier plus –59 or –51 as applicable
•Revenue Code: 490: ASC
•Procedure Code
•Fluoro or Interpretation Code -tc
•Supplies (99070)

CODING FOR MINIMALLY INVASIVE PROCEDURES

Jo Anne E. Burkhardt

Billing for minimally invasive procedures in pain management is a challenge for several reasons:

1. Payors are not all familiar with the effectiveness of treatment pathways or that pathways exist at all.
2. The technology used for pain procedures is advanced and does not have specific CPT codes for billing.
3. There are many local medical review policies that vary by locality, by level of service performed, bilateral rules, and multiple procedure rules.
4. The place of service may have a significant impact on reimbursement.

It is important for the pain biller to understand the local policies and to bill according to the rules of the payor. The following outlines generally accepted policies but these may vary by locality.

When pre-certification is attempted, it is important that all the clinical information about the patient is known to the person who attempts to pre-certify. If the payor denies the treatment ask how to appeal this decision. Have the patient contact his/her employer (if group coverage) and also ask the insurance company. Ask for the Medical Directors name and number and have the pain physician talk to the Medical Director.

Medicare and other carriers do not cover IDET and therefore an Advanced Beneficiary Notice is required if the procedure is done on a Medicare patient and advised for the other payors also. The patient will be responsible for payment. Payment policies should be established in the office for this procedures as the billed amount is significant.

LASE (LASER ASSISTED SPIRAL ENDOSCOPY) OR LADD (LASER ASSISTED DISC DECOMPRESSION)

The code used to bill this procedure is 62287. Payors will generally pay for this procedure but usually require pre-certification. Pre-certification is usually easier than for IDET because there is a CPT code for the service. It is helpful to develop similar materials for this service: a physician letter of medical necessity, a description of the service, and articles that support treatment effectiveness.

62287 is now bundled with 62310, 62311, 62318, 62319, 64479 and 64483 for those payors that follow the Correct Coding Initiative.

VERTEBROPLASTY

The code(s) used to bill this service are:

22520	thoracic; one vertebral body, unilateral or bilateral
22521	lumbar, one vertebral body, unilateral or bilateral
22522	each additional thoracic or lumbar vertebral body
76012	Fluoroscopic guidance
76013	CT guidance

Use the 26 modifier if equipment is not owned or leased.

Generally if medical necessity is documented this service is payable by most payors. It is advisable to pre-certify with the payor until the practice knows the specific payor rules.

When 72295-26 or 72285-26 are billed a formal radiological report must be on file as well as radiographic images and these codes are billable by level. Be sure that the pain physician is the only physician involved in the procedure.

NUCLEOPLASTY

The following is how to bill this procedure:

62287 Aspiration or decompression procedure, percuta neous, of a nucleus pulposus of intervertebral disk, any method, single or multiple levels, lumbar (e.g., manual or automated percutaneous diskectomy, per cutaneous laser diskectomy)

76003 Fluoroscopic guidance for needle placement (Use 26 modifier if the equipment is not owned or leased by the billing provider)

If a physician chooses to perform Diskography prior, during, or after performance of a percutaneous decompression nucleoplasty, a concise description of the findings should be recorded within the chart to assist in decision making and future follow-up. This evaluation may be facilitated with the use of standardized manflometric recording in conjunction with detailed anatomic and disc architectural descriptions (Derby, et. Al Spine 1999). If a physician chooses to perform diskography and percutaneous decompression Nucleoplasty in the same setting, he/she should separately document both procedural steps and findings. Codes used to bill for diskography and nucleoplasty are:

62287 Aspiration or decompression procedure, percuta neous of nucleus pulposus of intervertebral disk, any method, single or multiple levels, lumbar (e.g., manual or automated percutaneous diskectomy, per cutaneous laser diskecotomy)

Use a -26 modifier when the equipment is not owned or leased by the billing provider.

RADIOLOGY DICTATION REQUIREMENTS

Use of the C-arm for supervision and interpretation requires taking a copy of the film and including the following in the report:

General radiographic review of normal and abnormal anatomy

- Comparison with previous films, it any, to determine change over time
- Space where Omnipaque is present (intravascujar, subarachnoid, subdural, or epidural space, or outside the epidural space)
- Epidural catheter tip location (vertebral level) and position in the epidural space (anterior or posterior)
- Volume flow after 5 ml. of Omnipaque; upper and lower extents of flow as described by vertebral level
- Volume flow after 10 ml of Omnipaque 180 and comparison with the 5-mi injection
- Abnormalities and/or obstruction of flow and level
- Flow of Omnipaque outside the epidural space

This documentation MUST be present in the chart to qualify and justify billing for the interpretation of the films during the procedure. A radiologist must not present a second bill for this service.

ICD-9-CM DIAGNOSIS CODES

Claim forms must include the proper ICD-9-CM diagnosis code. Many payers now regularly publish policies in which they define specific diagnosis codes that they consider supportive of medical necessity for procedures or services. Providers should receive all such publications from their payers, especially if an appeal for non-payment is filed.

The following diagnosis codes may be appropriate for Nucleoplasty Therapy:

724.4	Lumbosacral radiculitis
729.2	Neuralgia, neuritis, and radiculitis, unspecified
No Code	Lumbar disc disruption syndrome
722.10	Lumbar disc derangement syndrome
722.10	Lumbar disc displacement syndrome
722.90	Discopathy
724.2	Low Back Pain with or without discopathic/radicu lar features
722.0	Cervical disc herniation(s)
722.10	Lumbar disc herniation(s)
722.11	Thoracic disc herniation(s)
122.83	Post-laminectomy syndrome, lumbar region
953.2	Injury to lumbar nerve root
953.3	Injury to sacral nerve root
953.4	Injury to lumbosacral plexus

KYPHOPLASTY

Kyphoplasty should be billed with code 22899, the unlisted code. Attach a copy of the operative report and an explanation of the reasons for treatment. It is good to obtain an Advance Beneficiary Notice (ABN) from the patient in case the procedure is not deemed to be medically necessary by the payor.

Some of the indications for this treatment are:

1. Osteoporotic vertebral collapse causing persistent dehabilitating pain, which has not responded to accepted standard medical treatment. Standard medical treatment may include analgesics, external bracing, and medical treatment of osteoporosis, with

or without bed rest.

2. For a patient who is bed-confined due to the pain, or has other complicating conditions, the symptoms should be present for at least two weeks.
3. For all other patients, the pain must be severe enough to cause significant immobility, impair activities of daily living and persist for at least four weeks.
4. Osteolytic vertebral metastasis or myeloma with severe back pain related to a destruction of the vertebral body, not involving the major part of the cortical bone.
5. Vertebral hemangiomas with aggressive clinical signs and/or radiological signs.
6. Painful vertebral eosinophilic granuloma with spinal instability.
7. For the relevant indications, a diagnostic imaging study must document a non-healing osteoporotic or pathologic fracture.
8. Other causes of pain, such as herniated intervertebral disk that is ruled out by CT or MRI.

Some conditions that may be considered medically not necessary by the payor:

1. Asymptomatic fractures.
2. Fractures healing by conservative means.
3. Kyphosis without fracture.
4. Prevention of fractures due to documented osteoporosis or prior fractures.
5. Treatment of secondary complications of kyphosis, such as reduced pulmonary function or gastrointestinal complications.

MICRODISCECTOMY

This procedure is billed with CPT codes 63075 through 63091, depending on the location and the number of segments.

TRANSPEDICULAR SELECTIVE ENDOSCOPIC DISKECTOMY AND LAMINOTOMY

Used to relieve pressure on the spinal cord and nerve roots caused by herniated disk. The codes to use for billing this procedure are 63055 through 63066. This may be done with diskography and epidurography.

CODING FOR RADIOLOGICAL SERVICES

Jo Anne E. Burkhardt

Pain physicians in some instances may also perform radiological services. When billing radiological services it is important to understand the extent of the pain physician's role.

Radiological services may be global, technical only, or professional only.

The technical component represents payment for the technician, the equipment and supplies. It should only be billed if the equipment is owned or leased by the billing provider.

The professional component represents payment for the supervision and interpretation of the services billed.

Global represents payment for both the professional and technical components.

A service may be billed globally only if the physician owns the equipment, hires or leases the technician and performs the professional component.

Some of the most common radiological services performed by the pain physician are:

EPIDUROGRAPHY

This is a formal study of the epidural space requiring a formal dictated report. It requires a diagnostic indication for performing the procedure.

The epidurogram report must include the following:

- A separate report should be dictated for the epidurogram that lists the following:
- General radiographic review of normal and abnormal anatomy
- Comparison with previous films, if any, to determine change over time
- Space where contrast is present (intravascular, subarachnoid, subdural, or epidural space, or outside the epidural space)
- Epidural catheter tip location and position in the epidural space (anterior or posterior)
- Volume flow after 5 cc contrast; upper and lower extents of flow as described by vertebral level (some injected spaces may not hold 5cc of contrast)
- Abnormalities and/or obstruction of flow and level
- Flow of contrast outside the epidural space
- Diagnostic reason for the epidurogram (may not be for needle placement or visualization)

To bill this service use code 72275-26 (if equipment is not owned or leased) or 72275 (if equipment is owned). This code may be billed for each spinal region examined. Medicare will only pay for the code once per session.

DISKOGRAPHY

The CPT codes are:

62290 Injection procedure, each level; lumbar
62291 Injection procedure, each level; cervical or thoracic
72295-26 Diskography, lumbar-Radiological supervision and interpretation
72285-26 Diskography, cervical/thoracic
or
76005-26 Fluoroscopy for needle localization.

If the physician does not dictate a formal report than 76005-26 should be reported instead of 72295-26 or 72285-26.

FLUOROSCOPY

The codes used to bill fluoroscopy vary based on the type of service.

76005 is billed for spinal injections (codes 62272-62282, 62360-62319, 64470-64484, and 64622-64627)

76003 should be billed for the other nerve blocks and injections such as 64400-64450, 64505-64530, 64600-64620, 64630 -64680.

76012 Fluoroscopy for vertebroplasty
76013 CT guidance for vertebroplasty

The -26 modifier is used when the equipment is not owned or leased by the billing provider.

ARTHROGRAM

To bill this service use 73542-26 if the equipment is not owned and 73542 if the equipment is owned.

A radiographic formal report must be written in order to bill this code. The x-rays should be kept on file to support this billing.

Other Services

72141 MRI, spinal canal and contents, cervical, w/o contrast
72158 MRI, spinal canal and contents, lumbar, w/o contrast
76499 Unlisted diagnostic radiologic procedure. Use this code when a radiologic service is provided and there is no code to specifically describe the service. When this code is used, file a copy of the film and the report. Describe the reason for the service.

SECTION 4

COMPLIANCE

THE MODERN AGE OF COMPLIANCE

Ronald H. Clark, JD

It certainly comes as no surprise to providers to suggest that today's health care fraud enforcement climate is very different from even a few years ago. The amount of resources dedicated to enforcement activities has grown dramatically each year since 1992. Civil actions and criminal prosecutions initiated by the Department of Justice ("DOJ") have increased sharply. On the civil side, the government's principal tool has been the False Claims Act, under which it can recover triple its damages plus a penalty of between $5,000 and $10,000 for each fraudulent request for reimbursement (1). Federal criminal prosecutors can allege kickback (2), mail fraud (3), making false statements in connection with claims submitted to Medicare or state health programs (4), and conspiracies to defraud the government (5). Moreover, providers have come to dread a new player in the enforcement game: qui tam lawsuits filed by "whistle blowers" on behalf of the government who will ultimately share as much as 30% of any recovery. As a result of this increased enforcement activity, the government has been recovering hundreds of millions of dollars from providers and imposing serious criminal sanctions on wrongdoers.

The government has begun to emphasize the importance of compliance programs. For example, as part of the $324 million National Medical Enterprises civil settlement in 1994, the government imposed a 22-page compliance program upon the company – a practice followed as well in the $160 million Caremark, Inc. settlement in 1995. In fact, by direction of Attorney General Reno, every settlement entered into by DOJ must contain some provisions addressing compliance procedures.

The Sentencing Guidelines for Organizations (1991) mandate lesser criminal penalties for companies which have "effective" compliance plans in operation (6). For example, under the Sentencing Guidelines, if two entities are guilty of the identical offense, the entity with a compliance program in place will receive a significantly reduced penalty compared with an entity which has no program in place. DOJ's Civil Division over the last several years has implemented a similar approach by treating civil defendants with meaningful compliance programs in a more lenient fashion than those without such plans.

The government's current enforcement philosophy emphasizes preventing violations by health care providers from arising, rather than just recovering monetary damages and penalties and imposing criminal sentences if violations should occur. This is why compliance programs have become so important: their goal is to prevent violations of law or regulations, or if violations do occur, afford a mechanism to rectify the problem and, perhaps, inform the government. Given this consideration, institution of a plan before a provider is investigated is considered a definite plus by the government.

GENERAL ENFORCEMENT ENVIRONMENT

In the current adverse enforcement environment, a compliance plan is the most effective strategy for a health care provider to implement in order to reduce its risk of being the target of federal investigation and enforcement action. That risk is now greater than it has ever been. While the Office of the Inspector General ("OIG"), Department of Health and Human Services, has always been the key agency involved in health care fraud investigations, other agencies are now joining the effort. For example, since Attorney General Reno designated health care fraud as her number two enforcement priority, DOJ has committed substantial additional investigative and prosectorial resources to this area (7).

The enhanced enforcement activity is also getting a boost from another source. During the last three years, qui tam, or "whistle blower" suits filed under the False Claims Act (8), have been a principal source of investigation and prosecution. These suits, often filed by disgruntled ex-employees, competitors, customers, or even former federal agents, trigger an investigation by the United States government. If DOJ determines that the allegations have merit, it will assume responsibility for litigating against the defendant under the False Claims Act, and when there is a recovery, the relator (i.e., the individual filing the complaint), is rewarded with 15-25% of the recovery. Even should the government fail to intervene in the case, the relator may prosecute the case on behalf on the United States, and, if successful, will recovery as much as 30% of the final award (9). During the past few years there have been several multi-million dollar settlements, and the press attention surrounding these awards has generated a flurry of additional qui tam actions.

GOVERNMENT-IMPOSED COMPLIANCE PROGRAMS

Public statements made by the enforcers suggest that stringent compliance programs will be imposed as part of any health care fraud settlement (10). The government will demand that those compliance programs include a number of severe provisions. For example, the compliance plan must have a minimum duration of five years, include authorization to interview employees without counsel present; and involve annual compliance reviews and audits conducted by independent third parties. There must be prompt disclosure of any credible evidence or civil or criminal misconduct by any employee or any person under contract to the disclosing entity. The company will be expected to waive the attorney-client privilege with respect to any complaint or subsequent investigation of a suspected violation. Finally, the compliance program will be fully imposed upon any subsequently acquired facilities or entities.

Even if a compliance plan has not been implemented before a government investigation and subsequent negotiations commence, counsel representing the provider should nonetheless prepare a compliance program draft and present it to the government as a basis for discussions. Taking the initiative during negotiations allows the provider, rather than the government, the opportunity to define the pertinent issues and choose the appropriate corrective devices (11). This consideration is especially important because the government will seek to impose a compliance program that is advantageous to it – and potentially expensive and disruptive to the provider – as part of any settlement.

OVERVIEW OF A COMPLIANCE PROGRAM

An effective compliance program consists of:

1. An internal compliance review or "legal audit" of the provider's operations (generally focused in one or more targeted areas, such as billing practices, marketing, contracts, referral patterns, etc.)
2. Identification of practices which are improper, illegal, or potentially abusive
3. Drafting an appropriate code of conduct for management and staff
4. Development and implementation of a training program for relevant staff
5. Periodic audit of the provider's future operations in these targeted areas

Based on the success of this program, the provider may wish to expand the compliance review to other areas as appropriate.

THE COMPLIANCE REVIEW, OR "LEGAL AUDIT"

The initial step in developing an effective compliance plan is to undertake a comprehensive compliance review, sometimes referred to as a "legal audit." The purpose of the compliance review is to ascertain whether the provider's current practices and procedures conform with all pertinent legal requirements. Such reviews particularly focus upon detecting any potential violations of the Medicare/Medicaid anti-kickback law, 42 U.S.C. § 1320a-7b(b), the Civil False Claims Act, 31 U.S.C. §§ 3729-33, and pertinent regulations. In that regard a typical review might examine such elements as leases and supplier contracts, particularly those with referral sources; physician contracts and methods for documenting physician performance of contractual obligations; procedure manuals; the integrity and accuracy of the provider's billing methods; document destruction and retention policies; any audits performed internally or by outside entities such as intermediaries and by outside entities such as intermediaries and governmental agencies; cost report preparation; possible "related party" transactions; and internal audit procedures.

If the preliminary review indicates the existence of potential regulatory problems, then those areas would be examined in depth, possibly with the assistance of outside consultants, in order to ascertain if the provider actually is vulnerable and to make recommendations as to how those existing problems can be corrected. Of course, protecting the attorney-client, attorney work product and self-evaluative privileges is a paramount consideration (12). As part of this process, it should be decided whether a written report is necessary or whether an oral briefing will suffice. Some attention should be given to whether the provider is required by law to make disclosure to the government of any irregularities, or if such disclosure tactically would be advisable as a prelude to possible negotiation.

Once any existing problems have been identified and addressed, or in the event that the initial review discloses no troublesome areas, the next step is to fashion a compliance program specifically designed to address the kinds of risks the provider faces in today's unfavorable enforcement climate. Each of the compliance plan's core elements should be developed in conjunction with the provider's management and in-house counsel reflecting the unique aspects of each provider's business activities.

DESIGNING THE PROVIDER'S CODE OF CONDUCT

The first item on the agenda in designing any compliance program to undertake an examination of the corporate goals and philosophy of the provider. This analysis serves as a necessary prelude to the development of a code of fundamental standards to be followed by management and staff. The government considers the corporate code of ethics as a key element of any compliance effort. This code should emphasize the provider's commitment to compliance and integrity in all of its operations and must be written so that all employees understand its full meaning.

Essentially, the code is a statement of the fundamental values upon which the provider stands, such as its promise to adhere to all pertinent laws and regulations, its dedication to advancing the effectiveness and quality of its services, and its commitment to treat its clients or customers in an honorable and ethical fashion. The government takes very seriously the need for a corporate code of ethics, and believes that any compliance program is deficient without one. Because the code of ethics is the core of the compliance program, it is essential to seek the input of management and employees (13).

THE CENTRAL ACTOR - THE COMPLIANCE OFFICER

A second major step is to develop procedures to implement the provider's code of ethics. Most providers create the position of "compliance officer" who has the responsibility for implementing the code of ethics. It is important that the compliance officer work independently of the company's operations, finance, and marketing functions. Generally, this individual has the ability to deal directly with the Board of Directors; often the compliance officer is supervised by an Executive Compliance Committee established by the Board. In addition, as part of the implementation program, most larger providers establish a hotline to facilitate anonymous reporting of any suspected improper activity. The compliance officer is responsible for documenting all hotline reports and corrective actions undertaken as a result of those reports. The compliance officer also oversees any internal audits and investigations generated as a result of the hotline reports and the internal investigation discussed above, which is undertaken as part of the initial establishment of the compliance program (14).

It is important that the compliance officer establish procedures through which employees can seek clarification of ethical issues arising under the code or make suggestions about the operational effectiveness of the compliance program. Not only is facilitating employee communications an effective device to assure smooth implementation of the compliance program, but it also serves to discourage employees from filing qui tam lawsuits out of frustration.

The implementation phase also involves the identification of those circumstances where the provider concludes it should notify the government of certain improprieties which have been discovered. Therefore, part of the compliance program is to set up procedures to enable a provider to identify those situations where notification is appropriate, and those where notification is not appropriate.

EMPLOYEE TRAINING

A third major component is the education of staff about the compliance program, the provider's obligations, and their own individual obligations and responsibilities. This training has a two-fold purpose:

- Educating the staff about the provider's philosophy and commitment to integrity;
- Focusing on the substantive "do's and don'ts" in connection with the staff's activities.

A central objective of staff training is to ensure that employees understand they have an explicit obligation to report all violations of the code and any suspected illegal conduct, and they will be disciplined should they violate that obligation. The government expects that staff education should not be a single event, but rather, an ongoing responsibility. In order to demonstrate the effectiveness of this training, it is advisable that providers document the progress of raising the consciousness of their staff through the periodic surveying of the employees and publishing of the results.

DELEGATION OF DISCRETIONARY AUTHORITY

One of the most important directives in the Sentencing Guidelines relates to delegation of discretionary authority to employees. The company must institute measures designed to foreclose delegation to individuals who the company knows, or should know through the exercise of reasonable diligence, have a "propensity" to engage in illegal activities. At a minimum, this guideline would seem to require some manner of evaluation of employees who exercise discretionary authority to ensure that no indicia of improper propensities are present. The provider should also undertake careful evaluation of prospective employees through appropriate background screening procedures. Consultation with experienced labor relations counsel is essential to ensure that only appropriate procedures are followed.

CERTAINTY OF DISCIPLINE

Monitoring procedures also should be instituted to ensure that any employee or member of management who acts contrary to the plan's ethical commitment, through violation of the code, pertinent law or regulation, receives immediate discipline. Usually the compliance officer reviews all disciplinary actions taken against any staff member to ascertain if they involve violations of the standards of conduct or the compliance plan and to determine if appropriate discipline has been imposed. The government looks to the certainty, consistency and severity of personnel actions as a vital indicator of the effectiveness of a compliance program. Once again, careful coordination with experienced labor counsel is essential in designing this element of the compliance plan.

CONTINUING COMPLIANCE

Finally, the responsibility under a compliance program is an ongoing one. As new government regulations and policies are promulgated, it is critical that the appropriate individuals in the field receive proper guidance according to prescribed procedures. Thus, it is important to have periodic updates for staff and for the provider to monitor the staff's understanding of the applicable rules. Usually, this obligation falls to the compliance officer as well.

MONITORING COMPLIANCE

The compliance officer should institute a plan for periodic internal audits of selected facets of the provider's operations. The areas to be focused on and audited should be those problem areas identified in the original compliance audit. The compliance officer will determine who the audit teams shall comprise based upon consideration of what particular expertise is required. Audit teams can consist of employees, outside accountants, consultants, and counsel depending upon the subject being audited.

A very useful monitoring device is exit interviewing. Usually it will be the responsibility of the compliance officer to make certain that an exit interview is conducted with each employee terminating employment. The purpose of this interview is to solicit information about possible violations of the Code so they may be investigated. A second purpose of the exit interview is to determine whether the departing employee has any suggestions for improving the compliance program, especially if the employee felt particular elements of the program were not working in a satisfactory fashion. Exit interviews can be followed up with subsequent post-employment questionnaires.

A final method through which the provider should monitor its performance is periodic internal audits of the compliance program itself. Those audits should focus on employee training in the compliance program, verify that any reports and inquiries received by the compliance officer have been investigated and resolved; ensure that reporting devices are working; guarantee that appropriate discipline has been imposed; and verify that management and staff have been informed of all new pertinent laws and regulations.

A PLAN TO RESPOND TO INVESTIGATIONS

A comprehensive compliance plan will also address how the provider and its employees should respond to external investigations by law enforcement or regulatory authorities. Many of the advantages of an effective compliance plan can be compromised by an ill-advised or uninformed response to an unanticipated inquiry. A proactive plan, prepared in advance, with clearly-established procedures and defined individual responsibilities, is a logical component to an overall compliance plan. A surprise inspection can often lead to further scrutiny of the organization, and the reaction to such an administrative inquiry can influence the course of the investigation. No matter how honest and law-abiding the company, a confused response to an investigation can never advance the organization's interests (15).

WHY INSTITUTE A COMPLIANCE PROGRAM NOW?

Given the above considerations, it is highly advantageous for any health care provider to give serious consideration to instituting an effective compliance plan. The increased number of government investigations, coupled with the virtual explosion of qui tam lawsuits against health care companies, makes it more likely that providers will encounter investigations and possible civil and criminal prosecution. An effective compliance plan can prevent violations of the law; it sends the right kind of signal to the government should a company come under enforcement scrutiny; it mitigates any penalties should enforcement action be taken (16); and it limits to an important extent the government imposing its own expensive and disruptive compliance program upon the provider. Most basically, compliance program are not only good investments, they are the ethical thing for the conscientious provider to do.

Endnotes

1. 31 U.S.C. §§ 3729-33.
2. Medicare/Medicaid Anti-Kickback Statute, 42 U.S.C. § 1320a-7b(b).
3. 18 U.S.C. §§ 1341, 1343, 1345.
4. 42 U.S.C. § 1320a-7b(a).
5. 18 U.S.C. § 286.
6. United State Sentencing Commission Guidelines, Sentencing for Organizations, 56 Fed. Reg. 22762 (May 16, 1991).

7. *See generally*, *Department of Justice, Health Care Fraud Report, Fiscal* 1994.
8. 31 U.S.C. § 3730.
9. *See* Bucy, *Civil Prosection of Health Care Fraud*, 30 Wake Forest L. Rev. 693, 707-721 (1995).
10. Comments by William Heffron, Esq., OIG, Office of Civil Fraud and Administrative Adjudication, before the Health Law Section of the District of Columbia Bar, May 3, 1995.
11. Preparation of a compliance program draft by the provider also serves as an effective device to deflate any extreme settlement demands asserted by the government because correcting the problems giving rise to the government's concerns is as fundamental to the Attorney General as securing a financial recovery. Moreover, by admitting that corrective action needs to be implemented, the focus of negotiations is upon resolving a problem, not arguing culpability.
12. Conway, Self-Evaluative Privilege and Corporate Compliance Audits, 68 S. Cal. L. Rev. 621 (1995).
13. See generally, Pitt and Groskaufmanis, Minimizing Corporate Civil and Criminal Liability: A Second Look at Corporate Codes of Conduct, 78 Geo. L.J. 1559 (1990).
14. See Webb and Molo, Some Practical Considerations in Developing Effective Compliance Programs: a Framework for Meeting the Requirements *of the Sentencing Guidelines*, 71 Wash. U.L.Q. 377, 388 (1993).

IMPLICATIONS OF MODEL COMPLIANCE PROGRAM FOR INTERVENTIONAL PAIN PHYSICIANS

William A. Sarraille, JD

The Office of the Inspector General for the Department of Health and Human Services (OIG) recently released a final model compliance program for small physician practices. The model plan shows a remarkable degree of flexibility reflective of the OIG's acknowledgment that small physician practices have such limited resources that they might not be in a position to implement a full compliance program. The OIG's final model plan incorporates many items suggested by the American Society of Interventional Pain Physicians (ASIPP) in written comments submitted by ASIPP to the agency.

AN "OPERATIONAL" APPROACH

In the past, OIG has stressed what it expects "out" of a voluntarily implemented compliance program, rather than how an organization can get "there" as a matter of process. Traditionally, the OIG has defined an "effective compliance program" by stating simply that it must include:

- a compliance officer and/or committee to direct the program, with the appropriate authority and direct access to the decision-makers in the organization,
- written standards of conduct and a written compliance plan,
- the development and use of corrective action procedures,
- compliance training,
- periodic monitoring and auditing,
- disciplinary protocols, and
- the screening of employees and contractors to ensure that they are not inappropriately delegated responsibility for sensitive functions.

This list of the necessary "outputs," though, does not tell providers anything about "how" to go about putting a compliance program in place.

Realizing that the "how" question is particularly important from the small physician practice perspective (because physician practices are more likely to feel overwhelmed in the absence of very practical advice from an operational point of view), the OIG took the unprecedented step in the final physician plan by emphasizing the outline of a compliance process, instead of a list of required end products. The OIG deserves a significant degree of praise for taking this approach, which ASIPP encouraged the OIG to follow. OIG also should be commended for recognizing that the process used by small practices may very well not lead to all of the elements of a traditional "effective compliance program" being implemented—simply because of resource, personnel, and time limitations.

The OIG suggests the following approach to the implementation of a compliance program in a small physician practice. Although the OIG's step by step approach will be the right process for some practices to adopt, it will not, as the OIG itself appears to concede, be the correct sequence for others. Blind adherence to the OIG's model would be ill-advised.

STEP ONE: AUDITING AND MONITORING

The first step that the OIG mentions is to audit and monitor the current situation. OIG believes that this can be accomplished by doing two things: (1) a review of the practice's existing "standards and procedures"[1] and (2) a "claims review."

In undertaking a claims review, the OIG stresses four areas of testing:

- adequate coding and documentation,

- completeness of documentation,
- medical necessity and reasonableness of the services, and
- a check to determine the presence of "incentives" for the over-utilization of services.

The OIG says that the review may be either prospective (claims not yet submitted) or retrospective (claims already submitted) in nature. The OIG states that the results of the review should be used as a benchmark, to assess compliance the success of compliance efforts on an on-going basis.

The OIG also writes that auditing and monitoring must have continuing application. At a minimum, annual audits must be undertaken. Reviews of no less than five services per provider should be completed.[2] The OIG cautions that negative audit results must lead to corrective action. According to the OIG, the appropriate response to an identified problem will depend on the circumstances. "In some cases," the OIG states, "it can be as straight-forward as generating a repayment with appropriate explanation." "In others," the OIG suggests, "the practice may want to consult with a billing/coding expert to determine the next best action."

STEP TWO: PRACTICE STANDARDS AND PROCEDURES

OIG says that the next step that a small physician practice should take is to develop written practice standards and procedures. The standards and procedures should address any areas of vulnerability identified in the baseline audit. Calling the standards and procedures "a central component of a compliance program," the OIG writes that small practices may look to programs developed by medical societies and associations, such as ASIPP, or by contractual partners, such as a physician practice management company, a management services organization, or the local hospital where services are provided. However, a practice should not just adopt a model program wholesale and simply install the "off the shelf" product—a point made in ASIPP's own model plan. The small practice's plan must be tailored to its needs and circumstances.

The OIG suggests that small practices consider developing a compliance binder that would include:

- written standards addressing the risk areas identified by OIG for small practices (more about those later),
- attachments consisting of OIG fraud alerts and advisory opinions, as well as the applicable Medicare bulletins, and
- clinical forms designed to secure appropriate and complete documentation.

The binder must be reasonably accessible to members of the practice and its staff. OIG encourages practices to train their new employees on the contents of the compliance binder "as soon as possible" as part of their orientation.

STEP THREE: COMPLIANCE OFFICER OR CONTACT

The OIG says that the next step that a small practice should consider is who will direct the compliance program on an on-going basis. Although "ideally" a single person will be selected as the compliance officer and will be responsible for the compliance program as a whole, the OIG acknowledges in its model plan that this might not be possible in a small practice with limited resources and personnel. Accordingly, OIG states that it is "acceptable" to "spread" the compliance functions over a number of "compliance contacts," so long as the division of responsibility is made clear in the practice's written plan.

The OIG's final plan also indicates that practices can "share" compliance officers retained on an independent contractor or other basis. The final plan's discussion of this option, however, is somewhat muted, as compared to the discussion of this same concept in the OIG's earlier proposed model. Critics, including ASIPP, had responded to this proposal raising a host of concerns—ranging from issues of privacy and confidentiality, the whistle-blower implications, and the potential anti-trust concerns. Although the final plan does not address most of these concerns, OIG does state that a shared compliance officer can create concerns if the compliance officer is so disengaged from a practice that he or she has no real connection to it. In other words, though it is often important to ensure that a compliance officer can act with independence, a compliance officer can be too detached to be effective.

Addressing other "sharing" issues, the OIG appears to have no particular difficulty with a physician practice using a hospital plan as a guide in developing its own program, or in making use of compliance training offered by a hospital. The OIG does express the concern, however, about a hospital's support of other physician compliance activities, including audits, unless the institution will be compensated at fair market value for those services. The OIG's concern is based on the Federal Anti-Kickback Statute. The OIG has apparently determined that there is a risk that hospitals will use free compliance services to reward or induce referrals in violation of the statute. Presumably, the OIG would have the same reaction to free compliance services offered by ambulatory surgery centers, as it would to those offered by hospitals.

Critics, including ASIPP, have questioned the wisdom of the OIG's position in this area. Institutions, like hospitals and ambulatory surgery centers, often have difficulty improving their compliance, because they are largely dependent on independent physicians for a number of critical decisions that affect compliance. Institutional providers can demonstrate the need for changes in behavior that will improve the compliance of both the practice and institution by providing free or discounted billing and coding audits for practices. Some critics do not see any particular anti-kickback risks where these services are provided to all physicians on staff who request them, not just "big referrers."

STEP FOUR: TRAINING AND EDUCATION

According to the OIG, the next step that a small practice should consider taking is the implementation of a program of training and education. "Ideally" the training will consist of both what the OIG refers to as "general" and "specific" training. General training consists of training on the practice's compliance standards and procedures, including the "nuts and bolts" of how the practice's compliance program operates. Specific training consists of training on particular compliance risk areas, like the waiver of co-payments and deductibles.

The OIG suggests that small practices create their training and education programs by answering three questions. First, the practice needs to determine who needs training—both general and specific. The implicit assumption in that statement, of course, is that not all practice personnel necessarily need compliance training. This would be the case, for instance, with very low-level employees who have no role in billing, coding, documentation or other substantive issues.

The second question is how should the training be delivered. The OIG states that training can be presented in live seminars or through newsletters, self-study, or in-services. Although this sounds as though the OIG is open to training programs that do not include any "live" sessions, the OIG cautions that training and education programs must be "effective."

The final question is when and how often should training be conducted. The OIG states that "at a minimum" training should occur on an annual basis.

In terms of topics for training, the OIG makes a number of recommendations. Training should include education on the practice's compliance program generally (and how it operates), including the means to report issues and concerns and the discipline that will be imposed where violations are found to exist. Two major goals of compliance training should be (1) to show employees how to conduct their responsibilities in compliance with federal law and (2) how compliance is a condition of employment. The OIG also recommends training on relevant statutes and regulations. The OIG provides a number of relevant legal authorities in an appedix to its final plan.

The OIG suggests that specific and "extensive" training on billing and coding issues be provided to all those involved "directly" in billing. Training topics should include:

- claims development and submission processes,
- the legal issues posed in signing materials for a physician without the physician's authorization,
- proper documentation of services,
- appropriate billing and coding standards and procedures, and
- the legal sanctions for deliberately or recklessly filing false claims.

Effective education includes having up-to-date reference materials, such as CPT and ICD-9 code books and carrier bulletins. Training on billing and coding issues may be obtained, the OIG notes, from community colleges, carriers, and professional associations.

STEP FIVE: CORRECTIVE ACTIONS

In the words of the OIG, "upon receipt of reports or reasonable indications or suspected noncompliance, it is important that the compliance contact or officer look into the allegations to determine whether a significant violation of applicable law or the requirements of the compliance program has indeed occurred, and to take decisive steps to correct the problem." The OIG stresses that, depending on the circumstances, refunds or disclosures may be required. OIG states its expectation that criminal violations will be reported to the government. Known overpayments, even in the absence of criminal wrong-doing, should result in repayments to the applicable payor. When problems are identified, it is important that the practice take steps quickly to ensure that the problem is not magnified or compounded.

In order to facilitate appropriate corrective action, the OIG suggests that practices create a variety of "monitors and warning indicators." These might include systems to check for:

- significant changes in the types of claims rejections,
- correspondence from carriers or intermediaries challenging the medical necessity of services or the validity of claims,
- illegal or unusual patterns in code utilization, and
- high volumes of unusual payment adjustments.

STEP SIX: COMMUNICATION

In other plans addressed to other types of providers prior to the issuance of the final small physician plan, the OIG had stressed the need for compliance programs to include a means of anonymous reporting of compliance issues, preferably through a telephone hotline. In announcing this component of the small physician plan, however, the OIG accepted that anonymity may simply not be possible in a small physician practice. Although OIG states its belief that e-mail or telephone anonymous reporting can be achieved by larger practices, OIG writes that an "open door" policy should be sufficient for small practices.

An open door policy consists of:

- mandatory reporting of conduct a reasonable person would believe to be erroneous or fraudulent,
- creation of a "user-friendly" process for reporting issues,
- the creation of a standard that makes the failure to report compliance issues grounds for instituting discipline, and
- the creation of a simple and readily accessible mechanism for processing compliance reports.

The practice must also implement and enforce a policy that the practice will not tolerate any retribution made for reporting a compliance concern in good faith.

An open door policy should also involve a clear system for effective communication between a small practice and a third party billing agent, to the extent the practice contracts with one. Such a system should include communication regarding:

- identified concerns,
- the initiation and results of audits,
- training needs,
- regulatory changes, and
- operational compliance matters.

STEP SEVEN: DISCIPLINARY PROTOCOLS

Despite criticism from many organizations, including ASIPP, that an emphasis on disciplinary protocols is inconsistent with the type of voluntary and collaborative process that compliance is supposed to entail, the OIG insists in its final plan that "consistent and appropriate sanctions" are a "necessary" component of an effective compliance program. They are necessary, OIG says, to "add credibility," if for no other reason. Inclusion of disciplinary guidelines in the practice's written standards and procedures is sufficient to meet the OIG's expectation that the standards related to discipline be "well-publicized."

RISK AREAS

The OIG's final plan lists a wide variety of risk areas that a small practice should address in its program. The tremendous number of risk areas, collected in an appendix to the final plan, are a source of concern for a number of commentators, including ASIPP. who are afraid that small physician practices will be overwhelmed by the laundry list of risk areas that they may elect not to create a compliance program. If that were to occur, the OIG will have hurt its own effort to create an environment of self-policing in physician services.

Interestingly, many of the identified risk areas relate to situations in which physicians interact with other types of providers—including durable medical equipment suppliers, home health agencies, clinical laboratories, hospitals, and others—who have been under the fraud and abuse microscope for a long time. Many of the listed items correspond to areas that the OIG has addressed previously in special fraud alerts and in advisory opinions. Although physicians have tended to equate the term "compliance" with "billing and coding" compliance, the OIG's list of risk areas reveals a much broader range of compliance issues and concerns, with particular emphasis on financial relationships between physicians and other providers.

Organized under four principal risk area headings, the OIG enumerated the following risk areas:

Coding and Billing Issues

- Billing for items or services not provided or not provided as claimed;
- Submitting claims for equipment, supplies, or services that are not reasonable and necessary;
- Double billing ;
- Billing for non-covered services as if they were covered services;
- Knowing misuse of provider numbers that result in improper payments;
- Unbundling;
- Failure to use coding modifiers appropriately;
- Clustering;
- Inappropriate use of advanced beneficiary notices (also known as waiver of liability forms);
- Problems related to the reassignment of the right to bill or collect; and
- Upcoding.

Ensuring Reasonable and Necessary Services

- Following local medical review policy restrictions;
- Appreciating and abiding by Medicare restrictions on the coverage of screening services;
- Inappropriate use and completion of certificates of medical necessity; and
- Not submitting non-covered services except to secure a denial for purposes of secondary coverage requirements.

Accurate and Complete Documentation of Various Elements

- The site of service;
- Appropriateness of the services;
- Accuracy of the billing;
- Identities of the care-givers; and
- Design of appropriate systems to ensure a legible and complete record showing:
- The reason for the encounter;
- " Any" relevant history;
- Physical examination findings;
- Prior [presumably relevant] diagnostic test results;
- The assessment, clinical impression, or diagnosis;
- The plan of care;
- Date and legible identity of the observer;
- The reasons for the ordering of diagnostic testing if those reasons are not "easily inferred" from the record;
- CPT and ICD-9 codes supported by the record;
- Correct use of coding modifiers;
- Accurate linkage of CPT codes to ICD-9 codes;
- Provision of accurate information to the Medicare program regarding other insurance coverages, where known;
- Appropriate documentation of participation in care and supervision of care under the teaching physician rules; and
- The identification of appropriate health risk factors, including the patient's progress, his or her responses to treatment, and any revisions in diagnoses.

Improper Inducements, Kickbacks, and Self-Referrals

- Financial relationships with hospitals, hospices, nursing facilities, home health agencies, and pharmaceutical companies, and others who are in a referral relationship (including non-federal program relationships because they can have an indirect effect on federal program referrals);
- Arrangements that do not reflect fair market value;
- Joint ventures with individuals or entities providing goods or services to the practice or its patients;
- Consulting contracts or medical directorships;
- Office and equipment leases with entities in referral relationships;
- Compliance with the OIG's restrictions on physician-hospital cost savings "gainsharing";
- Percentage compensation arrangements in third party billing contracts;
- Appropriate professional courtesy practices; and
- Solicitation of any gift or gratuity of more than nominal value.

DISCUSSION

As indicated earlier, commentators have roundly praised the OIG for showing a real measure of flexibility in its development of the final model plan. The final plan clearly states that, if a practice does not have sufficient resources, it can implement a compliance mechanism that represents something less than a full compliance program as set out in the definition of an "effective compliance program" that is contained in the United States Sentencing Commission Guidelines.

Despite this, however, some have questioned whether the OIG has really committed to recognizing the compliance efforts of small physician practices that do not implement a full compliance program. The OIG's discussion of this issue leaves it with room to argue that particular practices who fail to fully implement a compliance program did not abide by the agency's guidance.

For instance, at one point in the final model plan document, the OIG states that "full implementation of a compliance program may not be feasible for all physician practices." [Emphasis added]. The OIG also writes, at one point, that "some physicians may not fully implement all of the components of a [compliance] program." [Emphasis added]. The OIG also states that the "extent of implementation will depend on the size and resources of the practice." [Emphasis added].

The negative pregnant of these and similar statements may be that the OIG will dispute the sufficiency of compliance mechanisms, in False Claims Act or other enforcement actions, if the agency concludes that the practice could (and should) reasonably have done more. For large practices, the OIG states its expectation that those entities will combine the physician practice model compliance program and the OIG's third party billing company model compliance program to develop a "complete" compliance program.

The situation is made all the more unclear and frustrating by the OIG's studied refusal to define a "small physician practice." Despite repeated requests from medical societies, such as ASIPP, the OIG has not offered any real guidance on how to distinguish between small and large physician practices, other than to simply state that "small" practices are those that have the "financial and staffing resources that would prevent the implementation of a full scale, institutionally-structured compliance program." In a most unhelpful response to the repeated requests for guidance on this central question, the OIG has defended its failure to provide any instruction with the statement that the difference between a small and a large physician practice "cannot be determined by stating a particular number."

On a positive note, the OIG's final model program responds to the criticism made by many medical societies, including

ASIPP, that the original draft program incorrectly implied that compliance programs were required of physician groups. The OIG flatly states that "these Guidelines are not mandatory."

With that said, ASIPP and some other medical societies have expressed their concern with the failure of the draft plan to stress the responsibilities of others to work with physician practices in resolving the ambiguities currently endemic in the Medicare, Medicaid and other government-funded health care programs. Specifically, ASIPP called upon the OIG to stress its own responsibility and that of the Centers for Medicare and Medicaid Services(CMS), the Medicare carriers, the Medicare intermediaries and others to work to address these issues. ASIPP was particularly focused on this issue given the variable and inconsistent instructions issued by carriers and intermediaries on a host of interventional pain management procedure coding issues. Unfortunately, without even commenting on this request made by ASIPP and other medical societies, the final model plan fails to discuss in any significant way the responsibilities of governmental agencies in the compliance process, other than their enforcement powers.

The final plan also includes some reassuring words for physicians regarding the intent of the OIG in the exercise of its enforcement powers. The OIG states, for instance, that the False Claims Act is designed only to target intentional, knowing, or at least reckless conduct, not mere negligent errors or "honest mistakes." For many, though, those reassuring words ring hollow, as the dividing line between a "reckless" act and a merely "negligent" one is often in the eye of the beholder. The misuse of a single CPT code repeated over a period of time will be viewed by the federal government as a reckless pattern of misconduct, even though, from the provider's perspective, it represents a single, honest mistake in the evaluation of a single code.

The model plan also attempts to respond to the criticism of some that compliance program activities can have the unintended effect of distracting physicians from patient care activities. The OIG specifically acknowledges in the final plan that "patient care is and should be the first priority" for physicians. According to the OIG, however, "patient focus can be enhanced" through compliance activities.

CONCLUSION

Only time will tell whether the OIG's efforts at announcing what it viewed as flexible guidance will encourage more practices to implement at least some compliance mechanisms. Physician practices are clearly at greater risk today if they fail to do so in light of the publication of the OIG's final plan.

PHYSICIAN OFFICE COMPLIANCE PROGRAMS

Alan E. Reider, JD

The challenge to establishing an effective compliance program for a physician office is developing a program which is sufficiently comprehensive to cover the potential areas of fraud and abuse to which the physician is vulnerable, while, at the same time, recognizing that the program must be practical – outside major clinics or groups, a typical physician practice cannot afford to invest $100,000 or more in the establishment and operation of a compliance program. Admittedly, "comprehensive but practical" is a difficult balance to achieve. Nevertheless, because of the enforcement environment today, it is important for physicians to consider areas where they may be vulnerable, and take the necessary steps to address them.

SCOPE AND CONTENT OF COMPLIANCE REVIEW

It is critical for the physician practice to identify the particular areas of concern which should be the focus of the compliance review, and for the attorney to articulate clearly what areas of law will be addressed by the review. Generally, in light of the focus of current enforcement activities, the compliance audit addresses fraud and abuse concerns, including application of the federal anti-kickback and Stark laws, state anti-kickback and self-referral limitations, as well as fee split and corporate practice of medicine issues, plus general billing issues.

The mechanism for a physician compliance review is a "legal audit" of the practice's structure and procedures. The audit is designed to examine the internal procedures and records in connection with the following activities:

a. billing procedures;
b. contacts with outside suppliers, and consultants;
c. admission procedures and treatment protocols;
d. record retention practices;
e. leases or other contracts with potential referral sources;
f. recruitment and retention mechanisms;
g. advertising practices;
h. methods for securing informed patient consent; and
i. procedures relating to waiver of co-payment and deductible.

In addition, all corporate/partnership agreements are reviewed and the structure and operation of the practice is developed in detail.

A compliance review generally is conducted in four stages. First, the attorney will undertake an initial review of the most relevant documents, including all corporate and partnership practice materials, contracts with consultants, employment agreements, advertising materials, procedures for billing, any procedure manuals, and, perhaps most importantly, any audits, evaluations or reviews performed by an insurer, Medicare carrier, Medicaid agency, or similar agency during the past five years, as well as any correspondence from these entities relating to disputed claims.

Following the review of the documents an on-site review is conducted and key personnel are interviewed. In addition, there is often a "walk through" where the path of a patient is followed throughout the process, beginning with registration, through the visit and discharge. Then, following the on-site review, there is an exit conference where any immediate concerns which require immediate corrective action are identified. Finally, after all of the data has been assimilated, a report is issued to the physician identifying those areas of weakness which should be addressed to assure compliance in the future. In addition, to the extent that any issue has been identified which requires contacting appropriate agencies or insurers, recommendations will be made accordingly.

IMPLEMENTING A COMPLIANCE PROGRAM

While the legal audit is a helpful tool which can be of great value to the practice, a complete compliance program requires more – employee training, a hotline, and establishment of a corporate code of ethics are all elements of a complete compliance program, just as they are for major hospitals and national corporations. Obviously, the scope of a physician practice compliance program will not be as great or as broad as that described in the general introduction, but each of the key elements of a compliance program should be established for physician practices as well.

Physicians should recognize that a compliance program is designed not only to protect them in the case of an enforcement action, but also to prevent, or at least minimize, the risk of enforcement actions being taken. As noted previously, there is a significant opportunity to reduce the risk of a qui tam relator filing a complaint against a physician if that individual has been afforded a means to address his or her concerns to the physician directly. While many physician investigations have been triggered by qui tam complaints, we believe an effective compliance program will significantly reduce the likelihood of success by the relator in qui tam litigation.

CONCLUSION

Physicians should not overlook the many benefits from developing a compliance program for their practice. Certainly, the enforcement authorities have not overlooked physicians as potential targets for enforcement actions.

THE VALUE OF COMPLIANCE PROGRAMS

Carson P. Porter, JD

A recent decision of the Delaware Chancery Court recognizes the value of having a compliance program in place (1). In a suit brought by certain shareholders of Caremark International, Inc. seeking to require the members of the company's Board of Directors to reimburse the $250 million paid by Caremark to settle allegations of criminal violations of various provisions of the Medicare anti-fraud and abuse laws, the court dismissed the case on the grounds that the directors had performed their duties properly and cited the implementation of a compliance program as evidence of those efforts.

The suit alleged that members of the Caremark Board breached their fiduciary duty of care in connection with purported violations by Caremark employees of both federal and state laws pertaining to health care providers. Specifically, Caremark was under investigation by various federal and state agencies for entering into arrangements which purportedly violated regulations prohibiting health care providers from paying any form of remuneration to induce the referral of Medicare or Medicaid patients. Caremark had a practice of entering into contracts with physicians, some of whom prescribed or recommended services or products that Caremark provided to Medicare patients. These payments raised issues as to possible illegal kickbacks. After extended investigations and negotiations, Caremark agreed to settle the claims by paying a $250 million fine along with other requirements.

The court found that Caremark's Board had made prudent efforts to assure compliance with company policies prohibiting violations of rules. The record in the case supported the company's position that the Board had implemented several programs which were designed to educate employees as to the company's commitment to abide by all pertinent rules and regulations as well as establishing an internal audit process designed to assure compliance. After reviewing the legal precedents applicable, Judge Allen observed:

> ...I am of the view that a director's obligation includes a duty to attempt in good faith to assure that a corporate information and reporting system, which the board concludes is adequate, exists, and that failure to do so under some circumstances may...render a director liable for losses caused by noncompliance with applicable legal standards (2).

To establish a prima facie case, the court ruled:

In order to show that the Caremark directors breached their duty of care by failing adequately to control Caremark's employees, plaintiffs would have to show either (1) that the directors knew or (2) should have known that violations of law were occurring and, in either event, (3) that the directors took no steps in a good faith effort to prevent or remedy that situation, and (4) that such failure proximately resulted in the losses complained of...(3)

Following a detailed review of the entire record, Judge Allen dismissed the complaint and held:

> ...[I]n my opinion only a sustained or systematic failure of the board to exercise oversight such as an utter failure to attempt to assure a reasonable information and reporting system exists will establish the lack of good faith that is a necessary condition to liability. Such a test of liability for lack of good faith as evidenced by sustained or systematic failure of a director to exercise reasonable oversight is quite high...

Here the record supplies essentially no evidence that the

director defendants were guilty of a sustained failure to exercise their oversight function. To the contrary, insofar as I am able to tell…[Caremark's] information systems appear to have represented a good faith attempt to be informed of relevant facts. If the directors did not know the specifics of the activities that lead to the indictments, they cannot be faulted (4).

Due to the recognition afforded to decisions of the Delaware Chancery Court, the ruling in the Caremark case will likely establish that any health care provider would be well-advised to implement an effective compliance program. The effort by the board in the Caremark case relieved the directors from any personal liability for repaying the $250 million paid by the company in settlement.

Endnotes

1. *In re Caremark International, Inc. Derivative Litigation*, Civil Action No. 13670, Delaware Chancery Court (New Castle), September 25, 1996.
2. *Id*, at 39.
3. *Id*. at 40.
4. *Id*. at 42.

LEGAL AUDITS FOR COMPLIANCE PROGRAMS

Ronald H. Clark, JD

The foundation for a truly "effective" compliance plan is developed before the compliance program itself is designed and implemented. A rigorous "legal audit" or compliance review accomplishes this objective. The legal audit is a comprehensive internal investigation of the provider's operations, generally focused on one or more targeted areas. The purpose of the compliance review is to ascertain whether the provider's current practices and procedures conform with all pertinent legal requirement. Such reviews particularly focus upon detecting any potential violations of the Medicare/Medicaid Anti-Kickback Law, 42 U.S.C. § 1320a-7b(b), the Civil False Claims Act, 31 U.S.C. §§ 3729-33, and pertinent regulations.

The investigative techniques employed in a legal audit include reviewing pertinent documents and interviewing key individuals who are either identified in the document reviews or hold essential positions (the director of billing operations, for example). Each type of health care provider has certain unique facets of its operation that should be examined (*e.g.*, compliance with the new teaching physician rules in teaching hospitals); other issues should be examined for all providers (billing practices are a good example). A typical review might examine such elements as leases and supplier contracts, particularly those with referral sources; physician contracts and methods for documenting physician performance of contractual obligations; procedure manuals; the integrity and accuracy of the provider's billing methods; document destruction and retention policies; any audits performed internally or by outside entities such as intermediaries/carriers and governmental agencies; cost report preparation; possible "related party" transaction; and internal audit procedures.

Once the compliance review is completed, its diagnostic findings can serve multiple purposes. If the preliminary review indicates the existence of potential regulatory problems, then those areas would be examined in depth, possibly with the assistance of outside consultants, in order to ascertain if the provider actually is vulnerable and to make recommendations as to how those existing problems can be corrected. Of course protecting the attorney-client privileges is a paramount consideration. Before the compliance plan is instituted, any problems should be corrected and any necessary procedures implemented to foreclose their recurrence.

As regards designing the compliance program, the review's results should highlight any existing problems so that special attention can be devoted in the Standards of Conduct to preventing a reoccurrence. Addressing particular problem areas in the Standards also demonstrates to the government that the compliance plan is not an "off-the-shelf" document but a program custom designed for that particular provider. The compliance officer as well should be informed of the audit's results so that she may devote special attention to these potential problem areas. As part of this process it should be decided whether a written report is necessary or if an oral briefing or an "exit report" on the preliminary findings will suffice. Again, protecting privilege can be a paramount consideration at this stage.

It is also important that a determination be made, usually in conjunction with counsel, as to whether any existing problems require disclosure to the government and possible negotiation of a resolution. This frequently is a very difficult decision for the provider, who may feel that correction of a problem is sufficient action, especially given today's adverse enforcement environment which often seems to punish providers who are trying to act responsibly. On occasion, counsel may recommend some manner of disclosure, not necessarily under the Inspector General's "voluntary disclosure" program, in order that all regulatory problems (and potential sanctions) are elimi nated before the compliance plan begins operation.

The ideal situation is to have identified and corrected all regulatory problems prior to implementation of the compliance plan. Such action demonstrates to the government that the compliance plan is a serious undertaking and that the health care provider is prepared to swallow bitter medicine if necessary in order to cleanse its operations of any problems. Such action can lend an important element of credibility to the compliance plan. In addition, given the extraordinary importance of "whistle blower" or ***qui tam*** lawsuits under the False Claims Act (31 U.S.C. § 3730), correcting any problems which the legal audit uncovers can foreclose substantial expense and potential legal and administrative sanctions should a potential whistle blower become aware of them.

For any number of reasons, then, instituting a demanding legal audit as a preliminary step to the design and implementation of the compliance plan can be essential to successfully designing and implementing the kind of compliance program the Sentencing Guidelines and the government expect and demand.

MODEL COMPLIANCE PLAN FOR INTERVENTIONAL PAIN MEDICINE

William A. Sarraille, JD
Eileen Kahaner, JD

Pressures on physician practices have increased steadily over the past several years. With the wide variety of government and private health insurance programs in which patients and physicians are participating, each with its own set of complex rules and regulations, the burden to assure compliance with the rules of the programs has become enormous. The enhanced enforcement effort of both the government and private insurance has generated still further pressure on physician practices. Currently, the federal government is reporting more than 5,000 health care fraud and abuse cases and investigations on an annual basis. The number of such cases and investigations represents more than a 500 percent increase during a recent five-year period. The government's health care fraud and abuse offensive generally focuses on three sets of statutes. They are the Criminal and Civil False Claims Acts, the Federal Anti-Kickback Statute, and the Federal Self-Referral Law (more commonly known as the Stark Law).

False Claims Acts

The Criminal False Claims Act makes it a felony to make or cause to be made any "false statement or representation of material fact in any application for any benefit or payment under a Federal health care program," including requests for reimbursement. Penalties for violation of the Criminal False Claims Act include a term of imprisonment of not more than five years, fines up to $25,000 and exclusion from federally funded health care programs.

The Civil False Claims Act imposes liability if one knowingly submits or causes to be submitted a false or fraudulent claim for payment to the federal government. The Civil False Claims Act also prohibits knowingly using a false record to get a false claim paid, conspiring to get a false claim paid, and knowingly making or using a false record to avoid an existing obligation to pay the federal government. Penalties for violation of the federal Civil False Claims Act include treble damages, fines of $5,000 to $10,000 per claim, and possible exclusion from federally funded health care programs. Many states have enacted laws similar to this federal statute.

The Civil False Claims Act is the enforcement tool most commonly used by government officials. Potential False Claims Act issues include billing for medically unnecessary services, services not provided, or noncovered services; upcoming; and duplicate billing, among others. Unfortunately, the potential for False Claims Act exposure in the area of pain management is serious, despite the fact that practitioners are acting in good faith.

Although practices tend to dismiss the possibility that they could file for services not actually performed, many third party payors take the position that billing for "no shows" constitutes just such a practice. It is not unusual for "no shows" to be billed, particularly in connection with physical therapy and psychotherapy services. Because of the failure of the CPT system to timely include procedure codes for new procedures or to create separate procedure codes covering all of the anatomical sites that may be the focus of a particular service, the use of procedure codes that do not completely describe new procedures can give rise to allegations that a service was billed but was not rendered. Epiduroscopy and annuloplasty are among those new procedures that can create False Claims Act exposure for pain management anesthesiologists.

Billing for non-covered services is another major focus of False Claims Act liability that can expose pain management practices to serious consequences. Patient controlled analgesia is a service that is often billed to third party payers, even though most payers do not cover these services. Billing for physical therapy services where the patient is merely being "maintained" can also raise allegations of billing for non-covered services. Most payors do not cover most medical screening services. Accordingly, many payors take the position that services ordered on the basis of "rule-out" diagnoses constitute a non-covered screening service. Although many providers submit services requiring pre-certification even when a pre-certification has not been obtained, most payors take the position that such submissions are improper as the absence of a pre-certification necessarily means that the service is not covered.

Billing for medically unnecessary services is another significant source of potential exposure under the False Claims Act for pain management physicians. Payors are particularly aggressive in attacking the medical necessity of psychotherapy, physical therapy, clinical laboratory, and diagnostic imaging services. Pain management practitioners often incorrectly assume that the reason a service was ordered can be inferred from their chart entries.

Because of medical necessity documentation requirements, most payors require that claims for the placement of a catheter for treatment of post-operative pain must include an entry differentiating the catheter billed from the one placed principally for purposes of surgical anesthesia. The medical necessity of services ordered, as part of plans of care is becoming a particularly significant source of concern for payors. The medical necessity of psychotherapy services may be challenged where the patient is taking psychotropic medications or there is evidence of organic brain disease.

Miscoded services are another very important source of False Claims Act liability for pain management practices. Reliance on ASC "face" or admitting sheets, outdated "cheat sheets," and scrub technicians or other untrained personnel to select procedure and diagnoses codes often leads to miscoding problems.

Although many practitioners thought that the government would refrain from conducting an organized offensive in the area of evaluation and management coding until the debate regarding the 1997 guidelines had been resolved, the government is aggressively targeting many physicians, including pain management physicians, in this area. The focus on evaluation and management services has also led to organized attacks on the use of consultation codes, where the consulting physician actually takes over the treatment of the patient, rather than simply acting as a consultant. A related focus of government scrutiny is the inappropriate use of psychotherapy codes where services are billed at levels that cannot be supported by the actual time spent in face-to-face contact with the patient. In billing levels of service, bill the level that was performed, documented, <u>and</u> medically necessary.

Miscoded services can also be submitted because of supervision issues and problems. Services of providers such as clinical psychologists (CP), clinical social workers (MSW), nurse practitioners (NP) or physician assistants (PA) may be billed to Medicare and other federally-funded programs, depending on the facts surrounding the encounter at issue, either using the provider number of the CP, MSW, NP or PA (in which case the program will pay a percentage of the physician fee schedule amount for the service) or by complying with the "incident-to" billing rules. To use "incident-to" billing, however, the physician must be <u>physically on-site and immediately available</u> when the ancillary practitioner is providing services and the services must be an incidental component of the physician's service. A physician may only bill for the services of other non-physician providers, such as master's level psychologists, physical therapists, or physical therapy assistants, using the "incident-to" billing rules.

The submission of duplicate bills and fragmented claims are also a significant potential source of exposure for pain management physicians. Duplicate bills are often submitted to third party payors under the mistaken belief that the original claim has been lost or misplaced. The potential for False Claims Act liability increases when a practice has no system in place to identify and refund duplicate payments. The National Correct Coding Initiative specifies that certain less comprehensive services may not be billed to Medicare in addition to or instead of various more comprehensive procedure codes. Unfortunately, some pain management providers do not have a system in place to screen for National Correct Coding Initiative restrictions.

Anti-Kickback Laws

The Federal Anti-Kickback Law is a broad prohibition on the offer or receipt of anything of value (direct or indirect, overt or covert, in cash or in kind), which is intended to induce the referral of a patient for an item, or service that is reimbursed under a federal health care program, including Medicare and Medicaid. Many states have enacted similar state prohibitions. Violations of the federal law are punishable by a term of imprisonment not to exceed five years, trebled damages and penalties of up to $50,000 for <u>each violation</u>, and exclusion from federally funded health care programs.

In order to prevent application of the law to legitimate business relationships, a number of exceptions to the Federal Anti-Kickback Law have been created. These are commonly known as "safe harbors," and include protections for payments resulting from certain investments, payments for rentals of space and equipment, payments to bone fide employees, payments under contracts for services, payments relating to physician referral services, payment relating to the purchase and sale of physician practices, remuneration paid pursuant to warranties and in the form of discounts, remuneration to group purchasing organizations, and certain arrangements with preferred providers and in Medicare/Medicaid managed care arrangements. Potential kickback issues include direct and indirect relationships with referring physicians, hospitals, and clinical laboratories; courtesy discounts; and physician compensation arrangements.

Many common business arrangements have the potential to violate state or federal anti-kickback laws. Practices should not have any arrangements with hospitals, ambulatory surgery centers, durable medical equipment suppliers, diagnostic imaging centers, clinical laboratories, billing companies, or others that provide any form of payment or remuneration for referrals of patients for services that may be covered by a federally-funded health care program, unless the arrangement falls squarely and appropriately within one of the anti-kickback law safe harbors.

Suspect arrangements

- Hospital or ASC medical director positions where services are provided for no compensation or for compensation that is more than fair market value.
- Professional courtesy discounts, including waiver of co-payments or deductibles, where the practice submits a claim to the patient's insurance company (this may also be a violation of the provider agreement between the physician/practice and certain private payors) that does not reflect the discount or where the discount is given or taken in an effort to influence referrals.
- Waiving co-payments or deductibles without establishing the patient's indigence or making reasonable efforts to collect the fee;
- Discounts for the purchases of goods or services or for the sale of goods or services that are not based upon prompt payment;
- Space lease arrangements at a hospital office medical building that are not based upon fair market value;
- Stock options or other compensation from medical equipment suppliers and pharmaceutical companies whose products are used by the provider or the practice;
- Sale of pharmaceutical samples to beneficiaries
- Compensation arrangements with physicians or other practitioners that are based upon the volume or value of referrals for services within the practice;
- Favorable investment opportunities in ASCs that are based upon the volume or value of referrals for services to the ASC;
- Inducements given to beneficiaries that are known to or should have been known to affect the beneficiaries choice of provider, such as with cash or inappropriate medication dispensing practices;
- Free pain management screenings not undertaken as part of a health fair;
- Providing free transportation to assist patients in traveling to the practice, particularly if the service is advertised;
- Marketing activities to referral sources which include expensive meals, or tickets to entertainment and sporting events; and
- Percentage contracts with management service organizations or billing companies, which include marketing and billing and collection services.

Self-Referral Laws

The Federal Self-Referral Law, commonly known as the "Stark law," prohibits a physician from making referrals for certain "designated health services" when those services are (1) furnished by an entity with which the physician has a direct or indirect financial relationship, and (2) reimbursed by Medicare or Medicaid. Many states have enacted similar state provisions. The designated health services covered by the federal law include: clinical laboratory services; physical therapy services; occupational therapy services; radiology and ultrasound services (defined to include nuclear imaging services); radiation therapy services and supplies; durable medical equipment and supplies; parenteral and enteral nutrients and supplies; prosthetics, orthotics, and prosthetic devices; home health services; outpatient prescription drugs; and inpatient and outpatient hospital services. Violations of the statute are punishable with civil money penalties of up to $15,000 per claim and exclusion from federally funded health care programs.

Like the Federal Anti-Kickback Law, several exceptions to the Stark law have been added by statute and regulations, including physician services, in-office ancillary services, certain Medicare/Medicaid managed care arrangements, investments in publicly traded companies and mutual funds, ownership arrangements of hospitals and rural providers, payments for rental of equipment and space, payments in connection with bone fide employment arrangements, payments in connection with personal service arrangements, payments in connection with physician incentive plans and physician recruitment, isolated transactions, certain group practice arrangements, and payments for items or services at fair market value. Potential Stark Law issues, in addition to many of the issues identified above in the anti-kickback area, include financial interests in hospitals, ambulatory surgery centers, clinical laboratories, and diagnostic imaging centers.

Relationships that can create self-referral problems include ownership interests in or medical director agreements with a hospital or ASC,1/ investment interests in a clinical laboratory, diagnostic imaging center, physical therapy, occupational therapy or DME company, part-time employment or independent contractor agreements, free or discounted space or equipment leases, marketing agreements with entities owned by physician or hospital investors that do not reflect fair market value payments for necessary services; and practice compensation programs that reward shareholders or employee physicians based on orders of designated health services.

While there is no magic formula to ensure protection from government or private payor enforcement activities, one step that will enable a practice to operate more efficiently and minimize its exposure is the development of a health care fraud and abuse compliance program. Compliance programs have already become standard for large providers of health care. National suppliers and institutional providers of care have been developing compliance programs for the past several years. More recently, individual hospitals, nursing homes, and other institutional providers of care have implemented compliance programs as well. Within the last several years, many physician practices have been developing compliance programs as well. Physician practices would be wise to commit to compliance programs.

What Is a Compliance Program?

A compliance program is a series of internal controls that promote the prevention, detection, and resolution of conduct that may be inconsistent with applicable laws, regulations, rules, or program or practice policies. Compliance programs establish a mechanism for addressing questions about appropriate behavior, as well as investigating and correcting inappropriate activities. Since the effectiveness of the program is dependent upon the cooperation and commitment of all employees and other personnel involved with the practice, a compliance program also will establish a procedure for imposing discipline, when appropriate, and include a process to reduce the risk of similar problems recurring in the future.

A compliance program requires a practice to commit its culture and its resources in an appropriate fashion and at an appropriate level in order to assure compliance with applicable rules and regulations — instead of waiting for the government or an outside entity to identify problems and impose sanctions. While there will necessarily be a number of elements common to all physician practice compliance programs, the implementation and structure of each program should reflect the philosophy and culture of a particular practice and must be tailored to address that practice's needs.

What a Compliance Program Is Not

A compliance program is not a magic formula that will give a practice absolute protection from the risks inherent to government and private insurance payment programs. Even the most effective compliance program may not be able to avoid the imposition of some form of sanctions. Further, a compliance program is not a document that can be left on the shelf and be forgotten. To be effective, a compliance program must be a dynamic and ongoing process.

Why Should a Physician Practice Adopt a Compliance Program?

Compliance programs have their origin in the federal sentencing guidelines, a series of guidelines designed to assure consistency in the imposition of sanctions in criminal cases. Under the sentencing guidelines, when an individual or entity is sentenced as a result of a criminal conviction, the existence of an effective compliance program is considered a mitigating factor that can reduce the period of incarceration as well as the dollar amount of the criminal penalty imposed. Until the early 1990s, compliance programs were largely unknown in the health care industry. With the explosive increase in health care enforcement cases, however, the significance of compliance programs has become evident.

The major catalyst for development of compliance plans in the health care industry occurred in 1994 as a result of the settlement between National Medical Enterprises (NME) and the United States. In addition to agreeing to pay $379 million to settle allegations of false claims and kickbacks, NME agreed to adopt a corporate compliance program developed in coordination with the U.S. Department of Justice and the Office of the Inspector General of the Department of Health and Human Services (OIG). Since the resolution of the NME case, virtually every settlement between the government and a major provider of health care services has resulted in the imposition of a compliance program. Since 1994, the government has imposed corporate compliance programs on physician practices as well.

The pressure to implement a compliance program will continue to increase. The OIG has committed to develop model compliance programs for various facets of the health care industry. Already, OIG has published model programs for physicians and small group practices, laboratories, hospitals, home health agencies, billing companies, durable medical equipment suppliers, skilled nursing, facilities, hospices, and Medicare + Choice managed care organizations.

On December 24, 1997, the OIG published a notice in the Federal Register (62 Fed. Reg. 67392) that sets forth the criteria to be used by that office in exercising its permissive exclusion authority. In this notice, OIG explained what factors it considered in determining whether it should exclude from Medicare, Medicaid, and other federal health care programs, a provider found to have violated program rules and regulations. The adoption and operation of an effective compliance program are among the key factors OIG evaluates in its decision to exercise its discretionary exclusion authority.

Finally, practices should establish compliance programs because it makes good business sense. As noted above, the complexity of participating in the variety of government and private insurance programs has imposed an extraordinary burden on medical practices, and the potential for error is significant. While the majority of medical practices are committed to following the rules, government and private enforcement authorities are becoming less tolerant of any errors and wield tremendous power to impose sanctions. While not foolproof, a compliance program is the most effective way to reduce the likelihood that the occasional mistake will evolve into a pattern of inappropriate behavior inviting outside scrutiny and possible sanctions. The federal government has stated repeatedly that the voluntary adoption of an effective compliance program is the single most important step that health care providers are likely to be able to take to (1) reduce the risk of a criminal charge and (2) reduce any civil fines or penalties.

Elements of a Physician Practice Compliance Program

Under the federal sentencing guidelines, as well as under the model compliance programs developed by OIG to date, an effective compliance program must reflect the following seven elements:

1. **Written standards of conduct**. The practice must adopt a set of guidelines, as well as policies and procedures, to be followed by all personnel associated with the practice. These guidelines must reflect the practice's commitment to compliance in general, as well as address specific areas of concern for that practice. The standards of conduct should be more detailed if the practice does not already have a comprehensive policy and procedures manual. The OIG has suggested that a centralized repository of government and payor procedure manuals and publications may supplement the guidance of the practice's written standards of conduct.
2. **Designation of compliance officer or committee**. The practice must identify an individual or group of individuals responsible for the operation and monitoring of the compliance program, and who report directly to the governing body or other alternate decision-makers within the practice.
3. **Education and training for all personnel in the practice**. Programs must be developed to educate all personnel on an on-going basis about the existence of the compliance program and the rules and regulations with which the practice must comply.
4. **Effective mechanism for communication**. The practice must establish a reporting mechanism, through a telephone hotline or other process, for questions or complaints to be communicated to the compliance officer/committee without raising concerns about retaliation. Telephone hotlines are only usually used in larger practices or practices that have multiple offices, particularly those with geographically dispersed offices. Smaller practices typically use suggestion boxes to facilitate anonymous reporting. The compliance officer/committee must also be able to communicate with and disseminate information to all practice personnel.
5. **Internal investigation and disciplinary process**. The practice must develop a process to investigate allegations of impropriety and discipline individuals who have acted inappropriately.
6. **Periodic auditing and monitoring**. The practice must have a mechanism for performing periodic auditing and monitoring of its operation to assure compliance with applicable rules and regulations.
7. **Establishment of response mechanism**. The practice must develop a mechanism for responding to and correcting identified problems, and must develop a process for screening new personnel to prevent delegating authority to individuals who may have a propensity to engage in illegal activity.

Implementation of a Compliance Program

When a physician practice implements a compliance program, it must assure that the seven elements described above are followed. Given the diversity in size and structure of physician practices today, there is no single "best" compliance program. The following section describes one mechanism that a practice may use. Additional details addressing certain implementation issues and representative examples may be found in the attached materials. These examples are for demonstrative purposes only. Each practice should use, ignore, or amend them in light of the practice's particular needs, organizational structure, and available resources.

Suggested Implementation Steps

As the initial step in developing an effective compliance program, the practice should perform a comprehensive baseline audit of its operations, sometimes referred to as the "legal audit." The purpose of the baseline audit is to ascertain whether the practice's current practices and procedures conform with all pertinent legal requirements. The audit may be performed internally or by an independent third party. Because it is often difficult for a practice to be objective in conducting a baseline audit and to effectively challenge the assumptions from which it is operating, externally performed baseline audits generally appear to be more effective in identifying potential compliance issues. This baseline audit will assist in the development of the Standards of Conduct and will serve as the foundation for the education training programs.

The first step in the audit requires a review of key documents, including documents related to all contractual relationships, relationships with referral sources, the overall structure of the practice and its compliance with federal and state anti-kickback and self-referral laws, and billing and coding issues. Physician practices may identify other areas for review based upon their particular needs, such as licensing, antitrust considerations, compliance with Drug Enforcement Agency or Occupational Safety Hazards Act medical waste requirements, employee benefit issues, or tax issues.

As part of the general document review, all practices should undertake a thorough review of their billing and coding practices. This sub-component of the review should include locating and reviewing private or public payor procedure manuals and agreements, assessing the integrity and accuracy of the practice's billing methods, and reviewing any prior audits performed by internal or outside entities. The practice may also find it useful to evaluate its claims history for patterns of denial and overpayment.

A "walk-through" of the practice should be performed. During a walk-through, an imaginary patient and his paperwork is followed from check-in, through the office or in-patient visit, to the end stages of the billing process, which includes claim submission, payment posting and collections, denials and resubmissions, refunding of overpayments, and write-offs. This exercise is one of the best methods for obtaining a complete overview of a practice's operations. It often highlights areas of vulnerability and poor coordination, and offers staff an opportunity to raise questions or concerns about current practices that might not be expressed in a different forum.

The next step is to conduct interviews with members and employees of the practice. These interviews offer the opportunity for the people within the practice to (1) identify issues not already identified and (2) see the practice's interest in and commitment to act on any compliance concern they might have. Where interviews of all the members and employees do not make sense, would be too expensive, or would take too much time, sufficient interviews should be conducted to secure information and perspective from every level of the practice.

Many practices also find a medical chart review, performed internally or by an outside consultant, to be a very useful addition to the baseline audit as well. We recommend that at least eight services, and preferably ten to fifteen services, be reviewed for each clinician in the practice. Be careful to capture a range of services in the charts that are reviewed.

Using the findings of the baseline audit as a guide, the practice should adopt Standards of Conduct, supported by written policies and procedures. The Standards of Conduct form the foundation of the compliance program. They should reflect the general philosophy, mission, and culture of the practice, and should also focus on specific areas of compliance weakness that were identified in the baseline audit. Generally, the Standards of Conduct will include broad categories of the practice's operations, such as relationships with patients and vendors, compliance with federal and private program rules and regulations, conflict of interest concerns, and business conduct and practices, as well as specific areas of conduct with which all personnel are expected to comply. While certain standards are expected to be consistent among all medical practices, such as treating patients with dignity or assuring that claims submitted to payors are accurate and complete, there should also be specific components of the Standards of Conduct that are tailored to the needs and experiences of each practice. Practices should solicit suggestions from its members and employees about items to be included in the Standards.

Written policies and procedures should implement the Standards of Conduct by addressing the details of day-to-day operations. For most practices, these may already exist in some form but may not be compiled or circulated in a methodical way. Development of policies and procedures will continue after operation of the compliance plan has begun. Lack of policies and procedures should not delay moving forward with the other pieces of the compliance program. The practice should also consider updating clinical forms and clinical pathways and protocols.

A compliance officer and/or committee should be appointed as early as possible in the compliance plan development process. The compliance officer and/or committee must have access to the principals of the practice or other ultimate decision-makers, and must be an individual or individuals who other personnel will feel comfortable approaching with questions or concerns. Since the compliance officer and/or committee serves as the focal point for compliance activities, the individual or individuals should take an active role in the development of the compliance program. In particular, the compliance officer and/or committee should participate in developing the Standards of Conduct, and developing a process to communicate with and disseminate information to the individuals in the practice. The practice must also establish procedures for the compliance officer and/or committee to respond to any requests for information from personnel or to investigate and, where appropriate, take corrective action concerning any complaints that are filed. The document that describes these procedures and the other workings of the compliance program is called a Compliance Plan. Open discussion of ethical and legal issues without fear of retaliation is vital to the effectiveness of the compliance program and should be emphasized in the Compliance Plan. These procedures must maintain, within the limits of the law, and as otherwise consistent with the needs of the practice, the confidentiality of any individual who reports misconduct and must prohibit retaliation against any individual who, in good faith, reports a legal or ethical concern. Further, a disciplinary protocol should be established, and personnel should be advised of the sanctions that may be imposed for those who fail to follow the practice's Standards of Conduct and prescribed procedures, who violate applicable program rules and regulations, or who do not abide by the Compliance Plan. Finally, the practice should establish a mechanism to assure that delegation of authority is made only to those individuals who are trustworthy and have not been excluded from any of the federally funded health care programs.

Although not a specific requirement for a compliance program, it is also useful to develop an appendix to the Compliance Plan containing a plan for responding to government investigations and a document retention policy.

Compliance programs require commitment from all individuals in a practice. After the compliance program has been established, personnel should be informed about its existence and how it operates in an organized, thoughtfully designed training program. In the initial training that occurs under the compliance program, all personnel should also be educated about the fraud and abuse laws and regulations that affect the practice as well as the corrected policies and procedures implemented based on issues identified in the baseline audit. All new employees should be trained as part of their orientation. Live sessions are much more productive than written materials. At least annual training sessions and refresher courses must be conducted regarding the Standards of Conduct and the requirements of the Compliance Plan. Alternative training sources include attendance at commercial compliance seminars or educational seminars sponsored by hospitals or other providers affiliated with the practice.

An effective compliance program is a dynamic process that requires regular re-evaluation. Every practice should periodically assess the success of its initial program and revise any Standard of Conduct, procedure or policy as appropriate.

COMPLIANCE PLAN

Each employee and affiliate of the organization must recognize that he or she has assumed a number of responsibilities by joining the staff or affiliating with the organization. This document describes the two principal elements of those responsibilities.

A. *Conformity with the Standards of Conduct*

First, each employee or affiliate is responsible for making sure his or her conduct is in conformity with the Standards of Conduct listed here, any other organization policy, any third party payor requirements, and all applicable federal and state rules, regulations, and statutes.

If, at any time, you have a question as to whether a procedure or action is appropriate under the Standards, then you should ask your immediate supervisor. If you do not feel comfortable discussing the situation with your supervisor, or, if you have discussed the matter with your supervisor and you remain unclear as to what conduct is appropriate, then you should speak with one of the members of the Compliance Committee. The Suggested Compliance Committee members consist of:

Administrator
Director of Human Resources
Representative of Insurance Department
Clinical Director
Psychologist
Nursing Administrator
Clinical Coordinator
Physician(s)
Medical Director
Compliance Officer

The Compliance Committee was created so that any employee or affiliate who had a question about what was proper conduct could secure any needed information. The Compliance Committee will be able to answer questions about the Standards of Conduct and resolve disputed interpretations. The Compliance Committee also can and will take whatever action is necessary to investigate a complaint and institute corrective action.

B. *Reporting Violations of the Standards of Conduct*

Second, it is the responsibility of each employee or affiliate to report any violations of the Standards of Conduct, any other organization policy, any third party payor requirements, or any federal or state rule, regulation, or statute. A form that may be used to report such concerns is attached. In addition, issues may be raised anonymously by calling the organization's hotline at (270) 554-8373, ext. 131 or completing the report form attached as Exhibit 3. Because it is often difficult to explore issues raised anonymously (since the Compliance Committee cannot ask for additional information from an anonymous source), we prefer other types of reports of issues. If you decide to report an issue anonymously, please be as specific and detailed as you can possibly be to assist the Compliance Committee. Please give a detailed explanation of the issue, how long you believe it has been an issue, what documents or persons can help to further explain the issue, or that reflect or are involved in the conduct, and what steps, if any, have been taken to resolve or investigate the issue.

All organization employees and affiliates must follow the Standards of Conduct. Any violation of the Standards is a serious matter. Employees and affiliates may be subject to discipline, up to and including termination, for violations of these Standards. The organization's Standards of Conduct do not constitute an employment or other type of contract. You should not and may not interpret any of these Standards as a promise of continued employment or any other continued contractual or other relationship.

COMPLIANCE COMMITTEE

The suggested Compliance Committee shall consist of:

Administrator
Director of Human Resources
Representative of Insurance Department
Clinical Director
Psychologist
Nursing Administrator
Clinical Coordinator
Physician(s)
Medical Director
Compliance Officer

If a Committee member is involved personally and directly in any allegation that is raised, he or she will abstain from any consideration of any such allegation. If any Committee member is involved personally and directly in any allegation, the organization's attorneys will be notified and informed of the nature of the allegation.

INVESTIGATIVE PROTOCOL

A primary duty of the Compliance Committee shall be to facilitate reports of possible misconduct from the organization's employees. The Compliance Committee shall ensure that every report, whether written or oral, that is received shall be reviewed and evaluated. Reports will be forwarded to the organization's attorneys, as necessary or appropriate, the discretion of the Compliance Committee.

After consulting with the organization's attorneys, the Committee may determine that a report does not warrant investigation. If the Committee concludes, based upon its initial review of a report, that an investigation is warranted, the Committee may ask the organization's attorneys to conduct the investigation or it may conduct the investigation itself. Any investigation shall be completed in a timely fashion.

At the conclusion of any investigation, a report may be written to the organization's attorneys containing a summary of the reported allegation, the steps taken to investigate the report, the investigative findings, and the recommendations, if any, for corrective action. In consultation with the organization's attorneys, the Compliance Committee shall act on all investigatory conclusions in a timely fashion.

AUDIT PROTOCOL

The Compliance Committee shall institute a plan for periodic internal audits of certain facets of its operations. The areas that shall be audited are billing practices and procedures, procedures relating to the adequacy of chart documentation, utilization, and other matters. These audits shall be performed no less than monthly.

COMPLIANCE TRAINING

As part of its compliance program, the organization shall provide periodic training for its employees and, in its discretion, its affiliates. The focus of the training shall be the Standards of Conduct and the way in which the employee disciplinary system will be used to enforce the compliance program. Each employee and affiliate attending a program shall be required to sign an attendance sheet establishing attendance at each training session that is conducted. It is the responsibility of the Compliance Committee to maintain contact with outside counsel so that the organization is aware of new regulatory and legal developments affecting its operations. It is the responsibility of the Compliance Officer, or his or her designee, to ensure that each new employee or appropriate affiliate receives a copy of the compliance program. It is the Compliance Officer or his or her designee that shall be responsible for training all new employees regarding the requirements of this program and its importance to the organization.

EXIT INTERVIEWS

It shall be the responsibility of the Compliance Officer, or his or her designee, to conduct an exit interview with each employee terminating employment with the organization. The purpose of this interview shall be to solicit information about the level of the organization's compliance with the Standards of Conduct. A questionnaire attached as Exhibit 1 shall be completed at each exit interview.

DISCIPLINARY ACTIONS

It shall be the responsibility of the Compliance Committee to ensure that any employee found to have violated the Standards of Conduct is disciplined in an appropriate, measured, and consistent fashion. See Exhibit 2.

EXHIBIT 1
COMPLIANCE PROGRAM EXIT INTERVIEW

This form is an important part of the Organization Compliance Program. We ask that all employees and others who are terminating their relationship with the Organization take a few moments to respond to the questions that follow. Our goal is to find ways in which we can improve the ethics and compliance of our organization.

Name:______________________________

Please provide your current address and telephone number:______________________________

Please provide your address and telephone number following the termination of your employment with the Organization:

____

____

____

What is your position with the organization:

____

____

How long were you employed by the Organization?

____

____

During your affiliation with the Organization, have you ever-engaged in conduct that you believe was either unethical or illegal?

YES _____ NO _____

____

If yes, please describe that conduct, including the relevant dates.

____

____

During your affiliation with the Organization, have you ever been asked to engage in conduct that you believe was either unethical or illegal?

YES _____ NO _____

If yes, by whom? Please describe that conduct, including the relevant dates.

____

____

Have you ever witnessed conduct by an employee, affiliate, contractor or agent of the Organization that you believe was either unethical or illegal?

YES _____ NO _____

If yes, by whom? Please describe that conduct, including the relevant dates.

During your affiliation with the Organization, has there ever been anything that you have felt uncomfortable doing on behalf of the Organization?

YES _____ NO _____

If yes, please describe.

____

____

Have you ever removed Organization documents without returning them to Organization?

YES _____ NO _____

If yes, where are those documents now?

____

____

Have you ever given Organization documents to a third-party other than in furtherance of the Organization's business?

YES _____ NO _____

If yes, to whom and when?

____

____

Have you ever used the Compliance Hotline system?

YES _____ NO _____

If yes, were you satisfied with the results?

____

____

Do you have any recommendations for improving the Organization's compliance program or its ability to meet its ethical and legal obligations?

YES _____ NO _____. If yes, what are they?

____

____

____

EXHIBIT 2
DISCIPLINARY PROTOCOL

In order to make the organization's compliance program effective, the Compliance Officer, or his or her designee, must educate all employees so that they understand that the program includes the imposition of appropriate discipline for violations of the Standards of Conduct. Violations of the Standards of Conduct (including failure to report the misconduct of other employees) may result in punishment, including possible immediate termination of employment.

Managers must make serious and consistent attempts to identify any misconduct committed by any employees or others that they supervise. Managers will be subject to discipline for failure to detect compliance violations that occur to the extent that the manager fails to identify misconduct due to his or her negligence or other wrongful conduct.

Certain violations of the compliance program are particularly likely to justify immediate termination. These offenses include:

1. violation of any state or federal statute;
2. failure to report conduct by an organization employee or contractor that a reasonable person under the circumstances should have known was criminal or a violation of the law;
3. failure to report a violation of the Standards of Conduct by any organization employee or contractor that a reasonable person under the circumstances should have known was a violation of the Standards; and
4. willfully providing materially false information to the organization, its attorneys, a government agency, or other person in connection with any matter related to the organization or the provision of any health care service or item.

EXHIBIT 3
COMPLAINT POLICY

The Compliance Program reporting system was established to help organization personnel with questions, concerns, and complaints that cannot be properly addressed through traditional resolution processes. It is our intention to respond to each reasonable inquiry, which is made in good faith to the reporting system. It is the organization's policy that no retaliation or retribution occurs as a result of using the reporting system. It is also the organization's policy that the anonymity of individuals using the system be preserved, subject to the limits imposed by law. If you discuss your report with other individuals, your anonymity may not be preserved.

In the space provided below, please describe your question, concern or complaint. Feel free to attach additional sheets if necessary. Please be as specific as possible so that we may respond appropriately. Please attach copies of any relevant documents or other materials that you believe would assist in our appropriately investigating your report.

____

____

____

____

Name (optional): ____________________________

Address or phone number (optional): ___________

____

EXHIBIT 4
COMPLIANCE PROGRAM SEMI-ANNUAL SURVEY

This form is an important part of the Organization Compliance Program. We ask that all employees and affiliates of the organization take a few moments to respond to the questions that follow. Our goal is to find ways in which we can improve the ethics and compliance of our organization.

If you do not feel comfortable completing this form, but do have information that you believe is relevant to the organization's compliance efforts, please feel free to place an anonymous report in the organization's compliance hotline or complete and submit a report form. To the extent a report has not been made anonymously at any time in the past, will not be made anonymously within one week, or has not been made in completing a previous questionnaire, any compliance concerns that you may have must be reported here.

Name: ______________________

Please provide your current address and telephone number: ____________________________

What is your position with the organization?

____

____

How long have you been employed by the organization?

____

____

During your affiliation with the organization, have you ever-engaged in conduct that you believe was either unethical or illegal?

YES _____ NO _____

If yes, please describe that conduct, including the relevant dates.

____

____

During your affiliation with the organization, have you ever been asked to engage in conduct that you believe was either unethical or illegal?

YES _____ NO _____.

If yes, by whom? Please describe that conduct, including the relevant dates.

____

Have you ever witnessed conduct by an employee, affiliate, contractor or agent of the organization that you believe was either unethical or illegal?

YES _____ NO _____.

If yes, by whom? Please describe that conduct, including the relevant dates.

____

____

During your affiliation with the organization, has there ever been anything that you have felt uncomfortable doing on behalf of the organization?

YES _____ NO _____.

If yes, please describe.

____

____

Have you ever removed organization documents without returning them to organization?

YES _____ NO _____.

If yes, where are those documents now?

____

____

Have you ever given organization documents to a third-party other than in furtherance of the organization's business?

YES _____ NO _____.

If yes, to whom and when?

____

____

Have you ever used the Compliance hotline report system?
YES _____ NO _____.

If yes, were you satisfied with the results?

Do you have any recommendations for improving the organization's compliance program or its ability to meet its ethical and legal obligations?

YES _____ NO _____. If yes, what are they?

____

____

EXHIBIT 5

SAMPLE VERIFICATION CORRESPONDENCE

____

____

____

____

Dear _______________:

On _____________________, at approximately _________ am/pm, I spoke to you regarding a question concerning ______________________________

____

You informed me that

____

It is my understanding that the guidance that you provided is in accordance with the applicable rules and policies governing this issue, and I intend to act in reliance on this information. If my understandings are not correct, please write to me immediately to clarify the situation.

Thank you for your kind attention to this matter.

Sincerely,

____

STANDARDS OF CONDUCT

The organization is dedicated to furnishing quality medical treatment in accordance with all pertinent federal and state laws. The organization will take reasonable steps in an attempt to ensure that its staff acts in conformity with pertinent laws and regulations. The term "affiliates," as used in this document, means the organization's suppliers, vendors, independent contractors, and others, with whom the organization has a significant relationship. The following are the Standards of Conduct that the organization has adopted:

General Matters

1. All employees of the organization and its affiliates must cooperate fully and completely with any compliance program or initiative instituted by the organization.
2. All employees of the organization and its affiliates must fully and completely comply with the organization's policies and procedures.
3. Violations or suspected violations of the compliance program, these Standards or organization policies and procedures must be reported immediately to a supervisor or the compliance officer/committee. The organization will investigate reports promptly and fully, as appropriate under the circumstances.
4. All treatment recommended and provided by the organization and its affiliates will be medically necessary.
5. The organization and its affiliates will not over-utilize services or under-utilize services in treating their patients.
6. The organization and its affiliates will not directly or indirectly pay any person or any entity for patient referrals or for arranging for the purchase or lease of any item or service in violation of state of federal law. Except for certain exceptions, it may be illegal or unethical to offer any financial inducement, gift or bribe to prospective patients or others in order to encourage patients to undergo treatment.
7. The organization and its affiliates shall not refer patients to entities with which the organization, its employees, or its affiliates have a financial interest, except as permitted by the Federal Self-Referral Law or applicable state law.
8. The organization shall not enter into a financial relationship with a referral source or any other person in a position to make referrals unless the payments or other financial terms reflect fair market value in an arm's length transaction without regard to any referrals or other business between the parties.
9. The organization shall not enter into a financial relationship with a referral source or any other person in a position to make referrals unless the issue of fair market value has been assessed in some objective manner. Review of published data such as the AMA or MGMA physician compensation surveys or an independent appraisal shall satisfy this requirement, as will comparable bids or market quotations.
10. Except for the occasional modest expressions of gratitude from patients, employees should refuse gifts, loans, tickets, meals or anything of value offered by outside individuals or companies, including the organization's affiliates, unless receipt of the gift, loan, or other thing of value has been disclosed to the compliance officer/committee and the

compliance officer/committee, or their designee, believes that the receipt of the gift, loan, or other thing of value will not create any regulatory violation or potential conflict of interest.

11. No person or employee shall offer or give anything of monetary value, including gifts, gratuities, favors, entertainment, or loans to an employee or representative of a government agency or payor with which the organization has or is seeking to obtain contractual or other business or financial relations or that regulates any of the organization's activities or operations.

Quality of Care

1. All patients shall be treated with respect and dignity.
2. The organization shall only provide quality care that is both necessary and appropriate.
3. Informed consent shall be obtained for all treatment as appropriate and required under the circumstances.
4. Whenever the circumstances permit, patients and their representatives shall be given information regarding the reasons for the recommended treatment, how it will be accomplished, and the associated risks and benefits of available treatment options.
5. Patients and their representatives will be accorded appropriate confidentiality, privacy, security, counseling and opportunities for resolution of complaints.
6. The organization shall make no distinction in the care provided based on race, color, religion, national origin or ability to pay. Each patient, no matter what the payment source or level of reimbursement, shall be provided with a high level of superior care and cost-effective treatment.
7. All organization physicians, nurse practitioners, psychologists, and other clinicians will be licensed, credentialed and skilled at the services they perform, as appropriate and as required by law.
8. The organization will comply with all laws and regulations regarding patient rights. All personnel will receive training about patient rights in order to clearly understand their role in supporting them.
9. Patient telephone inquiries shall be referred to an appropriate clinician and the inquiry and the response given should be documented in the patient's chart.
10. On a periodic basis, the organization, through its compliance committee, will review and evaluate its procedures, medical standards and treatment results to ensure that its care remains of superior quality. Reviews shall occur no less frequently than on annual basis.

Records and Other Property

1. All organization records and documents are of a highly confidential nature. Except as required or authorized by law, they shall not be disclosed to or discussed with anyone not employed by or affiliated with the organization without the written permission of the organization or the relevant patient. Staff shall make every reasonable effort to ensure that their conversations and other communications appropriately respect patient confidentiality.
2. No property belonging to the organization may be removed from the organization without the permission of the organization.
3. Except as expressly permitted in writing, no employee may use or disclose to any person any trade secrets or other confidential or proprietary information belonging to the organization, including, but not limited to, records and files, patient lists, referral information, marketing materials, business records, financial documents, and any other papers, records, and documents the disclosure of which might adversely affect the organization.
4. Upon separation, no employee may take or retain any of the organization's papers, patient lists, fee books, patient records, files, or other documents, or copies of any such materials.
5. No edits should be made to clinical records unless the edit is properly undertaken. The appropriate manner in which to make an edit to a hardcopy document is to place a single line through the material to be edited, using a blue or black pen, and to date and sign the edit. In addition, where edits are made after the date of the original entry, the reason or the basis for the edit should be documented.
6. It shall be the responsibility of the compliance officer, or his designee, to ensure that all provider agreements, provider manuals, and provider billing instructions and circulars are maintained in centralized, well-organized binders.
7. It shall be the responsibility of the compliance officer, or his or her designee, to ensure that all Medicare instructions and bulletins regarding billing, coding, and coverage information is supplied to all clinicians, technical staff, scribes, billing department staff, and others with involvement in the billing and coding functions, including front desk and check out personnel. Recipients receipt of these materials should be documented.

Reporting, Survey, and Other Requirements

1. All employees and affiliates shall immediately report to the organization any contact, inquiry, investigation, proceeding, charge, or complaint involving any court of law, administrative tribunal, or state or federal agency that is related to the organization or its operations in any manner or that is related to

the provision of medical care, involves an allegation of moral turpitude, or is related to any alleged fraudulent act or omission.

2. Any employee or affiliate of the organization must immediately notify the organization in writing if he or she becomes the subject of or there is presently pending against him or her any request, inquiry, investigation, or proceeding the outcome of which could result in the suspension or revocation of his or her licensure or any professional membership or certification. Thereafter, any such employee or affiliate must keep the organization informed of the progress and outcome or resolution of such request, inquiry, investigation, or proceeding in a timely and complete fashion.
3. Any employee of the organization must immediately notify the organization if he or she is excluded, suspended, debarred, or removed, whether voluntarily or involuntarily, from any government or commercial payor plan or program.
4. On a semi-annual basis, each employee will fully and accurately complete a compliance questionnaire. See Exhibit 4 under Section II. It shall be the responsibility of the compliance officer, or his or her designee, to ensure that these questionnaires are distributed and completed in accordance with this policy.
5. Upon separation, all employees shall be asked to participate in an exit interview and provide complete and accurate information to the organization in connection with that interview. The exit interview will include the completion of a questionnaire. See Exhibit 1 under Section II. The exit interview shall be conducted by the Compliance Officer, or his or her designee.

Governmental and Other Inquiries or Communications

1. The organization will respond to any governmental inquiries as required by law.
2. The organization will provide accurate information in responding to any governmental, payor, or patient inquiries.
3. During a government investigation, no person shall conceal, destroy, or alter documents; knowingly make any false statements to the government's representatives; or attempt to cause another person to fail to provide accurate information or obstruct the inquiry.
4. Every contact with a payor or a governmental agency in which the organization receives coverage or other advice that the organization intends to rely upon in submitting claims or taking other action should be documented using a written communication. See Exhibit 5 under Section II.

Maintenance of Compliance Plan Documents

1. A bound copy of the current Standards of Conduct and Compliance Plan document shall be maintained at each employee's work station at all times.
2. It is the responsibility of the Compliance Officer, or his or her designee, to audit compliance with this requirement at least once each year.

Screening Obligation

1. On an annual basis, the Compliance Officer, or his or her designee, will check the Lists of Excluded Persons maintained by the Office of the Inspector General to the Department of Health and Human Services and the General Services Administration to ensure that each employee and affiliate has not been excluded from any federal program.
2. These lists shall also be queried any time that a new employee or affiliate is selected.

BILLING

General Matters

1. The organization will take reasonable steps to ensure that claims for reimbursement submitted to any federally funded health care program or other payer are accurate and in accordance with the services rendered.
2. Claim forms will be submitted in a timely manner taking all reasonable steps to ensure the accuracy of the date of service, the nature of the service, and all other information, including the signatures used.
3. The organization will select the most appropriate CPT codes, ICD-9 codes, and modifiers in describing procedures performed, regardless of the impact upon payment.
4. Super bills, billing instruction sheets, and other forms will not be designed in any way that inappropriately steers practitioners towards higher level procedure codes or diagnoses codes that will support third party payor coverage.
5. The organization shall take reasonable steps to ensure that services are documented appropriately as required by the applicable billing and coding requirements.
6. The organization shall take reasonable efforts to ensure that the federally funded health care programs and other payors are not billed for routine or screening services for which they do not provide coverage.
7. Where a service may be denied on grounds of medical necessity and the service is not of a type that is always or virtually always never covered by a payor, the patient shall complete a waiver of liability form before the service is provided that states why this specific service is

likely to be denied on the basis of medical necessity.

8. Claims shall not be submitted to third party payors for missed appointments.
9. Bills related to the provision of drugs or equipment shall not be issued until the drugs or items are actually dispensed or provided.
10. Except in connection with coordination of benefits, duplicate bills shall not be submitted to a third party payor until such time as the payor has indicated that the prior bill is lost or otherwise unavailable or at least 30 days have elapsed with no response from the third party. The third party payor's statements regarding the status of the prior bill should be documented.
11. Procedure and diagnosis codes should not be changed in rebilling denied claims unless a clinician involved in the service consents to the change after reviewing the patient's medical record or an oversight and/or mistake occurred.
12. The organization shall not provide out-of-network services in a PPO, HMO, or other plan at in-network fees if such discount is not permitted under applicable federal or state law. To the extent that such discounts are given, the discounts shall be listed on the claim forms for the services or otherwise disclosed in writing to the applicable payor.

Assignment Issues

1. No employee of the organization will bill any patient or any third party payor of the organization for any services rendered in connection with the employee's employment (ex. work related injury) by the organization.
2. If any employee receives any fees or charges for services performed during his or her employment by the organization, the employee shall remit such payment to the organization promptly.
3. The organization shall obtain patient written consent to bill and collect for services on an assigned basis before the organization bills any third party payors for such services.
4. It shall be the responsibility of the front desk personnel to verify the presence of such consent in the patient's medical record at the time of each patient visit or service.

New Services or Technologies

1. The organization shall not bill federally-funded programs for medical devices not approved for marketing by the Food and Drug Administration (FDA) or categorized by the FDA as Experimental/Investigational (also known as Category A). In addition, the organization shall not bill federally funded programs for the medical services related to the use of such devices.
2. The organization shall not bill federally funded health care programs for FDA-approved drugs used for an indication not specified in the labeling, unless such use is a generally accepted medical practice in the community.
3. Where no CPT code completely and accurately describes a new service or technology, the practice shall use the closest available code and will inform the carrier by letter and will seek advice and opinion.

Evaluation and Management Services

Persons involved in the process of documenting or selecting evaluation and management services shall read and review the applicable sections of the CPT manual.

1. Practitioners shall use the full range of evaluation and management codes, selecting the most appropriate level of service for each individual service based on the requirements for each level of service and the medical needs of the patient.
2. A level five evaluation and management service shall only be billed where the requirements of a comprehensive history, a comprehensive examination, and medical decision making of high complexity are present, are necessary, were performed, and were appropriately documented.
3. A level five evaluation and management service should reflect medical decision making of high complexity, meaning that an extensive number of diagnoses or management options are present, where there are extensive or complex data and other information reviewed, or where there is a high risk of complications and/or morbidity or mortality.
4. A level four evaluation and management service shall only be billed where the requirements of a comprehensive history, a comprehensive examination, and medical decision making of moderate complexity are present, are necessary, were performed, and were appropriately documented.
5. In documenting reviews of systems, positive findings must be specified in sufficient detail and may not be documented with a notation of "positive" only.
6. In documenting reviews of systems, negative findings must be explained where they are unexpected or unusual under the circumstances.
7. Time becomes the most significant factor in determining evaluation and management services when time spent counseling the patient or family members or others predominates, meaning that such time accounts for more than half of the time spent providing services.
8. Where counseling times are used as the basis for the selection of an evaluation and management service, the total counseling time shall be documented in the record.

9. Until such time as the Health Care Financing Administration acts, documentation of Medicare evaluation and management services shall meet the requirements of the proposed 1997 guidelines.

Consultations

1. Consultations will be billed when appropriate.
2. Consultations, including intra-organization consultations, must be requested by a physician or other practitioner.
3. The request for a consultation must be documented in the patient's medical record.
4. The report of a consultation must be sent to the physician or other practitioner requesting the service.
5. Consulting physicians shall order diagnostic services as appropriate and necessary.
6. Consulting physicians shall provide treatment to the extent such services are urgently needed by the patient.
7. Consulting physicians may not take over the treatment of the patient, except for urgently needed services.
8. Consulting physicians shall bill only for the appropriate level of consultation and as consistent with the applicable documentation standards.
9. Use of the terms "referring physician" or "referral" are not consistent with a request for a consultation.

Global Period Issues

1. The organization will not bill separately for services performed within a global period unless those services are separately identifiable.
2. The -25 modifier shall only be used to designate a separately identifiable service.
3. Care will be exercised in billing for anesthesiology services described by a CPT code that is not included in the anesthesiology section of the CPT manual (including CPTs 00100 to 00199), as the anesthesia component of such services may not be separately billable.

Psychotherapy Services

1. Psychotherapy services are billed based on the amount of face-to-face time spent in providing psychotherapy services to the patient. Accordingly, documentation of psychotherapy services should include start time, stop time, and total time.
2. For each Medicare patient receiving psychotherapy services, the organization shall obtain a statement of understanding from the patient that shall establish that the psychologist may and will consult with the patient's attending or primary care physician in accordance with acceptable professional ethical norms.
3. Psychotherapy services shall only be billed where a psychotherapy service is provided. Preparation for pain management services and emotional support in connection with pain management services may not qualify as psychotherapy services.
4. Psychologists shall not bill for CPT 90862, pharmacological management, with no more than limited psychotherapy, unless specifically permitted by state licensure and the applicable payor.

Physical Therapy Services

1. Prior to the receipt of physical therapy services, all Medicare beneficiaries shall sign appropriate waiver of liability forms acknowledging the statutory imposition of an annual cap on payments for medically necessary outpatient physical therapy services, and the possibility that the patient will be responsible for payment of medically necessary services that exceed the cap.
2. No Medicare patient will receive services provided by an independent physical therapist, or a physical therapist in private practice, without an appropriate written plan of care. The plan of care shall be reviewed and signed by the ordering physician at least every thirty days.
3. All employees of the organization who provide physical therapy services shall be appropriately licensed and credentialed.
4. A physician will provide on-site supervision and will be immediately available when physical therapy services are performed by employees of the organization and the services are billed under the provider number of the physician or as required by the Medicare program.

Diagnostic Services

1. Services shall not be billed on the basis of "rule out" diagnoses, unless a payor specifically covers screening services of the kind at issue.
2. All diagnostic tests must be ordered by a treating or consulting physician. All such orders must be documented in the patient's medical record. Verbal orders are sufficient for diagnostic services provided by a hospital or physician office provided that the verbal order is documented in the patient's medical record.
3. Unless a third party payor has given instructions to the contrary and those instructions are documented, the medical necessity of a diagnostic service must be determined based on the signs, symptoms, conditions, or diagnoses documented in the patient's medical record before the diagnostic service is provided.

Specific Services

1. Separate reimbursement shall not be sought for patient controlled analgesia services from third party payors who do not cover such services.
2. Claims for placement of a catheter for treatment of post-operative pain should be documented in the medical chart in a manner that differentiates the use of such catheter from any other catheter placed principally for purposes of surgical anesthesia.

Pre-Certification Issues

1. Services shall not be submitted to a third party payor where the organization knows that a condition of payment for the service is a pre-service certification and the organization has not secured such a certification, unless the organization believes that the pre-certification was improperly or incorrectly withheld.
2. The organization shall develop a sheet, organized by payor, that summarizes the applicable pre-service certification requirements.

Local Medical Review Policies

1. Medicare and other carriers issue local medical review policies that restrict the ability of providers to bill certain services unless certain enumerated conditions, signs, symptoms, or diagnoses are present.
2. The organization shall maintain centralized binders that include copies of all such limited medical review policies that are issued by payors and which are applicable to services or items offered by the organization.
3. Unless the organization disagrees in good faith with a particular local medical review policy and can articulate a reasonable basis for that disagreement, it shall only bill such payor in accordance with the requirements of such policy.
4. Where the organization disagrees in good faith with a local medical review policy of a payor, the organization shall take steps to document in a communication with the applicable payor the nature and the reasons for the organization's disagreement with the policy whenever a claim is submitted that does not comply with the local medical review policy.
5. The organization shall appeal all claims denied on the basis of the local medical review policy and press those appeals.
6. Under no circumstances will procedure or diagnosis codes be used that are not clinically appropriate in an effort to circumvent any local medical review policy.

Supervision Issues

1. Services of clinical psychologists, clinical social workers, nurse practitioners, physician assistants, and certified nurse specialists may be billed in the name of these practitioners to the Medicare program when various requirements are met.
2. Direct billing of Medicare services in the name of the clinical psychologist, clinical social worker, nurse practitioner, physician assistant, or certified nurse specialist is permitted where no facility or other provider will claim reimbursement for the services provided, regardless of where the services are provided.
3. Services billed directly to the Medicare program may be collected by an employer.
4. Services performed by a clinical psychologist, master's-level psychologist, clinical social worker, nurse practitioner, physician assistant, certified nurse specialist, or physical therapist, among others, may be billed "incident to" a physician services (so long as no direct bill from the limited license practitioner is submitted). Services of all other non-physician clinicians who are employees of the organization also may be billed as "incident-to."
5. All "incident to" services must be provided as an integral, though incidental, component of a physician service under the direct supervision of a physician.
6. Direct supervision means that the physician must be present in the office suite and readily available to give advice and direction during the entire time that the "incident to" service is provided.
7. All "incident to" services shall be provided by personnel in accordance with any state law requirements or restrictions, including any limitations on the scopes of organization.

ASC Services

1. Ambulatory surgical services procedures will not be billed to the Medicare program and other payors unless the applicable payor permits the procedure at issue to be performed in an ambulatory surgery center.
2. A list of services that may be performed in an ASC setting, organized by payor, shall be developed and maintained by the billing personnel.
3. The list of services that may be performed in an ASC shall be updated no less often than annually and immediately upon receipt of additional or updated information.
4. It shall be the responsibility of both the physician and billing department personnel to ensure that no billings are submitted to a payor that does

not recognize the suitability of a procedure in an ASC setting.

5. Designated health services within the meaning of the Federal Self-Referral Law or any corresponding state law shall not be provided by an ASC unless counsel has determined that the provision of such services does not violate any self-referral prohibition.

Use of Signature Stamps

1. Signature stamps will only be used where authorized by the practitioner involved.
2. Use of signature stamps will only be used by designated personnel.
3. Signature stamps shall be maintained in a secure location and will be maintained in a locked location after hours.
4. Signature stamps should not be used in securing a signature for a progress note or other medical record documentation for patient visits.
5. Signature stamps should not be used in connection with patient medical records, such as progress notes and operative reports.
6. The practitioner providing the service shall sign all patient medical records.

Collection of Co-Payments and Deductibles and Refunds of Overpayments

1. It is the policy of the organization to make a reasonable and good faith effort to collect any co-payment and/or deductible owed to it. The front desk will be responsible for collecting co-payments and deductibles.
2. A decision to waive a co-payment or deductible may be made in accordance with written guidelines developed by the organization, which employ appropriate standards for determining financial hardship. All waiver decisions will be appropriately documented.
3. The organization will refund any payer or patient overpayments in a timely fashion.
4. The organization shall seek to refund all over-payments within ninety (90) days of the date that they are identified.

Professional Courtesy

1. The organization shall not provide professional courtesy services to any person in a position to refer or to influence referrals.
2. Physicians and others employed by the organization in a position to refer or to influence shall not accept professional courtesy services

Conflicts of Interest and Related Matters

1. Employees of the organization shall report to the Compliance Officer, or his or her designee, any potential conflict of interests that arise in connection with their employment, including, but not limited to, any offers of incentive payments or free items or services offered by suppliers or vendors of the organization. Potential conflicts may also arise due to demands of outside activities that may distract or hinder performance of duties for the organization or cause use of organization resources for other than organization purposes.
2. Employees shall cooperate with the organization in resolving actual conflicts of interests.

Contracting and Affiliation Obligations

1. The organization shall require compliance with the organization's Compliance Program or their own program for all affiliates who are in a position to infer, are in a position to induce referrals, or suppliers or vendors with whom the organization has more than $25,000 in business on an annual basis.
2. The organization shall take reasonable steps to ensure that, on a prospective basis, all contracts or modifications to existing contracts with the affiliates listed above shall incorporate the organization's compliance plan by reference.
3. The Compliance Officer, or his or her designate, shall be responsible for ensuring that such affiliates receive any updated versions of the Compliance Plan.

Integrity of Financial Reporting and Funds Control

1. The organization shall take steps to ensure that all assets and liabilities are accounted for properly, in compliance with all tax and financial reporting requirements, generally accepted accounting principles and established accounting and financial policies of the organization, and that there are no unrecorded assets of the organization.
2. All items of income and expense and all assets and liabilities shall be entered on the financial records of the organization, and all transactions shall be executed in accordance with appropriate authorization from the appropriate organization officer.
3. All funds shall be controlled and dispersed in an ethical manner.

Marketing

1. Any marketing and advertising activities used to educate the public, provide information to the community, increase awareness of services, and to recruit colleagues will present truthful, and non-de-

ceptive information.

2. Claims made in marketing and advertising material that are capable of objective confirmation shall have a reasonable documented basis.

Integrity of Data Systems

1. The organization will establish procedures for maintaining the integrity of all electronic data collection systems, including regular back-ups on disk, tape or other format, regularly scheduled virus checks, and analysis of all systems for Year 2000 compliance.

2. The organization will develop procedures to prevent unauthorized access and disclosure of confidential electronic data.

POLICIES AND PROCEDURES

POLICY DESCRIPTION:	**Duties of the Compliance Officer**
REFERENCE NUMBER:	**COMPLY.001**
EFFECTIVE DATE:	**xx / xx / xxxx**

PURPOSE: To set forth the duties and responsibilities of the Organization's Compliance Officer.

SCOPE: This policy governs the conduct of the Compliance Officer, as well as the Compliance Officer's interactions with the Compliance Committee, the Organization's managers, the Board of Directors and all employees and contractors of the Organization and its other affiliates.

POLICY: The Compliance Officer shall serve as the focal point for the compliance activities of the Organization. The Compliance Officer shall be recruited by management and approved by the Board of Directors or other governing body. While the Compliance Officer is responsible for the implementation and day-to-day management of the Compliance Program, he or she shall be assisted by the Compliance Committee. In order to carry out his or her responsibilities, the Compliance Officer shall have direct access to the Board of Directors, the Organization's managers, and the principals of the Organization, as well as access to all documents and other information relevant to performing his or her duties.

DUTIES: In carrying out his or her responsibilities, the Compliance Officer shall:

Plan, implement and monitor the day-to-day operations of the Compliance Program.

Act as a liaison to Organization personnel with ethics or compliance questions or concerns by coordinating the timely resolution of those issues with appropriate Organization and other personnel.

In consultation with appropriate Organization officials and with the assistance of outside counsel, when appropriate, investigate issues and alleged violations of the law or of the Organization's Standards of Conduct, and oversee the implementation of any necessary corrective action.

Monitor compliance reports or complaints, and coordinate and track appropriate responses through the maintenance of a report log, including undertaking investigations or corrective actions, and ensuring that those submitting reports are able to maintain confidentiality as possible and appropriate in light of the requirements of law and the needs of the organization.

Develop and distribute policies and programs that (a) reduce the Organization's vulnerability to fraud and abuse, and (b) encourage Organization personnel to report violations of the Standards of Conduct or other improprieties or possible issues without fear of retaliation.

Develop, coordinate, and participate in compliance education and training programs for all employees and affiliates, as appropriate, of the Organization.

Assist the Compliance Committee in developing and coordinating internal compliance review and monitoring activities.

Monitor the screening process for new employees and contractors to ensure that the Organization does not hire persons or contract or maintain relationships with untrustworthy individuals or companies.

Review the exit interviews of all personnel who terminate their relationship with the Organization in order to identify potential compliance issues.

Ensure that all personnel are uniformly disciplined, in accordance with Organization policy, for any violations of the law, the Standards of Conduct, or any other Organization policies or procedures.

Ensure that overpayments are promptly refunded to patients, government programs, and other third party payors and, when appropriate and with the assistance of outside counsel, that violations of the law are reported to the appropriate government agencies as appropriate or as required under the circumstances.

Coordinate the dissemination of information on regulatory and legal developments affecting Organization operations, and maintain appropriate resources for obtaining access to updated information.

Coordinate periodic revisions to the Organization's Compliance Program and to its policies and procedures, as necessary, to respond to the needs of the Organization and to changes in the law and in the program requirements of federal, state and private health plans.

Report no less often than annually to the Board of Directors or other governing body and semi-annually to the Compliance Committee on the status of all significant compliance issues and the effectiveness of the Compliance Program. Such reports shall include information on the number of telephone hotline or other reports received and the number of investigations opened and closed during the preceding quarter or year, as well the reasons for any items on the report log that have not been closed within 90 days of receipt. See Responding to Compliance Telephone Hotline and Other Reports.

Serve on the Organization's Compliance Committee.

When appropriate, report directly to senior management, the Board of Directors, or principals of the Organization regarding any problems, issues, or concerns related to the Compliance Program.

Perform such other functions as may be assigned from time to time by the Board of Directors, the Compliance Committee, or the principals of the Organization.

POLICY DESCRIPTION:	**The Compliance Committee and Its Powers and Responsibilities**
REFERENCE NUMBER:	**COMPLY.002**
EFFECTIVE DATE:	**xx / xx / xxxx**

PURPOSE: To establish the composition and duties of the Organization's Compliance Committee.

SCOPE: This policy governs the conduct of the Compliance Committee, as well as its interactions with the Compliance Officer, the Board of Directors, and all employees and contractors of the Organization and affiliates.

POLICY: The Compliance Committee shall provide oversight, advice, and general guidance to the Board of Directors, the Compliance Officer, and employees or affiliates of the Organization on all matters relating to the operation of the Organization's Compliance Program. The primary mission of the Compliance Committee shall be to assist the Compliance Officer and the Board with respect to the Organization's compliance with applicable laws, the program requirements of federal, state and private health plans, the Standards of Conduct and other corporate policies and procedures.

The Compliance Committee shall be composed of the following individuals:

____

____

____

____

____

____

The Board of Directors designated ___________ as the Chair of the Compliance Committee. The Committee shall meet semi-annually, and more frequently, as necessary.

DUTIES: In carrying out its responsibilities, the Compliance Committee shall:

1. Ensure the continued operation and maintenance of the Organization's Compliance Program.
2. Provide oversight and guidance to the Compliance Officer to ensure the development of internal systems and controls to ensure compliance with the Standards of Conduct, applicable laws, and the program requirements of federal, state and private health plans.
3. Review the activities and performance of the Compliance Officer to ensure that his or her responsibilities are being carried out appropriately.
4. Review all decisions to initiate or defer a compliance investigation, oversee all compliance investigations, and review and respond to investigative reports and recommendations for corrective action.
5. Ensure that the Organization maintains an environment in which personnel are able to make telephone hotline or other reports or inquiries without fear of retaliation or retribution.
6. Monitor the compliance hotline system to ensure that reports are logged, investigated, and responded to in compliance with the Organization's policies and procedures.
7. Oversee education and training activities to en-

sure that all employees and contractors are properly trained on the Standards of Conduct, the operation of the Compliance Program, applicable laws, and the program requirements of federal, state and private health plans.

8. Ensure that the Organization has appropriate safeguards in place to prevent it from hiring or maintaining relationships with untrustworthy individuals or companies.
9. Oversee disciplinary actions to ensure that personnel are being disciplined uniformly and in accordance with Organization policy for violations of the Standards of Conduct, and, where necessary, that matters are reported in a timely fashion to appropriate authorities.
10. Ensure that overpayments are promptly refunded to patients, government programs, and other third party payors.
11. Oversee and evaluate the effectiveness of the Compliance Program.
12. Revise the Compliance Program and the Organization's policies and procedures, as necessary, to respond to the needs of the Organization and to changes in the law and in the program requirements of federal, state and private health plans.
13. Report regularly, and no less often than annually, to the Board of Directors or other governing body on the status of any significant compliance issues and the effectiveness of the Compliance Program.
14. Perform such other appropriate functions as may be assigned from time to time by the Board of Directors or principals of the Organization.

POLICY DESCRIPTION:	**Responding to Compliance Telephone Hotline or Other Reports**
REFERENCE NUMBER:	**COMPLY.003**
EFFECTIVE DATE:	**xx / xx / xxxx**

PURPOSE: To establish a process to receive and respond to inquiries, complaints and allegations of known, suspected, or possible inappropriate acts or violations of the Organization's Standards of Conduct.

SCOPE: This policy shall govern the conduct of the Compliance Officer, outside counsel, the Compliance Committee, and all Organization personnel, including affiliates of the Organization, involved in reporting, investigating or otherwise responding to inquiries, complaints, or allegations made in connection with the Organization's Compliance Program.

POLICY: All matters reported to the Compliance Officer through the compliance telephone hotline or other means shall be documented by the Compliance Officer and resolved, wherever possible, within 90 days. Alleged violations of applicable laws, program requirements of federal, state or private health plans, the Standards of Conduct, or other compliance policies or procedures shall be investigated in a timely fashion based on the circumstances. All reported matters will be handled in a manner that safeguards the confidentiality of the person making the report, as is possible and appropriate in light of the requirements of the law or the needs of the Organization. Where appropriate, prompt corrective action shall be implemented in response to reports.

PROCEDURE:

1. The Compliance Hotline.

An open line of communication between all Organization personnel and the Compliance Officer shall be maintained through the establishment of a compliance hotline. Personnel shall be encouraged to use the hotline to (a) report possible violations of the law, program requirements of federal, state or private health plans, the Standards of Conduct, or other Organization policies or procedures, (b) pose questions regarding compliance policies and procedures, and (c) make suggestions about improving the quality of care furnished to patients and reducing the risks to the Organization from fraud and abuse.

Reports to the hotline may be made on an anonymous basis, and shall be handled in a manner that safeguards the confidentiality of the person making the report. However, personnel shall be advised that there may be a point where their identity may become known or may be revealed in certain instances when governmental authorities become involved or in other situations. No person shall suffer retaliation or retribution for filing a report with the hotline in good faith. (See Non-Retaliation Policy.)

The compliance hotline is a combination of a telephone hotline and a system for receiving written reports. The Compliance Officer shall be responsible for operating or contracting with an outside vendor to operate a telephone hotline service. The Compliance Officer also shall be responsible for publishing the hotline number in the Compliance Plan and through other appropriate means. The vendor shall provide periodic reports to the Compliance Officer, summarizing the nature of all calls or other reports received substantially in the form attached hereto as Attachment A. Written reports may be submitted in any form, however, the Organization shall make available Report Forms similar to Attachment B. The Compliance Officer shall log this information into a compliance report log, using the form attached hereto as Attachment C, and shall respond to each report in accordance with the procedures set forth below.

Personnel also may access the hotline system through direct inquiries to the Compliance Officer in writing or via telephone. The Compliance Officer shall record direct inquiries on a form substantially similar to Attachment A. The Compliance Officer shall log all inquires into the compliance report log and respond to each report in accordance with the procedures set forth below.

Responding to Reports.

The Compliance Officer is responsible for coordinating the Organization's response to every credible inquiry, complaint, or allegation made via the compliance hotline or other means. The Compliance Officer shall ensure that every report or reasonable indication of suspected noncompliance is promptly investigated, evaluated and resolved, within 90 days, as is possible under the circumstances. Such matters shall be categorized into three general areas: (a) informational inquiries, (b) complaints not involving a violation of law or Organization policy, and (c) alleged violations.

The Compliance Officer shall maintain a compliance report log and case files to track hotline reports, other indications of suspected noncompliance, and the Organization's responses. The report log shall track the progress of activity relating to all such matters. The case files shall contain the working papers and backup material for each individual hotline report or allegation of noncompliance, including the response to any request for information, any investigative or audit activity, conclusions and supporting factors leading to a decision not to investigate, and any corrective action.

At the end of each quarter, the Compliance Officer shall submit to the Compliance Committee a summary of the hotline reports received and the Compliance Officer's written evaluation of such reports and of other indications of suspected noncompliance. In the event the Compliance Committee disagrees with the Compliance Officer's evaluation in any given case, it shall direct the Compliance Officer to follow the appropriate procedures set forth below.

The Compliance Officer's response to a hotline report or other indication of suspected noncompliance shall vary based on the nature of the report or matter, as follows:

Informational Inquiries.

The Compliance Officer shall respond to all requests for information concerning the compliance program, and shall forward to the appropriate department manager or other supervisory personnel any report that is a request for information or clarification concerning other Organization policies or procedures. The Compliance Officer or any individual to whom such an inquiry is forwarded must respond to the inquirer within 30 days, unless this is not possible under the circumstances. A copy of the response or a brief description of any communication must be prepared by or forwarded to the Compliance Officer for inclusion in the case file. If the person responsible for responding is unable to contact the inquirer, the report should document the efforts that were undertaken to respond to the inquiry.

If the inquiry was made anonymously, the Compliance Officer and the appropriate department manager or other supervisory personnel should evaluate the inquiry and the most appropriate method to respond. For example, information addressing the issue might be distributed at a regularly scheduled staff meeting or could be included in an Organization bulletin or newsletter.

Responses to both anonymous and non-anonymous inquiries should be shared with other personnel, as appropriate, so that standards, policies and procedures can be updated and improved to reflect any necessary changes or clarifications.

The Compliance Officer shall maintain case files for each inquiry. These files shall document the Organization's response to each inquiry and any necessary follow-up actions.

Reports Not Requiring Investigation or Responses.

Certain reports to the Compliance Officer may require no direct or immediate response. Reports which are determined to be venting of personal frustration and that do not involve requests for information nor alleged violations of applicable laws, program requirements of federal, state or private health plans, the Standards of Conduct, or other Organization policies or procedures shall be noted in the report log and included in the Compliance Officer's report to the Compliance Committee. In such circumstances, there is no need for further action.

Alleging Violations.

All matters that reasonably suggest violations of applicable laws, program requirements of a federal, state or private health plan, the Standards of Conduct, or other Organization policies or procedures shall be investigated in order to determine their veracity.

The Compliance Officer shall consult outside counsel immediately concerning any matter that involves a possible violation that relates to any: (a) financial or billing errors or improprieties which may result in repayment to a federal, state or private health plan of over $10,000, or (b) violations of law. The outside counsel shall be responsible for coordinating the investigation of all such violations in accordance with the procedures set forth below.

Individual case files shall be maintained for all reports: These files shall contain documentation of the alleged violation and a brief description of the investigative process and the results of the investigation, as well as a brief description of the corrective action implemented (including any disciplinary action taken). All reports and case files shall be maintained in a secure location, and the Compliance Officer shall take appropriate steps to prevent the destruction of documents or other evidence relevant to the investigation.

The Compliance Committee shall consult with outside counsel to determine the necessity of disclosing any violation of law that is discovered during the course of an investigation to appropriate government officials or licensing agencies or making any required refunds.

If, at any time during the evaluation of an allegation or during an investigation, the Compliance Officer, or a member of the Compliance Committee, is alleged to be personally or directly involved in any allegation, such person shall recuse himself or herself from consideration of any such allegation. If an investigation of alleged violation is undertaken and the Compliance Officer or outside counsel believes that the integrity of the investigation may be compromised because of the involvement of personnel that should reasonably be the subject of investigation, such personnel should be removed from the investigation.

Alleged Violations Not Meeting the Threshold.

The Compliance Officer shall coordinate the investigation of alleged violations not meeting the monetary or legal thresholds identified above. The Compliance Officer may conduct the investigation himself or herself, or with the assistance of other Organization personnel who are not involved personally or directly in the alleged violations under investigation. In many cases, it may be appropriate for the Compliance Officer to delegate the responsibility for the investigation to the department manager or supervisor responsible for the matters in question, with a requirement that findings and recommendations for corrective action be submitted to the Compliance Officer.

In coordinating the investigation, the Compliance Officer may retain outside consultants, if appropriate. The Compliance Officer also may request assistance from the outside counsel in coordinating and performing the investigation. The Compliance Officer shall have access to any documents or records necessary to perform the investigation. All matters concerning the investigation shall be considered confidential, as is possible and appropriate in light of any legal requirements or other needs of the Organization.

The Compliance Officer's quarterly report to the Compliance Committee shall document the progress of all investigations of violations not meeting the thresholds described above.

At the conclusion of an investigation, the Compliance Officer shall immediately inform the Compliance Committee in a brief writing of all findings and recommendations. The report shall contain a summary of the initial report, the steps taken to investigate the report, the investigative findings, and the recommendations for any corrective action.

If, at any time during the investigation, it appears that the matter constitutes a violation that meets the thresholds described above, or is likely to lead to discovery of such an alleged violation, then the Compliance Officer shall immediately contact outside counsel, who shall assume responsibility for conducting the investigation in accordance with the procedures set forth below.

Alleged Violations Meeting the Threshold.

The investigation of an alleged violation that meet the monetary and legal thresholds described above shall be coordinated by outside counsel with assistance, as appropriate, from the Compliance Officer or others. Outside counsel may retain outside consultants and/or others to assist in the investigation. Outside counsel shall have access to any documents or records necessary to perform the investigation. All matters concerning the investigation shall be considered confidential, as is possible and appropriate in light of the requirements of law and the other needs of the Organization. Outside counsel shall update the Compliance Committee on the progress of any alleged violations that are under investigation.

At the conclusion of the investigation, outside counsel shall immediately inform the Compliance Committee, in writing, of all findings and recommendations. The report shall contain a summary of the initial report, the steps taken to investigate the report, the investigative findings, and the recommendations, if any, for corrective action.

The Role of the Compliance Committee.

The Compliance Committee shall act on any report from the Compliance Officer or outside counsel in a timely fashion as appropriate under the circumstances. In the event the Compliance Officer or outside counsel concludes that no violation of applicable laws, program requirements of federal, state or private health plans, the Standards of Conduct, or other Organization policies or procedures has occurred, and should the Compliance Committee concur, then no further action shall be taken on that report.

Alleged Violations Not Meeting the Thresholds.

If the Compliance Officer concludes that a violation not meeting the thresholds described above has occurred, and if the Compliance Committee agrees, then copies of the report and recommendations to address the problem, and any evaluation and recommendations by the Committee, shall be forwarded to the Chief Executive Officer, Organization administrator, or equivalent person for his or her review. The recommendations shall be implemented.

In the event that the Compliance Committee disagrees with the recommendation of the Compliance Officer, it shall confer with the Compliance Officer and outside counsel, as necessary. If no agreement can be reached after these consultations, the issue shall be brought to the Board of Directors or the Organization principles. The Board of Directors or the Organization principals retain the final authority to decide what corrective action shall be taken.

Alleged Violations Meeting Thresholds.

If, as a result of his or her investigation, outside counsel concludes that a violation meeting the thresholds described above has occurred, and if the Compliance Committee agrees, then copies of the report and recommendations to address the problem, and any evaluation and recommendations by the Committee, shall be forwarded to the Chief Executive Officer, Organization Administrator or other equivalent person for his or her review. The recommendations shall address whether the results of the internal investigation should be disclosed to appropriate government officials and, if appropriate, the manner in which such disclosure should be made. The recommendations shall be implemented.

In the event that the Compliance Committee disagrees with the recommendation of outside counsel, the issue shall be brought to the Board of Directors or Organization principals. The Board of Directors or the Organization principals retain the final authority to decide what corrective action shall be taken.

Corrective Action.

Corrective action shall be implemented in response to all confirmed violations of applicable laws, the program requirements of federal, state or private health plans, the Standards of Conduct, or other Organization policies. Corrective action plans should address not only the immediate violation at hand, but also measures, which will prevent similar violations from recurring in the future.

Corrective action plans may involve imposing appropriate disciplinary action against the employees involved in accordance with Organization policy. See Discipline Policy. Depending on the circumstances, corrective action also may involve training, refunding overpayments to government or private payors, or voluntary disclosure to the appropriate government officials, as appropriate or required under the circumstances.

ATTACHMENT 'A'
HOTLINE REPORT

Note: The following report is proprietary information and is strictly confidential, any unauthorized disclosure is prohibited.

Call or Report Number: _______
(As Applicable)
Date: _____ Time: _____ Duration ofCall: ___

Call or Report Received By: __________

Introductory Questions: _________

Caller acknowledged hearing and understanding the pre-recorded message: Yes? No? N/A?

Caller acknowledged an understanding of anonymity/confidentiality limitations: Yes ? No ? N/A ?

Caller or reporter identified self: Yes ? No ?

Caller's or reporter's identity: __________

Caller's or reporter's division or general location: ________

If identity given, did caller or other reporter request confidentiality? Yes? No?

Type of call:

Informational: Caller or reporter sought assistance or guidance clarifying a rule, regulation, Organization policy, procedure, element of the Standards of Conduct, or other requirement.

Allegation or Complaint: Caller or reporter reported an alleged violation of law, regulation, policy, procedure, or Standards of Conduct.

Venting: Caller or reporter did not seek assistance or guidance or make an allegation.

Subject of Call or Report: ________________

Brief Description of Call: ________________

Summary of Details of Information Provided by Caller: All information presented by the caller or reporter as allegations, conclusions, facts, opinions, perceptions, etc. is attributed to the caller or reporter:

____

Has the caller or reporter spoken with his/her supervisor or other management personnel? Provide specific details, if possible:

Information provided to the caller or reporter (if any):

Arrangements made for follow-up contact (if any):

ATTACHMENT 'B'
COMPLIANCE PROGRAM REPORT FORM

The Compliance Program reporting system was established to help organization personnel with questions, concerns, and complaints that cannot be properly addressed through traditional resolution processes. It is our intention to respond to each reasonable inquiry, which is made in good faith to the reporting system. It is the organization's policy that no retaliation or retribution occurs as a result of using the reporting system. It is also the organization's policy that the anonymity of individuals using the system be preserved, subject to the limits imposed by law. If you discuss your report with other individuals, your anonymity may not be preserved.

In the space provided below, please describe your question, concern or complaint. Feel free to attach additional sheets if necessary. Please be as specific as possible so that we may respond appropriately. Please attach copies of any relevant documents or other materials that you believe would assist in our appropriately investigating your report.

____

Name (optional): __________________

Address or phone number (optional) : ____________

ATTACHMENT 'C'
CONFIDENTIAL

Compliance Hotline Report Log

Record Number or Other Report: ______________

Date Received Type of CallOr Other Report: _______

Subject of Call Brief Description: ______________

____

____

____

POLICY DESCRIPTION: **Non-Retaliation Policy**
REFERENCE NUMBER: **COMPLY.004**
EFFECTIVE DATE: **xx / xx / xxxx**

PURPOSE: To ensure that all personnel may raise compliance questions or concerns with their supervisor or with the Compliance Officer or a member of the Compliance Committee without fear of retribution or retaliation.

SCOPE: This policy is applicable to all personnel employed by or affiliated with the Organization.

POLICY: Employees or affiliates who, in good faith, report a possible violation of applicable laws, the program requirements of federal, state or private health plans, the Standards of Conduct or other Organization policies shall not be subject to retaliation, retribution or harassment. No supervisor, manager, employee or affiliate is permitted to engage in retaliation, retribution or any form of harassment against any person for reporting a compliance related issue or concern. Any supervisor, manager, employee or affiliate who engages in or condones conduct in violation of this policy shall be subject to discipline, up to and including immediate termination.

PROCEDURE: This policy shall be incorporated into the Organization's compliance training program, and shall be prominently highlighted in the Compliance Plan and in any other informational materials related to the compliance program.

Violations of this policy are to be reported to the Compliance Officer. The Compliance Officer shall be responsible for investigating alleged violations of this policy in accordance with the Organization's policies and procedures, subject to the direction and oversight of the Compliance Committee.

POLICY DESCRIPTION: **Exit Interviews**
REFERENCE NUMBER: **COMPLY.005**
EFFECTIVE DATE: **xx / xx / xxxx**

PURPOSE: To provide an additional means for identifying potential compliance issues.

SCOPE: This policy shall apply to all personnel who terminate their employment with the Organization.

POLICY: An exit interview shall be conducted for all personnel terminating their relationship with the Organization in order to solicit (a) information on the Organization's level of compliance with applicable laws, the program requirements of federal, state and private health plans, the Standards of Conduct, and other Organization policies, and (b) suggestions for improving compliance.

PROCEDURE: The Compliance Officer shall be responsible for ensuring that all personnel terminating their relationship with the Organization are asked to participate in an exit interview or complete the attached form.

The Compliance Officer shall be responsible for determining whether any information learned through the exit interview process requires

a. that the Compliance Officer conduct a follow-up interview either in person or via telephone, as appropriate,
b. further investigation in accordance with the Organization's policy on Responding to Compliance Telephone Hotline or Other Reports,
c. the development of an appropriate policy, or
d. other appropriate action.

Any significant developments arising out of the exit interviews shall be included in the Compliance Officer's quarterly report to the Compliance Committee.

Compliance Program Exit Interview

This form is an important part of the Organization Compliance Program. We ask that all employees and others who are terminating their relationship with the Organization take a few moments to respond to the questions that follow. Our goal is to find ways in which we can improve the ethics and compliance of our organization.

Name: ________________

Please provide your current address and telephone number:

____

Please provide your address and telephone number following the termination of your employment with the Organization:

____

What was your position with the Organization?

____

How long were you employed by the Organization?

During your affiliation with the Organization, have you ever-engaged in conduct that you believe was either unethical or illegal? YES _____ NO _____.

If yes, please describe that conduct, including the relevant dates.________________________________

During your affiliation with the Organization, have you ever been asked to engage in conduct that you believe was either unethical or illegal? YES _____ NO _____.

If yes, by whom? Please describe that conduct, including the relevant dates.________________________________

Have you ever witnessed conduct by an employee, affiliate, contractor or agent of the Organization that you believe was either unethical or illegal? YES _____ NO _____.

If yes, by whom? Please describe that conduct, including the relevant dates________________________________

During your affiliation with the Organization, has there ever been anything that you have felt uncomfortable doing on behalf of the Organization?

YES _____ NO _____.

If yes, please describe.

Have you ever removed Organization documents without returning them to Organization?

YES _____ NO _____.

If yes, where are those documents now?____________

Have you ever given Organization documents to a third-party

other than in furtherance of the Organization's business?

YES _____ NO _____.

If yes, to whom and when?_____________________

Have you ever used the Compliance hotline report system?

YES _____ NO _____.

If yes, were you satisfied with the results?

____

Do you have any recommendations for improving the Organization's compliance program or its ability to meet its ethical and legal obligations?

YES _____ NO _____. If yes, what are they?

POLICY DESCRIPTION: **Employee, Contractor and Affiliate Screening**
REFERENCE NUMBER: **COMPLY.006**
EFFECTIVE DATE: **xx / xx / xxxx**

PURPOSE: To prevent delegation of authority to persons who may have a propensity to engage in illegal activity

SCOPE: This policy is applicable to all new employees, affiliates and contractors of the Organization.

POLICY: The Organization shall take reasonable steps to refrain from employing or contracting with any individual or entity that (a) has been convicted of a criminal offense related to health care, or (b) is debarred, excluded or is otherwise ineligible for participation in federal or state health care programs.

PROCEDURE: The Human Resources Department shall develop and utilize application forms that will require each applicant for a position with the Organization, or with one of its affiliated physician organizations, to disclose whether the individual has ever been (a) convicted of a criminal offense, or (b) debarred, excluded or otherwise deemed ineligible to participate in a federal or state health care program.

For each new officer, manager, Patients Accounts Department employee, Medical Coding Department employee, Marketing Department employee, or other employee who will have discretionary authority to make decisions that may involve compliance with the law or compliance oversight responsibilities, the Human Resources Department shall conduct a reasonable and prudent background investigation that shall include, at a minimum, the following:

a reference check;

a criminal records check; and

a review of the Cumulative Sanctions Report maintained by the Office of the Inspector General of the Department of Health and Human Resources ("OIG") (www.dhhs.gov/ progorg/oig) and the List of Persons Excluded from Federal Procurement and Non-Procurement Programs maintained by the Government Services Administration ("GSA") (www.arnet.gov/epls).

The performance of these background investigations shall be documented and kept in the appropriate personnel files.

For each physician, nurse practitioner, psychologist or clinician employed or otherwise retained by the Organization or by one of its affiliated physician organizations, the Human Resources Department shall, in addition to its other credentialing activities related to licensure and hospital staff privileges, conduct a reasonable and prudent background investigation that shall include, at a minimum, the following:

a reference check;

a criminal records check; and

a review of the OIG and GSA lists.

The performance of these background investigations shall be documented and kept in the appropriate personnel files.

Before the Organization executes a contract with another Organization for the purchase or provision of any health care items or services, the Compliance Officer shall conduct a review of the OIG and GSA lists in order to determine whether the Organization has been debarred, excluded or otherwise deemed ineligible to participate in a federal or state health care program.

POLICY DESCRIPTION:	**Document Retention Policy for Compliance Program Documents and Documents Associated with Claims Processing**
REFERENCE NUMBER:	**COMPLY.007**
EFFECTIVE DATE:	**xx / xx / xxxx**

PURPOSE: To set forth the Organization's document retention/destruction policy.

SCOPE: This policy applies to the categories of documents generated and maintained by the Organization, which is specified below.

POLICY: The Organization maintains those documents required by law and necessary to its operations. Documents are retained long enough to satisfy specific legal requirements, and are destroyed at the expiration of the required retention period. Where documents are no longer required to be maintained by law or by the needs of the Organization, they will be destroyed. The Organization may, on occasion, retain certain key documents indefinitely for future reference.

PROCEDURE:

Documents developed in connection with the organization's compliance program, such as hotline reports, annual reports, and investigative files, shall be maintained for seven years from the date of creation.

Documents associated with claims processing, such as claims, denial reports, and credit and collection reports, shall be maintained for seven years from the date of creation.

Destruction of designated documents shall be suspended in the following circumstances:

- service of legal process;
- inquiries indicating the commencement of litigation; or
- notice from Counsel, the Compliance Officer, or the Office Administrator.

If the individual responsible for document destruction believes, for any reason, that a document or category of documents should not be destroyed, he or she should contact the Compliance Officer prior to destroying such documents.

POLICY DESCRIPTION:	**Refunding Overpayments**
REFERENCE NUMBER:	**COMPLY.008**
EFFECTIVE DATE:	**xx / xx / xxxx**

PURPOSE: To ensure the prompt refund of overpayments to patients and third party payors.

SCOPE: This policy applies to any overpayment received by the Organization, or by any of its affiliates or subsidiaries, from a patient or from a government or private health plan.

POLICY: Overpayments received from a patient or from any government or private health plan shall be promptly refunded.

PROCEDURE: No less than quarterly, the Patient Accounts Department will review and ensure that the refund of all credit balances have occurred promptly.

The Organization will notify patients and appropriate government or private health plans of any errors that involve an overpayment, and shall promptly make any refund that is necessary, normally within 90 days after receiving notice of the overpayment.

Anyone with knowledge of a potential reimbursement error that may require the return of any prior payments, other than a routine processing error, should provide the Administrator or the Compliance Officer with all information related to the potential error, with as much specificity as possible regarding the type of problem, the date and place of occurrence, and the dollar amount involved.

Processing or other billing errors should be corrected either by the individual who detects the error or by the person who committed the error, and any necessary payments should be promptly made. If errors involve aggregate amounts of greater than $5,000, the errors must be reported to the Compliance Officer.

This policy establishes a minimum course of action. The Compliance Officer, in consultation with outside counsel, shall be responsible for determining whether a reimbursement error involves a potential violation of applicable law, the program requirements of federal, state or private health plans, the Standards of Conduct or other Organization policies and procedures so as to warrant additional investigation and corrective action pursuant to the Organization's policy on Responding to Compliance Telephone Hotline and Other Reports.

POLICY DESCRIPTION:	**Compliance as an Element of Performance Evaluations**
REFERENCE NUMBER:	**COMPLY.009**
EFFECTIVE DATE:	**xx / xx / xxxx**

PURPOSE: To promote the Organization's commitment to compliance by including it as an element in evaluating managers, supervisors and employees.

SCOPE: This policy shall apply to the periodic performance evaluations of all managers, supervisors and employees.

POLICY: Promotion of, and adherence to, the provisions of the Organization's Compliance Program, including attendance at required training sessions, shall be a factor in evaluating the performance of all Organization employees, managers and supervisors, and will be considered in decisions regarding hiring, promotion and compensation for all personnel.

PROCEDURE: The Office Administrator shall ensure that the forms used in documenting the performance evaluations of Organization personnel include a provision for evaluation of mangers, supervisors and employees on their promotion of, and adherence to, the provisions of the Organization's Compliance Program.

POLICY DESCRIPTION:	**Documenting Discussions with Third Party Payors**
REFERENCE NUMBER:	**COMPLY.010**
EFFECTIVE DATE:	**xx / xx / xxxx**

PURPOSE: To ensure that discussions with third party payors on billing, coding or payment issues are properly documented.

SCOPE: This policy applies to any discussions on billing, coding or payment issues with any representative or agent of a federal, state or private health plan.

POLICY: All significant or substantial discussions on billing, coding or payment issues with any representative or agent of a federal, state or private health plan should be documented in writing by drafting a confirmation letter addressed to the person with whom the conversation occurred. A copy of the letter shall be furnished to the Compliance Officer.

PROCEDURE: The attached form shall be used for documenting discussions with third party payors.

VERIFICATION CORRESPONDENCE

Address:________________

____

Dear ________________:

On ____________________________, at approximately ___________ am/pm, I spoke to you regarding a question concerning ____

You informed me that ________________________

____

It is my understanding that the guidance that you provided is in accordance with the applicable rules and policies governing this issue, and I intend to act in reliance on this information. If my understandings are not correct, please write to me immediately to clarify the situation.

Thank you for your kind attention to this matter.

Sincerely,

____

POLICY DESCRIPTION:	**Waiver of Co-payment and Deductibles**
REFERENCE NUMBER:	**COMPLY.011**
EFFECTIVE DATE:	**xx / xx / xxxx**

PURPOSE: To establish specific and limited circumstances under which it is permissible to waive or reduce a patient's obligation to pay co-insurance or deductible amounts owed for the provision of medial services.

SCOPE: This policy is applicable to all services furnished by the Organization.

POLICY: It is the policy of the Organization to provide adequate and appropriate treatment to patients without regard to the source of payment, level of reimbursement or the patient's ability to pay. However, the Organization may waive or reduce co-payment or deductible amounts only for indigent patients or after all reasonable collection efforts have been exhausted.

1. **General Rule**. In general, no employee or member of the Center shall offer any kind of payment, including any kickback, bribe, or rebate, whether in cash or in kind, in any manner or form, including waiver of co-payments or deductibles, to any physician, patient, or other party to induce the referral of any health care business, patient, or other item of service to the Center.
2. **Exception for Financial Hardship**. Notwithstanding the general rule, the chief compliance officer may, on receipt of a request from a patient, waive co-payments or deductibles; provided, however, that such waivers shall be made only in documented cases of financial hardship. If a patient asks about waiver of co-payments or deductibles, staff should give the patient a Request to Waive Co-payment or Deductible Form and ask the patient to fill it out.
3. **Eligibility Criteria**. A patient is eligible for a waiver of the co-payment or deductible under this policy if the patient's gross family income for the 12 months before the date of the request is at or below 200 percent of the current federal poverty guidelines (as listed in the *Federal Register* for the current year – see below). If the patient's gross family income is above the federal poverty guidelines and seeks financial assistance the patient will be required to complete a financial statement form. Eligibility will be determined on an individual basis based on the patient's financial income and expense ratio.

Poverty Guidelines for the 48 Contiguous States & the District of Columbia (2001)

SIZE OF FAMILY UNIT	POVERTY GUIDELINE	200% OF POVERTY GUIDELINE
2	$11,610	$11,610
3	$14,630	$29,260
4	$17,650	$35,300
5	$20,670	$41,340
6	$23,690	$47,380
7	$26,710	$53,420
8	$29,730	$59,460

For families with more than 8 members, add $3,020 for each additional member to determine the poverty guideline ($6,040 to determine 200 percent of the poverty guideline. {Source: Federal Register, Feb. 16, 2001}

4. **Proof**. We will base our decision whether to grant a request to waive co-payments or deductibles on written documentation provided by the patient. The Center shall require the patient to submit one or more of the following documents:

   - W-2 withholding statements
   - Pay Stubs
   - An income tax return
   - Social Security Benefit Statement – form SSA-1099

We will keep all information relating to the request confidential, except as needed to comply with a court order or other legal requirement. If we deny a request to waive co-payments or deductibles and later receive additional documentation of financial hardship, we will reconsider the request based on the new documentation.

5. **Decision**. The chief compliance officer or medical director must approve any waiver of deductibles or co-payments.

POLICY DESCRIPTION: **Vendor - Promotional Training**
REFERENCE NUMBER: **COMPLY.012**
EFFECTIVE DATE: **xx / xx / xxxx**

PURPOSE: To establish the parameters for accepting invitations for vendor-promotional training.

SCOPE: This policy applies to all Organization employees and affiliates.

POLICY: "Vendor-promotional training" is defined as training or education provided by any person or entity for the purpose of promoting its products or services, including vendor-sponsored seminars. It does not include training provided under a contract with the Organization or by a contractor to facilitate use of products or services it furnishes under an existing contract with the Organization.

Vendor-promotional training, including travel and lodging, may be accepted when the business value to the Organization outweighs any recreational or entertainment value of the training event, provided that approval is obtained in advance from the Compliance Officer.

PROCEDURE: An employee or affiliate who receives an invitation to attend vendor-promotional training, which may include any travel, lodging, entertainment expenses or other benefits, must obtain the approval of the Compliance Office before accepting the invitation.

POLICY DESCRIPTION: **Responding to Government Investigations**
REFERENCE NUMBER: **COMPLY.013**
EFFECTIVE DATE: **xx / xx / xxxx**

PURPOSE: To organize and facilitate the Organization's response to, and cooperation with, any government investigation.

SCOPE: This policy shall apply whenever the Organization is (a) served with a search warrant or subpoena, or (b) is the subject of a government or regulatory agency investigation, audit, survey or inspection, other than routine licensing, certification or accreditation surveys.

POLICY: Each Organization office shall be responsible for designating one person to serve as its Coordinator for responding to search warrants, subpoenas or government investigations, audits, surveys or inspections. The names of the Coordinators shall be maintained by the Compliance Officer, who shall be responsible for providing them with a copy of this policy, arranging for outside counsel to conduct periodic training on their duties and responsibilities, and supervising them in their execution of this policy.

PROCEDURE: The Compliance Officer shall serve as the Coordinator for the headquarters location of the Organization. Other locations shall select local Coordinators as appropriate.

In the event of any calls or visits by investigators, whether scheduled or unscheduled, the Coordinator shall be the sole point of contact and communication. It shall be the responsibility of the Coordinator to:

immediately notify outside counsel;

verify the identity of the investigators, secure telephone numbers for each investigator or obtain a business card, and ascertain if the investigators are in contact with any attorneys at the United States Attorney's Office, the Criminal and/or Civil Divisions of the U.S. Department of Justice, the state Medicaid fraud unit, or any other federal, state or local law enforcement agency;

request inspection of any warrant, or other legal authority under which the investigators are acting, to ensure that the investigators have proper authorization, and retain a copy of each such document;

attempt to ascertain from the investigators the nature of the inquiry and the alleged violations or statutes that are the basis for the investigation;

ensure that Organization records are produced only under compulsion of a subpoena, search warrant or other legal authority and, whenever feasible, after consultation with outside counsel;

inform the investigators that the Coordinator has been designated to respond to their requests for access or information;

render courteous cooperation with the investigators, escort

them at all times while on the premises, and act as the sole representative handling oral communications with the investigators; and

be responsible for coordinating implementation of a response plan with outside counsel.

If a search warrant is executed, it shall be the responsibility of the Coordinator to monitor the actions of the search team, making notes of areas searched and preparing a general description of items seized. The Coordinator also shall ensure that once the search warrant has been executed, the agents have left behind an inventory listing of items seized, as required by law.

At the conclusion of any investigative visit, audit or inspection, the Coordinator shall request an exit conference in order to learn additional details of the investigation, if any violations have been discovered during inspections, and if the Organization will be involved in any further investigative activity.

The Coordinator shall immediately inform outside counsel of all information acquired regarding an investigation so that the Organization may undertake its own internal investigation.

The Organization's documents and records shall be organized in a manner which ensures that attorney-client privileged documents are maintained in a separate location and are clearly labeled as such.

The Compliance Officer shall, in consultation with outside counsel, provide training for all employees regarding their rights and obligations in the event of investigative or regulatory activities initiated at any of the Organization's corporate locations or offices. The training shall include the distribution of written guidelines and shall focus on the following:

Explaining the primary role of the local Coordinator and outside counsel in coordinating the Organization's response to all search warrants, subpoenas, government audits, surveys and inspections.

Employees shall be reminded that Organization documents and other confidential information may not be shared with others outside of the Organization unless the individuals (a) have a legitimate need to know the information and have agreed to maintain its confidentiality, or (b) otherwise have a legal right to the information.

Employees shall be instructed that, as a general rule, they should not give Organization documents or records to any government investigator, auditor, surveyor, or inspector without receiving authority to do so from their local Coordinator. With respect to situations involving search warrants, however, employees must be instructed on their obligation to avoid obstructing or interfering with the agents executing the warrant. Thus, employees should be advised that if the Coordinator is not available, they might need to cede to the authority of the government agent and surrender documents without the Coordinator's consent.

Employees should be informed that the government, as a routine matter, may attempt to interview them on the Organization's premises during the course of an audit, survey, the service of a subpoena or the execution of a search warrant, or at home in the evening or at other times. Employees should be advised that while the Organization intends to cooperate in all investigations, they have the right to decide for themselves whether and when to agree to an interview with a government investigator. It should be emphasized that the decision to consent to an interview is entirely the employee's to make. Furthermore, employees should be advised that if they choose to be interviewed, they have the right to request the presence of an Organization representative. Employees also should advise their local Coordinator of any contacts that they have with government agents or investigators.

All employees shall be instructed that during a government investigation, audit, survey or inspection, they must never conceal, destroy or alter any documents, lie, or make misleading statements to the government's representatives. They also must not attempt to cause any other person to fail to provide accurate information or obstruct, mislead or delay the communication of information or records to the appropriate authorities.

FEDERAL REGISTER
Vol. 66, No. 33
Notices
Department of Health and Human Services (HHS)
Annual Update of the HHS Poverty Guidelines

Date: Friday, February 16, 2001

Action: Notice

Summary: This notice provides an update of the HHS pov erty guidelines to account for last (calendar) year's increase in prices as measured by the Consumer Price Index.

Effective Date: These guidelines go into effect on the day they are published (unless an office administering a program using the guidelines specifies a different effective date for that particular program.)

Addresses: Office of the Assistant Secretary for Planning and Evaluation, Room 404E, Humphrey Building, Department of Health and Human Services (HHS), Washington, DC 20201.

For Further Information Contact:

For information about how the poverty guidelines are used or how income is defined in a particular program, contact the Federal (or other) office, which is responsible for that program.

For general information about the poverty guidelines (but NOT for information about a particular program-such as the Hill-Burton Uncompensated Services Program-that uses the poverty guidelines), contact Gordon Fisher, Office of the Assistant Secretary for Planning and Evaluation, Room 404E, Humphrey Building, Department of Health and Human Services, Washington, DC 20201 – Telephone: (202) 690-5880; persons with internet access may visit the poverty guidelines internet site at <http://aspe.hhs.gov/poverty/poverty.htm>.

For information about the Hill-Burton Uncompensated Services Program (no-fee or reduced fee health care services at certain hospitals and other health care facilities for certain persons unable to pay for such care), contact the office of the Director, Division of Facilities Compliance and Recovery, HRSA, HHS, Room 10C-16, Parklawn Building, 5600 Fishers Lane, Rockville, Maryland 20857 – Telephone: (301) 443-5656 or 1-800-638-0742 (for callers outside Maryland) or 1-800-492-0359 (for callers in Maryland); persons with internet access may visit the Division of Facilities Compliance and Recovery internet home page site at <http://www.hrsa.gov/osp/dfcr>. The Division of Facilities Compliance and Recovery notes that as set by 42 CFR 124.505 (b), the effective date of this update of the poverty guidelines for facilities obligated under the Hill-Burton Uncompensated Services Program is sixty days from the date of this publication.

For information about the percentage multiple of the poverty guidelines to be used on immigration forms such as INS Form I-864, Affidavit of Support, contact the U.S. Immigration and Naturalization Service. To get a copy of the most recent poverty guidelines published by the Immigration and Naturalization Service, call 1-800-375-5283 and ask for Form I-864. Persons with internet access may obtain the information from the Immigration and Naturalization Service internet site at http://www.ins.usdoj.gov/graphics/howdoi/affsupp.htm

For information about the Department of Labor's Lower Living Standard Income Level (an alternative eligibility criterion with the poverty guidelines for certain Workforce Investment Act programs and services), contact Ronald E. Putz, U.S. Department of Labor—telephone: (202) 693-3575, e-mail: rputz@doleta.gov>; persons with internet access may visit the Employment and Training Administration's Lower Living Standard Income Level internet site at <http://www.wdsc.org/11si1>.

For information about the number of people in poverty (since 1959) or about the Census Bureau (statistical) poverty thresholds, contact the HHES Division, Room G251, Federal Office Building #3, U.S. Bureau of the Census, Washington, DC 20233-8500 – Telephone: (301) 457-3242 or send e-mail to hhes-info@census.gov>; persons with internet access may visit the Poverty section of the Census Bureau's world wide web site at <http://www.census.gov/hhes/www/poverty/html>.

2001 Poverty Guidelines for the 48 Contiguous States and the District of Columbia

Size of Family Unit	Poverty Guideline
1	$ 8,590
2	$11,610
3	$14.630
4	$17,650
5	$ 20,670
6	$23,690
7	$26,710
8	$29,730

For family units with more than 8 members, add $3,020 for each additional member. (The same increment applies to smaller family sizes also, as can be seen in the figures above.)

2001 Poverty Guidelines for Alaska

Size of Family Unit	Poverty Guideline
1	$ 10,730
2	$14,510
3	$18,290
4	$22,070
5	$25,850
6	$29,630
7	$33,410
8	$37,190

For family units with more than 8 members, add $3,780 for each additional member. (The same increment applies to smaller family sizes also, as can be seen in the figures above.)

2001 Poverty Guidelines for Hawaii

Size of Family Unit	Poverty Guideline
1	$ 9,890
2	$13,360
3	$16,830
4	$20,300
5	$23,770
6	$27,240
7	$30,710
8	$34,180

For family units with more than 8 members, add $3,470 for each additional member. (The same increment applies to smaller family sizes also, as can be seen in the figures above.)

(Separate poverty guideline figures for Alaska and Hawaii reflect Office of Economic Opportunity administrative practice beginning in the 1966-1970 period. Note that the Census Bureau poverty thresholds-the primary version of the poverty measure-have never had the separate figures for Alaska and Hawaii. The poverty guidelines are not defined for Puerto Rico, the US Virgin Islands, American Samoa, Guam, the Republic of the Marshall Islands, The Federated States of Micronesia, The Commonwealth of the Northern Mariana Islands, and Palau. In cases in which a Federal program using the poverty guidelines serves any of those jurisdictions, the Federal office which administers the program is responsible for deciding whether to use the contiguous-states-and-DC guidelines for those jurisdictions or to follow some other procedure.)

The preceding figures are the 2001 update of the poverty guidelines required by section 673 (2) of the Omnibus Budget Reconciliation Act (OBRA) of 1981 (Pub. L. 97-35). As required by law, this update reflects last year's change in the Consumer Price Index (CPI-U); it was done using the same procedure used in previous years.

Section 673(2) of OBRA-1981 (42 USC 9902 (2)) requires the use of the poverty guidelines as an eligibility criterion for the Community Services Block Grant program. The poverty guidelines are also used as an eligibility criterion for the Community Services Block Grant program. The poverty guidelines are also used as an eligibility criterion by a number of other Federal programs (both HHS and non-HHS). Due to confusing legislative language dating back to 1972, the poverty guidelines have sometimes been mistakenly referred to as the "OMB" (Office of Management and Budget) poverty guidelines or poverty line. In fact, OMB has never issued the guidelines; the guidelines are issued each year by the Department of Health and Human Services (formerly by the Office of Economic Opportunity/Community Services Administration). The poverty guidelines may be formally referenced as "the poverty guidelines updated annually in the Federal Register by the US Department of Health and Human Services under authority of 42 USC 9902 (2)."

The poverty guidelines are a simplified version of the Federal Government's statistical poverty thresholds used by the Bureau of the Census to prepare its statistical estimates of the number of persons and families in poverty. The poverty guidelines issued by the Department of Health and Human Services are used for administrative purposes-for instance, for determining whether a person or family is financially eligible for assistance or services under a particular Federal program. The poverty thresholds are used primarily for statistical purposes. Since the poverty guidelines in this notice-the 2001 guidelines-reflect price changes through calendar year 2000, they are approximately equal to the poverty thresholds for calendar year 2000 which the Census Bureau will issue in September or October 2001. (A preliminary version of the 2000 thresholds is now available from the Census Bureau).

In certain cases, as noted in the relevant authorizing legislation or program regulations, a program uses the poverty guidelines as only one of several eligibility criteria, or uses a percentage multiple of the guidelines (for example, 125 percent or 185 percent of the guidelines). Non-Federal organizations which use the poverty guidelines under their own authority in non-Federally-funded activities also have the option of choosing to use a percentage multiple of the guidelines such as 125 percent or 185 percent.

While many programs use the guidelines to classify persons or families as either eligible or ineligible, some other programs use the guidelines for the purpose of giving priority to lower-income persons or families in the provision of assistance or services.

In some cases, these poverty guidelines may not become effective for a particular program until a regulation or notice specifically applying to the program in question has been issued.

The poverty guidelines give above should be used for both farm and non-farm families. Similarly, these guidelines should be used for both aged and non-aged units. The poverty guidelines have never had an aged/non-aged distinction; only the Census Bureau (statistical) poverty thresholds have separate figures for aged and non-aged one-person and two-person units.

Definitions:

There is no universal administrative definition of "family," "family unit," or "household" that is valid for all programs that use the poverty guidelines. Federal programs in some cases use administrative definitions that differ somewhat from the statistical definitions given below; the Federal office, which administers a program, has the responsibility for making decisions about administrative definitions. Similarly, non-Federal organizations which use the poverty guidelines in non-Federally-funded activities may use administrative definitions that differ from the statistical definitions given below. In either case, to find out the precise definitions used by a particular program, one must consult the office or organization administering the program in question.

The following statistical definitions (derived for the most part from language used in US Bureau of the Census, Current Population Reports, Series P60-185 and earlier reports in the same series) are made available for illustrative purposes only; in other words, these statistical definitions are not binding for administrative purposes.

a. Family. A family is a group of two or more persons related by birth, marriage, or adoption who live together, all such related persons are considered as members of one family. For instance, if an older married couple, their daughter and her husband and two children, and the older couple's nephew all lived in the same house or apartment, they would all be considered members of a single family.

b. Unrelated Individual. An unrelated individual is a person 15 years old or over (other than an inmate of an institution) who is not living with any relatives. An unrelated individual may be the only person living in a house or apartment, or may be living in a house or apartment (or in group quarters such as a rooming house) in which one or more persons also live who are not related to the individual in question by birth, marriage, or adoption. Examples of unrelated individuals residing with others include a lodger, a foster child, a ward, or an employee.

c. Household. As defined by the Bureau of the Census for statistical purposes, a household consists of all the persons who occupy a housing unit (house or apartment), whether they are related to each other or not. If a family and an unrelated individual, or two unrelated individuals, are living in the same housing unit, they would constitute two family units (see next item), but only one household. Some programs, such as the Food Stamp Program and the Low-Income Home Energy Assistance Program, employ administrative variations of the "household" concept in determining income eligibility. A number of other programs use administrative variations of the "family" concept in determining income eligibility. Depending on the precise program definition used, programs using a "family" concept would generally apply the poverty guidelines separately to each family and/or unrelated individual within a household if the household includes more than one family and/or unrelated individual.

d. Family unit. "Family unit" is not an official US Bureau of Census term, although it has been used in the poverty guidelines Federal Register notice since 1978. As used here, either an unrelated individual or a family (as defined above) constitutes a family unit. In other words, a family unit of size one is an unrelated individual, while a family unit of two/three/ etc. is the same as a family of two/three/etc.

Note that this notice no longer provides a definition of "income." This is for two reasons. First, there is no universal administrative definition of "income" that is valid for all programs that use the poverty guidelines. Second, in the past there has been confusion regarding important differences between the statistical definition of income and various administrative definitions of "income" or "countable income." The precise definition of "income" for a particular program is very sensitive to the specific needs and purposes of that program. To determine, for example, whether or not taxes, college scholarships, or other particular types of income should be counted as "income" in determining eligibility for a specific program, one must consult the office or organization administering the program in question; that office or organization has the responsibility for making decisions about the definition of "income" used by the program (to the extend that the definition is not already contained in legislation or regulations.)

Dated: February 13, 2001

Tommy G. Thompson,

Secretary of Health and Human Services

(FR Doc. 01-4036, Filed 2/15/01: 8:45am)

Billing Code 4154-05-P

AN INTRODUCTION TO HIPAA

Laxmaiah Manchikanti, MD

The Health Insurance Portability and Accountability Act of 1996 (HIPAA) was passed by Congress and enacted into law in August 1996. Its original purpose was simply to provide portability of group health insurance for Americans, not control fraud and abuse, and not provide so-called administrative simplification. While portability is the primary subject of one section of HIPAA, it is a relatively small aspect of the overall legislation. Portability is not only totally separate from, but completely unrelated to Title II of HIPAA, consisting of the so-called administrative "simplification provisions" governing privacy and security of health data and related subjects involving the transmission and processing of the data. Another major part of legislation, unrelated to portability is expansion of fraud and abuse authority. Thus, the title may sound benign, but it is malignant.

As with many other legislations affecting medical practice in the United States this federal legislation is lengthy, complicated, and confusing due to the fact that Congress attached many provisions to HIPAA that will have little or nothing to do with its name and original purpose. The proposed regulations and the final regulations implementing HIPAA already have filled more than 500 densely packed small script pages of the Federal Register.

HIPAA establishes four types of federal standards instead of only assisting with portability of insurance and expanding fraud and abuse investigations. These standards include the following:

- Transaction standards

  HIPAA requires health plans to conduct these particular transactions electronically when they are asked to by a provider

- Privacy standards

  HIPAA provides standards to protect the privacy of sensitive personal health information whether that information is stored electronically or in any other form

- Security standards

  HIPAA provides standards to protect the security and integrity of personal health information when it is stored electronically

- Uniform identifiers

  HIPAA provides systems of uniform federal identifiers for health care providers, health plans, employers, and individuals.

While HIPAA affects every participant in the American health care system, it is fair to say that its most direct impact will be felt by health care providers, health care plans, and health care clearing houses which are termed as "covered entities." In addition, HIPAA also indirectly affects the business partners and business associates of the covered entities.

HISTORY

On August 1 and 2, 1996, Congress cleared for the president's signature the Health Insurance Portability and Accountability Act of 1996, also known as Kennedy – Kassebaum Bill. This was enacted without much descent. The House vote approving the conference report on the Bill was 421 to 2, the Senate vote was 98 to 0. Press was extremely favorable. After all this was about portability and accountability, which is good for the public. President Clinton happily signed the Bill into law on August 21, 1996.

However, the review of this Bill brings many memories of President Clinton's Health Care Reform proposals of 1993. We were presented the most far - reaching program of social engineering to be attempted in the United States since the passage of Medicare and Medicaid in 1965. By September 1994, the plan was in critical condition. Finally, this health plan failed mainly because too many people concluded that it was not credible. Some believed that health care reform failed because people don't trust government to manage their medical care. Unfortunately, mostly unknown to Americans, ignored by republican congress, the 1996 Act contained major provisions of the Clinton administration's previously rejected 1993 Health Security Act (1). The most feared provisions of the 1993 proposal – potentially threatening innocent physicians with federal criminal penalties and jeopardizing the privacy of doctor-patient relations through a nationwide electronic database – became law in 1996 with enactment of HIPAA legislation virtually without opposition enacted by a republican congress and signed by a democratic president.

The Health Insurance Portability and Accountability Act of 1996 contained some features that most Americans value highly, including portability provisions to prevent loss of health insurance triggered by employment changes, significant health insurance access and renewability guarantees, and also, on an experimental basis, medical savings accounts re-established greater individual financial stakes resulting in cost consciousness in making health care choices. However, neither the congress nor the press told the medical profession or for that matter the public about the provisions, including heavy federal criminal sanctions, potentially threatening innocent physicians and a national electronic database threatening the privacy of individual's medical records. Most of these provisions appear in Title II of the new law under the heading "preventing health care fraud and abuse; administrative simplification" (3).

One of the undisclosed purposes of the 1996 law is to limit Medicare fraud, with an estimated cost of $18 billion annually in 1996. Accordingly, HIPAA establishes a "fraud and abuse control program" to be administered by the department of Health and Human Services. This is similar to proposals by the Clinton Administration in 1993, which empowered the Secretary of HHS, to "conduct investigations, audits, evaluations, and inspections relating to the delivery of and payment for health care in the United States," to "arrange for the sharing of data with representatives of health plans," and, to secure "qualified immunity" for those who provide information to the secretary or the attorney general.

IMPLICATIONS TO INTERVENTIONAL PAIN MEDICINE

While HIPAA provides patients with portability and accountability of healthcare, it also provides providers with a major fraud and abuse initiative, along with so-called administrative simplification providing transaction standards, privacy standards, security standards and uniform identifiers.

Fraud and Abuse

HIPAA of 1996 is the most sweeping legislation in medical fraud and abuse. The HIPAA added substantial funding for fraud and abuse activities for several agencies, including the Office of Inspector General (OIG), the Federal Bureau of Investigations (FBI) and Centers for Medicare and Medicaid Services (CMS). Additional funding for fraud and abuse prosecutary efforts will be achieved through incentives and recoveries from successful prosecuted cases. The act provides incentives for the various enforcement agencies to identify and prosecute fraud cases.

Until HIPAA, the Inspector General only dealt with Medicare and Medicaid. However, with HIPAA, there are additional requirements that all law enforcement agencies coordinate efforts to oppose healthcare fraud and abuse in the public and private sector. To achieve this, most of the funding is devoted to the hiring of additional investigators and other enforcement personnel.

HIPAA does not explicitly define terms such as defraud, but it establishes some new federal healthcare crimes, broadly classified as follows:

- Making materially false statements
- Healthcare fraud,
- Embezzlement of monies under control of a health benefit program,
- Obstructing an investigation,
- Money laundering.

Unfortunately, under the HIPAA, these categories of crimes apply also to private payors, not just Medicare or Medicaid.

Some of the HIPAA provisions are as follows:

- Medicare and Medicaid exclusion penalties also apply to all other federal healthcare programs, such as CHAMPUS, Veteran's Affairs, Black Lung, and Federal Employee Health Benefits program.
- The HIPAA allows imposition of $10,000 per day fines for organization that continue any "investor" relationship or continue employing a person who has been excluded from any federal healthcare program.

- HIPAA increases civil monetary policies from $2,000 to $10,000 per infraction plus three times the amount of the overpayment.
- HIPAA requires mandatory exclusion from Medicare for 5 to 10 years for certain offenses.
- HIPAA makes "deliberate ignorance" or "reckless disregard of the truth" tests as to whether an individual should have known that an activity was fraudulent.
- HIPAA specifically defines upcoding of evaluation and management or other services.
- HIPAA establishes a penalty of $5,000 or three times the cost of services for any physician who certifies unneeded home healthcare.
- HIPAA also makes healthcare fraud, embezzlement, false statements, money laundering and obstruction of any healthcare investigation a federal criminal offense.

One silver lining is that HIPAA also requires the government to issue advisory opinions on a limited list of issues to help physicians and others determine beforehand whether an arrangement might pose a problem.

Standardized Transactions

Administrative simplification is also known as standardized transactions and code sets. Its purpose is to encourage the efficient use of electronic data interchange.

The healthcare industry spends a significant percentage of its resources on administrative overhead, including eligibility verification, enrollment, referral authorization and various transactions related to the development, support and payment of claims for healthcare services. Currently, healthcare administration involves a vast array of paper trails, telephone calls, and logistical delays. In an effort to relieve a substantial portion of this burden, HIPAA Administrative Simplification Provisions seek to standardize the format for electronic data interchange and create single identification numbers for industry participants. Thus, these provisions create uniform national standards to ten specific transactions (Table 1) between providers, payors, and purchasers, which may greatly simplify the administrative transaction process. Thus, it is

Table 1. *The ten specific transaction standards under HIPAA administrative simplification*

Transaction	Standard
Health plan enrollment	Benefit Enrollment and Maintenance,
Premium payment	Payment Order/Remittance Advice
Claims submission	Health Care Claim: Institutional Health Care Claim: Professional Health Care Claim: Dental *NCPDP Telecommunications Standard Implementation Guide*, Version 5 Release 1 and equivalent *NCPDP Batch Standard Implementation Guide*, Version 1 Release 0
Claims status	Health Care Claim Status Request and Response
Remittance	Health Care Claim Payment/Advice *NCPDP Telecommunications Standard Implementation Guide*, Version 5 Release 1 and equivalent *NCPDP Batch Standard Implementation Guide*
Coordination of benefits	Health Care Claim: Institutional Health Care Claim: Professional Health Care Claim: Dental *NCPDP Telecommunications Standard Implementation Guide*, Version 5 Release 1 and equivalent *NCPDP Batch Standard Implementation Guide*, Version 1 Release 0
Eligibility	Health Care Eligibility Benefit Inquiry and Response *NCPDP Telecommunications Standard Implementation Guide*, Version 5 Release 1 and equivalent *NCPDP Batch Standard Implementation Guide*, Version 1 Release 0
Referral authorization	Health Care Services Review Information
First report of injury	None recommended in the proposed rule ASCX12N and IAI/ABC alternatives will continue to be evaluated for possible adoption as a final standard
Claims attachments	(Not published to date)

expected that healthcare industry will experience substantial reductions in the cost of administrative operations. Even though transition to a single set of standards will be costly, the savings, once all the parties to healthcare electronic transaction are using the same information, the same forms, and the same formats, will be considerable. In fact, HHS estimated savings of nearly $30 billion over a ten-year period.

A standard transaction is one that complies with transaction standards. HIPAA also requires HHS to use code sets in connection with the transaction standards. The American Medical Association's Current Procedural Terminology and the International Classification of Diseases are two of the recognized code sets.

All covered entities including health plans, health clearing houses, billing companies, and healthcare providers have to comply with the relevant standards and code sets when processing electronic claims or remittances. However, physicians may continue to file paper claims in any format they wish and transmit the information to clearing houses that will transmit the information into the appropriate format. HIPAA established penalties for non-compliance; as much as $100 per claim.

Impact of HIPAA administrative simplification on providers and payors is not only complex and also is expensive. It is expected that proposed rules for administrative simplification will involve enormous cost and logistical issues related to these changes. While HHS has estimated savings of $30 billion over a period of ten years, the healthcare industry has estimated expenses to the industry of as much as $250 billion over the next 2 to 5 years in an attempt to comply with HIPAA standards. Thus, some have stated that the HIPAA expense of administrative simplification, simply exceeds the entire issue of Y2K.

The Final Rule on transaction standards and code sets was published on August 17, 2000. The effective date specified in the Final Rule was October 16, 2000. Any of the specified transactions, when conducted electronically, must be conducted as standard transactions starting 24 months after the effective date. This means that a health plan, provider, or healthcare clearinghouse must comply with the standards no later than October 16, 2002. However, on November 27, 2001, the senate passed a bill giving covered entities a 1-year extension to comply with the transaction and code sets provision. Subsequently, on December 4, 2001, the House of Representatives also passed its bill delaying implementation until October 16, 2003.

PRIVACY STANDARDS

The HIPAA Privacy Rule is longer than all other sections of HIPAA put together. In fact, to many of the people and organizations affected by HIPAA, the Privacy Rule itself consists of the entire HIPAA. The Rule is not only lengthy but complex. However, for physicians, the Privacy Rule may not have as many implications as fraud and abuse does.

The HIPAA Privacy Rule or Confidentiality and Security Act requires all covered entities that engage in HIPAA transactions to protect individually identifiable health information against disclosure to unauthorized parties. The Final Rule states that the protected health information is, "individually identifiable health information that is transmitted or maintained, in any form or medium, by an entity covered under HIPAA administrative simplification." Privacy standards also describe individually identifiable health information as any information, including demographic information, collected from an individual that (A) is created or received by a healthcare provider, health plan, employer or healthcare clearinghouse; and (B) relates to the past, present, or future physical or mental health or condition of an individual; the provision of healthcare to an individual; or the past, present, or future payment for the provision of healthcare to an individual, and (i) identifies the individual or (ii) with respect to which, there is reasonable basis to believe that the information can be used to identify the individual.

Data elements that make information individually identifiable include the following; name, address, employer, relatives' names, date of birth, telephone and fax numbers, e-mail addresses, social security number, medical record numbers, member or account number, certificate/license number, voice/fingerprints, photos, or other number, code or characteristics such as occupation.

Thus, health plans, healthcare clearinghouses, and healthcare providers who transmit health information electronically in connection with a standard transaction, including claims, coordination of benefits, payment and remittance advice, claims status, etc., are covered entities. However, employee health benefit plans are excluded if they are self-administered and have fewer than forty participants.

The Privacy Rule will have significant impact on interventional pain management practices. Practices will need to ensure that health information is not disclosed for non-health purposes without explicit authorization from the patient. All disclosures must be limited to the minimum necessary. However, the minimum necessary standards will not apply to disclosure of medical records for treatment information. Further, practices are required to provide patients clear written information on how the practice may use and disclose health information.

SECURITY STANDARDS

HIPAA's security provisions, generally deal with unintentional release of health-related information. Most specifically, they address the steps that must be taken by a covered entity to prevent the unintentional disclosure, destruction, or corruption of personal health information maintained or transmitted by health plans, healthcare providers and healthcare clearinghouses.

The security standards apply to all information that is transmitted, received, recorded or stored electronically. They apply to information that is transmitted as part of a standard transaction, but they also apply to information that they just collected, stored, or accessed electronically for purposes other than conducting a standard transaction. It appears that security standards have broader applications than the transaction standards. Thus, they carry broader implications for health plans, healthcare providers and healthcare clearinghouses that transmit, receive or store information electronically.

Multiple aspects of security include the integrity of the information retrieved from a data system is the same as the information that originally was entered into it; confidentiality in a data system is available only to authorized individuals, or is only transmitted to and received by intended recipients; and availability of the information when it is needed by authorized users.

Categories of security standards include administrative procedures for managing the development and implementation of measures to protect data and ensure appropriate conduct of personnel; physical safeguards that protect the physical computer systems and related buildings and equipment from environmental hazards and intrusion; technical security services for protecting, controlling and monitoring access to information; and technical security mechanisms for preventing unauthorized data to be transmitted over a communications network.

IDENTIFIERS

One of the objectives of HIPAA is to deal with highly variable and complex regulations of individual health plans created over the years for identifying the people they cover, the employees those people work for, and the healthcare providers who send them claims. It is presumed that the lack of standardization has added cost to healthcare system, slowed down reimbursement, and contributed to mistakes.

The purpose of the National Provider Identification System is to replace the fragmented systems of identifiers being used by various programs. The National Provider Identification (NPI) is an 8-place alphanumeric identifier. The NPI System has the capacity to assign unique identifiers to about 20 billion providers. The NPI will eventually replace the Unique Physician Identification Number (UPIN).

CONCLUSION

Even though the Health Insurance Portability and Accountability Act of 1996, also known as Kennedy-Kassebaum Act, started as an independent simple act to protect the Health Insurance Portability for employees, it evolved into a complex, complicated healthcare regulation. While it sounds benign, biopsy results are malignant. The regulation was almost unanimous and bipartisan passed by a republican congress and signed by a democratic president, without consideration that this legislation embodied the principles of the Clinton Healthcare Act of 1993. Since its proposal, many changes have occurred with the establishment of the administrative simplifications of Title II, as well as the extension of its implementation. In the coming years, HIPAA will not only take center stage in the practice of interventional pain medicine, but also will be an expensive proposition. One can only hope that it will truly lead to simplification, savings, and improved patient care.

REFERENCES

1. Twight C. Medicare's progeny: The 1996 Health Care Legislation. In Feldmen RD (ed), *American Health Care*, The Independent Institute, New Brunswick, 2000; pp 87-118.
2. Derthick M. Policymaking for Social Security. Brookings Institution, Washington, DC, 1979.
3. Goldberg RM. "The Birth of Clintoncare Jr. . . ." *Wall Street Journal,* August 5, A18.

HIPAA PRIVACY REGULATIONS: PRACTICAL INFORMATION FOR PHYSICIANS

Erin Brisbay McMahon, JD
Tracy Lee-Huber, JD

One of the main goals of the federal Health Insurance Portability and Accountability Act (HIPAA) was to protect the security and privacy of patient data. HIPAA gave Congress until August 21, 1999 to enact comprehensive health privacy legislation. Because Congress failed to act, however, HIPAA's provisions then gave the Department of Health and Human Services (DHHS) the authority to promulgate privacy regulations.

Final HIPAA privacy regulations were issued on December 28, 2000, and were to be effective February 26, 2001. Due to an administrative glitch delaying their effective date, however, the privacy regulations underwent another public comment period that ended March 30, 2001. Much to the dismay of the health care industry and to the surprise of everyone else, the Bush administration decided to forego further delays in implementing the comprehensive privacy regulations. Thus, the HIPAA privacy regulations that were issued in December became effective on April 14, 2001, and physicians' offices must be in compliance with them by April 14, 2003.

The privacy regulations, as they exist currently, are more than 1,500 pages in length including the rules, comments, and the predicted impact of the regulations on the health care industry. The last comment period produced at lease 7,500 additional comments on the controversial regulations. This article is intended to highlight and simplify, to the extent possible, the practical aspects of the regulations for physicians.

COVERED ENTITIES

The burden of complying with the HIPAA privacy regulations is placed squarely upon "covered entities." Covered entities are defined as health plans, health care clearinghouses, or health care providers. A health care provider is defined as a provider of medical or health services and any other person or organization who furnishes, bills, or is paid for health care in the normal course of business. Therefore, physicians have an obligation to implement the privacy regulations. As a covered entity, physicians may not use or disclose protected health information except as permitted or required by the regulations.

PROTECTED INFORMATION

The privacy regulations are intended to protect *all medical records* and *individually identifiable health information* held, created, or disclosed by a physician. As the regulations exist currently, they broadly protect health information communicated electronically, on paper or orally. The proposed regulations only covered electronic records or any paper records that had at some point been in electronic form. However, the final regulations were expanded to cover all mediums in which health information could be transmitted.

Opponents have heavily criticized the regulations for their restrictive nature on physician communications and for the burden that the regulations place on the provision of health care. For example, opponents argue that the regulations will inhibit physicians from speaking freely with one another, their staff, or even with the patient while rendering health services if someone unauthorized were present to hear protected health information. Providers unsuccessfully argued for the final regulations to cover only electronically transmitted health information.

Individually identifiable health information (IIHI) is a subset of health information, including demographic information collected from the individual, that is created or received by a health care provider, health plan, employer or health care clearinghouse. Protected IIHI must relate to the past, present, or future physical or mental health or condition of an individual; the provision of health care to an individual; or the past, present, or future payment for the provision of health care to an individual. For IIHI to be protected, it must also identify the individual or give the physician a reasonable basis to believe that the information in question can be used to identify the individual. Given the above factors, it is hard to imagine any information that would be excluded from protection by the physician in his or her practice.

MINIMUM NECESSARY INFORMATION

Not only does the physician have an obligation to protect a patient's health information, but that physician must limit the amount of information used, requested or disclosed to the "minimum necessary" to accomplish an intended use, disclosure, or request. This minimum necessary obligation also applies to a physician's workforce.

Under the regulations, a physician has a duty to limit the access of his/her workforce to certain designated protected health information. A physician must identify those classes of individuals in his/her workforce who need access to protected health information in order to carry out their duties. Also, a physician must identify the categories of protected health information to which workforce access is needed and set any conditions appropriate to such access.

In line with the minimum necessary requirements, a physician's office must implement policies and procedures for any type of disclosure that it makes on a *routine* basis so that it limits the protected health information disclosed to the amount reasonably necessary to achieve the purpose of the disclosure. For all non-routine disclosures, a physician must (a) develop criteria designed to limit the protected health information disclosed to the information reasonably necessary to achieve the purpose for which disclosure is sought and (b) review requests for disclosure on an individual basis in accordance with such criteria. Obviously, a physician's workforce must be trained on the above policies and procedures in order for the members of the workforce to carry out their respective duties.

The minimum necessary requirement does not apply to disclosures to or requests by a health care provider for treatment; to disclosures to the individual who is the subject of the privacy information; to disclosures made to the Secretary of Health and Human Services pursuant to an investigation for violation of the privacy regulations; or to disclosures that are required by law or by the privacy regulations. Even with these exclusions, there remains a debate between proponents of the privacy regulations and health care providers as to whether or not the minimum necessary requirement will dangerously hinder the ability of health professionals to provide unrestrictive treatment to their patients.

PERMITTED AND REQUIRED DISCLOSURES

The general rule under the HIPAA privacy regulations is that a physician is allowed to use or disclose protected health information if it is:

- disclosed to the individual who is the subject of the information;
- pursuant to a valid consent to carry out treatment, payment or health care operations;
- pursuant to a valid authorization;
- without consent, if consent is not required under the regulations; or
- without written consent, if the individual was informed in advance of the use or disclosure and had the opportunity to agree to or to prohibit the disclosure.

A physician will be confronted with the regulations most frequently in the circumstance where the physician must obtain the consent of the patient to use or disclose personal health information in order to carry out treatment, payment, or health care operations. The regulations require the physician to obtain the individual's consent prior to using or disclosing such protected health information to carry out treatment, payment or health care operations.

A physician is not required to obtain the patient's consent in certain limited situations. For instance, a physician does not need a patient's consent to use or disclose health information if the physician has an "indirect treatment relationship" with the individual, such as where the physician is reading an x-ray on the orders of a second physician who will report the results of the x-ray to the patient. Nor does the physician need the patient's consent in emergency treatment situations if the physician attempts to obtain the consent as soon as reasonably practicable after the delivery of treatment. Also, if a physician is unable to obtain the consent of an individual because of language or other communication barriers, the physician may use or disclose the protected health information if the individual's consent is clearly inferred from the circumstances. However, a physician who fails to obtain consent, as required, must document his or her attempt to obtain consent and the reason why consent was not obtained.

Furthermore, a physician may condition treatment of a patient on the provision of consent. A consent to carry out treatment, payment or health care operations must be, among other things, visually and organizationally separate from other written legal permission; in plain language; separately signed and dated by the individual; and inform the individual of his or her rights in and to the protected information. If a physician receives any other consent or written legal permission from an individual for a disclosure of protected health information to carry out treatment, payment or health care operations, the physician must follow the more restrictive consent.

Another important part of the regulations is the physician's obligation to obtain the patient's authorization if he or she wants to use the patient's protected health information or disclose the protected health information for a purpose other than carrying out treatment, payment or health care operations. A physician may not use an individual's protected health information or make a disclosure of that information to a third party without a valid authorization.

A valid authorization consists of, among other things, a description of the information to be used or disclosed; the identification of the person or class of persons allowed to make the requested use or disclosure; a signature of the individual and the date; and a statement of the individual's right to revoke the authorization. An individual may revoke an authorization at any time provided that the revocation is in writing and the physician has not taken action in reliance on it. A physician must document and retain any authorizations as well as provide the individual with a copy of the signed authorization.

PATIENTS' RIGHTS

As one would expect from the pro-patient nature of the privacy regulations, the patient has an array of rights with respect to the use or disclosure of his or her individual health information. With few exceptions, an individual has the right to adequate notice of the uses and disclosures of protected health information; to know his or her individual rights to the protected health information; and to know the physician's legal duties with respect to the protected health information. The patient's rights manifest themselves in the form of a comprehensive notice that must be given by the physician to his or her patients.

The physician must provide a notice to the patient that is written in plain language containing information as to how the patient's protected information may be used or disclosed. The notice must also contain a description, and at least one example, of the types and uses and disclosures that the physician is permitted to make for treatment, payment and health care operations. Furthermore, the notice must set forth a description of each scenario in which the physician is required or permitted to use or disclose protected health information without the individual's written consent or authorization. The physician must inform the patient that, other than the exceptions listed above, uses and disclosures will be made only with the individual's written authorization and that the individual may revoke that authorization.

A statement of the individual's rights with respect to protected health information, and a brief description of how the individual may exercise these rights, must also be contained in the notice. The following are individual rights of a patient that must be provided in the physician's notice:

- the right to request restrictions on certain uses and disclosures of protected health information;
- the right to receive confidential communications of protected health information;
- the right to inspect, copy, and amend protected health information;
- the right to receive an accounting of disclosures of protected health information; and
- the right to obtain a paper copy of the physician's notice upon request.

The physician's legal duties under the privacy regulations must also be placed in his or her notice to the patient. The notice must state that the physician reserves the right to change the terms of his or her notice and to make new provisions effective for all protected health information retained by the physician. However, the physician must promptly revise and distribute his or her notice whenever there is a material change. The notice must briefly describe how patients may file a complaint with the physician if they believe that their privacy rights have been violated. Correspondingly, the notice must state that the individual will not suffer retaliation for filing a complaint and designate the name, title, and telephone number of a person or office to contact with concerns.

OBLIGATIONS OF THE PHYSICIAN

The notice requirements contained in the HIPAA privacy regulations are only one piece of the physician's obligation puzzle. The physician must implement and maintain various policies and procedures as well as have in place appropriate administrative, technical, and physical safeguards in the workplace to protect the privacy of health information from any intentional or unintentional use or disclosure that would violate the regulations.

The privacy regulations require that a physician designate a privacy official who is responsible for the development and implementation of the above policies and procedures, and a contact person responsible for receiving complaints and for providing information about matters covered by the notice. As part of the implementation process, the physician must train all members of his or her workforce on established policies and procedures as necessary and appropriate for all members to carry out their duties with respect to protected health information. The physician must accurately document personnel designations and any training conducted by the physician. Likewise, the physician must apply appropriate sanctions against members of the workforce who fail to comply with established policies and procedures.

The physician also has an obligation to provide a process for individuals to make complaints concerning the physician's policies or procedures or the physician's compliance with such policies and procedures. The physician must document all complaints. The physician may not intimidate, threaten, coerce, discriminate against, or take other retaliatory actions against any individual for the exercise of his or her rights under the privacy regulations.

The privacy regulations require the physician to mitigate, to the extent practicable, any harmful effect that is known to the physician of a use or disclosure of protected health information in violation of the physician's policies and procedures or the privacy regulations. This responsibility of mitigating harmful effects from uses or disclosures of health information also applies to the physician when he or she deals with business associates. The regulations define a business associate as a person who performs or assists in the performance of a function or activity involving the use or disclosure of individually identifiable health information. Examples of business associates include: claim processors, data analysts, attorneys, accountants, and consultants. A physician may disclose protected health information to a business associate and may allow a business associate to create or receive protected health information on the physician's behalf only if the physician obtains adequate assurances that the business associate will properly protect the information. To assure adequate protection, the physician must enter into a written contract with the business associate.

The contract must establish the permitted and required uses and disclosures of the health information by the business associate; must authorize termination of the contract if the business associate violates a material term of the contract; and must outline mandatory obligations of the business associate under the privacy regulations. A physician is noncompliant with the regulations if he or she knew of a pattern of activity or practice of the business associate that violated their agreement unless the physician took action to cure the breach. If actions by the physician to cure the business associate's breach are unsuccessful the physician must terminate the contract, if feasible, or if not, report the problem to the Secretary of Health and Human Services.

INVESTIGATIONS AND REVIEWS

The Secretary of Health and Human Services may conduct compliance reviews of the physician's office to determine whether the physician is complying with the privacy regulations. Physicians are expected to keep records and to submit compliance reports to the Secretary so that he may determine whether a physician is complying with the privacy regulations. Furthermore, the physician must permit access to information during his or her normal business hours unless the Secretary determines that such information may be hidden or destroyed. If so, the physician must permit access by the Secretary at any time. If the Secretary receives a complaint about a physician, the Secretary may investigate the complaint by reviewing the physician's policies and procedures. The physician must fully comply with the investigation.

STEPS TOWARD COMPLIANCE

Now that the privacy regulations are finalized, there are several steps that physicians may take today to get their practices in compliance mode. Physicians should do a comprehensive study of their practices to determine how patient information flows in and out of their organizations. If a physician has not done so already, he or she should quickly designate a compliance officer in order to begin determining what policies and procedures are necessary for compliance. It may be prudent for physicians to consider hiring a compliance officer from outside his or her current staff.

Physicians should evaluate the capacity of their current software and review the technical requirements for implementation of the transaction and code set requirements found in a separate section of the HIPAA regulations. Moreover, physicians need to consider budgetary concerns that will arise from the implementation of the expansive privacy regulations.

Tommy Thompson, the Secretary of DHHS, announced that DHHS will issue guidelines in the coming months on how the rule should be implemented in order to help providers with compliance. Thompson has stated that the guidelines will clarify some of the confusion regarding the impact the regulations might have on health care delivery and access.

PENALTIES

The stakes for noncompliance with the HIPAA privacy standards are high. A physician failing to comply with the regulations can be subject to civil or criminal liability. The civil monetary penalties are $100 per incident, up to $25,000 per person, per year, per standard. There will be federal criminal penalties for physicians that knowingly and improperly disclose protected health information or obtain protected health information under false pretenses. Penalties will be higher for actions designed to generate monetary gain. The criminal penalties range up to $50,000 and one year in prison for obtaining or disclosing protected health information; up to $100,000 and up to five years in prison for obtaining protected health information under false pretenses; or up to $250,000 and up to ten years in prison for obtaining or disclosing protected health information with the intent to sell, transfer or use it for commercial advantage, personal gain or malicious harm.

COMPLIANCE DEADLINE

Physicians will have two years in which to come into compliance with the privacy regulations. Thus, physicians must comply with the HIPAA regulations by April 14, 2003. Given the magnitude of these regulations, it is imperative that physicians begin drafting a compliance plan and begin practicing the implementation of that plan today in order to meet the 2003 deadline.

HIPAA PRIVACY GUIDANCE

William A. Sarraille, JD
Anna Spencer, JD

On Friday, July 6, 2001, the United States Department of Health and Human Services ("the Department") released its first guidance document on the Privacy Standards issued recently under the Health Insurance Portability and Accountability Act of 1996 ("HIPAA"). Aimed at trying to respond to growing fears among providers about the likely impact and cost of the Privacy Standards, the guidance provides some comfort on a number of issues and points to plans to address other areas of concern. Although helpful, the guidance still leaves many issues unanswered.

The guidance issued by the Department is clearly designed to address several topics that have been the subject of debate under the Privacy Standards. Each of the topics covered in the guidance includes a brief summary of the relevant rules and then provides questions and answers relevant to that issue.

In addition, as noted above, the document also outlines modifications that will be made in the future related to address various issues. The guidance notes that these modifications, unlike this guidance document, will consist of a formal rule-making under the Administrative Procedures Act, with proposed rules issued by the Department.

The guidance also notes that this document is intended as only one of several technical assistance materials to be issued and that the driving force, or the primary goal, behind the guidance to be issued is to ensure that the Privacy Standards do not interfere with access to or the quality of health care services.

The document indicates that one area where the Department will alter the existing Privacy Standards is prescriptions telephoned into pharmacies. The change will permit pharmacists to fill prescriptions telephoned in by a patient's doctor, even if the pharmacist has not secured a patient's written consent to use or disclose protected health information at the time the order is telephoned in to the pharmacy. The Department acknowledges the problem under the Privacy Standards, as currently drafted, that would not permit telephoned-in prescriptions without prior patient consent.

The guidance also clarifies that a pharmacist may provide advice about over-the-counter medications without obtaining a customer's prior consent, provided the pharmacist does not create or keep a record of the protected health information. The guidance notes that in this case, the only interaction or disclosure of information is a conversation between the pharmacist and customer.

The guidance acknowledges a problem with the current Privacy Standards when it comes to physicians and other providers to whom a patient is referred and their ability to use or act on any information they receive in the referral to schedule appointments, surgery or other procedures, if the patient has not already signed a consent for the provider receiving the referral to use that information. The Department will alter the Standards to allow the provider receiving the referral to use protected health information in connection with the referral before the patient comes into the office.

The third change relates to allowable communications. The guidance states that the Department will be changing the Standards to increase the confidence of Covered Entities (including providers) that they are free to engage in whatever communications are required for quick, effective, high quality health care, including routine oral communications with family members, discussions with staff about treatment decisions, and using patient names to locate patients within waiting areas.

Changes will also be proposed to increase providers' confi

dence that certain common practices, such as the use of sign-up sheets and x-ray light boards and the maintenance of patient medical charts at bedside, are not prohibited under the Privacy Standards.

Significantly, the guidance clarifies that a health care provider may rely on his or her professional judgment in determining whether there is an emergency which would justify foregoing the consent requirement, as is permitted by the Privacy Standards.

The guidance discusses the difference between consents, which are brief, simple documents which permit uses and disclosures for treatment, payment and health care operations, and authorizations, which are more detailed, specific documents which give covered entities permission to use protected health information for purposes generally other than treatment, payments or health care operations, or to disclose protected health information to a third party specified by an individual. For example, a Covered Entity would need an authorization for individuals to sell a patient mailing list, to disclose information to an employer for employment decisions, or to disclose information for eligibility for life insurance.

The guidance addressed the minimum necessary requirement, which is a major source of concern for providers. The Standards require, even where use of protected health information is permitted, that the use be the "minimum necessary" for the stated purpose. For routine disclosures, Covered Entities must have policies and procedures aimed at limiting protected health information disclosed to the minimum necessary. For non-routine disclosures, a Covered Entity must make and develop criteria to guide case-by-case determinations of minimum necessary.

In a positive development, the guidance emphasizes that the minimum necessary requirement should not impede the delivery of health care, because disclosures <u>for treatment purposes</u> between health care providers are explicitly exempted from minimum necessary requirements. Further, the Department states that the minimum necessary requirement is not intended as a strict standard — that Covered Entities need not limit uses and disclosures of information to those that are absolutely needed to serve a purpose. Instead, the Department announces a "reasonableness" standard that calls for an approach consistent with best practices and the guidelines used by many providers currently for limiting unnecessary sharing of medical information.

The guidance clarifies that the minimum necessary standard does not require Covered Entities to re-design their facilities, although it notes that Covered Entities may need to make certain adjustments to their facilities to minimize access to protected health information, such as isolating and locking file cabinets or record rooms. The guidance also notes that the minimum necessary requirement does not apply to disclosures to third parties, as authorized by an individual, or to disclosures by providers to federal or state agencies, such as the Social Security Administration.

The next topic covered by the guidance relates to oral communications. Here, the guidance emphasizes that Covered Entities are free to engage in oral communications as required for quick, effective and high quality health care. It notes that the Department will be making modifications to their Privacy Standards to make sure that this critical point is clear. Although the Privacy Standards require Covered Entities to take reasonable safeguards to prevent intentional or unintentional uses and disclosures in violation of the rule, the rule is not intended to prohibit providers from talking to each other and their patients.

It noted that sometimes "overheard communications" are unavoidable. For example, in a busy treatment area, it may be necessary for providers to speak loudly for treatment purposes. All the rule requires is that, where it is reasonable to do so, Covered Entities should use safeguards for oral communications, such as admonishing employees to speak quietly, where possible. It does not require sound-proofing of rooms, or other measures that eliminate all risk. Another example given of an adjustment a Covered Entity may take that could constitute a reasonable safeguard with respect to oral communications is adding a curtain or screen to areas where oral communications often occur between doctors and patients.

The next topic covered by the guidance relates to business associates, such as consultants, accountants, lawyers, billing companies, and others who supply services to providers and receive protected health information. The guidance clarifies that the Privacy Standards do not "pass through" the requirements of the rule to business associates. The "assurance" that Covered Entities must obtain prior to disclosure to business associates imposes obligations that are more narrow than the provisions of the rule. It also notes that a Covered Entity is not liable for privacy violations of a business associate. Instead, a Covered Entity may be considered to violate the Privacy Standards only if it fails to take curative steps when it becomes aware of a material breach by the business associate of its business associate agreement.

Another section in the guidance relates to parents and minors. This section provides assurances that, with a few miner exceptions, the Privacy Standards allow parents, when acting as their minor children's personal representative, to have access to their children's health information. It also clarifies that the rule does not provide rights to minors to obtain treatment without parental consent.

Marketing is another topic covered by the guidance. Here the guidance reviews the basic framework for the rules on marketing, where individual authorization is required, unless an exception applies. Marketing is broadly defined as a communication about a product or a service, a purpose of which is to encourage recipients of the communication to purchase or use the product or service.

Exceptions to the authorization requirement include: (1) face-to-face communication with an individual (for example, providing patients with samples during an office visit); (2) providing products of nominal value; or (3) a communication which concerns the health-related products and services of the Covered Entity, if the Covered Entity allows the individual to opt out of receiving further marketing materials and meets other requirements.

If an activity does not fall within the definition of marketing, but qualifies as a treatment or health care operation, all that is needed is a basic consent. For example, if the communication is part of a provider's treatment of a patient (such as recommending a specific brand name drug) or if the communication is made in the course of managing an individual's treatment (such as reminders for appointments), these communications are not considered marketing activities.

Finally, the guidance makes clear that the rule does not prevent issuing reports to consumer credit reporting agencies regarding delinquent accounts. This is because the rule's definition of permitted disclosures for payment purposes includes disclosures to consumer reporting agencies. These permitted disclosures are limited, however, to the following information about the individual: name and address, date of birth, Social Security Number, payment history, and account number. In addition, the disclosure of the name and address of the health care provider or health plan making the report is allowed.

With more guidance to come, providers struggling with the Privacy Standards will need to keep abreast of the Department's future efforts at clarification.

HIPAA STANDARDS FOR HEALTH CARE ELECTRONIC TRANSACTIONS

Erin Brisbay McMahon, JD

The Department for Health and Human Services (HHS) has issued the final rule that will govern electronic exchanges of financial and administrative information in the health care industry. The standards for health care electronic transactions were published in the August 17, 2000 edition of the *Federal Register* and can be found at http://aspe.hhs.gov/admnsimp/Index.htm. Technical corrections were published in the November 24, 2000 edition of the *Federal Register* and can be found at the same website address. HHS was required to adopt the standards pursuant to the administrative simplification provisions in the Health Insurance Portability and Accountability Act of 1996 (HIPAA). Congress and the regulators hope that the standards will simplify electronic transactions and result in cost savings throughout the industry. According to HHS, about 400 different formats currently exist for electronic health care claims. Once compliance with this rule is required (October 2002 for most health care entities to which the rule applies unless an extension plan is submitted), a physician will be able to submit an electronic claim in the standard transaction format to virtually any health plan in the United States and the health plan will have to accept it.

The rule applies to health care plans and health care clearinghouses. Health care plans include most private sector health plans that provide or pay the cost of medical care (e.g., managed care organizations), and all governmental health plans (including Medicare and Medicaid). Health care clearinghouses are public or private entities that either (1) take information received from another entity (e.g., a physician group practice) in a nonstandard format or containing nonstandard data content and convert it into a standard transaction or standard data elements for a receiving entity (e.g., a health plan) or (2) receive a standard transaction from another entity (e.g., a health plan) and convert it into nonstandard format or nonstandard data content for a receiving entity (e.g., a physician group practice). The rule also applies to all health care providers who transmit any health information in electronic form in connection with a transaction covered by the rule.

HEALTH CARE TRANSACTIONS SUBJECT TO THE RULE

Under the rule, an electronic transaction involves information exchanges between two parties to carry out financial or administrative activities related to health care. Transactions subject to the rule include the following types of electronic data interchange:

- Health claims and equivalent encounter information
- Enrollment and disenrollment in a health plan
- Eligibility for a health plan
- Health care payment and remittance advice
- Health plan premium payments
- Health claim status
- Referral certification and authorization
- Coordination of benefits

Thus, health plans will be able to pay physicians, authorize services, certify referrals, and coordinate benefits using a standard electronic format for each transaction. Physicians also will be able to use a standard format to determine a patient's eligibility for insurance coverage, file a claim, ask about the status of a claim, request authorizations for services or specialist referrals, and receive electronic remittances to post receivables. HHS will eventually adopt standards for claims attachments and the first report of injury.

Conflicting state laws will be superseded by the standards, although HHS is developing an exception process pursuant to HIPAA. Specific exceptions to the standards may also be allowed for entities wishing to test (1) a modification to the existing standard or (2) a different standard.

STANDARDS

HIPAA required HHS to adopt data and format standards, if possible, that were developed by private sector standards development organizations accredited by the American National Standards Institute (ANSI). ANSI Accredited Standards Committee (ASC) X12N standards, Version 4010, were adopted for all transactions except retail pharmacy transactions, which will be governed by the National Council for Prescription Drugs Programs (NCPDP) standards, the NCPDP Telecommunications Standard Format Version 5.1 and NCPDP Batch Standard Version 1.0.

When conducting a transaction covered by the rule, physicians are required to use applicable medical data code sets as specified in the implementation specification that is valid at the time the health care is furnished. Under the rule, a "code set" is any set of codes used for encoding data elements, such as tables of terms, medical concepts, medical diagnostic codes, or medical procedure codes. The standard medical data code sets that must be used to code standard transactions are as follows:

International Classification of Diseases, 9th Edition, Clinical Modification, (ICD-9-CM), Volumes 1 and 2 (including The Official ICD-9-CM Guidelines for Coding and Reporting), as maintained and distributed by HHS, for the following conditions:

- Diseases.
- Injuries.
- Impairments.
- Other health problems and their manifestations.
- Causes of injury, disease, impairment, or other health problems.

International Classification of Diseases, 9th Edition, Clinical Modification, Volume 3 Procedures (including the Official ICD-9-CM Guidelines for Coding and Reporting), as maintained and distributed by HHS, for the following procedures or other actions taken for diseases, injuries, and impairments on hospital inpatients reported by hospitals:

- Prevention.
- Diagnosis.
- Treatment.
- Management.

National Drug Codes (NDC), as maintained and distributed by HHS, in collaboration with drug manufacturers, for the following:

- Drugs.
- Biologics.

Note : According to a letter dated May 29, 2001 from Tommy Thompson, Secretary of HHS, to John Lumpkin, Chair of the National Committee on Vital and Health Statistics, drugs and biologics will be covered by HCPCS (see below) because of the difficulty of switching to the NDC. As of this writing, the regulations implementing this change have not been proposed.

Code on Dental Procedures and Nomenclature, as maintained and distributed by the American Dental Association, for dental services.

The combination of ***Health Care Financing Administration Common Procedure Coding System (HCPCS),*** as maintained and distributed by HHS, and ***Current Procedural Terminology, Fourth Edition (CPT-4),*** as maintained and distributed by the American Medical Association, for physician services and other health care services. These services include, but are not limited to, the following:

- Physician services.
- Physical and occupational therapy services.
- Radiologic procedures.
- Clinical laboratory tests.
- Other medical diagnostic procedures.
- Hearing and vision services.
- Transportation services including ambulance.

The ***Health Care Financing Administration Common Procedure Coding System (HCPCS),*** as maintained and distributed by HHS, for all other substances, equipment, supplies, or other items used in health care services. These items include, but are not limited to, the following:

- Medical supplies.
- Orthotic and prosthetic devices.
- Durable medical equipment.

Local and proprietary codes currently used by health plans can no longer be used in electronic transactions governed by the rule after the compliance date (unless an extension plan is submitted, the compliance date is October 16, 2002, except for small health plans, which have until October 16, 2003). The Implementation Guides and Data Dictionaries for Transactions Standards can be downloaded from http://aspe.hhs.gov/admnsimp/Index.htm.

CLEARINGHOUSES

Physicians may choose to use a business associate (a person who performs an activity falling under the rule on behalf of the physician), including a health care clearinghouse, to conduct transactions covered by the rule. However, the physician must contractually require the business associate (1) to comply with all applicable requirements of the rule and (2) to insist via written contract that the business associate's agents and subcontractors comply with the rule. Health care clearinghouses may prove useful to physicians who prefer to store data in a format that does not translate into a standard transaction.

INTRACORPORATE TRANSACTIONS

When conducting electronic transactions within corporate boundaries, two questions must be asked to determine if a standard format must be used:

(1) Is the transaction initiated by a health plan, clearinghouse, or provider subject to the rule or its business associate? If not, the standard need not be followed.

(2) Is the transaction one for which the Secretary has adopted a standard? If so, the standard has to be used. If not, then the standard need not be followed. For purposes of this question, the definitions of the transactions themselves, as stipulated in subparts K-R of the regulation, must be consulted to determine if the Secretary has adopted a standard for the transaction.

MODES OF TRANSMISSION

The rule applies to transactions sent over the Internet. However, a physician using a "direct data entry" process, where data are directly keyed into a health plan's computer using dumb terminals or computer browser screens, must comply with the data requirements of the applicable standard, but need not comply with the format portion of the standard.

HEALTH CARE CLAIMS

The rule does not require physicians to submit claims transactions electronically, but all transactions submitted electronically must comply with the standards. For example, a physician could send an electronic health care claim standard transaction for Patient A to health plan Z, and could also send a paper claim for patient B to health plan Z. The same physician could send an electronic health care claim standard transaction to health plan S and send paper claims to health plan T.

Under HIPAA, health plans subject to the rule must accept the standard claim submitted electronically. They cannot:

- require physicians to make changes or additions to the standard claim;
- delay or reject a transaction, or attempt to adversely affect a physician practice or the transaction, because the transaction is a standard one;
- reject a standard transaction on the basis that it contains data elements not needed or used by the health plan; or
- offer incentives for physicians to conduct a transaction covered by the rule as a direct data entry.

Further, health plans that operate as clearinghouses or that require a physician to use a clearinghouse to receive, process, or transmit a standard transaction cannot charge fees or costs in excess of the fees or costs for normal telecommunications that a physician practice incurs when it directly transmits or receives a standard transaction to or from a health plan.

Until a standard is adopted for electronic health claims attachments and compliance is required with that standard, health plans can continue to require health claim attachments to be submitted on paper.

Health plans may continue to provide physicians with information regarding their processing or adjudication policies. However, this information cannot be used to modify a standard adopted by HHS and cannot include:

- instructions to change the definition, data condition, or use of a data element or segment in a standard;
- requests for data elements or segments not in the maximum defined data set in the applicable implementation guide;
- requests for codes or data elements that are either marked "not used" in the implementation specifications or are not in the standard's implementation specifications; or
- rules that change the meaning or intent of a standard's implementation specifications.

Similarly, provider contracts with health plans cannot provide for any of the above. This means that physicians choosing to engage in electronic transactions covered by the rule must review their provider contracts with health plans and revise them so that renewals of the contracts occurring on and after October 16, 2002 state that electronic standard transactions must comply with the regulation.

It is important to note that while health plans covered by the rule must accept and process any claim that meets the national standard, they do not have to pay the claim if it is not for a covered service. HHS gives the following example: Medicare currently requires providers to bill for certain services only in specified circumstances. In October 2002, however, Medicare will have to process all claims that meet HIPAA specifications. This does not mean that Medicare has to change a payment policy that denies coverage for cosmetic face lifts; if a claim for a face lift for cosmetic purposes is received after the compliance date, Medicare will have to process the bill, but will not have to pay the claim if its payment policy then in force denies such a claim as a noncovered service.

ENFORCEMENT AND IMPLEMENTATION

HIPAA gives the Secretary of HHS the authority to impose monetary penalties for failure to comply with a standard. The Secretary is required by statute to impose penalties of not more than $100 per violation on any person or entity who fails to comply with a standard. However, the total amount imposed on any one person in each calendar year cannot exceed $25,000 for violations of one requirement. The Secretary will eventually adopt a regulation addressing specific enforcement procedures.

In an HHS press release dated August 11, 2000, Secretary Shalala cautioned that this rule was released under the assumption that, by the compliance date, HHS' proposed regulation on privacy of medical records (November 3, 1999 *Federal Register*) would also be in effect, or that Congress would have enacted such protections. The privacy rule was issued as a final rule on December 28, 2000, but will not be enforced until April 14, 2003. During the Clinton administration, HHS said it would seriously consider suspending or withdrawing the transaction regulation, pending appropriate privacy protections. The Bush administration appears to wish to proceed with enforcement of the transaction regulation even though it precedes the compliance date of the privacy regulation.

ADMINISTRATIVE SIMPLIFICATION COMPLIANCE ACT

On December 27, 2001, President Bush signed into law H.R. 3323, the Administrative Simplification Compliance Act (Public Law 107-105). This law provides for a one-year extension of the date for complying with the HIPAA standard transactions and code set requirements (to October 16, 2003) for any health care plan (except small plans), health care clearinghouse, or health care provider that submits to HHS a plan of how the plan, clearinghouse, or provider will come into compliance with the requirements by October 16, 2003.

The plan must be submitted by October 15, 2002 and shall summarize the following:

- An analysis reflecting the extent to which, and the reasons why, the person is not in compliance.
- A budget, schedule, work plan, and implementation strategy for achieving compliance.
- Whether the person plans to use or might use a contractor or other vendor to assist the person in achieving compliance.
- ·A timeframe for testing that begins not later than April 16, 2003.

The law also requires HHS to develop and promulgate a model compliance form for the plan by March 31, 2002, and to allow for compliance plans to be submitted electronically. This legislation does not change the compliance deadlines for the Privacy Rule (April 14, 2003 for all covered entities except small health plans; April 14, 2004 for small health plans). Failure to comply with the transactions regulation by October 16, 2002 or to submit an extension plan by October 15, 2002 can result in exclusion of participation in Medicare.

The law also requires that, by October16, 2003, providers stop submitting paper claims and submit only electronic claims to Medicare. There are waivers for certain small providers or if no method exists for electronic submission of claims by October 16, 2003.

Additional information on the administrative simplification regulations of HIPAA, as well as a "Frequently Asked Questions" section on the electronic transactions standards rule, can be found at http://aspe.hhs.gov/admnsimp/Index.htm.

IMPLEMENTATION OF THE HIPAA PRIVACY STANDARDS: REAL LIFE EXAMPLES

William A. Sarraille, JD
Anna Spencer, JD
Jerome T. Levy, JD
Connie Raffa, JD
Eileen Kahaner, JD
Kathleen Cheney, JD

Although there is, at this point, a good deal of information available about the basic prohibitions and obligations imposed by the Privacy Standards (the Standards) under the Health Insurance Portability and Accountability Act (HIPAA), relatively little has been published on how the Standards will affect the day-to-day operations of various types of health care operations in specific situations, despite the almost universal acknowledgment that the Standards will, in fact, have a sweeping effect on those operations. In our presentations on the Standards for international pain practices, hospitals, ambulatory surgery centers, and others, we have noted the frustration of providers who have expressed a desire to "get beyond the basics" and to see, in tangible ways, how specific operations and recurrent issues will have to be confronted in light of the Standards. Accordingly, we have shifted many of our presentations to ones that focus on hypotheticals that deal with the difficult and quite specific issues which our clients are beginning to struggle with from a HIPAA compliance perspective. This article is designed to take some of the hypotheticals that we have discussed and present them to our readership. Our hope is that this discussion will begin to help international pain practices really understand the specific impact of HIPAA on their day-to-day operations.

Although the need to move forward quickly with changes designed to comply with the HIPAA Standards is clear, organizations, other than small health plans, will have until April 14, 2003 to comply with those Standards. Small health plans will have until April 14, 2004. As many international pain practices are realizing, the compliance deadline, despite being the better part of two years away, is frighteningly close in light of how much needs to be accomplished to ensure compliance.

The Department of Health and Human Services, acting with the Office of Civil Rights, has pledged to release a series of guidance documents over the next twelve months or so, which should measurably improve the difficult task of taking the Standards' often quite generalized language. In addition, there is the prospect that some not insignificant modifications to the Standards themselves will be made on consent, the minimum necessary, and other selected components of the Standards. Still, the need to press forward with implementation now is all too clear.

ARE YOU A COVERED ENTITY?

Pain Associates is a small practice that keeps its medical records on paper and in file drawers. It does not have any electronic medical records; it only uses its computer for accounting, scheduling and other fairly limited purposes.

Do the Standards apply to Pain Associates? What if the practice hires a billing company which files electronic health care claims on its behalf?

The Standards only apply to covered entities which is defined to include health plans, health care clearinghouse and those health care providers who engage in "electronic standard transactions" such as filing health care claims electronically. So, based on the facts presented here, Pain Associates is not a covered entity.

However, if Pain Associates were to hire a billing company to engage in standard transactions on its behalf, the Standards would apply to the practice. Having a billing company submit bills electronically for the practice would clearly convert Pain Associates into a covered entity. The practice may not escape the requirements of the rule by outsourcing the billing function. In addition, even though the practice itself only holds protected health information (PHI) in paper records, the Standards would protect the use and disclosure of PHI contained in those records, as well as the electronic records held by the billing company. This is because the definition of PHI includes any health information, in whatever form, which identifies an individual.

Additionally, if the practice submits one health care claim electronically itself, the Privacy Standards would apply to the practice. There is no minimum threshold for the number of claims submitted by a practice electronically for the requirements of the Standards to be triggered. So, hypothetically, if a covered entity engages in just one standard electronic transaction, it must meet the requirements of the Standards.

MISUSE OF PHI IN A GROUP HEALTH PLAN

The Angel City Physician Clinic, which has 250 employees, including three interventional pain physicians establishes a group health plan for the benefit of its employees. A couple of employees of the company perform administrative functions for the group health plan. They sometimes have access to PHI as a consequence. One of these employees learns that someone in the company has contracted hepatitis and tells her boss about the condition. The Clinic Administrator, fearful of the cost implications of the employee's condition, decides to include the employee in a reduction in force.

Would this disclosure by the group health plan violate the Standards?

Yes. It is often the case that ERISA group health plans do not have their own employees, so employees of the plan sponsor are named as fiduciaries to undertake administrative duties. This relationship poses the danger that information related to the health condition of employees will be improperly shared between the health plan and the plan sponsor. The rule permits group health plans to disclose PHI to plan sponsors for plan administration purposes, but not for employment-related actions. Thus, the disclosure by the employee working in plan administration to the boss for reasons other than plan administration would be a clear violation of the Standards. The consequences of such a violation to the company are enormous, given the criminal sanctions under the Standards.

IDENTIFYING BUSINESS ASSOCIATES

Comprehensive Pain Care, P.A. hires a law firm to defend it in a malpractice case. Ambulatory Surgery Centers, Inc. discloses PHI to a health plan for payment purposes.

Which of these entities, the law firm or the health plan, would be considered a business associate under the Standards such that a business associate contract would be required?

The law firm. A business associate is defined under the rule as an entity which (1) performs a function involving PHI *for or on behalf of* a covered entity or (2) provides specified services, such as legal and accounting services which involve the disclosure of PHI, *to* a covered entity. The law firm, because it would be defending the practice in a legal action and the practice would have to disclose PHI to the law firm to enable it to do that, is a business associate. Therefore, the law firm and the practice would have to enter into a contract which protects the use and disclosure of PHI by the law firm before disclosure is made. The health plan would not be a business associate of the ambulatory surgery center because it would not be performing a function for or on behalf of the ASC or providing one of the specified services to it. When it pays for services performed by the ASC, it is undertaking a task for its own business purposes, not as a contractor to the ASC.

COVERED ENTITY'S RESPONSIBILITY FOR BUSINESS ASSOCIATE'S MISUSE OF PHI

An interventional pain practice hires an accounting firm to provide it with on-going analysis of its operations to better improve its efficiency and profitability. The accounting firm issues a report to the practice. An employee of the accounting firm uses the PHI his employer gathered during the contract and faxes it to a number that he thinks is one used by the practice. Unfortunately, it is not. It is the fax number of the patient's brother, who was listed as a contact for the patient on the medical records in the event of an emergency.

Would the practice be subject to penalties under the rule for the actions of the accounting firm and its employee?

It depends. Clearly, the disclosure of PHI by the accounting firm would violate the terms of the business associate contract as the disclosure was not made for the purposes of improving the business operations of the hospital. Under the Standards, covered entities are not required to actively monitor their business associates, but they will be held responsible for business associate violations where they have knowledge of an improper use or disclosure by the business associate, and fail to take appropriate corrective action. Assuming the practice was not aware of the disclosure of its PHI and took appropriate corrective action once (and if it became aware of the misuse of the PHI), the practice would not have violated the Standards.

DE-IDENTIFYING INFORMATION

A consulting company, We Have All the Answers, Inc., consults with an interventional pain practice on how it may improve its billings and collections. In order to do this, the consulting company must have access to practice bills and the medical information contained in the bills. If the practice discloses this information to the consulting company, it must have patient consent and a business associate contract which allows the disclosure. Further, it must ensure that it provides the minimum necessary PHI to accomplish the billing and collection review.

Does the practice have another option besides the above?

Yes. The practice could create de-identified information and provide only that information to the consulting company. The practice would need to remove the name, telephone number, fax number, address, social security number, medical record number, photographic image and any other identifier from the record which could be used to identify an individual. Or, it could remove fewer identifiers than is required to meet this safe harbor, if a person with appropriate statistical and scientific knowledge determines that the risk of identification would be small. The Standards do not apply to the use and disclosure of de-identified information. So, the practice could disclose the de-identified information to anyone for any purpose assuming that it did not also disclose the key to the information.

If the consulting company needed to be able to refer the practice to particular health records, the practice could assign dummy numbers for that purpose which the practice could later use to match information with a particular record. Covered entities may use codes and similar means of marking records so that they may be linked or later re-identified, if the code does not contain information about the subject of the individual (such as a code that is derivative of an individual's social security number). The covered entity is also prohibited from disclosing the mechanism for re-identification, such as tables, algorithms, or other tools that could be used to link the information.

The problem with the de-identification approach, of course, is that it can be so costly to employ. The cost grows with the number and volume of documents that must be "scrubbed."

DISCLOSURES TO OVERSIGHT AGENCIES

An insurance company acts as the Part B Carrier to Pain Consultants, P.A. The physician practice submits a large number of Medicare claims for a particular injection procedure so that the practice's utilization rates of this procedure appear aberrant, even though they are not. The Carrier suspects billing fraud and requests medical records from the practice as part of a post-payment audit.

May the practice disclose this information without permission from the patient under the Privacy Standards?

Yes. The Privacy Standards permit covered entities to disclose PHI to health oversight agencies, such as the OIG and those who act on behalf of such agencies for the purposes of oversight activities, without obtaining permission (consent, verbal agreement or authorization) from the individual who is the subject of the records. Therefore, the disclosure of PHI by the physician practice to the Carrier would not violate the Standards.

LEGAL REQUESTS FOR INFORMATION

A person injured in a car crash is treated at an ambulatory surgery center. The ASC receives a request for medical records from an attorney who represents the driver in the automobile accident. The request states that the attorney represents the driver who has been sued for negligence by the patient and to send the records to the lawyer within 15 days of receipt of the letter.

May the center disclose the patient's records to the attorney without an authorization from the patient?

No. Although there is a category of permissible uses and disclosure which permits the use and disclosure of PHI for judicial and administrative purposes without patient permission, the rule permits disclosure only upon (1) an order from a court or administrative tribunal OR (2) upon proof that the person seeking disclosure attempted to notify the individual who is the subject of the information and the individual did not object, or that a qualified protective order was obtained. It does not matter that state law might permit the disclosure under the theory that the patient waives his right to confidentiality by filing suit in a claim that puts his health condition at issue. To release the information, the patient would have to sign a specific authorization for this purpose.

WHAT ABOUT MARKETING AND FUNDRAISING?

A large community hospital has recently established a new pain center. The hospital sends flyers announcing the new pain center to all persons who have been admitted to the hospital within the past six years. It also accesses it records to determine who has received pain treatments at the hospital in the past six years. These individuals receive solicitations to try and raise money for the development of the new pain center. The hospital also posts on its web site a positive testimonial from a patient who received injections at the center, but does not obtain the individual's authorization to do so.

Are these activities permitted under the Privacy Standards?

The Standards define marketing as a communication about a product or service designed to encourage the recipient of the communication to purchase or use the product or service. In response to significant comments to the Standards, the Standards permit numerous forms of marketing activities without the need for an individual authorization. For instance, a covered entity may use and disclose protected health information for marketing its health-related products and services if certain requirements are met. First, the communication must identify the covered entity, state if the covered entity will be paid for making the communication, and state that the individual may opt-out of future communications. Additionally, if the covered entity has used PHI to target individuals based upon their health status, the covered entity must make a determination that the service being advertised would be beneficial to the individual. It also must explain why the individual has been targeted to receive the flyers.

In order to be compliant with the rules, all flyers announcing the pain center must specifically identify the hospital. In addition, the flyers should indicate how the recipient of the flyer may opt out of future communications.

It would be inappropriate for the hospital to target past pain patients for pain center solicitations unless the patient had signed an individual authorization specific to the intended use. It is important to distinguish marketing from fundraising activities under these rules. Fundraising is a solicitation for the purpose of raising funds to benefit a covered entity. In comparison to marketing activities, fundraising activities are much more restricted under the Privacy Standards. According to the rules, general fundraising may not be targeted to an individual based upon the past health status of the individual. Instead, PHI used for fundraising, without a specific patient authorization, must be limited to demographic information and dates of treatment. Diagnosis or nature of the services received is not considered "demographic information." Demographic information includes name, address and other contact information, age, gender and insurance status.

Finally, under the new Standards, it is impermissible to post a patient testimonial without permission from the individual. This use requires a specific written authorization from the individual.

PARTICIPATION ON A PROVIDER COMMITTEE

One of the physicians with staff privileges at a community hospital is asked to participate in the hospital's quality assurance reviews.

May the physician participate in this review of PHI, even though the review does not involve the physician's own patients?

Yes. Under the Standards, providers in an organized health care arrangement may share information to support the health care operations of the enterprise, even though the sharing may not directly benefit a particular participant of the arrangement. Organized health care arrangements are arrangements which involve clinical or operational integration among legally separate covered entities. Individuals who obtain services from them have an expectation that operations are integrated and jointly managed.

The definition of health care operations includes quality assessment and improvement activities of a covered entity or of an organized health care arrangement in which a covered entity participates. Therefore, the physician on staff at the hospital may review information containing PHI for quality assurance purposes, even though the information does not relate to his own patients.

PICKING UP MEDICATIONS FOR A FRIEND

An elderly woman is bedridden and is unable to leave the house to pick up her pain medication. She calls a friend of hers and asks her to pick up her prescription for her. Her friend goes to the pharmacy and asks to pick up the woman's medication.

May the pharmacist give the prescription medication to the friend?

Yes. One of the permissible disclosures under the Standards is for disclosures to persons assisting in a patient's care. If an individual is present, this type of disclosure may be made, where the covered entity simply obtains the affected individual's oral agreement. The agreement does not have to be written; it may even be inferred from the circumstances. If an individual is not present, or is incapacitated, a covered entity may release the information if it determines, in the exercise of its reasonable professional judgment, that the disclosure is in the best interests of the patient and it discloses only the PHI relevant to the person's involvement in the patient's care. So, the pharmacist in this example may disclose PHI to the patient's friend if it is in the patient's best interests, but it must restrict the amount of information given about the patient.

Of course, the rule leaves open exactly what information could be disclosed to a friend in this kind of situation. It is common today for pharmacists to attach on the outside of a bag containing the medication a sheet which describes what the medication is for, the instructions for its use and information about combining the medication with other medications the patient may be taking. In a case like the one presented here, the pharmacist might be under an obligation to place this sort of information within the bag.

What information could be disclosed to the friend would

probably depend on the circumstances. If a friend or spouse had to assist the patient with taking the medication, the pharmacist could probably disclose more information regarding the recommended doses and need for the medication.

DISCLOSURES FOR LAW ENFORCEMENT PURPOSES

An interventional pain management physician prescribes narcotics for some of his patients that suffer from chronic pain. One day, an agent from the Drug Enforcement Agency (DEA) appears at the physician's office with a subpoena for some of the physician's medical records. The physician has been targeted for investigation because the physician allegedly has irregular patterns of prescribing controlling substances.

May the physician release PHI as requested by the DEA agent consistent with the Privacy Standards?

Under the Privacy Standards, disclosures to law enforcement agents are permissible without individual authorization only under certain circumstances. One circumstance where it is permissible for a provider to disclose PHI to law enforcement officials is where the disclosure is required by law. A covered entity may disclose PHI in compliance with a court order or a court-ordered warrant, or a subpoena or summons issued by a judicial officer, or a grand jury subpoena. So, it would clearly be permissible for the pain physician in our hypothetical to disclose the information requested by the DEA agent.

WHAT IS THE NOTICE OF PRIVATE PRACTICE?

Mr. Green, a 38-year-old man, is referred to Dr. Smith for evaluation of chronic pain. In addition to other elements of the plan, Dr. Smith assesses the medical management and finds the patient is not as compliant as he should be with his medications. Dr.Smith also learns that Mr. Green has a tendency to miss appointments. To improve Mr. Green's compliance, involving the lower back Dr. Smith's group has started mailing medication and appointment reminders to existing patients. Like other conscientious physician groups, Dr. Smith's practice also is concerned about its own compliance activities. As a result, the practice has decided to contract with an outside law firm to coordinate annual chart audits. The practice also has hired an external billing company to perform billing and collection services on behalf of the practice. When Mr. Green presents at the admission's window of Dr. Smith's practice, he is given a "Notice of Privacy Practices."

Why is he given this document and what is it?

The Privacy Standards require covered entities, such as physician practices, to develop a "Notice of Privacy Practices" that must be shared with any individual who provides PHI to the covered entity. It must be provided to a patient in writing no later than the first time that the practice sees the patient after the Privacy Standards implementation deadline of April 14, 2003.

The Notice of Privacy Practices is a complete, and detailed description of a covered entity's possible uses and disclosures of PHI. It explains how the provider will use and disclose PHI obtained from a patient. The Notice also explains the rights of individuals under the Privacy Standards and the legal obligations of the covered entity with respect to PHI. In general, health care providers must post the Notice prominently, and must furnish a copy to each individual when the individual first receives care.

The detailed elements that must be contained within the Notice are specified in the Privacy Standards. While many of the elements appear generic, every covered entity must customize the Notice to its own behavior.

The Notice must include a description and at least one example of the types of uses and disclosures that the covered entity expects to make. Treatment, payment, and health care operations each require a separate example. Dr. Smith's Notice might reference the outside billing company or auditor as an expected recipient of Mr. Green's PHI.

Since the practice contacts patients with appointment reminders, Dr. Smith's Notice also will need a separate explanation about this intended use. Another separate statement also would be required if the practice intended to send individuals information about treatment alternatives, or other services that may be of interest.

The Notice also must include a general description of other permitted uses for which neither written consent nor an authorization are required. This includes disclosure to individuals involved in the patient's care or payment related to the individual's care, such as family members, relatives, or close personal friends. It also includes a general discussion of the public policy exceptions to the consent/agreement/authorization requirements.

Dr. Smith's practice, like all covered entities, must establish policies and procedures to implement the individual rights mandated under the Privacy Standards. The Notice must explain these rights and how an individual may exercise them.

Finally, the Notice must contain certain contact information about how to file a complaint with the Secretary of the Department of Health and Human Services and the health care provider, and must provide the name and telephone number of a person at the covered entity who may be contacted for more information about the Privacy Standards.

Covered entities should think carefully when developing their Notice. Making revisions may result in significant costs because covered entities must inform individuals when the Notice is amended and offer them a revised Notice. It is important to draft this document correctly in the first instance.

PSYCHOTHERAPY NOTES

A psychologist provides psychotherapy as part of Pain Consultants, P.A. One of the patients of the psychologist is a resident of a Nursing Facility. The Nursing Facility has requested copies of the psychotherapy records to substantiate the medical necessity of the services. The pain practice submits bills to Medicare electronically and is a covered entity under the Standards.

Is the psychologist permitted to disclose his or her psychotherapy notes to the Nursing Facility?

No, unless an authorization is obtained. In general, a covered entity must obtain an authorization for any use or disclosure of psychotherapy notes. There are limited exceptions to this rule, none of which are applicable here. Psychotherapy notes are notes kept by mental health professionals to document or analyze the contents of conversations during private, group, or family counseling sessions and are separated from the rest of an individual's medical record. Psychotherapy notes exclude medication prescription and monitoring, counseling session start and stop times, the modalities and frequencies of treatment furnished, results of clinical tests, and any summary of diagnosis, functional status, the treatment plan, symptoms, prognosis, and progress to date. Because the term psychotherapy notes is defined to exclude information necessary for treatment and payment, it was thought that there should be little need to use or disclose the notes of conversations between psychotherapists and their patients. In this way, the Privacy Standards provide special protections to psychotherapy notes.

A valid authorization to disclose psychotherapy notes must contain at least the following elements:

- a description of the notes to be disclosed;
- the name of the psychotherapist being authorized to make the requested disclosure;
- the name or identity of the person or class or persons to whom the disclosure is to be made;
- an expiration date or expiration event;
- a statement of the individual's right to revoke the authorization in writing and the exceptions to the right to revoke;
- a statement that information used or disclosed pursuant to the authorization may be subject to redisclosure by the recipient and no longer be protected by the privacy Standards;
- signature of the individual and date; and
- if the authorization is signed by a personal representative, a description of such representative's authority to act for the individual.

FAMILY MEMBERS INVOLVED IN CARE COMMUNICATIONS

Mrs. Johnson is 60 years old, has chronic pain, heart disease, diabetes, arthritis, depression, and some hearing loss. The patient's primary language is Spanish. Although the patient understands most English and can speak some English, the patient is most comfortable in her native language. The patient's daughter has always handled patient's affairs, including communicating with her mother's health care providers on symptoms, course of treatment, medication, tests, obtaining copies of medical records, and all medical decisions. The daughter also translates for the mother when appropriate during medical visits and about follow-up decisions.

How do the HIPAA Privacy standards impact the daughter's role in managing her mother's care?

The health care entities (insurance payors, nursing home, home health agencies, physicians, etc.) must make sure that there is appropriate permission from the patient for information to be shared with the daughter. In a case such as this, a verbal agreement from the patient should be sufficient. The consent may also be inferred by the circumstances. The minimum necessary restriction would still apply, however.

CONCLUSION

The Privacy Standards will pose many implementation challenges, but with more information about how to respond to specific situations, those implementation challenges may seem somewhat less daunting.

STARK II RULES AND INTERVENTIONAL PAIN MEDICINE

William A. Sarraille, JD

After many delays and much anticipation, the Health Care Financing Administration (HCFA) has released Phase I of its Stark II final rules. Although the final rules are being hailed for the relief they have brought to a series of problems under the Federal Physician Self-Referral Statute, a number of difficult questions remain. This article summarizes the most important portions of the Stark II rules, which promise to reshape physician contracting and compensation in interventional pain physician services.

BACKGROUND

The original Stark Law, commonly referred to as "Stark I," was enacted in 1989. Stark I prohibited a physician from ordering a clinical laboratory test or service from an entity with which the physician, or an immediate family member, had a financial relationship if the test or service was reimbursable by Medicare, unless an exception to the law applies. The term "financial relationship" includes both investment interests and compensation arrangements. Stark I became effective on January 1, 1992.

The Stark Law was amended in 1993. The amendments are commonly referred to as "Stark II." Stark II extended the referral prohibition to services reimbursable under Medicaid and greatly expanded the list of items and services covered by the law i.e., "designated health services" or "DHS". The Stark II expansion had a tremendous effect on interventional pain physicians, precisely because of the breadth of the list of designated heath services added by the amendment. Those services included hospital outpatient and inpatient services, physical therapy services, radiology services, and outpatient prescription drugs. Stark II became effective on January 1, 1995.

PHASE I

As indicated above, HCFA will issue the final Stark rules in two phases. The rules published on Jan. 4, 2001 represent "Phase I" and are focused mainly on the scope of the referral prohibition, the in-office ancillary services exception for group practices, and certain new exceptions. Phase II, in turn, will focus on the remaining provisions in the statute, largely compensation exception issues and the statute's application to Medicaid. Although a "60-day" hold has been placed on the Stark II regulations by the Bush Administration, no significant change of the Phase I provisions is anticipated.

Because of the significant changes made in Phase I, HCFA published these final rules with a 90-day comment period. HCFA will accept comments on Phase I until April 4, 2001. The American Society of Interventional Pain Physicians (ASIPP) will be filing comments. According to Phase I, these comments will be incorporated in Phase II, which HCFA claims it will publish shortly afterwards. Obviously, Phase II will not be published until at least the end of the comment period for Phase I, and likely substantially after that. This could create an unfortunate situation where the effective date for the delayed implementation of some Phase I obligations may occur before the Phase II rules are issued, which, in several cases, may be needed to clarify issues that relate to Phase I.

In order to allow for both the comment period and time for providers "engaged in business arrangements affected by Phase I . . . to restructure those arrangements to comply" with the final Stark rules, HCFA has generally delayed the effective date of new requirements created by Phase I for one year. Because HCFA also says that the statute and statutory requirements are currently effective, there is a good deal of uncertainty surrounding what requirements are statutory and, therefore, currently in effect, and what requirements are "new" and not yet effective.

REFERRAL DEFINITION ISSUES

Under Phase I of the Stark regulations, a "referral" means either of the following:

1. A request by a physician for, or ordering of, or certifying or recertifying of the need for, any designated health service, including a request for a consultation with another physician, as well as any test or procedure ordered by or to be performed by (or under the supervision of) that other physician; or
2. A request by a physician that includes the provision of any designated health service or the establishment of a plan of care by a physician that includes the provision of such a designated health service, or the certifying or recertifying of the need for such a designated health service.

Phase I of the regulations makes clear that the term "referral" does not include a designated health service ordered and personally performed by the same physician. If an interventional pain physician were to personally perform a radiology technical component (such as fluoroscopy) or a related professional component service, those services would not involve a "referral" within the meaning of the Stark Law. In the preamble to the Phase I regulations, however, HCFA states that services performed by others, including the ordering physician's employee, or other physicians in the practice, are still included in the definition of referral.

Despite this, HCFA noted that it recognizes that, in many cases, services performed by a physician's employees are, for practical purposes, tantamount to services performed by the physician. The example HCFA used is a physician's assistant applying a neck brace ordered by a physician for an individual when the face-to-face physical examination by the physician, indicated the need for the adjusted neck brace. HCFA noted that it specifically seeks comments as to whether services performed by a physician's employees should be treated as the physician's personally performed services. ASIPP will be submitting comments on this issue as well.

HCFA also stated that it was establishing an exception for indirect and oral referrals. An interventional pain physician may have a patient referred by an orthopedic surgeon with whom the pain physician has a financial relationship, but the patient does not say that he was referred by the orthopedic surgeon. When there is no written order or other documentation of the referral, the provider of designated health services will only be held responsible for the indirect or oral referral when it knows or has reason to suspect the identity of the physician who prescribed or ordered the designated health service or made the referral.

HCFA also stated that a referral by a nurse practitioner or physician assistant could be imputed to an employer physician if the physician controls or influences the nonphysician's referral. HCFA noted that these nonphysicians may not always act independently of their employers. Clearly, when these nonphysician services are billed incident to an interventional pain physician's or another physician's services, an imputation will be made.

HCFA further noted that the direction or steering of a patient to an entity does not need to be in writing for a "referral" to occur. Nor does it have to be absolute. Rather, it need only be reasonably intended to result in the patient receiving the service from the entity. HCFA noted that a physician can make a referral of DHS to an entity, even though the referral is first directed or routed through another physician or entity, if the physician has reason to know the identity of the actual provider of the service.

"VOLUME OR VALUE" OF REFERRALS AND "OTHER BUSINESSGENERATED" STANDARDS

Virtually all of the noteworthy exceptions to the Stark Law include a requirement that prohibits payments related to the volume or value of referrals or other business generated between the parties. In a significant departure from the proposed rules, HCFA now takes the position that time-based or unit-of-service-based payments do not necessarily violate this requirement and may be protected, so long as the payment per unit is at fair market value at inception and does not subsequently change during the term in any manner that takes into account designated health services referrals. For example, compensation arrangements based upon a percentage of gross revenues, collections, or expenses will not satisfy the requirements of this exception. A compensation arrangement based upon a percentage of a fee schedule could satisfy the exception, if there were a single fixed fee for each service (i.e., there were not multiple payments amounts from different payors). Given the prominence of "percentage" contracts in interventional pain physician and other physician services, this restriction could force major changes in existing compensation arrangements.

In the case of exceptions that include the additional restriction that the payment not take into account "other business generated between the parties," such as in the space and equipment lease exceptions, the per-unit payment also may not take into account any other business, such as an non-federal health care business, generated by the referring physician. Thus, compensation arrangements should be structured to be consistent with fair market value for the work performed, not inflated to compensate for the physician's ability to generate additional revenue.

Unfortunately, Phase I of the final Stark rules does not address the "commercially reasonable even in the absence of referrals" standard that is an additional requirement for some of the Stark Law exceptions. Accordingly, it is unclear if this standard would not be met where, for instance, a per unit approach is taken and the physician involved is responsible for generating a majority of the units with his or her own referrals.

HCFA notes that the fact that a contract requires referrals to certain providers does not vitiate the exception, provided that the contract expressly provides exceptions for situations when the patient expresses a different choice, when the patient's insurer determines the provider, or when the referral is not in the best medical interest of the patient in the physician's judgment. HCFA points out that, even if an arrangement does meet a Stark Law exception, it could still run afoul of the Federal Anti-Kickback Statute.

THE IN-OFFICE ANCILLARY SERVICES EXCEPTION

The Stark Law's prohibition on referrals does not apply to services that meet the "in-office ancillary services" exception. This exception is the primary mechanism that interventional pain physicians and other physicians use to protect referrals for designated health care services made within their practices. It generally allows interventional pain physicians and other physicians to order designated health services from their own practices so long as (1) the services are personally performed by the ordering physician or another physician member of the ordering physician's group practice or (2) the service is provided by a non-physician within the group practice who is directly supervised by the ordering physician or another physician member of the ordering physician's group practice. The exception contains additional detailed requirements relating to (1) the locations where in-office ancillary services may be performed and (2) how they may be billed, which are discussed below.

In the final rule, HCFA has attempted to administratively simplify the exception, while retaining what HCFA believes was Congress' intent to protect only those services that are actually ancillary to the physician's practice. This effort results in positive changes with respect to the supervision requirements of the exception, but imposes new limits on the locations where services may be furnished. ASIPP pushed aggressively for the changes in the supervision standards.

Scope of Designated Health Services that Can be In-Office Ancillary Services

The 1998 proposed rule suggested that a DHS would be considered furnished in the location where the service was actually performed or where the patient received and began to use the item. In response to confusion about the applicability of the exception to outpatient prescription drugs and ambulatory infusion pumps, the final rule takes a slightly broader approach to the furnishing of items. The final rule recognizes an item as being furnished when the item is dispensed to the patient in a manner that is sufficient to meet the applicable payment and coverage rules. This new definition, along with changes in the supervision requirements (discussed below), may improve the ability of interventional pain physicians to provide both infusion and outpatient drug services.

Direct Supervision

What Does It Mean to Provide Direct Supervision?

The statute requires in-office ancillary services to be furnished either (1) personally by the referring physician or another physician member of the same group practice, or (2) by non-physicians who are directly supervised by the referring physician or other physician group member. In keeping with ASIPP's lobbying proposal, the final regulation defines "direct supervision" as that level of supervision that would satisfy the supervision requirements under the applicable Medicare payment or coverage rules for the particular service at issue.

The definition of "direct supervision" adopted under the final rule is a significant change from the proposed regulation and an important victory for interventional pain physicians. In the proposed regulation, HCFA required the physician to be present in the office suite where the services are being provided and (with a very limited exception) to be immediately available throughout the entire service. For interventional pain physicians who must leave their offices and perform procedures in a hospital outpatient department or an ambulatory surgery center, the direct supervision standard, as it was interpreted by HCFA, was a major obstacle and was inconsistent with the supervision called for under the applicable standards of care. For example, simple radiology services may be furnished under general physician supervision.

In responding to the concerns raised by ASIPP and others, HCFA changed, as noted above, the supervision standard under the in-office ancillary services exception to require only that level of supervision otherwise required by the Medicare payment and coverage rules. In a number of cases, such as simple radiology services and clinical laboratory services, the Medicare payment and coverage rules only require general supervision of non-physicians providing those services. General supervision does not require the physician supervisor to be present in the office suite when the service is provided.

Providers should remember, however, this revision to the in-office ancillary service supervision standard has no impact on physician services that are furnished as incident-to services. In other words, if an interventional pain physician elects to furnish certain DHS as "incident-to services," all the coverage requirements for incident-to services, including the applicable direct supervision standard, must be satisfied.

Who May Provide "Direct Supervision"?

In the proposed regulation, HCFA proposed eliminating independent contractors as members of a group practice. While this proposal improves the ability of a small physician group to qualify as a group practice (see the discussion below about the definition of a "group practice"), the proposal prohibited independent contractors from being eligible to supervise nonphysician employees who were furnishing potential in-office ancillary services. In response to concerns raised about this issue, the final regulation permits independent contractors to supervise in-office ancillary services, if certain conditions are met.

To supervise designated health services, an independent contractor must furnish patient care services to the group practice's patients in the group practice's facilities, under a contractual arrangement with the group practice. Furthermore, the contract must contain the same restrictions on compensation that apply to members of the group practice (discussed later) or it must satisfy the requirements of the personal services exception to the Stark Law. Finally, the arrangement between the group and the independent contractor must comply with the Medicare reassignment rules.

The Building Requirements

The in-office ancillary services exception also requires that the services be furnished in a building in which the referring physician, or another physician who is a member of the same group practice, furnishes physician services that are unrelated to the furnishing of DHS. Alternatively, if the physician who makes the referral is a member of a group practice, the services may be performed in another building used by the group for the provision of all or some of the group's clinical laboratory services or for the centralized provision of other DHS.

Same Building

The final rule permits in-office ancillary services to be furnished in the same building in which the referring physician or another group practice member furnishes substantial physician services unrelated to the furnishing of DHS payable by any payor. "A building" is defined as any structure or combination of structures having a single United States Postal Service street address. It does not include parking lots or parking garages where mobile equipment may be located.

The rule also prohibits the receipt of the DHS (whether covered by private or government payor) from being the primary reason the patient comes in contact with the referring physician or group practice. Highly specialized physicians may find this criterion difficult to satisfy if their practice is focused in areas considered DHS, such as radiology or other imaging services. HCFA states that its intention is to "preclude single service DHS enterprises from the in-office ancillary services exception" and ensure that the exception protects only those services related to the physician's practice.

Centralized Building

An alternative to the same building requirement is the "centralized building" standard. The final rule permits services to be furnished in a centralized building that is used by a group practice for the provision of some or all of the group practice's clinical laboratory services or other DHS. The centralized building does not need to service all of the group's offices or furnish all of the group's DHS.

The centralized building alternative may only be used when the referring physician is a member of the group practice. It may not be used for services referred by an independent contractor. In-office services referred by independent contractors must be meet the "same building" standard.

The centralized building standard requires the space for furnishing the DHS to be used exclusively by the group, on a full-time basis (7 days per week, 24 hours per day). The ownership or lease of the space must be for at least six months. One significant impact of the new rule is that part-time arrangements of space for the furnishing of DHS, such as one day rentals of MRI or ultrasound laboratories or physical therapy units, will not satisfy the centralized building requirement. If a group wishes to use space on a part-time basis or lease space from another group on a part-time basis, the DHS services must satisfy the same building requirements.

Mobile Units

The preamble discusses the applicability of the building standard to the provision of ancillary services through mobile units. A mobile unit will not satisfy the "same building" standard since the definition of a building excludes parking lots and parking garages where mobile units might be placed. Furthermore, HCFA considers mobile units whose use is shared by multiple physician groups not to be "in-office" services. Nevertheless, HCFA recognizes certain mobile unit arrangements as compliant with the "centralized building" standard. The group practice must exclusively own (or lease) the mobile unit to circulate among its group practice locations.

The Billing Requirements

The exception imposes limits on who may submit a bill for a DHS. To address how to bill for services of independent contractors, who are physicians in a group practice but not members, HCFA has interpreted the statute to permit billing by a group practice for physicians who are "in the group." The final regulation also permits billing by entities wholly-owned by the physician (or group practice) performing or supervising the services. The wholly-owned requirement may limit the ability of physicians or groups to use the in-office ancillary services exception in shared facility arrangements.

In the past, small group practices and solo practitioners had indicated the efficiencies that sharing certain facilities permitted. While rejecting a suggestion to adopt a new exception for shared facilities, the preamble acknowledges the appropriateness of the in-office ancillary services exception to DHS services furnished in a shared facility. Unfortunately, the exception's use may be hampered by its strict billing limitations which require that the "shared facility" bill in the name of the practice wishing to rely upon the exception.

GROUP PRACTICE DEFINITION

Among the most troubling aspects of the 1998 proposed rule was its treatment of the definition of a "group practice" for purposes of the Stark Law. This definition is critical because it is, in most cases, a threshold requirement for the all-important in-office ancillary services exception discussed above.

Most of the problems with the 1998 proposed rule's group practice definition resulted from HCFA's efforts to target "sham group practices" and "loose confederations" of physicians bound together – in HCFA's view at least – to circumvent the law's prohibitions. Thus, the proposed rule included a "unified business test" that would have prohibited different accounting and profit distribution systems for satellite offices or for different specialties within a group practice. Other proposals would have excluded sole shareholder practices from the definition of a *bona fide* group, and barred the payment of productivity bonuses that included any portion of a physician's own orders for designated health services (even if the physician personally performed the services). In response to criticism that these proposals would have excluded many *bona fide* group practices, intruded too far into the financial operations of physician practices, HCFA substantially revised the group practice definition in the final rule.

The final rules create a substantially more flexible "unified business" test that will permit group practices to maintain separate cost centers for different practice locations or specialties, at least with respect to non-designated health services and, in some cases, with respect to designated health services, so long as the compensation method is not directly related to the volume or value of referrals and other conditions are satisfied. To meet the revised unified business test, a group practice must be organized and operated on a *bona fide* basis as a single integrated business enterprise with legal and organizational integration. While HCFA's new rule sets general parameters indicative of integration, it does not dictate specific compensation practices.

The final rules also allow a group to consist of almost any kind of legally organized entity, owned by virtually any combination of individuals and other entities, provided that there are at least two physicians providing services to patients as group practitioners. As a result, sole shareholder entities will qualify as a group practice, as long the group employs at least one other physician.

As under the proposed rule, independent contractors are no longer considered "members" of a group. This provision helps groups in meeting the so-called "substantially all test" for group practice status, which requires that at least 75 percent of the services of a group's members must be provided through the group, in aggregate. By limiting members to owners and employees of the group, it will be easier for groups that use part-time independent contractor physicians to fulfill this requirement. As indicated above, HCFA also liberalized the direct supervision standard in the in-office ancillary services exception to permit supervision by independent contractors. Under the new rules, groups also may pay productivity bonuses to independent contractor physicians.

The final rules provide additional revisions to the productivity bonus rules, so that group practices may pay physicians in the group bonuses based directly on the services they perform. However, the final rule continues to prohibit groups from paying physicians bonuses based directly on their referrals of designated health services that are performed by someone else.

The final rules also promulgate specific methods for paying productivity bonuses and distributing profits which HCFA deems to be only "indirectly" related to referral income. In other words, if a group practice wants absolute assurance that its bonuses or profit shares are not "directly" related to referrals, the group may employ one of the listed methodologies set forth in the regulations. However, groups are not required to use these methodologies. In fact, the regulations make clear that other methods are acceptable so long as they are reasonable, objectively verifiable and no more than indirectly related to designated health service referrals. HCFA's newfound flexibility, however, does not save the Stark Law's group practice definition from remaining a painfully detailed and highly technical morass.

NEW REGULATORY EXCEPTIONS

Fair Market Value Compensation

In the 1998 proposed rule, HCFA proposed a new fair market value exception for compensation arrangements that met certain criteria. Phase I of the final regulation adopts this fair market value compensation exception, with certain revisions. HCFA clarifies and emphasizes that, although there was some confusion regarding the scope of the proposed fair market value exception, it is only intended to cover items or services provided by a physician (or immediate family member) to an entity, not by an entity to a physician. Significantly, HCFA will permit the parties to an arrangement to utilize this exception, even if another exception could potentially apply to the arrangement. In other good news for practitioners, HCFA also eliminated a requirement from the proposal that the written agreement cross-reference all other agreements between the parties.

HCFA also revised the exception to state that an arrangement under the exception must (1) not violate the Anti-Kickback Statute, (2) comply with an Anti-Kickback Statute safe-harbor, or (3) have been blessed by the Office of Inspector General in the form of an official advisory opinion. If an arrangement does not fit within a safe-harbor or receive an advisory opinion, however, meeting this exception may be an exercise in clairvoyance. This is because a determination of a "violation" of the Anti-Kickback Statute requires an understanding of the intent of *both* parties to the arrangement. HCFA acknowledges this fact but notes that it believes it would be "unusual" for only one party to an arrangement to have the intent to violate the kickback statute.

Non-Monetary Compensation up to $300

In this final rule, HCFA significantly revised its previously proposed *de minimis* exception to be more flexible in a move that should protect Christmas gifts and the like. HCFA eliminated the previous $50 per encounter limit, meaning that the value of a particular gift can be any amount, so long as the annual aggregate value of all gifts from that source to the referring physician does not exceed $300. HCFA also added a protective measure that would disqualify from this exception gifts that are solicited by the physicians.

In addition, HCFA eliminated the "similarly situated" standard contained in the original proposal, which would have required that any *de minimis* compensation be made available to all similarly situated individuals. Because the "similarly situated" standard was intended to ensure that gifts were not given primarily to reward high-referrers, HCFA felt that a better approach was to prohibit gifts that take into account the volume or value of referrals or other business generated between the parties. HCFA also points out that the exception covers gifts to individual physicians, not to groups or entities. This seems an absurd distinction.

HCFA makes explicit that "professional courtesy" is not covered by this or any other exception, and solicits comments on appropriate conditions for such an exception. Accordingly, if the Stark Law would otherwise be triggered, no exception to the Stark Law will protect professional courtesy exchanges, at least at present.

Medical Staff Benefits

HCFA added a new exception that would allow certain "incidental benefits" of "low value" when provided by hospitals to their medical staffs, such as parking, internet access, and duplication services. Although far from perfect, this new exception is of significant value to hospitals and their medical staff, including interventional pain physicians. HCFA specifically states, however, that medical transcription services and the provision of malpractice insurance and are not covered by this exception. In order to be excepted, the benefit(s) provided from the hospital to the medical staff member must be:

1. Offered by a hospital to all members of the medical staff without regard to the volume or value of referrals or other business generated between the parties;
2. Offered only during periods when the medical staff members are making rounds or performing other duties that benefit the hospital and its patients;
3. Provided by the hospital and used by the medical staff members only on the hospital's main campus;
4. Reasonably related to the provision of or designed to facilitate the delivery of medical services at the hospital;
5. Consistent with the types of benefits offered to medical staff members by other hospitals within the same region or comparable regions; and
6. Of "low value," meaning less than $25, per occurrence.

DEFINITIONS OF THE DESIGNATED HEALTH SERVICES

In a welcome display of clarity, HCFA has chosen to define several of the designated health services by listing the applicable CPT and HCPCS codes. Beginning with this final rule, HCFA will list annually in the *Federal Register* the particular CPT codes that define clinical laboratory services, physical therapy, occupational therapy, radiology and certain other imaging services covered by the Stark Law. Although the regulation contains general definitions of these services, the published list of codes will be controlling.

HCFA excepts from the term "designated health services" those services that would otherwise be considered designated health services but are paid for by Medicare as part of a separate composite payment for a group of services as a separate benefit. For example, HCFA will not apply the prohibition on referrals to services paid for under the ASC rate. Notably, however, certain composite rate services will not be able to meet this exception, including inpatient hospital services.

Professional Services as Designated Health Services

In the final rules, HCFA clarified its position that the professional components of health services are included under the definition of designated health services. Many commenters on the proposed rule had suggested that the professional component of the various services, especially clinical laboratory and radiology services, were not covered, and not intended to be covered, by the self-referral prohibition. HCFA declined to adopt this interpretation or definition, but noted that "as a practical matter" they believed that the professional components of many designated health services will be excluded from the definition of referral, as they would be personally performed by the referring physician.

Radiology and Certain Other Imaging Services

HCFA has redefined the category of "radiology and certain other imaging services" to clarify what imaging services are included in this category. In particular, HCFA has slightly modified its 1998 proposal to exclude radiology services that were peripheral, incidental, or secondary to a nondesignated health services from the operation of the Stark Law. Under the final rules, any radiology procedures that are integral to the performance of, and performed during, a nonradiology medical procedure are not considered part of this designated health service. X-ray, fluoroscopy, and ultrasound services that are part of invasive procedures requiring the insertion of a needle, catheter, tube, or probe have been excluded from this category (i.e., fluoroscopic guidance in an interventional procedure). However, HCFA warns that such procedures could still be considered designated health services, if they are, for instance, provided in a hospital and are, therefore, inpatient or outpatient hospital services under the Stark Law.

Outpatient and Inpatient Hospital Services

HCFA largely retained the proposed definitions of outpatient and inpatient hospital services. Of particular importance, however, HCFA discusses at length "under arrangements" relationships which some interventional pain physicians are entering into in the wake of the collapse of Medicare outpatient pain procedure rates. In "under arrangements" relationships, a hospital outsources a portion of its services to an outside third party that provides the services. The hospital pays the outsourced provider, bills Medicare for the services, and remains ultimately responsible for the services.

HCFA noted the pervasive nature of many of these arrangements and realized that prohibiting them on the grounds that the physician was an "owner" of the outsourced entity providing the service would significantly disrupt patient care. HCFA stated that it will treat under arrangements relationships between hospitals and physician owned entities as only "compensation relationships," which means they will be protected if they meet an applicable exception, such as a space lease or personal service exception. It should be possible to protect most of those relationships under these exceptions. HCFA cautioned, however, that it may reconsider its decision if it suspects the arrangements are abused. HCFA also warned hospitals and physician groups that such relationships must still comply with the Anti-Kickback Statute.

HCFA also clarified that the professional services of physicians, physician assistants, and certain other practitioners are not considered inpatient or outpatient hospital services (and thus not "designated health services"), if Medicare reimburses the services independently and not as part of the inpatient or outpatient hospital service.

Outpatient Prescription Drugs

Outpatient prescription drugs are considered designated health services subject to the general prohibition on referrals. In Phase I, HCFA revised the definition of outpatient prescription drugs to make clear that it includes all prescription drugs covered by Medicare Part B. In the preamble to Phase I, HCFA noted that the breadth of its definition of outpatient prescription drugs is ameliorated to a large extent by its expansion of the in-office ancillary services exception, which includes greater flexibility with respect to the direct supervision requirement.

CONCLUSION

With the Department of Justice having recently announced that it is investigating over fifty False Claims Act cases that include allegations of Stark Law violations, Stark Law compliance is all the more critical in the wake of the Stark II final rules.

NEEDLESTICK SAFETY AND PREVENTION

Mark F. Tatelbaum, JD
William A. Sarraille, JD

On November 6, 2000, President Clinton signed into law the Needlestick Safety and Prevention Act to revise the Occupational Safety and Health Administration's (OSHA) standard regulating occupational exposure to bloodborne pathogens, including the human immunodeficiency virus, the hepatitis B virus, and the hepatitis C virus. On January 18, 2001, OSHA published in the Federal Register its regulations reflecting the Act and its requirments. The effective date of the regulations is April 18, 2001. They impose additional administrative responsibilities in the way that hospitals, ambulatory surgical centers (ASCs), pain management practices, and other health care providers manage their sharps protection procedures. The Act and the regulations have had a profound effect already on interventional pain management.

THE INITIAL BLOODBORNE PATHOGENS STANDARD

OSHA issued the Initial Standard regulating occupational exposure to bloodborne pathogens in 1991. This standard applied to all occupational exposure to blood or other potentially infectious material. Occupational exposure was defined to mean "reasonably anticipated skin, eye, mucous membrane, or parenteral contact with blood or other potentially infectious material that may result from the performance of an employee's duties." The Initial Standard required employers to maintain certain procedures to protect their employees from contamination from bloodborne pathogens.

Specifically, the Initial Standard required employers to establish a written "Exposure Control Plan" designed to eliminate or minimize employee exposure. The Initial Standard required "engineering controls" to isolate or remove the bloodborne pathogen hazards from the workplace. It also required employers to review and update their Plan, at least annually and more often, as necessary, so that it reflects new or modified tasks and procedures which affect operational exposure and new or revised employee positions subject to occupational exposure. The Initial Standard also required that employers maintain accurate medical records for each employee with occupational exposure.

THE NEEDLESTICK SAFETY AND PREVENTION ACT

The Needlestick Safety and Prevention Act seeks to further reduce health care workers' exposure to bloodborne pathogens by imposing additional requirements upon employers, such as hospitals and ASCs, concerning their sharps procedures. Unless superceded by OSHA, the Act requires hospitals and ASCs, among others, to review and update their Plans to reflect changes in technology, consider and implement new technologies, solicit input from employees, and maintain a sharps injury log.

THE REVISED STANDARD

Consistent with the Act, OSHA's regulations (1) modify the definition of "engineering controls" and adds definitions for the terms "sharps with engineered sharps injury protection" and "needleless systems," (2) requires employers to consider and implement new technologies when they update their "exposure control plan," (3) requires employers to solicit employee input with respect to appropriate engineering controls, and (4) requires employers to maintain a sharps injury log.

DEFINITIONS

In the final rule, OSHA modifies the definition of the term "engineering control" to clarify that it includes all control measures that isolate or remove a hazard from the workplace, such as "sharps with engineered sharps injury protections," "needleless systems," and all other medical devices designed to reduce the risk of percutaneous exposure to bloodborne pathogens. OSHA defines the term "sharps with engineered sharps injury protection" as a nonneedle sharp or needle device used for withdrawing body fluids, accessing a vein or artery, or administering medications or other fluids, with a built-in safety feature or mechanism that effectively reduces the risk of an exposure incident. OSHA defines the term "needleless systems" as a device that does not use needles for: (1) the collection of bodily fluids or withdrawal of body fluids after initial venous or arterial access is established; (2) administration of medication or fluids; or (3) any other procedure involving the potential for occupational exposure to bloodborne pathogens due to percuatneious injuries from contaminated sharps.

Although OSHA states in the final rule that it does not intend these definitional changes to impose new requirements upon employers, such as hospitals and ASCs, they most certainly will require additional work. The definition changes will require employers to evaluate "sharps with engineered sharps injury protections," "needleless systems," and all other new medical devices that function as "engineering controls," and may require employers to modify their Plans to incorporate these technologies.

CONSIDERATION AND IMPLEMENTATION OF NEW TECHNOLOGY

In this change, OSHA intends to impose new obligations on employers whose businesses affect interstate commerce, and whose employees are exposed to bloodborne pathogens. Affected employers will include hospitals, ASCs, and other health care facilities, as well as pain management practices and other physician practices in many circumstances. The regulation requires employers to account for innovations in technological developments that reduce the risk of exposure incidents. Employers must consider and implement "appropriate commercially available and effective safer medical devices" designed to eliminate or minimize occupation exposure, on at least an annual basis. The consideration undertaken must be documented.

Unfortunately for hospitals ASCs and others the regulation does not offer much guidance as to how this consideration and implementation is to be conducted. The preamble to the regulation states only that a device will be considered to be "appropriate" if it will not jeopardize patient or employee safety, and is not medically contraindicated. OSHA further states that the determination of whether a device is "effective" should be based on a "reasonable judgment" that the device will make an exposure incident less likely. Nowhere, however, does OSHA indicate when it considers a device to be "available in the marketplace." Nor, does OSHA state what it will consider to be a "safer medical device."

This lack of guidance presents a host of uncertainties in the efforts of hospitals ASCs and others to comply with the final rule. For example, at what point can technology be said to have established that it eliminates or reduces exposure to bloodborne pathogens, such that it must be reflected in the Plan? When does a device become recognized as "safer?" Additionally, when is a device considered "effective?" Is effectiveness tied to Food and Drug Administration approval? Further, at what point does a device become "available in the marketplace?" How many units must be on sale for this standard to be met? What efforts must a hospital or ASC or others undertake to acquire the device? Is there a cost limit? If the hospital or ASC or others determine that the device is "safer," "appropriate," "commercially available," and "effective," and thus must implement the use of the device, from a practical perspective, how can it force a non-employee physician to use such device. If it does force the physician to use the device, e.g. through the medical staff bylaws, what is the increased liability risk to the facility for a bad outcome? For now, the best course will be for hospitals, ASCs and others to fully document their determinations, and the reasoning for them.

EMPLOYEE INPUT

In addition to requiring that employers, such as hospitals and ASCs, consider and implement new technologies, OSHA also requires that they solicit the input of their employees. Specifically, OSHA will require employers to seek input from non-managerial employees who are responsible for direct patient care, and who may be potentially exposed to injuries from contaminated sharps. Employees must be asked to identify, evaluate, and select effective engineering and work practice controls. The solicitation for input must be documented in a employer's Plan.

There are no specific procedures as to how an employer must obtain employee input. A hospital, ASC or others are afforded the flexibility to solicit input in the manner in which it deems appropriate. The steps taken to solicit input must be reasonable, however. OSHA suggests what reasonable steps may be. OSHA states that a dental office employing two hygienists for instance, may choose to have periodic conversations with the hygienists. A large hospital would likely find that an effective process for soliciting employee input requires the implementation of more formal procedures OSHA adds. Methods for soliciting employee input may include involvement in informal problem-solving groups; participation in safety audits; worksite inspections; exposure incident investigations; participation in the evaluation of devices through pilot testing; and involvement in a safety and health committee properly constituted and operated in conformance with the National Labor Relations Board.

RECORDKEEPING

Not only must hospitals, ASCs and others now consider and implement new technologies and solicit employee input in the identification, evaluation, and selection of controls, they must also under the final rule, maintain a sharps injury log for the purpose of identifying high risk areas and for evaluating devices. The log must be maintained so as to protect the confidentiality of the injured employee. The log must contain at a minimum: (1) the type and brand of the device involved in the incident, (2) the department or work area where the exposure incident occurred, and (3) an explanation of how the incident occurred.

As with other requirements of the final rule, OSHA does not provide a sample or recommended format for the sharps log. OSHA states in the preamble, that employers are permitted to determine the format in which the log is maintained (e.g. paper or electronic), and may include information in addition to that required by the standard so long as the privacy of injured workers is protected. Employers may use the OSHA 300 Log of Work-Related Injuries and Illnesses and the OSHA 301 Injury and Illness Incident Report to meet the sharps injury log requirements, provided that certain conditions are satisfied.

CONCLUSION

Congress and OSHA should be commended for acting to protect the country's health care workers by reducing their exposure to bloodborne pathogens. Despite this worthwhile endeavor, however, practical questions about implementing the new requirements are a source of major concern.

The House Committee on Education and the Workforce stated in the legislative history to the Act that the statute was not meant to disturb the underlying flexible, performance-oriented nature of the Initial Standard. It also specifically stated that it "did not expect an OSHA inspector to substitute his judgment for that of the professional, clinical, and medical judgment of health care professionals responsible for patient safety." Only time will tell if OSHA will honor this Congressional intent.

The effective date of these revisions was April 18, 2001. Exposure Control Plans that are reviewed and updated on or after this date must incorporate these revised standards. The Act and the implementation regulations have already reshaped practices across the country.

ANTI-KICKBACK SAFE HARBORS

William A. Sarraille, JD
Robert WanermanJD

On November 19, 1999, the HHS Office of Inspector General (OIG) published a final rule adding eight new anti-kickback safe harbors and clarifying six of the existing safe harbors (2). The new and revised safe harbors are the first major revisions to the regulations since they were were first published in 1991, and have been under consideration by the OIG for over five years. Among the changes are several provisions that may affect pain management practices in a variety of clinical settings. This article will focus on the impact of those changes, and whether practices need to review their existing agreements for compliance purposes. The effect of their changes on pain practices is clear and significant.

INTRODUCTION TO THE FEDERAL ANTI-KICKBACK LAW AND RELATED LAWS

Under the Federal health care anti-kickback law, which was first enacted in 1972, it is a felony to knowingly and willfully offer, solicit, pay, or receive anything of value, whether directly or indirectly, in exchange for or to induce the referral of items or services for which a Federal health care program may make payment (3). Violations of the law are punishable by criminal fines of up to $25,000 per offense, incarceration for up to five years, or both. In addition, a violation of the anti-kickback law may trigger two civil sanctions: first, the OIG may exclude the offending individual or entity from participation in the Medicare and Medicaid programs; second, the OIG can impose a civil monetary penalty of $50,000 per violation plus up to three times the amount of the underlying remuneration (4).

In 1987, Congress recognized the extraordinary breadth of the anti-kickback law and amended it to require the Secretary of Health and Human Services to publish regulations that specify those payment practices that will not be exempted from the reach of the law. Any transaction that fits squarely within the published "safe harbors" is not subject to prosecution or sanction; all others will be evaluated on a case-by-case basis to determine if a violation has occurred and if enforcement is warranted.

The first group of safe harbors were published in 1991, and covered ten areas, including investment interests, rentals of space and equipment, personal service and management agreements, sales of practices, payments to employees, discounts, and referral services. The next year, safe harbors covering managed care arrangements were published. By 1996, the numerous changes in health care delivery led Congress to mandate that the OIG publish annual solicitations for both modifications to existing safe harbors and for new safe harbors.

The conduct targeted in the anti-kickback law and the exceptions overlap with the Stark anti-referral law, named for its primary sponsor in Congress (5). However, the two are distinct and should not be confused. Under Stark, a physician is prohibited from referring a patient to an entity in which he or she (or a member of the physician's immediate family) has either an ownership interest or compensation arrangement for one of a list of "designated health services" that may be covered under Medicare or Medicaid unless a specific exception in the law applies to the circumstances (6).

If a referral is made by a physician for a designated health service such as a radiology service, on prescription drug or a physical therapy service and that physician (or an immediate family member) has an ownership interest or compensation arrangement in the entity receiving the referral that is not permitted under the statute, then the physician is exposed to a range of sanctions. Payment for the services rendered must be denied, and the physician may be subject to civil monetary penalties and to exclusion from participation in the Medicare and State health care programs (7).

Many of the Stark exceptions cover the same ground as the anti-kickback safe harbors, such as investment interests, rental of space and equipment, personal service agreements, and payments to employees. However, the scope of the exceptions are not always identical. For this reason, several commentators suggested that the OIG amend the existing safe harbors to conform to the Stark exceptions. The OIG declined this invitation, citing the differences in the scope and structure of the two laws. The anti-kickback law is a criminal statute, and the intent of the parties is a key element of any violation; by contrast, the Stark law is a civil statute, and the intent of the parties is irrelevant. Similarly, if a transaction does not fit within an anti-kickback safe harbor, it is not necessarily illegal; however, the failure to fit within a Stark exception is a violation of that law. The OIG further noted that it is possible for a transaction to violate the anti-kickback law even if the agreement satisfies a Stark exception.

In addition to the federal laws, many states have enacted counterparts to the anti-kickback and anti-referral laws. These laws should also be consulted to fully assess whether or not a particular transaction poses a financial risk to the practice.

THE NEW AND REVISED SAFE HARBORS

As discussed above, a comprehensive treatment of each of the new and revised safe harbors is beyond the scope of this article. In addition to the specific revisions discussed below, the OIG crafted a set of safe harbors designed to provide incentives including investments in practices located in medically underserved areas, and for recruiting practitioners to provide services in those areas.

Ambulatory Surgical Centers

The new regulations establish a safe harbor for investments in ambulatory surgical centers ("ASCs"), a huge site-of-service for the delivery of pain services. Given the variety of ASCs, the OIG has identified four distinct entities that qualify for safe harbor protection: (1) surgeon-owned ASCs, at which all physician-investors are either general surgeons or group practices composed of surgeons engaged in the same specialty with the ability to refer patients; (2) single-specialty ASCs, where all physician-investors are engaged in the same specialty or subspecialty, such as Interventional pain management; (3) multi-specialty ASCs, where the physician-investors can be a mix of specialties; and (4) hospital-physician ASCs, where the investors consist of at least one hospital and physicians, group practices, or non-referral sources.

In each category, safe harbor protection for an ASC is available if the investors also include individuals or entities without any ability to refer patients to the ASC or to generate business either for the ASC or any of its investors. In the OIG's view, the key to ASC safe harbor is to protect those investments that represent a legitimate extension of the physician's or group's office practice.

In order to qualify for safe harbor protection, the minimum criteria that an ASC must meet include:

- certification under the Medicare program(including a requirement that the operating and recovery space in the facility be dedicated exclusively to the ASC);
- any physician investment interest must be fully disclosed to a program beneficiary who may be referred to the ASC;
- no investment in the ASC can be made with funds loaned from the ASC or from other investors;
- investment interests in the ASC cannot be offered on terms linked to the value or volume of referrals to the ASC;
- all payments to investors must be directly proportional to the individual's or entity's capital investment in the ASC (including the fair market value of any pre-operative services rendered);
- all ancillary services must be a integral part of the primary procedure performed at the ASC, and cannot be billed separately to Medicare or to any federal health care program; and
- neither the ASC nor physicians practicing at the ASC may discriminate against federal health program beneficiaries.

In addition, for the surgeon-owned, single specialty, and multi-specialty ASCs, the OIG further requires that each of the physician-investors derive at least one-third of their aggregate medical practice income from all sources during the preceding fiscal year or 12-month period from performing procedures covered by Medicare that require an ASC setting. Under the OIG's view, if an ASC represents an extension of a traditional office practice, then there is a minimal risk that the referring physician will refer patients to other investors. However, the rule does not mandate that the physician-investor derive at least one-third of his or her income from procedures performed at the ASC in which he or she has an investment interest. While this may appear to contradict the concept of an ASC as an extension of the office practice, it makes it easier to satisfy this requirement and allows for variations in such factors as quality, scope of specialty, and convenience for the patient.

In addition to the "one-third income" test for ASCs, the OIG has added an additional burden for multi-specialty ASCs. In order to minimize the potential for abusive cross-referrals within multi-specialty groups, each member of this category of physician-investors must also meet the requirement that at least one-third of his or her procedures that require an ASC or hospital surgical setting be performed at the ASC in which each group member is investing. Thus, in order to comply with the "one-third-income" and "one-third procedures" tests in this safe harbor, some multi-specialty group practices may actually be forced to "lock in" a referral mechanism.

This restriction may be particularly frustrating, since the safe harbor will not protect an ASC owned by a specialty group practice if any member of the group does not derive at least one-third of his or her medical practice income from surgical or other procedures performed in the ASC. As a result, if a practice consisting of three anesthesiologists owns and operates an ASC and one anesthesiologist provides only general anesthesiology, that ASC may not qualify for safe harbor protection, unless this anesthesiologist is considered not to be in a position to refer, a point not addressed in the final rule. In addition, the literal language of these safe harbors does not include practices owned by physicians and mid-level practitioners, such as CRNAs.

The new regulations take a more skeptical view of ASCs that are joint ventures between hospitals and physicians or physician groups. In the preamble to the regulations, the OIG stated its belief that such joint ventures are often susceptible to fraud and abuse. Nevertheless, in order to avoid placing hospitals at a competitive disadvantage, the OIG extended safe harbor protection to hospital/physician ASCs under limited circumstances. In addition to the limits discussed above governing the terms of the investment and the payments to investors, safe harbor protection is available for hospital/physician ASCs only if the hospital cannot be in a position to make or influence referrals to the ASC or to any of the investors in the ASC.

However, this requirement may effectively render the safe harbor meaningless, as OIG takes the position that hospitals can and do exercise control over referrals to ASCs. This problem may be avoided if the hospital expressly states in its by-laws or in any joint venture agreement that it will not interfere in any way with the exercise of a physician's judgment involving referrals and will not take any action to advertise or otherwise market the ASC. The safe harbor rule does not state whether even these precautions would be sufficient though there is some expectation that OIG will clarify this issue soon.

Under the hospital/physician ASC safe harbor, the physical space for the ASC must be dedicated space, and cannot be used to treat the hospital's outpatients. If the space for the ASC or the equipment used in the ASC is leased from the hospital, or if the hospital provides services to the ASC, then these agreements must also satisfy the existing safe harbors for space rental, equipment rental, or personal services and management contracts as set out in other safe harbors (8). Finally, the hospital cannot include the costs associated with the ASC on its cost report unless expressly authorized by HCFA.

As discussed above, the OIG's rationale for extending safe harbor protection to ASCs is that they represent a legitimate extension of a physician's or group's office practice. Yet, the OIG's application of this reasoning appears to be inconsistent and artificially restrictive. While the OIG received comments urging it to include other entities within the scope of this safe harbor based on the "extension of practice" concept, it declined to do so. The OIG's reasoning was that these entities, including physical therapy centers and diagnostic imaging centers, do not provide a cost savings to the programs when compared with hospital inpatient and outpatient surgery departments. By doing so, the OIG refused to recognize that many of these other entities are genuine extensions of specialty practices, and when operated as free-standing entities may deliver these services more efficiently and economically than their hospital-based counterparts.

Another anomaly in the revised safe harbors is the imposition of a requirement that physician-owned ASCs must disclose their ownership interests, while other physician-owned entities that qualify for protection under the small entity safe harbor need not make the same type of disclosure (9). Moreover, the safe harbors take inconsistent positions when it comes to separately billable ancillary services. While these services are not separately billable under the ASC safe harbor, they are protected under another safe harbor. These inconsistencies may produce the unintended result that ASCs may be unwilling or unable to compete effectively with hospitals over a broader range of services than just surgical and other procedures.

Investment Interests in Group Practices

In most group practices, the total income of the group is shared among its members or shareholders. Part of that pooled income often includes income generated as the result of a referral from one group member to another. It was unclear before the final rule was issued if that fact had any potential anti-kickback law implications. Although some have welcomed the final rule's creation of a group practice safe harbor, others question why it was developed and have expressed concern that the existence of such a safe harbor implies that even internal group practice arrangements are not free from scrutiny under the anti-kickback statute.

A new safe harbor expressly protects investments by individual physicians in group practices provided that the practice meets the definition of a group practice in the Stark law, with some modification. Under that law, a physician who has an ownership interest in or a compensation arrangement with a group practice will not violate that law if he or she makes a referral to that group for a designated health service payable under Medicare or a State health care program, where certain conditions are met (10). Under the safe harbor, a qualifying group may consist of individual licensed professionals who practice in a group, or can consist of a solo practice in which the solo practitioner's professional corporation provides the services.

One notable omission from the scope of this safe harbor is the inclusion of mid-level practitioners, such as CRNAs, Nurse Practitioners and Clinical Nurse Specialists, as potential investors when permitted by state law. The OIG's reasoning was that because it was incorporating the Stark Law exception, which only addresses financial interests of physicians, it was not prepared to go beyond the scope of that law. Nevertheless, the OIG did not foreclose a possible broadening of this safe harbor in its future rulemaking.

In order to qualify for this safe harbor, the equity interests in the group must be held by licensed professionals (or an individual professional corporation in the case of a solo practice) who practice in the group. Investment interests that take the form of bonds, notes, or other debt instruments are not considered in determining whether or not safe harbor protection is available; as a result, an equity interest in a group practice could be acquired with a loan from the group without jeopardizing the safe harbor protection. The equity interests must be in the group itself, and not in a subdivision of the group.

Finally, any distribution of profits derived from in-office ancillary services will be protected only if those services meet the Stark law's definition of in-office ancillary services (11). The OIG was particularly concerned that investments by members of a group practice in entities that provide ancillary services created the potential for overutilization and abuse of those services. As a result, an investment by a pain management practice in a physical therapy company will not qualify for safe harbor protection. Nevertheless, the OIG did acknowledge that while this safe harbor might not be available for ancillary service providers, the investment interest might still qualify for the small entity safe harbor, which was amended in the same rulemaking package.

Referral Agreements for Specialty Services

Physicians may refer patients to a specialist or subspecialist with the expectation that the patient will be referred back when the patient has reached a particular level of recovery. For example, an orthopedist or neurologist may refer a patient for pain management services with the understanding that the patient will be referred back in the future. Surprisingly, the anti-kickback law does not define the term "referral," even though offering or receiving anything of value in exchange for a referral is a crime.

The new safe harbor insulates those agreements in which a practitioner (or specialist) agrees to refer particular patients to a specialist or subspecialist in exchange for referring the same patient back at an agreed time or circumstance that is clinically appropriate. The referral must cover a service that is outside the scope of the referring practitioner's expertise, but is within the expertise of the practitioner receiving the referral. The only permissible remuneration in this setting is the payments received from patients or third-party payors (including Medicare or Medicaid). Although the proposed rule would have extended the safe harbor protection to referrals between primary care physicians and specialists who split a global fee under a co-management arrangement, the OIG deleted this proposal from the final rule on the belief that the potential for abuse was too great. Accordingly, safe harbor protection is not be available where the parties bill the Medicare program using the -54 or -55 modifiers to designate a split of a global fee. As the OIG reiterated, such practices are not necessarily illegal. The only inference that can be drawn is that splitting a global fee is not insulated from possible review by the government.

Clarifications to Existing Safe Harbors

Investment Interests

A safe harbor currently provides protection for investments in large entities traded on a national securities exchange (those with a capitalization of at least $50 million) and small entities, which must satisfy the "60-40" rules (i.e., no more than 40% of the investment interests may be held by individuals in a position to refer to the entity, and no more than 40% of the gross revenues may be derived from referrals generated by investors) (12).

The clarifications specify that for investments in large entities, the investment interest must be obtained on the same terms as those available to the public through a securities broker. The OIG was particularly concerned that some health care companies had acquired physician practices in exchange for stock or stock options valued at a special insider price. In the OIG's view, the spread between the market price and the insider price could be a vehicle for hiding payments for referrals. Under the final rule, however, stock and stock options may be protected by the safe harbor protection even if they are provided as compensation to physicians when the public could only acquire similar interests through a stock exchange transaction.

For small entities, the OIG has amended the rule to prohibit loans made to an investor by individuals or entities acting on behalf of the investment entity. The safe harbor also precludes loan guarantees or collateral assignments on behalf of the health care entity in order to allow an investor to obtain a bank loan for the purpose of acquiring the investment interest in the entity. The preamble expressly includes prohibitions on loans by hospitals, nursing homes, or other institutions in this category. The preamble also clarifies that the analysis under the 60-40 revenue test refers to revenue related to the furnishing of health care items or services.

Rentals and Contracts

The OIG published two clarifications to the existing safe harbors covering rentals and service contracts (13). First, it substituted the word "term" for "period" when describing the length of any agreement. Second, in the context of the requirement in the safe harbors that the agreement or contract serve a "legitimate business purpose," the OIG substituted the phrase "commercially reasonable business purpose" when describing the use of the rented space, equipment, or services. The OIG explained that it was shifting the test under these safe harbors to examine whether or not the underlying agreement serves a commercially reasonable business purpose of the lessee or purchaser. This can be viewed as a restriction on the old safe harbor, since a legitimate business purpose need not depend on measurements of the amount of space or equipment needed for the renter's or lessor's business. Therefore, the definition of what is commercially reasonable is not entirely subjective; if the OIG were to see that a portion of the space, equipment, or services involved was not reasonably calculated to further the lessee's or purchaser's commercially reasonable business objectives, it might conclude that safe harbor protection was not warranted. In addition, the preamble expressly excludes cost-or risk-sharing arrangements, joint research programs, and data collection arrangements from the scope of its definition of "commercially reasonable" business objectives.

In the OIG's discussion of these new rules, it provided some practical guidance covering the ability of an entity to terminate a contract or lease while not violating the provision in these safe harbors that the underlying agreement have a term of at least one year. It stated that a termination "for cause" can still comply with the safe harbor if the agreement defines the conditions that permit a termination "for cause," and also specifies that the terms of the agreement (or any other financial arrangement between the parties) cannot be renegotiated during the term of that agreement. The OIG refused to recognize any set of circumstances under which safe harbor protection would still be available if an agreement were terminated without cause. Notwithstanding the OIG's concern that terminations without cause could camouflage payments under a sham agreement, that ability could provide an incentive for lessors or management companies to impose onerous terms on providers by expanding the scope of "for cause" termination clauses.

Discounts

The existing safe harbor for discounts was clarified in two important respects (14). First, the OIG specifically extended safe harbor protection to rebate programs involving all types of providers, which are defined as any discount that is not given at the time of the sale. The rebate terms must be disclosed to the buyer at the time of the initial sale or first installment sale. Second, the OIG clarified the obligations that a seller must meet to comply with the safe harbor. If the seller reports the discount to the buyer and provides the buyer with a notice reasonably calculated to inform the buyer of its obligation to inform the Federal health care programs of the discount, the seller will be protected notwithstanding any failure by the buyer to perform in accord with the safe harbor given the growing regulatory focus on relationship between device and pharmaceutical companies, on the one hand, and interventional pain physicians on the other, this safe harbor is increasingly important.

The OIG provided additional technical amendments to the discount safe harbor that may make it easier to implement and administer. It noted that the obligation of charge-based buyers to disclose the amount of the discount on any claims submitted to Federally-funded health care programs was being eliminated. In addition, the OIG acknowledged that there are economic benefits to offering a discount on one good or service in order to provide an incentive to purchase another good or service provided by the same source, where the net value of the goods or services can be reported; in such cases, the buyer may be able to take advantage of lower prices offered as part of a volume discount. Finally, the OIG stated that safe harbor protection is available for coupons and credits, but are not available for discounts that are made available to one class of buyer and not made available to the Federal health care programs. The latter point is consistent with the OIG's policy that discounts or other inducements offered by clinical laboratories to hospitals for private pay or HMO patients in the hope of capturing their Medicare and Medicaid business is a potential anti-kickback violation.

CONCLUSIONS

The additions and amendments made by the OIG to the anti-kickback safe harbors, to varying degrees, recognize the pace of changes in the structure and organization of health care providers brought about by changes in reimbursement by government and private payors as well as changes brought about by the expanded enforcement of fraud and abuse laws by the OIG. Although the changes do not completely endorse all of these changes, or even fully acknowledge the benefits of many legitimate practices, the new and revised safe harbors are a beginning. At a minimum, practices should carefully evaluate any agreements affected by the changes in the regulations, and may wish to revisit proposed transactions to determine if they now qualify for safe harbor protection.

REFERENCES

1. 64 Federal Register 63,518 (Nov. 19, 1999).
2. 42 U.S.C. § 1320a-7b(b).
3. 42 U.S.C. §§ 1320a-7(b)(7) and 1320a-7a(a) (7).
4. 42 U.S.C. § 1395nn.
5. The Stark "designated health services" include physical therapy services, radiology services, durable medical equipment and supplies, home health services, outpatient prescription drugs, and inpatient and outpatient hospital services.
6. 42 U.S.C. § 1395nn (g).
7. 42 C.F.R. § 1001.952(b) – (d).
8. The small entity safe harbor is codified at 42 C.F.R. § 1001.952(a).
9. 42 U.S.C. § 1395nn(h) (4).
10. 42 U.S.C. § 1395nn(b) (2).
11. 42 C.F.R. § 1001.952(a).
12. 42 C.F.R. §§ 1001.952(b) – (d).
13. 42 C.F.R. § 1001.952(h).

ANY WILLING PROVIDER LAWS

Erin Brisbay McMahon, JD

Historically, insurance companies and managed care organizations were not required to contract with every healthcare provider within their geographical service areas. Antitrust and other common theories used by providers to challenge exclusion from a network were generally unsuccessful. Beginning in the late 1980's, physicians and other healthcare providers successfully lobbied state legislatures for relief in the form of "any willing provider" laws (1).

Any willing provider laws can be viewed as a creative offshoot of the "essential facility" theory developed in the antitrust case law. Simply stated, healthcare providers perceive that access to payors' networks is essential to their ability to stay in business. Under antitrust case law precedent, however, a provider in an essential facility case had to prove that the particular insurer or managed care organization that was excluding him or her had market power amounting to a monopoly, which was extremely hard to do, given the number of insurance companies and managed care organizations in existence. Any willing provider and similar laws, on the other hand, are based on the assumption that all the entities covered by the law, whether they are HMOs, PPOs, insurers, or nonprofit hospital corporations, are essential facilities.

Most any willing provider laws limit an insurer's and/or a managed care plan's discretion to exclude providers (2). These laws have evolved into four permutations: (a) true any willing provider laws, which require the insurer/managed care organization to include in its network any provider willing to accept the terms and conditions imposed by the insurer/managed care organization (2), (b) freedom of choice laws, which mandate that an insured/covered person be allowed to utilize the provider of his or her choice (2), (c) assignment laws, which require insurers/managed care organizations to reimburse nonparticipating providers (i.e., providers not admitted to the network) who have rendered services to an insured/covered person, who have a written assignment of benefits, and who have notified insurer/managed care organization of the assignment (1), and (d) nondiscrimination laws, which provide that insurers/managed care organizations cannot unfairly discriminate against a healthcare provider if the service provided is a covered service and is within the scope of the provider's license.

Table 1 summarizes current any willing provider laws of all four types, except that it excludes statutes relating solely to one or more of the following groups: chiropractors, dentists, pharmacists, nurse midwives, podiatrists, optometrists, and psychiatric services provided in psychiatric hospitals.

As Table 1 shows, insurers and managed care organizations have, with mixed success, used the federal Employee Retirement Income Security Act (ERISA) to challenge any willing provider laws. Three provisions of ERISA have been involved in the legal battles between insurers and managed care organizations on the one hand, and providers on the other: the preemption clause, the savings clause, and the deemer clause. ERISA's preemption clause supersedes state laws insofar as they relate to employee benefit plans, including plans offering health insurance (3).[1] Consequently, state laws relating to employee benefit plans are preempted (i.e., rendered invalid and unenforceable), unless they fall within ERISA's savings clause, which provides, among other things, that state laws that regulate insurance are saved from preemption (4). Even laws that regulate insurance and are saved from preemption, however, cannot be applied to regulate self-insured plans because they may not be "deemed" to be insurance companies or to be engaged in the business of insurance (5).

1 Some employee benefit plans are exempt from ERISA, most notably church plans and government plans. *See* 29 U.S.C. § 1003(b).

Table 1. *Any Willing Provider and Similar Laws*

ALABAMA

Type of Law: Ala. Code §27-1-19 Modified FOC/assignment provision
Which Providers Are Covered?: Healthcare providers, including physicians, dentists, pharmacists, podiatrists, chiropractors, optometrists, durable medical equipment, and home care providers.
Which Entities/Types of Policies Must Comply?: Persons, firms, corporations, associations, HMOs, health insurance service or preferred provider organizations, non-profit health service organizations, and employer sponsored health benefit companies providing health, accident, dental, or workers'compensation insurance coverage.
Description: The contract providing coverage to an insured Amay not exclude the right of assignment of benefits to any provider at the same benefit rate as paid to a contract provider."

ALASKA

Type of Law: Alaska Stat.§21.36.090 Non-discrimination
Which Providers Are Covered?: Physicians, dentists, osteopaths, optometrists, chiropractors, nurse midwives, advanced nurse practitioners, naturopaths, physical therapists, occupational therapists, marital and family therapists, psychologists, psychological associates, or licensed clinical social workers, or certified direct-entry midwives.
Which Entities/Types of Policies Must Comply?: Companies that issue group health insurance policies that extend coverage on an expense incurred basis, and HMOs or non-profit organizations that issue group service or indemnity type contracts.
Description: Entity may not practice or permit unfair discrimination against one of the providers listed if the service is covered by the policy in question and is within the scope of the provider's occupational license.

ARIZONA

Type of Law: A.R.S. §20-833 FOC
Which Providers Are Covered?: Hospitals, dentists, physicians, optometrists.
Which Entities/Types of Policies Must Comply?: Not-for-profit hospital, medical, dental, and optometric service corporations.
Description: Corporations covered by the statute cannot influence subscribers in the subscribers' free choice of a hospital, physician, dentist, or optometrist other than to limit their benefits to participating hospitals, physicians, dentists and optometrists.

Type of Law: A.R.S. §20-1403 AWP
Which Providers Are Covered?: Hospitals, nurses, and physicians (might also be interpreted to include podiatrists, chiropractors, dentists, naturopaths, homeopathic physicians, dispensing opticians, optometrists, osteopaths, pharmacists, physical therapists, psychologists, physician assistants, radiological technologists, midwives, counselors, occupational therapists, respiratory therapists, acupuncturists, athletic trainers and hearing aid dispensers)
Which Entities/Types of Policies Must Comply?: Any group disability policy.
Description: Policy cannot require that services be rendered by a particular hospital or person.

Type of Law: A.R.S. §20-1406.02 FOC
Which Providers Are Covered?: Psychologists
Which Entities/Types of Policies Must Comply?: Group disability insurance contracts and blanket disability insurance contracts.
Description: If services are within the lawful scope of the practice of a psychologist, the subscriber may choose either a physician or a psychologist to render the services.

ARKANSAS

Type of Law: A.C.A. 23-99-204 AWP
Which Providers Are Covered?: Physicians and surgeons (M.D.'s & D.O.'s), podiatrists, chiropractors, physical therapists, speech pathologists, audiologists, dentists, optometrists, hospitals, hospital-based services, psychologists, licensed professional counselors, respiratory therapists, pharmacists, occupational therapists, long-term care facilities, home health care and hospice care, licensed ambulatory surgery centers, rural health clinics, licensed certified social workers, licensed psychological examiners, advanced practice nurses, licensed dietitians,

Note to Table: AWP = Any Willing Provider Law: FOC = Freedom of Choice Law:
This table excludes statutes relating solely to one or more of the following groups: chiropractors, dentists, pharmacists, nurse midwives, podiatrists, optometrists, and psychiatric services provided in psychiatric hospitals.
Sources: BNA's Health Law & Business Portfolios No. 1000, Doc. 8 (2000); Vickie Yates Brown, "Provider Credentialing & Termination: What Works?" Paper presented at the 10th Annual Managed Care Law Conference (Apr. 1999); Current statutes and administrative regulations.

Table 1. *Continues....*

community mental health centers or clinics, certified orthotists and prosthetists.
Which Entities/Types of Policies Must Comply?: Insurance companies, hospital and medical service corporations, HMOs, PPOs, PHOs, TPAs, and PBMs authorized to administer, offer or provide a health benefit plan.
Description: Covered entities must give health care providers listed the opportunity to participate in their plan if providers are willing to accept the plan's terms and conditions. The U.S. Court of Appeals for the Eighth Circuit ruled that Arkansas' any-willing-provider statute was preempted by ERISA. Prudential Ins. Co. v. National Park Medical Ctr., 154 F.3d 812 (8th Cir. 1998).

Type of Law: A.C.A. 23-79-114 Non-discrimination/FOC
Which Providers Are Covered?: Physicians, chiropractors, optometrists, podiatrists, psychologists, dentists, CRNAs.
Which Entities/Types of Policies Must Comply?: Entities issuing individual or group policies for accident and health insurance or entities issuing policies, contracts, plans, or agreements for hospital or medical service or indemnity or reimbursement.
Description: The person entitled to benefits or the person performing the services is entitled to payment or reimbursement on an equal basis for the service if the policy, contract, plan, or agreement provides for payment or reimbursement for the service if provided by a physician; freedom of choice between physicians and optometrists, podiatrists, psychologists, dentists, or CRNAs.

DELAWARE

Type of Law: 18 Del. Code Ann. §3528 FOC
Which Providers Are Covered?: Hospitals, nurses, and physicians (medical or surgical services).
Which Entities/Types of Policies Must Comply?: Group health insurers.
Description: Policy cannot require that services be rendered by a particular hospital or person.

GEORGIA

Type of Law: Ga. Code Ann. 33-20-16 AWP
Which Providers Are Covered?: Physicians, dentists, podiatrists, health care providers.
Which Entities/Types of Policies Must Comply?: Health care corporations. (defined in §33-20-3 as a corporation established to administer one or more health plans)
Description: Appropriately licensed providers who are reputable and in good standing shall have the right to become participating physicians or approved health care providers or both under terms or conditions imposed on other participating physicians or approved health care providers.

Type of Law: Ga. Code Ann. §33-30-25 AWP
Which Providers Are Covered?: Health care providers.
Which Entities/Types of Policies Must Comply?: Insurers, fraternal benefit societies, health care plans, nonprofit medical service or hospital corporations, or HMOs that are authorized to sell accident and sickness insurance contracts and that are offering preferred provider arrangements.
Description: Entities covered may impose "reasonable limits" on the number or classes of preferred providers that meet the entities' standards. However, a covered entity must not discriminate on the basis of religion, race, color, national origin, age, sex, or marital or corporate status, and must give all licensed and qualified providers within a defined service area who satisfy the entity's standards an opportunity to become a preferred provider.

Type of Law: Ga. Code Ann. §33-18-17 FOC
Which Providers Are Covered?: Physicians, dentists and podiatrists.
Which Entities/Types of Policies Must Comply?: Not-for-profit medical service corporations.
Description: Contracts issued by corporations cannot limit freedom of choice with the respect to the providers covered.

Type of Law: Ga. Code Ann. §33-18-18 AWP
Which Providers Are Covered?: Physicians, dentists and podiatrists.
Which Entities/Types of Policies Must Comply?: Not-for-profit medical service corporations.

Note to Table: AWP = Any Willing Provider Law: FOC = Freedom of Choice Law:
This table excludes statutes relating solely to one or more of the following groups: chiropractors, dentists, pharmacists, nurse midwives, podiatrists, optometrists, and psychiatric services provided in psychiatric hospitals.
Sources: BNA's Health Law & Business Portfolios No. 1000, Doc. 8 (2000); Vickie Yates Brown, "Provider Credentialing & Termination: What Works?" Paper presented at the 10th Annual Managed Care Law Conference (Apr. 1999); Current statutes and administrative regulations.

Table 1. *Continues....*

Description: Physicians, dentists, and podiatrists licensed to practice in Georgia who are reputable and in good standing shall have the right to become a participating physician in the medical service corporation operating in the county in which s/he resides or practices, under such terms and conditions as are imposed on other participating physicians under similar circumstances.

Type of Law: Ga. Code Ann. §33-24-54 Modified FOC/assignment
Which Providers Are Covered?: Non-participating or non-preferred providers, including physicians, pharmacists, dentists, chiropractors, optometrists, podiatrists, osteopaths, and psychologists.
Which Entities/Types of Policies Must Comply?: Entities issuing/administering accident and sickness insurance policies, subscriber contracts or self-insured health benefit plans.
Description: Entities issuing accident and sickness insurance policies, subscriber contracts, or self-insured health benefit plans that provide benefits payable to participating or preferred providers shall be required to pay benefits either directly to licensed non-participating or non-preferred providers who have rendered health care services, have a written assignment of benefits, and have given written notice of such assignment to the entity or jointly to such non-participating or non-preferred providers and to the insured, subscriber, or other covered person.

IDAHO

Type of Law: Idaho Code §41-3927 AWP
Which Providers Are Covered?: Health care providers.
Which Entities/Types of Policies Must Comply?: Managed care organizations.
Description: Organizations issuing benefits must be willing to contract with all qualified providers who meet the requirements of the organization, practice within the general area served by the organization, wish to become participating providers, and are qualified to practice under Idaho law.

Type of Law: Idaho Code §41-2872 AWP
Which Providers Are Covered?: Health care providers.
Which Entities/Types of Policies Must Comply?: Stock or mutual insurers.
Description: Insurers issuing benefits must be willing to contract with all qualified providers who meet the requirements of the insurer, practice within the general area served by the insurer, wish to become participating providers, and are qualified to practice Idaho law.

Type of Law: Idaho Code §41-3408 AWP
Which Providers Are Covered?: Chiropractors, dentists, optometrists, osteopaths, pharmacists, physicians, and podiatrists.
Which Entities/Types of Policies Must Comply?: Hospital and professional service corporations (provide all or part of one or more health care services for prepayments).
Description: Corporation must be willing to contract with designated providers who are qualified to practice under Idaho law, who desire to become participant licensees, and who practice within the general area served by the corporation.

ILLINOIS

Type of Law: 215 Ill. Comp. Stat. 5/370h AWP
Which Providers Are Covered?: Noninstitutional providers (persons licensed under Medical Practice Act).
Which Entities/Types of Policies Must Comply?: Insurance companies and administrators.
Description: Entities regulated must be willing to contract with any noninstitutional providers who meet the established terms and conditions. The terms and conditions may not Adiscriminate unreasonably against or among noninstitutional providers."

KENTUCKY

Type of Law: KRS 304.17A-270 AWP
Which Providers Are Covered?: Facilities or services required to be licensed under KRS 216B, pharmacists, physicians, osteopaths, podiatrists, chiropractors, dentists, optometrists, physician assistants, nurse practitioners, and other health care practitioners as determined by administrative regulations promulgated under KRS Chapter 13A.
Which Entities/Types of Policies Must Comply?: Health insurers (insurance companies, HMOs, self-insurer or MEWA not exempt from

Note to Table: AWP = Any Willing Provider Law: FOC = Freedom of Choice Law:
This table excludes statutes relating solely to one or more of the following groups: chiropractors, dentists, pharmacists, nurse midwives, podiatrists, optometrists, and psychiatric services provided in psychiatric hospitals.
Sources: BNA's Health Law & Business Portfolios No. 1000, Doc. 8 (2000); Vickie Yates Brown, "Provider Credentialing & Termination: What Works?" Paper presented at the 10th Annual Managed Care Law Conference (Apr. 1999); Current statutes and administrative regulations.

Table 1. *Continues....*

state regulation by ERISA, provider-sponsored integrated health delivery network, self-insured employer-organized association, or nonprofit hospital, medical-surgical, dental, or health service corporation).
Description: "A health insurer shall not discriminate against any provider who is located within the geographic coverage area of the health benefit plan and who is willing to meet the terms and conditions for participation established by the health insurer, including the Kentucky State Medicaid program and Medicaid partnerships." The Sixth Circuit has found that this statute regulates insurance and is therefore saved from ERISA preemption. Kentucky Ass'n of Health Plans v. Nichols, 227 F.3d 352 (6th Cir. 2000).

Type of Law: La. Rev. Stat. Ann. §40:1300.145 (Rural Hospital Preservation Act) AWP
Which Providers Are Covered?: Rural hospitals and physicians practicing in such hospitals.
Which Entities/Types of Policies Must Comply?: Managed care organizations including but not limited to HMOs, PPOs, and other entities authorized by law to bear risk for the payment of health care services.
Description: Managed care organizations must "offer rural hospitals and hospitals located in parishes with a population of sixty-five thousand or less, and physicians practicing at such hospitals, participation as providers in the managed care organizations on terms and conditions that are no more restrictive than [those] applicable to other hospitals and physicians practicing at such hospitals."

MICHIGAN

Type of Law: M.C.L.A. §500.3529 Non-discrimination
Which Providers Are Covered?: Health professionals.
Which Entities/Types of Policies Must Comply?: HMOs.
Description: HMOs may contract with or employ health professionals on the basis of cost, quality, availability of services to the membership, conformity to the administrative procedures of the HMO, and other factors relevant to delivery of economical, quality care, but shall not discriminate solely on the basis of the class of health professionals to which the health professional belongs.

MINNESOTA

Type of Law: Minn. Stat. §62Q.095 AWP
Which Providers Are Covered?: Allied independent health providers (independently enrolled audiologists, chiropractors, dietitians, home health care providers, licensed marriage and family therapists, nurse practitioners or advanced practice nurses, occupational therapists, optometrists, opticians, outpatient chemical dependency counselors, pharmacists (not employed by or based on the premises of the health plan company), physical therapists, podiatrists, licensed psychologists, psychological practitioners, licensed social workers, speech therapists).
Which Entities/Types of Policies Must Comply?: Health plan companies, except any health plan company with 50,000 or fewer enrollees and those exempt under subdivision 6. (Subdivision 6 exempts staff-model health plan companies as defined in §295.50, subdivision 12b.) Health plan companies include insurance companies, nonprofit health service plan corporations, HMOs, fraternal benefit societies, joint self-insured employee health plans, integrated service networks, and community integrated service networks.
Description: Health plan company must "establish an expanded network of allied independent health providers, in addition to a preferred network." For acceptance into the expanded network, a provider must (1) meet the company's credentialing standards; (2) agree to the terms and requirements of the company's provider agreement and (3) agree to adhere to th" Amanaged care protocols"of the health plan company.

MISSISSIPPI

Type of Law: Miss. Code §83-41-417 AWP
Which Providers Are Covered?: Health care providers.
Which Entities/Types of Policies Must Comply?: HMOs and managed care entities.
Description: HMOs and managed care entities must establish procedures to give interested health care providers located in the geographic area served an opportunity to apply for participation.

Type of Law: Miss. Code §83-41-211 FOC
Which Providers Are Covered?: Psychologists, licensed professional counselors, and licensed clinical social workers.
Which Entities/Types of Policies Must Comply?: Insurance policies, medical service plans, hospital service contracts, or hospital and medical service contracts that provide for reimbursement for any diagnosis and treatment of mental, nervous or emotional disorders only.

Note to Table: AWP = Any Willing Provider Law: FOC = Freedom of Choice Law:
This table excludes statutes relating solely to one or more of the following groups: chiropractors, dentists, pharmacists, nurse midwives, podiatrists, optometrists, and psychiatric services provided in psychiatric hospitals.
Sources: BNA's Health Law & Business Portfolios No. 1000, Doc. 8 (2000); Vickie Yates Brown, "Provider Credentialing & Termination: What Works?" Paper presented at the 10th Annual Managed Care Law Conference (Apr. 1999); Current statutes and administrative regulations.

Table 1. *Continues....*

Description: Insured is entitled to reimbursement for services rendered by duly licensed physician or by duly licensed psychologist, professional counselor, or clinical social worker provided that the diagnosis and treatment is within the lawful scope of practice of the licensee.

MONTANA

Type of Law: Mont. Code Ann. §33-22-1704 AWP
Which Providers Are Covered?: Health care providers.
Which Entities/Types of Policies Must Comply?: Health care insurers (insurer that provides disability coverage, a health service corporation, a fraternal benefit society, and any other entity providing health coverage except an HMO) entering into preferred provider agreements.
Description: A preferred provider agreement must provide all healthcare providers with the opportunity to participate on the basis of a competitive bid or offer.

NEW MEXICO

Type of Law: NMS §59A-22-32 FOC
Which Providers Are Covered?: Hospitals, physicians, optometrists, psychologists, podiatrists, certified nurse-midwives, registered lay midwives, or registered nurses in expanded practice, chiropractors, dentists, osteopaths, acupuncturists.
Which Entities/Types of Policies Must Comply?: Health insurance policies, contracts, or health care plans.
Description: Insured shall have full freedom of choice in the selection of the covered providers within the area and limits of coverage offered.

NEW YORK

Type of Law: New York Insurance Code §4235 FOC
Which Providers Are Covered?: Physical therapists, podiatrists, optometrists, dentists, licensed health professionals, speech-language pathologists or audiologists, psychiatrists or psychologists, and chiropractors.
Which Entities/Types of Policies Must Comply?: Group accident, group health or group accident and health insurance.
Description: Subscribers shall be entitled to reimbursement whether a service is performed by a physician or one of the covered providers.

OHIO

Type of Law: Ohio Rev. Code Ann. 3923.23 Modified FOC
Which Providers Are Covered?: Licensed osteopath, optometrist, chiropractor or podiatrist.
Which Entities/Types of Policies Must Comply?: Insurers.
Description: Reimbursement for such providers shall not be denied when such service is rendered by a person so licensed.

OKLAHOMA

Type of Law: Okla. Stat. tit. 36, §3634 FOC
Which Providers Are Covered?: Podiatrists, psychologists, licensed and certified clinical social workers.
Which Entities/Types of Policies Must Comply?: Health insurers.
Description: Beneficiaries may select any licensed/qualified practitioner to perform podiatry services, psychological services, or licensed and certified clinical social work services covered by an insurance policy, provided that in the case of a PPO, the podiatrist, psychologist, or clinical social worker is a contracting provider.

Type of Law: Okla. Stat. tit. 36, §6055 FOC
Which Providers Are Covered?: Health care practitioners.
Which Entities/Types of Policies Must Comply?: Accident and health insurance policies.
Description: Insured may select practitioners to perform service as long as the service falls within the licensed scope of practice of the practitioners.

Note to Table: AWP = Any Willing Provider Law: FOC = Freedom of Choice Law:
This table excludes statutes relating solely to one or more of the following groups: chiropractors, dentists, pharmacists, nurse midwives, podiatrists, optometrists, and psychiatric services provided in psychiatric hospitals.
Sources: BNA's Health Law & Business Portfolios No. 1000, Doc. 8 (2000); Vickie Yates Brown, "Provider Credentialing & Termination: What Works?" Paper presented at the 10th Annual Managed Care Law Conference (Apr. 1999); Current statutes and administrative regulations.

Table 1. *Continues....*

PENNSYLVANIA

Type of Law: 40 P.S. §1511 modified FOC
Which Providers Are Covered?: Person licensed in Pennsylvania to practice medicine, osteopathy, dentistry, chiropractic, podiatry or physical therapy.
Which Entities/Types of Policies Must Comply?: Any insurance policy, self-insured sickness, health and/or welfare plan.
Description: Reimbursement shall not be denied when such service is rendered by a person so licensed.

RHODE ISLAND

Type of Law: R.I. Gen. Laws §23-17.13-3 modified AWP
Which Providers Are Covered?: Health care providers.
Which Entities/Types of Policies Must Comply?: Health plans.
Description: (c) Issuance of certification— (7) A health plan shall not exclude a provider of covered services from participation in its provider network based solely on: (a) The providers degree or license as applicable under state law; or (b) The provides lack of affiliation with, or admitting privileges at a hospital, if such lack of affiliation is due solely to the provider's type of license.

SOUTH DAKOTA

Type of Law: SDCL §58-17-54 modified FOC
Which Providers Are Covered?: Physicians, CRNAs, psychologists, dentists, osteopaths, licensed social workers, optometrists, chiropractors, podiatrists, physician assistants, and nurse practitioners and midwives.
Which Entities/Types of Policies Must Comply?: Health insurance policies and contracts.
Description: Reimbursement may not be denied for a covered service it is rendered by a provider that is covered by the statute.

TEXAS

Type of Law: Tex. Ins. Code Ann. §20A.14(g), (h) FOC/AWP (see also 28 TAC §11.1402)
Which Providers Are Covered?: Health care providers.
Which Entities/Types of Policies Must Comply?: Health maintenance organizations.
Description: (g) Licensed providers or providers otherwise authorized to practice in Texas who comply with terms and conditions set by an HMO may not be denied participation "on the sole basis of type of license or authorization."
(h) HMOs shall provide a 20-day period during each year in which providers or physicians in the geographic service area may apply to participate in providing health care services.

Type of Law: 28 TAC §3.3704 FOC
Which Providers Are Covered?: Hospitals, physicians and practitioners.
Which Entities/Types of Policies Must Comply?: Preferred provider benefit plans.
Description: Plan cannot require that a service be rendered by a particular hospital, physician, or practitioner. Insureds must be provided with reasonable access to all classes direct and of physicians and practitioners licensed to treat illness or injuries and to provide services covered by the plan. The insurer cannot restrict the rights of an insured to exercise full freedom of choice in the selection of a physician or a provider.

UTAH

Type of Law: Utah Code Ann.§31A-22-617AWP
Which Providers Are Covered?: Health care providers (defined in § 78-14-3 as hospitals, physicians, registered nurses, licensed practical nurses, nurse-midwives, dentists, dental hygienists, optometrists, clinical laboratory technologists, pharmacists, physical therapists, podiatrists, psychologists, chiropractic physicians, naturopathic physicians, osteopathic physicians and surgeons, audiologists, speech-language pathologists, clinical social workers, certified social workers, social service workers, marriage and family counselors, practitioners of obstetrics or others rendering similar care or services)
Which Entities/Types of Policies Must Comply?: Insurers, third-party administrators.
Description: Insurers cannot unfairly discriminate between classes of providers. Insurers must allow providers to apply for and be designated

Note to Table: AWP = Any Willing Provider Law: FOC = Freedom of Choice Law:
This table excludes statutes relating solely to one or more of the following groups: chiropractors, dentists, pharmacists, nurse midwivès, podiatrists, optometrists, and psychiatric services provided in psychiatric hospitals.
Sources: BNA's Health Law & Business Portfolios No. 1000, Doc. 8 (2000); Vickie Yates Brown, "Provider Credentialing & Termination: What Works?" Paper presented at the 10th Annual Managed Care Law Conference (Apr. 1999); Current statutes and administrative regulations.

Table 1. *Continues....*

as preferred providers if they agree to meet established terms and conditions. Nevertheless, "reasonable limitations" may be placed on the number of designated preferred providers based on substantial economic grounds, or expected use of particular services based on prior provider-patient profiles.

VIRGINIA

Type of Law: Va. Code Ann.§38.2-3407AWP
Which Providers Are Covered?: Hospitals, physicians, chiropractors, optometrists, opticians, professional counselors, psychologists, clinical social workers, podiatrists, physical therapists, chiropodists, clinical nurse specialists who render mental health services , audiologists, speech pathologists, certified nurse midwives, acupuncturists, and marriage and family therapists.
Which Entities/Types of Policies Must Comply?: Insurers offering or administering preferred provider policies or contracts that limit the providers eligible for payment as preferred providers.
Description: Insurers shall establish terms and conditions that must be met in order to receive payment as a preferred provider. The terms and conditions "shall not discriminate unreasonably against or among such health care providers." Insurers must not exclude any hospital, physician, or other type of provider listed who is willing to meet the terms and conditions. The U.S. Court of Appeals for the Fourth Circuit found that Va. Code Ann. §38.2-3407 regulates the business of insurance and thus escapes preemption by ERISA. Stuart Circle Hosp. Corp. v. Aetna Health Management, 995 F.2d 500 (4th Cir.), cert. denied, 510 U.S. 1003 (1993).

Type of Law: Va. Code Ann.§38.2-4209modified AWP
Which Providers Are Covered?: Hospitals, physicians, other health care providers (podiatrists, chiropodists, optometrists, opticians, chiropractors, professional counselors, psychologists, physical therapists, clinical social workers, clinical nurse specialists who render mental health services, certified nurse midwives, acupuncturists, audiologists or speech pathologists).
Which Entities/Types of Policies Must Comply?: Non-stock corporations.
Description: Providers who are willing to accept established terms and conditions may qualify for payment under preferred provider subscription contracts.

WASHINGTON

Type of Law: RCWA 48.43.045AWP
Which Providers Are Covered?: Health care providers.
Which Entities/Types of Policies Must Comply?: All health plans.
Description: All health plans must permit every category of health care provider to provide health services or care for conditions included in the basic health plan services to the extent that the provision of such health services or care is within the health care provider'spermitted scope of practice and the providers agree to abide by standards related to the provision, utilization review, and cost containment of health services, management and administrative procedures, and provision of cost effective and clinically efficacious health services. The Ninth Circuit has held that this law is not preempted by ERISA. Washington Physicians Serv. Ass'n v. Gregoire, 147 F.3d 1039 (9th Cir. 1998), cert. denied, 525 U.S. 1141 (1999).

WEST VIRGINIA

Type of Law: W. Va. Code §33-15-14 non-discrimination
Which Providers Are Covered?: Medical physicians, osteopathic physicians, podiatric physicians, chiropractic physicians, midwives and nurse practitioners.
Which Entities/Types of Policies Must Comply?: Health insurance policies, health care service plans or other contracts.
Description: If policy, plan or contract provides for payment of a medical procedure, it will be construed to include payment to all providers covered by the statute who render that procedure. Any limitation or condition places upon services, diagnoses or treatment by, or payment to such licensed providers shall apply equally to all such types of licensed providers without unfair discrimination.

Note to Table: AWP = Any Willing Provider Law: FOC = Freedom of Choice Law:
This table excludes statutes relating solely to one or more of the following groups: chiropractors, dentists, pharmacists, nurse midwives, podiatrists, optometrists, and psychiatric services provided in psychiatric hospitals.
Sources: BNA's Health Law & Business Portfolios No. 1000, Doc. 8 (2000); Vickie Yates Brown, "Provider Credentialing & Termination: What Works?" Paper presented at the 10th Annual Managed Care Law Conference (Apr. 1999); Current statutes and administrative regulations.

Table 1. *Continues....*

WISCONSIN

Type of Law: W.S.A. 628.36 FOC/AWP
Which Providers Are Covered?: Health care professionals, health care facilities, health care services and organizations.
Which Entities/Types of Policies Must Comply?: Health care plans, except for HMOs, PPOs, and limited service health organizations.
Description: Plans may not prevent any person covered from choosing freely among providers who have agreed to participate in the plan and abide by its terms, except by requiring the person covered to select primary providers to be used when reasonably possible. No provider may be denied the opportunity to participate in a health care plan other than an HMO, a limited service health organization or a preferred provider plan, except for cause related to malpractice.

WYOMING

Type of Law: Wyo. Stat. §26-22-503 AWP
Which Providers Are Covered?: Providers.
Which Entities/Types of Policies Must Comply?: Groups, insurers.
Description: Groups or insurers must grant any provider willing to meet the established requirements the right to enter into contracts relating to heath care services.

Type of Law: Wyo. Stat. §26-34-134 AWP
Which Providers Are Covered?: Providers (any physician, hospital, HMO, or other person licensed or otherwise authorized to furnish health care services in the state in which the services are rendered).
Which Entities/Types of Policies Must Comply?: HMOs.
Description: Providers willing to meet an HMO's established terms shall not be denied the right to contract with the HMO. ("This subsection shall not be construed to require any health maintenance organization to involuntarily employ any person....") An HMO may not discriminate against a provider on the basis of the provider's academic degree.

Note to Table: AWP = Any Willing Provider Law: FOC = Freedom of Choice Law:
This table excludes statutes relating solely to one or more of the following groups: chiropractors, dentists, pharmacists, nurse midwives, podiatrists, optometrists, and psychiatric services provided in psychiatric hospitals.
Sources: BNA's Health Law & Business Portfolios No. 1000, Doc. 8 (2000); Vickie Yates Brown, "Provider Credentialing & Termination: What Works?" Paper presented at the 10th Annual Managed Care Law Conference (Apr. 1999); Current statutes and administrative regulations.

Almost all the courts addressing whether ERISA preempts an any willing provider law have found that the law in question relates to an employee benefit plan, either because (a) the statute makes a direct reference to ERISA plans or (b) has a connection with employee benefit plans because it affects the benefits available, or both (6). The few laws that have escaped the preemption clause did so because they made no reference to ERISA plans or were worded in such a way that the courts could state that they did not operate directly on ERISA plans, and the courts found that the laws did not mandate the structure of benefit plans (7).

The real battleground in cases challenging the validity of any willing provider laws under ERISA has been whether the laws are considered to regulate insurance or not. If so, they are saved from ERISA preemption by the savings clause. Courts employ a two-part test to determine whether a state law regulates insurance. First, they ask whether, under a common sense view of the matter, the law regulates insurance. Second, they consider three factors employed to determine whether the law constitutes the "business of insurance" under the McCarran-Ferguson Act: (a) does the law have the effect of transferring or spreading the policyholder's risk; (b) is the practice an integral part of the policy relationship between the insurer and the insured; and (c) is the law limited to entities within the insurance industry. Under the common-sense test, courts look at whether the law regulates entities other than insurance companies. Of late, courts have been less willing to accept the argument that an HMO is fundamentally different from an insurance company, and if the statute has been carefully worded so that it does not regulate third-party administrators or ERISA plans, chances are that the law will pass the common-sense test as a law regulating insurance (8).

Courts also appear to be reading the McCarran-Ferguson factors more broadly than in the past. They have found that any willing provider laws affect the policyholder's risk, reasoning that whereas the insured/covered person might have to pay out of his or her own pocket to gain access to a provider in the absence of such a statute, the presence of such a statute spreads the cost component of the policyholder's risk among all the insureds by prohibiting the unreasonable restriction of providers. The second factor, courts have held, is met because the statutes effectively create a mandatory contract term by expanding the pool of providers from a closed to an open pool, thereby directly impacting the insurer-insured relationship. The third factor – the statute's limitation to entities within the insurance industry – will most likely be met if the court has already found that, under the common-sense test, the law does not regulate entities other than companies engaged in the business of insurance (8).

Given the wealth of case law that has developed on the subject, it should not be a difficult task at this stage for providers to craft any willing provider laws that would escape ERISA preemption or at least have a very good chance of doing so. Faced with the uncertainty of whether an ERISA preemption argument will be a winning one, many insurers and managed care organizations have turned to the language of the statutes and developed "terms and conditions" that may be difficult for many providers to satisfy, thus effectively limiting their panel to a select group of providers (1). At least one state's insurance department has issued an advisory opinion in which it set forth examples of acceptable terms and conditions (medical licensure, specialty board certification, medical malpractice history, valid DEA number, and hospital privileges) versus examples of unacceptable terms and conditions (required membership in a certain professional organization, professional enhancements, a medical degree from a particular university, a certain age, gender, race, sexual orientation or disability, and limiting the number of providers in a provider category based on the determination that the insurer's network is adequate) (9).

Whether any willing provider laws are of value to providers depends, then, on whether the laws themselves are carefully crafted so as to avoid, as much as possible, the risk of ERISA preemption, and whether insurers and managed care organizations will establish "reasonable" terms and conditions of participation. If significant court battles begin to ensue over what terms and conditions are reasonable, providers might want to return to the legislatures and ask them to amend the statutes to define what terms and conditions are *per se* unreasonable.

REFERENCES

1. Schroder, Jr., Jack S. Credentialing Strategies for a Changing Environment: Establishing and Operating an Effective Program, *BNA Health Law & Business Portfolios* No. 1000, § 1000.09(C)(2) (2002).
2. Davis, Gary S. Managed Care Contracting: Advising the Provider, *BNA Health Law & Business Portfolios* No. 1800, § 1800.10(A)(2) (2002).
3. *See* 29 U.S.C. § 1144(a).
4. *See* 29 U.S.C. § 1144(b)(2)(A).
5. *See* 29 U.S.C. § 1144(b)(2)(B).
6. *See, e.g., Kentucky Ass'n of Health Plans, Inc. v. Nichols*, 227 F.3d 352 (6th Cir. 2000), *petition for cert. filed,* 69 U.S.L.W. 3646 (U.S. Mar. 22, 2001) (No. 00-1471); *Prudential Ins. Co. v. National Park Med. Center, Inc.*, 154 F.3d 812 (8th Cir. 1998); *Texas Pharmacy Ass'n v. Prudential Ins. Co.*, 105 F.3d 1035 (5th Cir. 1997), *cert. denied*, 522 U.S. 820 (1997); *CIGNA Healthplan of Louisiana, Inc. v. Louisiana ex rel. Ieyoub*, 82 F.3d 642 (5th Cir. 1996), *cert. denied*, 519 U.S. 964 (1996); *Stuart Circle Hosp. Corp. v. Aetna Health Management*, 995 F.2d 500 (4th Cir.), *cert. denied*, 510 U.S. 1003 (1993).
7. *See, e.g., Washington Physicians Serv. Ass'n v. Gregoire*, 147 F.3d 1039 (9th Cir. 1998); *cert. denied*, 525 U.S. 1141 (1999); *American Drug Stores, Inc. v. Harvard Pilgrim Health Care, Inc.* 973 F. Supp. 60 (D. Mass. 1997).
8. *See, e.g., Kentucky Ass'n of Health Plans, Inc. v. Nichols*, 227 F.3d 352 (6th Cir. 2000), *petition for cert. filed,* 69 U.S.L.W. 3646 (U.S. Mar. 22, 2001) (No. 00-1471); *Washington Physicians Serv. Ass'n v. Gregoire*, 147 F.3d 1039 (9th Cir. 1998); *cert. denied*, 525 U.S. 1141 (1999); *American Drug Stores, Inc. v. Harvard Pilgrim Health Care, Inc.* 973 F. Supp. 60 (D. Mass. 1997).
9. Kentucky Department of Insurance Advisory Opinion 99-08.

SECTION 5

APPENDICES

APPENDIX A

i. PATIENT QUESTIONNAIRE

COMPREHENSIVE MEDICAL HISTORY

Dear Sir / Madam:

You have an appointment at Pain Management Center for evaluation and assistance with your pain problem. In order to do this properly, it is essential that we learn as much about you as we can, and that we learn it directly from you. Pain is a very complex matter and we have found it essential to know many things about you that you may not readily see as important.

This questionnaire requests a great deal of such personal information. PLEASE READ CARE FULLY AND ANSWER EACH AND EVERY QUESTION. This is YOUR personal account of YOUR problem.

The information you provide is strictly confidential, for center use only, and cannot and will not be released to anyone else without your specific written permission. Please return the completed forms in the enclosed self addressed envelope or bring it with you.

Thank you in advance for your help.

____

Medical Director

Date: ____________________

I. A. Name ________________________________ S.S. # ______/______/______
First Middle Initial Last

B. Sex: ☐ M ☐ F C. Race __________ D. Age ______ E. DOB __________

F. Address ______________ City __________ State _____ Zip __________

E Mail Address ____________________ Tel. __________

G. Occupation ______________ H. Employer ______________

I. Nearest Relative's Name ____________________ Tel. __________

II. A. Referring Physician ______________________________
Name and Address

B. Family Physician ______________________________
Name and Address

III. A. Describe the pain for which you are now seeking help in one sentence. (Example: "My back hurts.")

____

IV. A. **H/O PRESENT ILLNESS PLEASE LIST ONLY RELEVANT PROBLEMS**

PROBLEM(S)

1. ☐ Headaches Since: ______________________________
2. ☐ Neck Pain Since: ______________________________
3. ☐ Shoulder Pain R L Since: ______________________________
4. ☐ Upper Extremity Pain Since: ______________________________
   (any part from arm to fingers) R L ______________________________
5. ☐ Thoracic Spine Pain Since: ______________________________
6. ☐ Chest Wall Pain Since: ______________________________
   (not heart related chest pain) ______________________________
7. ☐ Low Back Pain Since: ______________________________
8. ☐ Hip Pain R L Since: ______________________________
9. ☐ Lower Extremity Pain Since: ______________________________
   (any part from thigh to toes) R L ______________________________
10. ☐ Abdominal Wall Pain R L Since: ______________________________
11. ☐ Abdominal Pain Since: ______________________________
12. ☐ Groin Pain R L Since: ______________________________
13. ☐ Other __________ Since: ______________________________

B. **PRESENT PAIN HISTORY:** *(If your problem is headache only, without neck or face pain, please go to question IV D.)* For any other problem or headache with neck or face pain, complete this section.

1. PAIN RATIO (mark which item best describes the ratio between pain in your back/leg or neck/arm)

FOR BACK PAIN	FOR NECK PAIN
☐ Back pain only; no leg pain	☐ Neck pain only; no arm pain
☐ Back pain worse than leg pain	☐ Neck pain worse than arm pain
☐ Back pain and leg pain equal	☐ Neck pain and arm pain equal
☐ Leg pain worse than back pain	☐ Arm pain worse than neck pain
☐ Leg pain only; no back pain	☐ Arm pain only; no neck pain

2. Please mark which of these words best describe your pain. Put the mark on the line which gives the intensity of that particular quality of your pain. (only mark applicable ones not all)

	Mild	Moderate	Severe	Unbearable	
1. Sharp	☐	☐	☐	☐	1.
2. Shooting	☐	☐	☐	☐	2.
3. Throbbing	☐	☐	☐	☐	3.
4. Cramping	☐	☐	☐	☐	4.
5. Stabbing	☐	☐	☐	☐	5.
6. Gnawing	☐	☐	☐	☐	6.
7. Hot Burning	☐	☐	☐	☐	7.
8. Aching	☐	☐	☐	☐	8.
9. Heavy	☐	☐	☐	☐	9.
10. Tender	☐	☐	☐	☐	10.
11. Splitting	☐	☐	☐	☐	11.
12. Tiring Exhausting	☐	☐	☐	☐	12.
13. Sickening	☐	☐	☐	☐	13.
14. Fearful	☐	☐	☐	☐	14.
15. Punishing Cruel	☐	☐	☐	☐	15.

3. How much time during an average day (24 hour period) are you in pain?

☐ few hours ☐ less than 1/3rd of time ☐ almost 50% of time ☐ almost 2/3rds of time
☐ almost 24 hours ☐ anytime that I am not lying down ☐ pain is not present daily

4. Do you have any of the following related to pain: (only mark applicable ones not all)

☐ 1. Numbness	☐ 4. Weakness
☐ 2. Tingling	☐ 5. Problems with Bowels related to pain
☐ 3. Pins & Needles	☐ 6. Problems with Bladder related to pain

5. PAIN INTENSITY

On a scale of 1 to 10, with "0" representing no pain, "1" representing a nuisance which would not interfere with daily activities (i.e., toothache) while "10" would be the most severe pain imaginable (suicidal pain, having a baby or pain of a kidney stone), which number would describe your pain:

	Less Pain ← → More Pain
1. What is your pain like today?	0 1 2 3 4 5 6 7 8 9 10
2. What is your least pain?	0 1 2 3 4 5 6 7 8 9 10
3. What is your worst pain?	0 1 2 3 4 5 6 7 8 9 10
4. Overall average pain?	0 1 2 3 4 5 6 7 8 9 10

5. How many extremely bad days (horrible or excruciating pain) in a week do you experience? _____

6. FACTORS CHANGING PAIN (Do any of the following make your pain change?)

		No Change	Somewhat Worse	A Lot Worse	Some Better	Complete Relief Pain Free	
1.	Sitting	☐	☐	☐	☐	☐	1.
2.	Standing	☐	☐	☐	☐	☐	2.
3.	Walking	☐	☐	☐	☐	☐	3.
4.	Bending Forward	☐	☐	☐	☐	☐	4.
5.	Bending Backward	☐	☐	☐	☐	☐	5.
6.	Bending to Same Side	☐	☐	☐	☐	☐	6.
7.	Bending to Opposite Side	☐	☐	☐	☐	☐	7.
8.	Lying Down / Resting	☐	☐	☐	☐	☐	8.
9.	Driving	☐	☐	☐	☐	☐	9.
10.	Lifting	☐	☐	☐	☐	☐	10.
11.	Coughing / Sneezing	☐	☐	☐	☐	☐	11.
12.	Cold Weather	☐	☐	☐	☐	☐	12.
13.	Damp Weather	☐	☐	☐	☐	☐	13.
14.	Sexual Activity	☐	☐	☐	☐	☐	14.
15.	Overhead Activity	☐	☐	☐	☐	☐	15.
16.	Other________________						16.

7. Are you able to perform any of the following without assistance?

1. Walk	☐ No ☐ Yes	4. Climb Stairs	☐ No ☐ Yes
2. Sit	☐ No ☐ Yes	5. Dress Self	☐ No ☐ Yes
3. Stand	☐ No ☐ Yes	6. Drive Car	☐ No ☐ Yes

8. EFFECT OF PAIN ON ACTIVITIES

(a) Please place a mark in the box which best describes the change in your condition now (after pain).

My desire to participate and actual participation in:	No Change	Decreased Some	Decreased Quite A Bit	Disappeared	Increased Somewhat	Increased Quite A Bit	
1. Personal Activities	☐	☐	☐	☐	☐	☐	1.
2. Household Cleaning, etc.	☐	☐	☐	☐	☐	☐	2.
3. Family Activities	☐	☐	☐	☐	☐	☐	3.
4. Recreation & Hobbies	☐	☐	☐	☐	☐	☐	4.
5. Sexual Relations	☐	☐	☐	☐	☐	☐	5.
6. Physical Exercise	☐	☐	☐	☐	☐	☐	6.
7. Watching TV	☐	☐	☐	☐	☐	☐	7.

(b) How often do you have to stop your activities and sit down or lie down to control your pain?

☐ Rarely not daily ☐ Approximately once per day ☐ Several times per day

☐ I spend almost all day lying or sitting to control my pain

What aspect of your pain, or which pain, is the most bothersome to you and why? ______________

____

9. PAIN DIAGRAM (please mark the actual or exact location of pain):

Please read these instructions very carefully. We want you to indicate on the drawings on this page ACCURATELY where your pain is and how much pain you feel. Please read all instructions CAREFULLY.

1. Mark on the drawing the spot where your pain usually is or starts. Mark this with an "X". If the pain starts at that spot (X) and travels to another part of your body, draw a line from the spot (X) where it starts to where it ends. If it is a whole area (example: whole arm, whole leg, etc.) that hurts, shade in that area.
2. We also want to know how much pain you feel. Look at the list of words below, which most people agree describes intensity of pain. Each word has a number.

1 = MILD OR JUST FEELING OF DISCOMFORT
2 = MODERATE OR UNCOMFORTABLE
3 = SEVERE OR DISTRESSING
4 =VERY SEVERE OR HORRIBLE
5 = EXCRUCIATING OR UNBEARABLE

REMEMBER TO:

SHOW WHERE YOUR PAIN USUALLY IS OR STARTS (X).

SHOW IF THE PAIN TRAVELS OR RADIATES.

SHOW IF THE PAIN IS EXTERNAL IN SKIN (E) OR DEEP IN MUSCLES OR BONES (I) OR BOTH (E & I).

SHOW OR RATE HOW MUCH PAIN YOU FEEL (1 5).

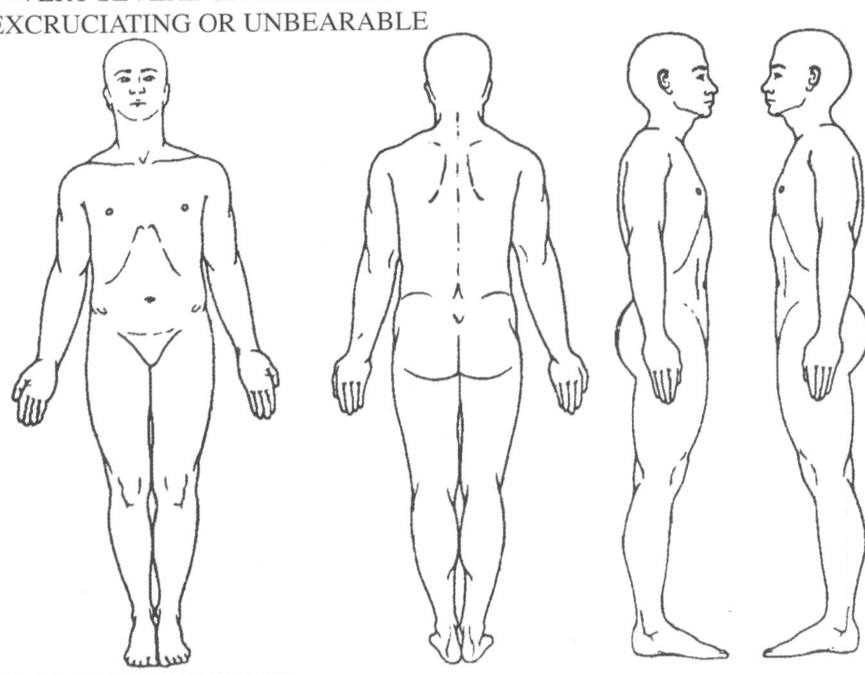

NOTES FOR STAFF ONLY (PLEASE DO NOT WRITE HERE): ______________________

____

____

____

____

____

____

____

C. **SLEEP PATTERN**

1. Has your sleeping pattern changed due to pain? ☐ No ☐ Yes ______________
2. Do you have a problem falling asleep? ☐ No ☐ Yes If yes, how many nights a week? ________
3. How many times do you wake up at night?____________ How many nights a week? __________
4. When do you go to sleep?__________ 5. How many hours do you try to sleep each night? __________
6. How many hours do you actually sleep?______________________
7. How do you feel when you wake up in the morning?______________________
8. Do you sleep during the daytime? ☐ No ☐ Yes If yes, how long? ______________

D. **HEADACHE QUESTIONS** *(If you do not have any headaches, please skip this section.)*

1. When did you first develop headaches? (approx. date or year) ______
2. Do you have more than one type of headache? ☐ No ☐ Yes ______
3. Where is your headache located? ☐ Neck ☐ Back of the head ☐ Eyes ☐ Face ☐ Temples
4. Where does your headache start? ☐ Neck ☐ Back of the head ☐ Behind eyes ☐ ______
5. How often and what time of the day do you have headaches? ______
6. Which of the following words do you use to describe your headache?
   ☐ Throbbing ☐ Pounding ☐ Splitting ☐ Pulsating ☐ Piercing ☐ Dull ☐ Aching ☐ Tight
   ☐ Other ______
7. How long does one episode of headache last? Shortest ______ Longest ______
8. What physical or environmental factors trigger the headache or make it worse? ☐ Bright light
   ☐ Tobacco ☐ Alcohol ☐ Exercise ☐ Loud Noises ☐ Sex ☐ Changes in weather
   ☐ Increased physical activity ☐ Travel ☐ Other ______
9. Have you noticed if any foods trigger your headache? ☐ No ☐ Yes If yes, list ______
   ______
10. Do you have any craving for any particular foods prior to a headache occurrence? ☐ No ☐ Yes
    If yes, list ______
11. i. If female, do you get headaches before, during or after menstrual cycle? ______
    ii. Have you had: ☐ Hysterectomy ☐ Ovaries removed
    iii. Do you have any problems with hormones? ☐ No ☐ Yes
    iv. Do you take any hormones? ☐ No ☐ Yes ______
12. How is your headache controlled? ______
    ______
13. Do you experience any of the following? (only mark applicable ones not all)

	Before Headache	During Headache	After Headache
Nausea	☐	☐	☐
Vomiting	☐	☐	☐
Dizziness	☐	☐	☐
Abnormal Sensations	☐	☐	☐
Aura	☐	☐	☐
Sound Sensitivity	☐	☐	☐
Light Sensitivity	☐	☐	☐
Other ______	☐	☐	☐

14. Can you tell when you are going to have a headache? If so, explain ______
    ______
    ______

THANK YOU FOR YOUR PATIENCE
YOU ARE DOING GOOD, PLEASE CONTINUE!

V. PAST, FAMILY, AND SOCIAL HISTORY ☐ No problems in past

A. **PAST PAIN HISTORY (DO NOT describe present problem.)** (mark only applicable ones not all)

1. ☐ Motor vehicle injury(ies) ____
2. ☐ Work related injury(ies) ____
3. ☐ Any other injury(ies) ____
4. ☐ Headache ____
5. ☐ Pain in Neck ____
6. ☐ Pain in Upper Extremities ____
7. ☐ Pain in Upper Back ____
8. ☐ Pain in Mid Back ____
9. ☐ Chest Wall Pain ____
10. ☐ Pain in Lower Back ____
11. ☐ Pain in Lower Extremities ____
12. ☐ Pain in Joints (example: shoulder, hip or knee) ____
13. ☐ Arthritis ____
14. ☐ Other ____

B. **EVALUATION AND TREATMENT HISTORY FOR PAIN**

1. Please list all doctors, chiropractors, therapists and emergency room doctors you have seen for your problem and when you first saw them.

PROVIDER SEEN	APPROX. # OF TIMES	DURING THE YEARS

2. Total number of providers seen: ____
3. Which of the following tests have been performed? (mark only applicable ones not all)

☐ a) Regular X Rays of ____
☐ b) CT Scan of ____
☐ c) Myelogram of ____
☐ d) MRI Scan of ____
☐ e) Discogram of ____
☐ f) Bone Scan of ____
☐ g) Nerve Conduction of ____
☐ h) Other____ ____

4. Please list all operations you have **ever** had for the pain (not other surgeries).
   PLEASE INCLUDE YEAR AND DOCTOR'S NAME
   1. ______
   2. ______
   3. ______
   4. ______
   5. ______
5. Please describe other treatments, in sequence, since this problem started, with months / years.
   1. ☐ Chiropractic Treatment ______
   2. ☐ Physical Therapy ______
   3. ☐ Psychotherapy ______
   4. ☐ Epidurals ______
   5. ☐ Nerve Blocks ______
   6. ☐ Cortisone Injections ______
   7. ☐ Cortisone By Mouth ______
   8. ☐ Other ______
6. a. What medicines are you now taking for pain, anxiety, etc., and how often for each? (do not list here medicines taken for medical problems)

	Medication	Dose	Frequency	Date Started	Time of Last Dose
i.					
ii.					
iii.					
iv.					
v.					

   How much relief do you obtain from drugs? ______
   Duration of relief: ______ Side effects: ______

   b. What other medicines (if any) and how long have you used them in the past?
   ______
   ______

C. i. FAMILY PAIN HISTORY ☐ No problems

	Relationship		Relationship		Relationship
1. ☐ Migraine	______	7. ☐ Shoulder Pain	______	14. ☐ Multiple Sclerosis	______
2. ☐ Headaches	______	8. ☐ Arm Pain	______	15. ☐ Epilepsy	______
3. ☐ Neck Pain	______	9. ☐ Hip Pain	______	16. ☐ Depression	______
4. ☐ Upper / Mid Back Pain	______	10. ☐ Leg Pain	______	17. ☐ Panic Disorder	______
5. ☐ Chest Wall Pain (not related to heart)	______	11. ☐ Arthritis	______	18. ☐ Schizophrenia	______
		12. ☐ Fibromyalgia	______	19. ☐ Alcoholism	______
6. ☐ Low Back Pain	______	13. ☐ Lupus	______	20. ☐ Drug Abuse	______
				21. ☐ Suicide	______

ii. FAMILY MEDICAL HISTORY ☐ No problems

1. ☐ High Blood Pressure	______	5. ☐ Bronchial Asthma	______
2. ☐ Heart Attack	______	6. ☐ Bleeding Disorder	______
3. ☐ Heart Disease	______	7. ☐ Hepatitis	______
4. ☐ Diabetes	______	8. ☐	______

D. **ENVIRONMENTAL INFORMATION**

1. List all the areas you have lived in (example: Paducah, KY): ____________________
2. Education: Highest grade completed ____________________
3. Marital status: ☐ Married ☐ Separated ☐ Divorced ☐ Widowed ☐ Single How long? ____
4. Do you live: ☐ Alone ☐ with Spouse ☐ with Parents ☐ Other ____________________
5. Previous marriages: ☐ None ☐ Yes If yes, how many? ____________________
6. Number of children: Male ________ Female ________ Ages of children ____________________
7. If married, which of the below best describes your marriage?
   ☐ Completely satisfactory ☐ Satisfactory ☐ Tolerable ☐ Intolerable ☐ No opinion
8. Has your pain problem changed your relationship with your spouse and family? ☐ No ☐ Yes
   If yes, describe ____________________
9. Excessive exposure at home to: ☐ None ☐ Fumes ☐ Dust ☐ Solvents ☐ Noise

E. **OCCUPATIONAL HISTORY:** ☐ Disabled since _______ ☐ Retired since _______ ☐ Homemaker

(If disabled, retired, over 65, or homemaker you may skip this section.)

1. Please list all previous occupations / jobs you have held in the last 10 years. (Attach separate sheet if necessary.) ____________________
   ____
2. Please describe your current job (if unemployed, your very last job). ____________________
   ____
   a. How long have you held this job? __________ 2. How many hours per week do your work? ______
   b. Does your work involve:
      Standing: ☐ No ☐ Yes If yes, how long at a time? ____________________
      Driving: ☐ No ☐ Yes If yes, how long at a time? ____________________
      Walking: ☐ No ☐ Yes If yes, how long at a time? ____________________
      Lifting: ☐ No ☐ Yes If yes, how many lbs. more than 6 8 times per hour? __________
      If yes, how many lbs. less than 6 times per hour? __________
      Sitting: ☐ No ☐ Yes If yes, how many hours per day? ____________________
   c. Does your work involve vibration (i.e., machinery, driving, etc.)? ☐ No ☐ Yes
      If yes, what is source of vibration? ____________________
   d. Excessive exposure at work to: ☐ Fumes ☐ Dust ☐ Solvents ☐ Noise
   e. Have you missed much work because of your current or previous illness, injury or pain?
      ☐ No ☐ Yes When was the last day you worked "full duty"? ____________________
   f. If you are not working, are you currently receiving wage compensation? ☐ No ☐ Yes

F. **HABITS**

1. SMOKING: a. Do you smoke now? ☐ No ☐ Yes Smoking since? ______________
   How many cigarettes per day?______________Cigars per day?______________Pipe? __________
   b. Have you ever smoked? ☐ No ☐ Yes Explain ____________________
2. ALCOHOL: a. Do you drink alcohol? ☐ No ☐ Yes If yes, how much? ______________
   b. Have you ever had problems with alcohol? ☐ No ☐ Yes If yes, explain ______________
3. CAFFEINATED DRINKS: Do you consume drinks with caffeine? ☐ No ☐ Yes
   If yes, ☐ Coffee ☐ Tea ☐ Iced Tea ☐ Colas ☐ Other ____________No. of Cups Daily ____
4. DRUGS: Do you use any street drugs? ☐ No ☐ Yes If yes, explain ______________

G. **HOBBIES:** List your hobbies: ____________________

Are you participating now? ☐ No ☐ Yes If yes, describe: ____________________

VI. A. MEDICAL HISTORY (answer only applicable ones do not mark all)

1. Constitutional Symptoms ☐ No Problems
- ☐ Weight loss _________ lbs., during ___________
- ☐ Weight gain _________lbs., during ___________
- ☐ Recurrent fever
- ☐ General weakness
- ☐ Fatigue
- ☐ ________________________________

2. Skin ☐ No Problems
- ☐ Dry skin
- ☐ Recurrent rashes
- ☐ Eczema
- ☐ Itching
- ☐ Changes in skin color
- ☐ Changes in hair or nails
- ☐ ________________________________

3. Hematologic / Lymphatic ☐ No Problems
- ☐ Swollen glands
- ☐ Low blood count (anemia)
- ☐ Easy bruising
- ☐ Easy bleeding
- ☐ Slow to heal after cuts
- ☐ h/o blood transfusions
- ☐ Enlarged glands
- ☐ Phlebitis
- ☐ HIV positive
- ☐ on blood thinners
- ☐ ________________________________

4. Head / Face ☐ No Problems
- ☐ Headaches
- ☐ h/o head injury without residual problems
- ☐ h/o head injury with residual problems of ________________________________
- ☐ Facial pain
- ☐ TMJ R L
- ☐ Tic douloureux R L _______________
- ☐ ________________________________

5. Eyes ☐ No Problems
- ☐ Nearsighted
- ☐ Farsighted
- ☐ Wear glasses
- ☐ Wear contact lenses
- ☐ Cataracts at present time R L
- ☐ Cataract surgery R L
- ☐ Conjunctivitis R L
- ☐ Glaucoma R L
- ☐ Double vision R L
- ☐ Blurred vision R L
- ☐ ________________________________

6. Ear / Nose / Mouth

i. Ears ☐ No Problems
- ☐ Hard of hearing R L
- ☐ Hearing aids R L
- ☐ Chronic ear discharge R L
- ☐ Vertigo
- ☐ Ringing in ears R L
- ☐ ________________________________

ii. Nose / Sinuses ☐ No Problems
- ☐ Sinus discharge
- ☐ Nasal discharge
- ☐ Repeated nosebleeds
- ☐ Deviated nasal septum
- ☐ Chronic sinus problems
- ☐ Chronic stuffy nose
- ☐ Hay fever
- ☐ Nasal polyps
- ☐ ________________________________

iii. Mouth / Throat ☐ No Problems
- ☐ Loose Teeth / No Teeth
- ☐ Dentures ___Full ___Partial
- ☐ Bleeding gums
- ☐ Dry mouth
- ☐ Sore throat
- ☐ Hoarseness
- ☐ Vocal cord polyps
- ☐ Trouble swallowing
- ☐ ________________________________

7. Chest / Breasts ☐ No Problems
- ☐ Breast masses
- ☐ Breast surgery
- ☐ Chest surgery
- ☐ ________________________________

8. Respiratory ☐ No Problems
- ☐ Recurrent cough
- ☐ Chronic bronchitis
- ☐ Emphysema
- ☐ COPD
- ☐ Bronchial asthma
- ☐ Tuberculosis
- ☐ Wheezing
- ☐ ________________________________

9. Cardiac / Peripheral Vascular

i. Cardiac ☐ No Problems
- ☐ Heart trouble
- ☐ Swelling of feet
- ☐ High blood pressure
- ☐ Chest pain
- ☐ Heart attack
- ☐ Bypass surgery
- ☐ Angioplasty
- ☐ Mitral valve prolapse
- ☐ Heart murmur

- ☐ Valvular surgery
- ☐ Heart failure
- ☐ Shortness of breath with walking
- ☐ ____________________

ii. Peripheral Vascular ☐ No Problems

- ☐ Poor circulation in arm R L
- ☐ Blood clots in arm R L
- ☐ Varicose veins R L
- ☐ Poor circulation in legs R L
- ☐ Blood clots in leg R L
- ☐ Vascular surgery R L
- ☐ ____________________

10. Hepatic Biliary / Gastrointestinal / Abdominal

i. Hepatic Biliary ☐ No Problems

- ☐ Any liver disease
- ☐ h/o hepatitis Active______ Inactive ______
- ☐ h/o jaundice due to liver disease
- ☐ h/o jaundice due to gallbladder disease
- ☐ Gallbladder problems
- ☐ ____________________

ii. Gastrointestinal ☐ No Problems

- ☐ Loss of appetite
- ☐ Abdominal pain
- ☐ Problems with gas
- ☐ Heartburn
- ☐ Recurrent nausea
- ☐ Recurrent vomiting
- ☐ Recurrent diarrhea
- ☐ Recurrent constipation
- ☐ Ulcer
- ☐ Hiatal hernia
- ☐ Regurgitation
- ☐ Reflux
- ☐ Indigestion
- ☐ h/o vomiting blood
- ☐ Blood in stools
- ☐ Loss of control of bowels
- ☐ ____________________

11. Urinary ☐ No Problems

- ☐ Frequent urination
- ☐ Difficulty with urination
- ☐ Burning
- ☐ Inability to control
- ☐ Loss of control
- ☐ Blood in urine
- ☐ Kidney stones
- ☐ ____________________

12. Genital / Reproductive

Male ☐ No Problems

- ☐ Discharge
- ☐ Pain in testicle(s) R L
- ☐ Lumps in testicle(s) R L
- ☐ Hydrocele R L
- ☐ Sexually transmitted disease(s)
- ☐ Sexual dysfunction
- ☐ ____________________

Female ☐ No Problems

- ☐ Menstruation regular____ irregular____
- ☐ LMP
- ☐ Post Menopausal Syndrome since ________
- ☐ Recurrent vaginal discharge
- ☐ No. of pregnancies ____ miscarriages____
- ☐ Cesarean sections 1 2 3 4
- ☐ Uterus removed
- ☐ Ovaries removed R L
- ☐ D & C (s)
- ☐ On hormones
- ☐ h/o cancer of uterus ovary(ies)
- ☐ Sexual dysfunction
- ☐ Sexually transmitted disease(s)
- ☐ ____________________

13. Endocrine ☐ No Problems

- ☐ Excessive thirst or urination
- ☐ Heat intolerance
- ☐ Cold intolerance
- ☐ Change in hat or glove size
- ☐ Thyroid trouble ___ underative ___overactive
- ☐ Sugar diabetes since ________________
  Insulin dependent ________________
- ☐ Disease of pituitary gland
- ☐ Disease of adrenal gland
- ☐ ____________________

14. Musculoskeletal ☐ No Problems

- ☐ Muscle cramps
- ☐ Stiff joints ________________
- ☐ Swelling of joints
- ☐ Generalized arthritis
- ☐ Rheumatoid arthritis
- ☐ Fibromyalgia syndrome
- ☐ Osteoporosis
- ☐ Neck pain
- ☐ Upper back pain
- ☐ Low back pain
- ☐ Heel spur(s) how many____________
- ☐ Gout
- ☐ Difficulty with walking
- ☐ Cold upper extremity(ies) R L
- ☐ Cold lower extremity(ies) R L
- ☐ Pain in feet
- ☐ ____________________

15. Neurological / Psychiatric

i. Neurological ☐ No Problems

- ☐ Frequent or recurrent headaches
- ☐ Fainting
- ☐ Blackouts
- ☐ Stroke
- ☐ Dizzy spells
- ☐ Gait difficulties
- ☐ Seizures
- ☐ Epilepsy
- ☐ Tremors
- ☐ Neuropathy
- ☐ Weakness
- ☐ Paralysis
- ☐ ____________________

ii. Psychiatric ☐ No Problems
☐ Problems with concentration
☐ Confusion
☐ Problems with thinking or thought process
☐ Problems with memory
☐ Depressed
☐ Anxious
☐ Shaky
☐ Agitated
☐ ____________________

16. Other ☐ No Problems
☐ Chicken Pox
☐ Rheumatic Fever
☐ Cancer
☐ Polio
☐ ____________________

17. i. Allergies ☐ No Problems
Drug Allergies ____________________
____
____
Food Allergies ____________________
____
____
Environmental Allergies ____________________
____
____

ii. Immunologic ☐ No Problems
☐ Immunologic disorders____________
☐ AIDS
☐ Lupus

B. Previous hospitalizations without surgery (include year and doctor's name)

1. ____________________
2. ____________________
3. ____________________
4. ____________________
5. ____________________

C. Previous surgeries (include year and doctor's name)

1. ____________________
2. ____________________
3. ____________________
4. ____________________
5. ____________________
6. ____________________

D. List all medications you currently take (prescription and nonprescription including aspirin, Tylenol, etc.)

	Medication	Dose	Frequency	Date Started	Time of Last Dose
1.					
2.					
3.					
4.					
5.					
6.					
7.					
8.					

YOU ARE ALMOST DONE GREAT JOB! PLEASE CONTINUE!

VII. PSYCHOLOGICAL HISTORY (Please answer as honestly as possible.)

This section asks some questions which may be repetitive and a few of the statements may seem unusual. Please do not be concerned, as these questions are included to describe people with many types of problems.

A. 1. Number of brothers and sisters: Older B_____ S_____ Younger B_____ S_____

2. Were you raised by: ☐ Mother & Father ☐ Mother ☐ Father ☐ Other _______________

3. Give a description of your father's personality: _______________

4. Give a description of your mother's personality: _______________

5. Your childhood and home life while growing up were: (choose one)
☐ Happy ☐ Very Happy ☐ Neither Happy nor Unhappy ☐ Unhappy

B. **YOUR PAST / PRESENT EXPERIENCES**

1. Problems with memory ☐ No ☐ Yes
2. Flashbacks ☐ No ☐ Yes
3. Unusual experiences ☐ No ☐ Yes
4. Dizziness ☐ No ☐ Yes
5. Physical violence ☐ No ☐ Yes
6. Sexual abuse ☐ No ☐ Yes
7. Arrests ☐ No ☐ Yes
8. Jail sentences ☐ No ☐ Yes

C. **STRESS / ANXIETY**

Have you been tense, nervous or anxious? ☐ No ☐ Yes

1. Do you have excessive worry and anxiety about a number of events or activities? ☐ No ☐ Yes
2. Do you experience these worries and anxieties most of the time? ☐ No ☐ Yes
3. Do you find it difficult to control your worries? ☐ No ☐ Yes
4. Are your worries and anxieties associated with:
   a. Restlessness or feeling keyed up or on edge? ☐ No ☐ Yes
   b. Being easily fatigued? ☐ No ☐ Yes
   c. Having difficulty concentrating so that your mind goes blank? ☐ No ☐ Yes
   d. Irritability or muscle tension? ☐ No ☐ Yes
   e. Sleep disturbance (difficulty falling or staying asleep, or restless)? ☐ No ☐ Yes
5. Do you have panic attacks (intense fear of impending doom)?_______________ ☐ No ☐ Yes
6. Do you have any phobias?_______________ ☐ No ☐ Yes
7. Have you ever had a traumatic experience?_______________ ☐ No ☐ Yes

D. **DEPRESSION**

1. Do you feel depressed (sad, empty)? ☐ No ☐ Mildly ☐ Moderately ☐ Significantly
2. Do you feel depressed most of each day? ☐ No ☐ Yes
3. Do you feel depressed nearly every day? ☐ No ☐ Yes
4. Does your family and/or friends think you are depressed? ☐ No ☐ Yes
5. Are you irritable (cranky, cross, grouchy) or restless and agitated? ☐ No ☐ Yes
6. Have you lost interest in all, or almost all, activities, most of the time? ☐ No ☐ Yes
7. Have you lost or gained a significant amount of weight over the past few months? ☐ No ☐ Yes
   Is this due to change in appetite? ☐ No ☐ Yes
8. Do you have trouble getting to sleep or awaken frequently and can't get back to sleep? ☐ No ☐ Yes
9. Do you sleep too much? ☐ No ☐ Yes
10. Do you feel sluggish and slow and you can't seem to get going? ☐ No ☐ Yes
    Does this happen nearly every day? ☐ No ☐ Yes

11. Do you experience fatigue or loss of energy? ☐ No ☐ Yes
    Does this happen nearly every day? ☐ No ☐ Yes
12. Do you feel worthless or guilty most of the time? ☐ No ☐ Yes
13. Has your ability to think, concentrate and make decisions diminished? ☐ No ☐ Yes
14. Do you have thoughts of ending your own life (suicide)? ☐ No ☐ Yes
    If yes, do you have a plan? ☐ No ☐ Yes
15. Have you ever attempted suicide? ☐ No ☐ Yes
    If yes, how many times?______________ When was the last attempt?______________________

E. **PREVIOUS PSYCHIATRIC HISTORY**

1. Have you ever had psychiatric / psychological treatment or evaluation? ☐ No ☐ Yes
   If yes, by whom and how many times?________________________________
   Medication ____ ☐ No ☐ Yes
   Psychotherapy ____ ☐ No ☐ Yes
   Most recent treatment or visit on_______________________________________

VIII. A. **LITIGATION**

i. You have or plan to have an attorney helping you? ☐ No ☐ Yes If yes, list name and address of attorney and how he / she is helping, etc.____

ii. Have you had any lawsuits in the past? Explain____

____

IX. TREATMENT GOALS Describe goals of your treatment.

☐ Return to work ☐ Have sexual relations
☐ Be more active and functional ☐ Participate in sports
☐ Play with kids and grandkids ☐ ________________________________

X. CERTIFICATION

I certify that I have answered truthfully all the questions, and have not knowingly withheld any information concerning any of the above problems, either past or present.

______________________________ ______________________________
Your Signature Witness

______________________________ ______________________________
Date Date

THANK YOU!

______________________________ ______________________________
Signature of Reviewing Physician Date

APPENDIX A

ii. PHYSICIAN ASSESSMENT FORM

INITIAL ASSESSMENT

INITIAL EVALUATION

☐ ____________________

Name ______________________________ Date ______________________

History Provided By: ______________________ Quality: ______________________

History of Present Illness:

Symptomatology: ☐ Location ☐ Quality ☐ Severity ☐ Duration ☐ Timing

☐ Context ☐ Modifying factors ☐ Associated signs & symptoms

Systems	Multisystems	Single System	
		Musculoskeletal	Neurologic
Constitutional	Two elements	Two elements	Two elements
Musculoskeletal	Six elements	Five elements	Three elements
Neurological	Three elements	Two elemenets	Sixteen elements
Cardiovascular	Seven elements	One element (Peripheral)	Three elements
Chest / breasts	Two elements		
Ears, nose, mouth and throat	Six elements		
Eyes	Three elements		One element (Ophthalmoscopy)
Genitourinary	Four elements male Seven elements female		
Gastrointestinal	Five elements		
Lymphatic	Four elements	One element	
Psychiatric	Four elements	Two elements	
Respiratory	Four elements		
Skin	Two elements	One element	

PSYCHOSOCIAL EVALUATION

P3 ☐ No ☐ Yes MCMI III ☐ No ☐ Yes

I. PAIN PATIENT PROFILE (P3)

A. VALIDITY ☐ No ☐ Yes

B. DEPRESSION

	Patient's T Score		
Below Average Pain Patient	29	45	
Average Pain Patient	46	54	______________
Above Average Pain Patient	55	71	

C. ANXIETY

	Patient's T Score		
Below Average Pain Patient	29	45	
Average Pain Patient	46	55	______________
Above Average Pain Patient	56	71	

D. SOMATIZATION

	Patient's T Score		
Below Average Pain Patient	21	44	
Average Pain Patient	45	55	______________
Above Average Pain Patient	56	99	

II. MCMI III

A. VALIDITY ☐ No ☐ Yes

B. GROSS PSYCHOLOGICAL PROFILE

1. ☐ None
2. ☐ Mild
3. ☐ Mild to Moderate
4. ☐ Moderate
5. ☐ Moderately Severe
6. ☐ Severe

C. DEPRESSION

MCMI Dysthymic BR________________________ Diagnosis: ☐ No ☐ Yes 300.40

Major Depression BR __________________ Diagnosis: ☐ No ☐ Yes 296.3

D. ANXIETY

MCMI Anxiety BR ________________________ Diagnosis: ☐ No ☐ Yes 300.02

E. SOMATIZATION

MCMI Somatoform BR______________________ Diagnosis: ☐ No ☐ Yes 300.81

F. OTHER PSYCHOLOGICAL PROBLEMS

☐ 1. None
☐ 2. Psychoactive substance abuse
☐ 3. Schizophrenia
☐ 4. Bipolar Disorder
☐ 5. Thought Disorder
☐ 6. Delusional Disorder
☐ 7. ________________________
☐ 8. ________________________

FUNCTIONAL ASSESSMENT

1. PERCEIVED FUNCTION:

Sitting ____________ at a time Driving ____________ at a time
Standing ____________ at a time Walking ____________ at a time
Balancing ____________ Stooping ____________
Lifting ____________ Carrying ____________
Kneeling ____________ Squatting ____________
Reaching Straight ____________ Overhead ____________
Pushing / Pulling ____________ Other ____________

2. RANGE OF MOTION: ☐ **Arcon** ☐ **Cybex EDI** ☐ ____________

Cervical ☐ Valid ☐ Invalid ____________
Lumbar ☐ Valid ☐ Invalid ____________

3. GRIP STRENGTH: Valid ____________ Invalid ____________

4. LIFT CAPACITY: Static: Valid ____________ of 4 categories

PHYSICAL EVALUATION

1. INITIAL OBSERVATION:

i. Arrived: ☐ On time ☐ Late ☐ Early ____________
ii. ☐ Accompanied by ____________ to center ☐ arrived alone to center
iii. ☐ Accompanied by ____________ to exam ☐ arrived to examination, alone
iv. Greeting manner: ☐ Pleasant ☐ Unpleasant ☐ Without any feeling ☐ ____________
v. Any unusual or noteworthy initial behavior:
☐ None ____________ ☐ Nervous ____________ ☐ Overreacting ____________
vi. Tatoos: ☐ None ☐ 1 ☐ 2 ☐ 3 ☐ 4 ☐ 5 ☐ Numerous
vii. Reinforcement by spouse or other: ☐ Yes ☐ No By: ____________
viii. Other ____________

2. CONSTITUTIONAL: (Need at least 3) (Describe positive and negative)

i. Height ____________ Weight ____________
ii. Pulse rate ____________ mt ____________ reg ____________ irr ____________ reg irr
iii. Blood pressure ____________ mm/hg ____________ supine ____________ sitting ____________ standing
iv. Respirations ____________ /mt
v. Temperature ____________ °F ____________ Oral ____________ Axillary

3. GENERAL APPEARANCE: (Describe positive and negative)

☐ WNL

i.	Development	________Well developed	________Poorly developed	
ii.	Nutrition	________Well nourished	________Undernourished	
iii.	Build	________normal	________thin	________overweight
		________somewhat obese	________obese	
iv.	Body habitus	________independent	________walked with a cane	
		________walked with walker	________wheelchair bound	________bedridden
v.	Deformities	________no physical disabilities	________disabilities	
vi.	Grooming	________well groomed	________poorly groomed	________casual

4. SKIN: (Describe positive and negative)

☐ WNL

	Scars	Rashes	Lesions	Ulcers	Café au lait spots
Head	____	____	____	____	____
Face	____	____	____	____	____
Neck	____	____	____	____	____
Thoracic Spine	____	____	____	____	____
Chest	____	____	____	____	____
Lumbar Spine	____	____	____	____	____
Abdomen	____	____	____	____	____
Upper Extremity (Right)	____	____	____	____	____
Upper Extremity (Left)	____	____	____	____	____
Lower Extremity (Right)	____	____	____	____	____
Lower Extremity (Left)	____	____	____	____	____

5. HEMATOLOGIC / LYMPHATIC: (Describe positive and negative)

☐ WNL

________Anemic ________Cyanosis

Enlarged lymph nodes:

________Neck R L	________Supraclavicular R L
________Axilla R L	________Groin R L
________Popliteal R L	________Other ________________

6. EYES: ☐ WNL

☐ Wearing glasses	☐ Wearing contacts	
☐ Erythema R L	☐ Sty R L	☐ Chalazion R L
☐ Conjunctivitis	☐ Ectropion R L	☐ Ptosis R L
☐ Proptosis R L	☐ Nystagmus R L	☐ Strabismus R L
☐ Swelling R L	☐ Abnormal pupillary reaction	☐ ____________

Ophthalmoscopy ☐ WNL ______________________________

7. EARS, NOSE, MOUTH & THROAT: ☐ ALL WNL

i. Ears: ☐ WNL

__________Lesions R L __________Discharge R L __________Hard of Hearing R L

ii. Nose / Sinuses: ☐ WNL

__________Lesions __________Discharge __________Sinus Tenderness R L

iii. Mouth & Throat: ☐ WNL

________No teeth ________Missing teeth ________Partials ________Dentures

________Full dentures ________Gingivitis

________Pallor________________________ ________Cyanosis________________________

8. CHEST: ☐ WNL Breasts ☐ Deferred

________Scars Midline R L ________Tenderness Midline R L

________Masses R L ____

9. RESPIRATORY: ☐ WNL

________Shortness of breath ________Intercostal retraction ________Visible respiratory effort

________Dullness ________Flatness ________Hyper resonance ________Rubs R L

________Prolonged expiration R L ________Wheezing R L ________Rales R L ________Ronchi R L

10. CARDIOVASCULAR / PERIPHERAL VASCULAR:

i. Cardiovascular: ☐ WNL

________Abnormal PMI ________Tachycardia ________Bradycardia ________Abnormal carotid pulses

________Irregular cardiac rhythm ________Murmur: Grade_______ Type_______

ii. Peripheral Vascular: (Describe positive and negative)

☐ WNL

	UE	LE		UE	LE
Varicosities	R L	R L	Swelling	R L	R L
Abnormal Pulses	R L	R L	Edema	R L	R L
Temperature Change	R L	R L	Tenderness	R L	R L

11. GASTROINTESTINAL (ABDOMINAL): ☐ WNL

________Tenderness ________Masses ________Rigidity

________Enlarged liver ________Palpable spleen ________Incisional hernia

________Inguinal hernia R L ________Abnormal bowel sounds ________________________

12. GENITOURINARY:

Male: ☐ WNL ☐ Deferred

________Hydrocele R L ________Spermatocele R L ________Tenderness of cord R L

________Testicular mass R L ________Penile warts Prostate ______enlarged ______tender

________Nodular ________Asymmetric ________________________

Female: ☐ WNL ☐ Deferred

________lesions ________masses ________discharge

________cystocele ________rectocele

13. PSYCHIATRIC: (Describe positive and negative)

☐ WNL

Lack of orientation to	______time	______place	______person
Abnormal mood and affect	______depressed	______anxious	
Shaky	______agitated	______irritated	
Lack of memory	______recent	______remote	
______Lack of concentration	______Lack of attention span		
Language difficulty	______naming objects	______repeating phrases	______speech
Lack of knowledge	______current events	______past history	

14. MUSCULOSKELETAL (NEUROLOGICAL):

i. Dominance: ☐ Right handed ☐ Left handed ☐ ____________________

ii. Posture:

i. Cervical Lordosis ____________		☐ Normal	☐ Increased	☐ Decreased
ii. Lumbar Lordosis ____________		☐ Normal	☐ Increased	☐ Decreased
iii. Kyphosis ____________	☐ None	☐ Mild	☐ Moderate	☐ Severe
iv. Scoliosis ____________	☐ None	☐ Mild	☐ Moderate	☐ Severe

iii. Gait:

i. Straight Line	____________	☐ Normal	☐ Limp	☐ Unable
ii. On Heels	____________	☐ Normal	☐ Limp	☐ Unable
iii. On Toes	____________	☐ Normal	☐ Limp	☐ Unable

iv. Coordination: ☐ WNL

Abnormal:
________________finger / nose
________________heel / knee / shin
________________rapid alternating movements in upper extremities
________________rapid alternating movements in lower extremities

v. Head / Face / Neck: ☐ WNL

Abnormal:

Head:
______lesions R L ______masses R L ______effusions R L
______crepitus R L ______asymmetry ______defects R L ______tenderness R L

Face:
______lesions R L ______masses R L ______effusions R L
______crepitus R L ______asymmetry ______defects R L ______tenderness R L
______TMJ tenderness R L ______Enlarged salivary glands R L
______Supraorbital tenderness R L ______Supratrochlear tenderness R L
______Auriculotemporal tenderness R L ______ ____________________

Neck:
______lesions R L ______masses R L ______effusions R L
______crepitus R L ______asymmetry ______defects R L
______thyromegaly ______jugular distension R L

vi. Cranial Nerves: ☐ WNL

Testing of Cranial Nerves (Abnormals)

_____2nd (visual acuity) _______________ R ☐ _______________ L ☐ _______________

_____3rd, 4th & 6th (pupils) _______________ R ☐ _______________ L ☐ _______________

_____5th (facial sensation) _______________ R ☐ _______________ L ☐ _______________

_____7th (facial symmetry, strength) _______________ R ☐ _______________ L ☐ _______________

_____8th (hearing w/ tuning fork) _______________ R ☐ _______________ L ☐ _______________

_____9th (palate movement) _______________ R ☐ _______________ L ☐ _______________

_____11th (shoulder shrug strength) _______________ R ☐ _______________ L ☐ _______________

_____12th (tongue protrusion) _______________ R ☐ _______________ L ☐ _______________

vii. Cervical Spine: ☐ WNL

A. Inspection: i. ☐ WNL

scar(s) _____anteriorly in neck _____posteriorly in neck _____shoulder R L _____arm R L
_____forearm R L _____hand R L _____finger(s) R L

B. Inspection / Palpation: i. ☐ WNL

_____masses M R L _____lesions M R L _____effusion R L _____defect R L
_____contracture R L _____dislocation R L _____subluxation R L _____laxity R L
_____fasciculations R L _____discoloration R L _____amputation R L
_____crepitus M R L _____swelling M R L

Palpation: ii.

ii. ☐ WNL	RIGHT			MIDLINE / SPINOUS PROCESS TENDERNESS	LEFT		
	Tenderness	Spasm	Trigger Points	Levels	Tenderness	Spasm	Trigger Points
Superficial							
Non Anatomic				Severity			
Paravertebral				0 1 2 3			
Suboccipital w/o HA							
Suboccipital w/ HA							
Periauricular w/o HA							
Periauricular w/ HA							
Upper Trapezius							
Shoulder							
AC Joint							
Arm							
Elbow							
Forearm							
Wrist							
Fingers							

C. Cervical Range of Motion: h WNL

	Reduced	Normal	Increased	Pain				Better	
				None	Mild	Moderate	Severe	Some Relief	Complete Relief
Flexion									
Extension									
Right lateral rotation									
Right lateral flexion									
Left lateral rotation									
Left lateral flexion									

		RIGHT	LEFT
D.	Shoulders (ROM):	N ↓ ↑	N ↓ ↑
	Impingement:	+ -	+ -
E.	Elbow:	______	______
F.	Wrist:	______	______
G.	Hand:	______	______
H.	Fingers:	______	______

I. Motor Examination:

			Focal Deficits
Motor Strength in extremities	______	______	______
Grip Strength	______	______	______
Wasting	______	______	
Tone	______	______	

J. Sensory Examination: ______ ______ ______

K. Reflexes:

Biceps (C5, C6)	______	______
Triceps (C6, C7)	______	______
Brachioradialis (C5, C6)	______	______

L. Other Signs:

Adsons'	+ -	+ -
Tinel's	+ -	+ -
Phalen's	+ -	+ -

M. Non-Physiological Signs:

i. Tenderness ______ + ______ - ______

ii. Distraction ______ + ______ - ______

iii. Simulation ______ + ______ - ______

iv. Regional ______ + ______ - ______

v. Overreaction ______ + ______ - ______

Positive in ________ out of 5 categories

viii. Thoracic Spine / Ribs: ☐ WNL

A. Inspection: i. ☐ WNL ____________________

Scar(s) ____ thoracic spine M R L

B. Inspection / Palpation: ii. ☐ WNL

_____masses M R L _____lesions M R L _____effusion R L _____defect R L
_____contracture R L _____dislocation R L _____subluxation R L _____laxity R L
_____fasciculations R L _____discoloration R L _____amputation R L
_____crepitus M R L _____swelling M R L

ii. ☐ WNL	RIGHT			MIDLINE / SPINOUS PROCESS TENDERNESS	LEFT		
	Tenderness	Spasm	Trigger Points	Levels	Tenderness	Spasm	Trigger Points
Superficial				Severity 0 1 2 3			
Non Anatomic							
Paravertebral							
Upper Trapezius							
Suprascapular							
Supraspinatus							
Infraspinatus							
Middle Trapezius							
Chest Wall							

ix. Lumbar Spine / Pelvis: ☐ WNL

A. Inspection: i. ☐ WNL

Scar(s) _____lumbar spine _____hip(s) R L _____thigh(s) R L
_____knee(s) R L _____leg(s) R L _____ankle(s) R L
_____feet R L ____________ ____________

B. Inspection / Palpation: ii. ☐ WNL

_____masses M R L _____lesions M R L _____effusion R L _____defect R L
_____contracture R L _____dislocation R L _____subluxation R L _____laxity R L
_____fasciculations R L _____discoloration R L _____amputation R L
_____crepitus M R L _____swelling M R L

ii. ☐ WNL	RIGHT			MIDLINE / SPINOUS PROCESS TENDERNESS	LEFT		
	Tenderness	Spasm	Trigger Points	Levels	Tenderness	Spasm	Trigger Points
Superficial				Severity			
Non Anatomic				0 1 2 3			
Paravertebral							
Sciatic Notch							
SI Joint							
Ilio Lumbar							
Glut Max							
Glut Med							
Groin							
Ischial Tuberosities							
Hips							
Knees							
Ankles							
Foot							
Toes							
Other							

C. Lumbar Range of Motion: ☐ WNL

	Reduced	**Normal**	**Increased**	**Pain**				**Better**	
				None	Mild	Moderate	Severe	Some Better	Complete Relief
Flexion									
Deflexion									
Extension									
Right lateral rotation									
Right lateral flexion									
Left lateral rotation									
Left lateral flexion									

	RIGHT	LEFT
D. Hip:	N ↓ ↑	N ↓ ↑
Patrick Fabere's Test:	+ -	+ -
E. Knee:	______	______
F. Ankle:	______	______
G. Foot:	______	______
H. Toes:	______	______

	RIGHT	LEFT	Focal Deficits
I. Motor Examination:			
Strength	________	________	________
Wasting	________	________	
Tone	________	________	
J. Sensory Examination:	________	________	________
K. Reflexes:			
Quadriceps Femoralis (L3, L4)	________	________	
Achilles (L5, S1)	________	________	
Superficial	________	________	
L. Straight Leg Raising			
Sitting	________	________	
Supine			
Active	________	________	
Passive	________	________	
Back Pain	+ -	+ -	
Sciatic Tension Signs	+ -	+ -	

M. Waddell's Non-Physiological signs:

i. Tenderness ________ + ________ - ________
ii. Simulation ________ + ________ - ________
iii. Distraction ________ + ________ - ________
iv. Regional ________ + ________ - ________
v. Overreaction ________ + ________ - ________

Positive in ________ out of 5 categories

x. Fibromyalgia Screen h **Negative** h **Positive**

Bilateral Tenderness present in following:

Suboccipital ________________ Lateral Epicondylec(s) ________________
Cervical C4 - 6 ________________ Greater Trochanters ________________
Second Costochondral Junction ________ Knee Medial (Fat Pad) ________________
Trapezius ________________ Gluteus Maximus ________________
Supraspinatus ________________

Other: ____
____
____
____
____
____
____
____
____

SYMPTOM MAGNIFICATION

1. **Lack of Strategy to Control Symptoms** ☐ Yes ☐ No ☐ N/A
2. **Lack of Control over Environment** ☐ Yes ☐ No ☐ N/A
3. **OVERT PAIN BEHAVIOR:**

   i. PAIN BEHAVIOR (Keefe and Block, Behavioral Theory, 1982)

(1) Guarding	☐ Yes	☐ No	(5) Sighing	☐ Yes	☐ No
(2) Bracing	☐ Yes	☐ No	(6) Pacing	☐ Yes	☐ No
(3) Rubbing	☐ Yes	☐ No	(7) Shifting	☐ Yes	☐ No
(4) Grimacing	☐ Yes	☐ No	(8) Other	☐ Yes	☐ No

   Positive (> 2 signs) __________ Negative (< 2 signs) __________ NA __________

   ii. MCGILL'S PAIN QUESTIONNAIRE Positive __________ Negative __________

   iii. PAIN RATING Positive __________ Negative __________

   iv. PAIN DIAGRAM Positive __________ Negative __________

   SUMMARY OF CATEGORY

   Positive (> 2 categories) __________ Negative (≤ 2 categories) __________ NA __________

4. LACK OF OBJECTIVE FINDINGS

   i. No paravertebral muscle spasm ☐ Yes ☐ No ☐ N/A __________________

   ii. No motor weakness ☐ Yes ☐ No ☐ N/A __________________

   iii. No sensory deficit ☐ Yes ☐ No ☐ N/A __________________

   iv. No alteration of reflexes ☐ Yes ☐ No ☐ N/A __________________

   v. No positive nerve tension signs ☐ Yes ☐ No ☐ N/A __________________

   vi. No evidence of trigger points ☐ Yes ☐ No ☐ N/A __________________

   SUMMARY OF CATEGORY

   Positive (all yes) __________ Negative (at least 1 No) __________ NA __________

5. LACK OF LABORATORY EVIDENCE

   i. Radiological (No abnormalities) ☐ Yes ☐ No ☐ NA

   ii. Electrodiagnostic (No abnormalities) ☐ Yes ☐ No ☐ NA

   SUMMARY OF CATEGORY

   Positive (all yes) __________ Negative (at least 1 No) __________ NA __________

6. CERVICAL SYMPTOMS OF ABNORMAL ILLNESS BEHAVIOR

i. Pain	☐ Anatomic distribution	☐ Whole arm pain
ii. Numbness	☐ Dermatomal	☐ Whole arm numbness
iii. Weakness	☐ Myotomal	☐ Whole arm giving way
iv. Time Pattern	☐ Varies with time and activity	☐ Never free of pain
v. Response to Treatment	☐ Variable benefit	☐ Intolerance of treatments ☐ Emergency admission(s) to hospital

   Positive (> 3 symptoms) ☐ __________ Negative (< 2 symptoms) ☐ __________ NA __________

7. <u>CERVICAL SIGNS OF ABNORMAL ILLNESS BEHAVIOR</u>

i. Tenderness	☐ Anatomic distribution	☐ Non anatomic
ii. Distraction	☐ No change or limited	☐ Improves with distraction
iii. Simulation	☐ No neck pain	☐ Neck pain
iv. Regional	☐ Anatomical	☐ Non anatomical
v. Overreaction	☐ None or Minimal	☐ Present

Positive (> 3 signs) ☐ __________ Negative (< 3 signs) ☐ __________ NA __________

8. <u>WADDELL'S SYMPTOMS OF ABNORMAL ILLNESS BEHAVIOR (LUMBAR)</u>

	Normal Illness Behavior	Abnormal Illness Behavior
i. Pain	☐ Anatomic distribution	☐ Whole leg pain
		☐ Tailbone pain
ii. Numbness	☐ Dermatomal	☐ Whole leg numbness
iii. Weakness	☐ Myotomal	☐ Whole leg giving way
iv. Time Pattern	☐ Varies with time and activity	☐ Never free of pain
v. Response to Treatment	☐ Variable benefit	☐ Intolerance of treatments
		☐ Emergency admission(s) to hospital

Positive (≥ 3 symptoms) ☐ __________ Negative (< 3 symptoms) ☐ __________ NA __________

9. <u>WADDELL'S SIGNS OF ABNORMAL ILLNESS BEHAVIOR (LUMBAR)</u>

i. Tenderness	☐ Anatomic distribution	☐ Non anatomic
ii. Simulation	☐ No lumbar pain	☐ Lumbar pain
iii. Distraction	☐ Limited	☐ Improves with distraction
iv. Regional	☐ Anatomical	☐ Non anatomical
v. Overreaction	☐ None or minimal	☐ Present

Positive (≥ 3 signs) ☐ __________ Negative (< 3 signs) ☐ __________ NA __________

10. <u>LACK OF MAXIMUM VOLUNTARY EFFORT</u>	YES	NO	NA
i. COV's > 14 hand grip	☐	☐	☐
ii. COV's > 14 static strength	☐	☐	☐
iii. Invalid range of motion inclinometry	☐	☐	☐

Positive (> 2 or > 50%) __________ Negative (< 2 or < 50%) __________ NA __________

11. <u>LACK OF COOPERATION</u>	YES	NO	NA
i. In completing questionnaire	☐	☐	☐
ii. With psychological evaluation	☐	☐	☐
iii. With physical evaluation	☐	☐	☐

Positive __________ Negative __________ NA __________

12. <u>SOMATOFORM IMPLICATIONS</u>	YES	NO	NA
i. MCMI Somatization	☐	☐	☐
ii. P3 Somatization	☐	☐	☐

Positive __________ Negative __________ NA __________

Diagnosis

☐ Positive ≥ __________ ☐ Borderline ≥ __________ ☐ Negative < __________

ICD 9 DIAGNOSTIC CODING

MUSCULOSKELETAL AND NERVOUS SYSTEM

	Cervical	Thoracic	Lumbosacral
1. Disc displacement w/o myelopathy (disc herniation, radiculitis, extrusion, protrusion, prolapse, discogenic syndrome)	722.0	722.11	722.10
2. Disc displacement w/ myelopathy	722.71	722.72	722.73
3. Degeneration of intervertebral disc (includes narrowing of disc space)	722.4	722.51	722.52
4. Facet arthropathy or spondylosis w/o myelopathy, dorsal arthritis, osteoarthritis, spondylarthritis	721.0	721.2	721.3
5. Spondylosis w/ myelopathy (anterior / vert artery compression, spondylogenic compression of cord)	721.1	721.41	721.42
6. Spinal stenosis	723.0	724.04	724.02
7. Radiculitis	723.4	724.4 (unspec.)	724.4 (unspec.)
8. Strain	847.0	847.1	847.2
9. Post laminectomy syndrome	722.81	722.82	722.83
10. Epidural fibrosis	349.2	349.2	349.2
11. Schmorl's nodes	722.39	722.31	722.32
12. Calcification of disc, cartilage, discitis	722.91	722.92	722.93
13. Plexus lesions (thoracic outlet syndrome brachial plexus, lumbar plexus)	353.0		353.1
14. Root lesions (NES) neuritis	353.2	353.3	353.4
15. Closed fracture	805.0	805.2	805.4 l 805.6 s
16. Spina bifida	741.91	741.92	741.93
17. Spina bifida occulta	756.17	756.17	756.17
18. Congenital spondylolysis	756.11	756.11	756.11
19. Acquired degenerative spondylolysis	738.4	738.4	738.4
20. Acquired spondylolisthesis	738.4	738.4	738.4
21. Congenital spondylolisthesis	756.12	756.12	756.12
22. Pain	723.1	724.1	724.2

23. Osteoporosis			41. Non specific neuritis		729.2
Unspecified		733.00	42. Torticollis		
Post menopausal		733.01	Congenital		754.1
Idiopathic		733.02	Hysterical		300.11
Disuse		733.03	Spasmodic		333.83
Drug induced		733.09	Traumatic		347.0
24. Osteoarthritis			43. SLE		695.4
Generalized 715.0			44. Hemiplegia Flaccid		342.0
Localized primary		715.1	45. Hemiplegia Spastic		342.1
Localized secondary		715.2	46. Neuritis of sciatic nerve		355.0
Localized non specific		715.3	47. Carpal tunnel syndrome		354.0
Multiple sites		715.8	48. Median nerve neuritis		354.1
Spine w/o myelopathy		721.90	49. Ulnar nerve neuritis		354.2
Spine w/ myelopathy		721.91	50. Radial nerve neuritis		354.3
25. Rheumatoid arthritis		714.0	51. Pleuritic pain		786.52
Ankylosing spondylitis		720.0	52. Rib pain		786.50
26. Sacroiliitis		720.2	53. Pain in extremity		729.5
27. Sacroiliac pain		724.6	54. Intercostal pain		786.59
28. Coccygodynia		724.79	55. Intercostal neuritis		353.3
29. Sciatica		724.3	56. Tietze's syndrome		733.6
30. Vertebrogenic pain		724.5	57. Peripheral neuropathy		
31. Meralgia paresthetica		355.1	Idiopathic		356.4
32. Ilioinguinal neuritis		353.7	Hereditary		356.0
33. Cauda equina syndrome w/o neuro / bla		344.60	Diabetic		357.2
			Alcoholic		357.5
34. Cauda equina syndrome w/ neuro / bla		344.61	Due to Drug		357.6
			58. Other mononeuritis (U.E.)		354.8
35. Psoriatic arthropathy		696.0	59. Other mononeuritis (L.E.)		355.9
36. Psoriasis		696.1	60. Myofacial Syndrome		729.1
37. Medial popliteal neuritis		355.4	61. Post herpetic neuralgia unspecified		053.13
38. Tarsal tunnel syndrome		355.5			
39. Plantar neuritis		355.6	62. Musculoskeletal disease		723.9
40. Multiple sclerosis		340.0			

PAIN

Anus		569.42	Generalized		780.9	Spermatic cord		608.9
Bladder		788.9	Groin		789.0	Testis		608.9
Bone		733.90	Heart		786.51	Throat		784.1
Breast		611.71	Infraorbital		350.1	Tongue		529.6
Chest (central)		786.50	Kidney		788.0	Tooth		525.9
Atypical		786.59	Laryngeal		784.1	Umbilicus		789.0
Midsternal		786.51	Mouth		528.9	Urinary (organ) sys		788.0
Musculoskeletal		786.59	Nose		478.1	Uterus / Vagina		625.9
Substernal		786.51	Ocular / Ophthalmic		379.91	PAINFUL		
Wall (anterior)		786.52	Penis		607.9	Coitus		
Ear		388.70	Perineum (female)		625.9	Female		625.0
Epigastric, epig.		789.0	Preauricular		388.70	Male		608.89
Flank		789.0	Scrotum		608.9	Psychogenic		302.76
Gas (intestinal)		787.3	Sinus		478.1	Menstruation		625.3
Gastric		536.8	Skin		782.0	Micturition		788.1

PALSY

Brachial plexus		353.0	Progressive supranuclear		333.0
Hemiplegic		343.1	Pseudobulbar NEC		335.23
Monoplegic		343.3	Radial nerve (acute)		354.3
Paraplegic		343.0	Seventh nerve		351.0
Quadriplegic		343.2	Shaking		332.0
Spastic, no congenital or infantile		344.89	Spastic (cerebral) (spinal)		343.9
Facial		351.0	Hemiplegic		343.1
Glossopharyngeal		352.2	Ulnar nerve (tardy)		354.2
Median nerve (tardy)		354.0	Wasting		335.21
Peroneal nerve (acute) (tardy)		355.3			

HEADACHES

Intractable migraine w/ aura		346.01	Unspecified trigeminal		350.9
Non intractable migraine w/ aura		346.00	Bell's palsy		351.0
Intractable migraine w/o aura		346.11	Unspecified facial nerve disorder		351.9
Non intractable migraine w/o aura		346.10	PHN trigeminal		053.12
Intractable cluster		346.21	PHN polyneuropathy		053.13
Non intractable cluster		346.20	Temporal arteritis		446.5
Intractable, hemiplegic / ophthalmic		346.81	Jaw pain		526.9
Non intractable hemiplegic / ophthal		346.80	TMJ		524.62
Unspecified migraine		346.9	Multiple sclerosis		340
Post lumbar puncture headache		349.0	Auriculotemporal neuritis		729.2
Tension headache psychogenic		307.81	Supraorbital neuritis		729.2
Trigeminal neuralgia		350.1	Infratrochlear neuritis		350.8
Headache (non specific)		784.0	Supratrochlear neuritis		350.8
Atypical face pain		350.2	Infraorbital		350.8
Specified trigeminal		350.8	Occipital neuritis		729.2

RSD / CAUSALGIA / NEUROPATHY

Reflex Sympathetic Dystrophy of upper limb		337.21	Causalgia, NOS		355.9
Reflex Sympathetic Dystrophy of lower limb		337.22	Algoneurodystrophy (disuse or Sudek's Atrophy)		733.7
Reflex Sympathetic Dystrophy of specified area		337.29	Unspecified disorder of autonomic nervous system		337.9
Reflex Sympathetic Dystrophy, unspec		337.20	Idiopathic peripheral autonomic neuropathy		337.0
Causalgia of upper limb		354.4	Diabetic autonomic neuropathy		337.1
Causalgia of lower limb		355.71	Phantom limb pain		353.6

SHOULDER / ELBOW / HAND

Shoulder pain		719.41	Contusion of elbow		923.11
Adhesive capsulitis of shoulder		726.0	Osteoarthritis of elbow		715.12
Periarthritis of shoulder		726.2	Traumatic arthritis of elbow		716.12
Supraspinatus syndrome		726.10	Medial epicondylitis		726.31
Calcifying tendinitis of shoulder		726.11	Lateral epicondylitis		726.32
Bicipital tenosynovitis		726.12	Olecranon bursitis		726.33
Complete rupture of rotator cuff		727.61	Bursitis of occupational origin		727.2
Rotator cuff syndrome		726.10	Wrist pain		719.43
Scapulohumeral fibrositis		726.2	Contusion of wrist		923.21
Bursitis of occupational origin		726.2	Hand pain		719.44
Subacromial bursitis		098.52	Finger pain		729.5
Subcoracoid bursitis		726.19	Contusion of hand		923.20
Subdeltoid bursitis		726.19	Metacarpophalyngeal pain		719.44
Contusion of shoulder		923.00	Osteoarthritis of wrist		715.13
Osteoarthritis of shoulder		715.11	Traumatic arthritis of wrist		716.12
Traumatic arthritis of shoulder		716.11	Osteoarthritis of multiple joints		715.19
Osteoarthritis of AC joint		715.11	Traumatic arthritis of multiple joints		716.19
Traumatic arthritis of AC joint		716.11	Pain in multiple sites		719.49
Elbow pain		719.42			

PELVIS / HIP / KNEE / ANKLE

Pelvic or hip pain		719.45	Derangement of lateral meniscus		717.4
Osteoarthritis of hip		715.15	Ankle or foot pain		719.47
Traumatic arthritis of hip		716.15	Osteoarthritis of ankle / foot		715.17
Knee pain		719.46	Traumatic arthritis of ankle		716.17
Osteoarthritis of knee		715.16	Metatarsophalyngeal		719.47
Traumatic arthritis of knee		716.16	Toe pain		729.5
Internal derangement of knee		717	Osteoarthritis of multiple joints		715.19
Old bucket handle tear of medial		717.0	Traumatic arthritis of multiple joints		716.19
Tibial pain		733.90			

MEDICAL DIAGNOSES

CONSTITUTIONAL		CARDIOVASCULAR		Gastric Hyperacidity	
Obesity		Hypertension		Esophagitis	
Overweight		Mitral Valve Prolapse		Hiatal Hernia	
		Mitral Valve Stenosis		Gastroesophageal Reflux	
HEMATOLOGIC / LYMPH		Mitral Valve Incompetence		Irritable Bowel Syndrome	
Anemia		Aortic Valve Incompetence			
Lymph Adenopathy		Aortic Valve Stenosis		GENITOURINARY	
Multiple Myeloma		Congestive Heart Failure		Ureteric Caliculi	
Leukemia		CAD		Bladder Caliculi	
HIV Positive		CAD with Angina		Erectile Dysfunction	
AIDS		CAD with Myocardial Infar			
		CAD with Angioplasty		ENDOCRINE	
EYES / EARS / NOSE / MOUTH		CAD with Stent		Diabetes Mellitus	
Glaucoma		Peripheral Edema		Diabetes Inspidus	
Cataract(s) R L		Deep Vein Thrombosis		Hypothyroidism	
Hard of Hearing R L		Peripheral Vascular Disease		Hypoadrenalism	
Vertigo		Varicose Veins R L			
Deviated Nasal Septum		Anticoagulant Therapy		NEUROLOGICAL	
Vocal Cord Polyps				Stroke	
				Coordination Deficiency	
RESPIRATORY					
Chronic Bronchitis		GASTRO / HEPATIC			
Emphysema		Hepatitis A			
COPD		Hepatitis B			
Bronchial Asthma		Hepatitis C			
Active Tuberculosis		Cholecystitis			
Inactive Tuberculosis		Pancreatitis			
		Constipation			

PSYCHOLOGICAL / DRUG DEPENDENCE

Generalized anxiety disorder		300.02	Barbiturates / hypnotics		304.1
Anxiety (unspecified)		300.00	Cocaine		304.2
Major depression recurrent		296.3	Cannabis (Marijuana)		304.3
Major depression single episode		296.2	Amphetamine		304.4
Dysthymia		300.40	Hallucinogen (LSD)		304.5
Somatization disorder		300.81	Opioid + any other drugs		304.6
Panic disorder		300.01	Combination of other (not opioid)		304.8
Agoraphobia with panic disorder		300.21	Alcohol abuse		305.0
Post traumatic stress disorder		309.81	Tobacco abuse		305.1
Acute stress disorder		308.3	Cannabis abuse		305.2
Obsessive compulsive disorder		300.3	Barbiturate / hypnotic abuse		305.4
Schizophrenia unspecified		295.0	Opioid abuse		305.5
Psychogenic pain		307.89	Laxative other		305.9
Opioid type		304.0	Unspecified		304.9

OTHER

MEDICAL DECISION MAKING

i. REVIEW OF INVESTIGATIONS / OUTSIDE REPORTS: ☐ Yes ☐ None available ☐ Requested ☐ Dictated

Actual films, EMC, NCV, etc. ☐ Dictated ______

Discussion with Radiologist, etc. ☐ Dictated ______

______

______

ii. REVIEW OF RECORDS ☐ Yes ☐ None available ☐ Requested ☐ Dictated

______

______

______

______

iii. IMPRESSION

PHYSICAL ☐ Dictated ☐ See coding section ☐ None ______

______

______

______

______

MEDICAL ☐ Dictated ☐ See coding section ☐ None ______

______

______

______

______

PSYCHOLOGICAL ☐ Dictated ☐ See coding section ☐ None ______

☐ Depression ☐ General Anxiety Disorder ☐ Somatization Disorder

☐ ______

______

______

iv. PLAN

Investigations ☐ None ordered ☐ Ordered ______

______

______

______

______

a. Drugs

1. ☐ None ______
2. ☐ To continue ______

   ______
3. ☐ Will start ______

   ______
4. ☐ Will wean off ______

   ______
5. ☐ ______

b. Physical therapy
1. ☐ None due to lack of response or significant progress in past ____________
2. ☐ None due to increased pain with physical therapy in past ____________
3. ☐ None due to patient's refusal to undergo physical therapy ____________
4. ☐ None due to the condition which is not amenable to physical therapy / rehab ________
5. ☐ Will continue at ____________
6. ☐ Will start at ____________
7. ☐ Will consider later ____________
8. ☐ Will manage with home exercise program ____________
9. ☐ ____________

c. Psychotherapy
1. ☐ None due to lack of major psychological problems ____________
2. ☐ None due to patient's refusal to undergo psychological intervention ____________
3. ☐ Will continue ____________
4. ☐ Will start at ____________
5. ☐ Will consider later ____________
6. ☐ ____________

d. Injections
1. ☐ None due to ____________
2. ☐ Will consider later ____________
3. ☐ Will start with: ☐ C / T / L Facet Blocks ☐ C / T / L Discography
☐ C / T / L / S Transforaminal Epidurals ☐ C / T / Lum / Caudal Epidural
☐ C / T / L Symp Block ☐ ____________
4. ☐ Follow if necessary with: ☐ Facet Blocks ☐ Epidurals ☐ Hyertonic ☐ RFTN
☐ Endoscopy ☐ Cryo ☐ IDET ☐ ____________
5. ☐ ____________

v. DURATION OF TREATMENT
1. ☐ No Rx 2. ☐ 2 4 weeks 3. ☐ 4 6 weeks 4. ☐ 6 8 weeks 5. ☐ 9 12 weeks
____

vi. PROGNOSIS
1. ☐ Very good 2. ☐ Good 3. ☐ Good to fair 4. ☐ Fair
5. ☐ Fair to poor 6. ☐ Poor

vii. DISCUSSION ____________
____

viii. DISCHARGE / DISPOSITION ____________
____

SIGNATURE OF PHYSICIAN ____________ **DATE** ____________

APPENDIX - B

1997 Documentation Guidelines for Evaluation and Management Services

REPRODUCED FROM

CENTERS FOR MEDICARE AND MEDICAL SERVICES

http://www.hcfa.gov/medlearn/emdoc.htm

1997 DOCUMENTATION GUIDELINES FOR EVALUATION AND MANAGEMENT SERVICES

I. INTRODUCTION

WHAT IS DOCUMENTATION AND WHY IS IT IMPORTANT?

Medical record documentation is required to record pertinent facts, findings, and observations about an individual's health history including past and present illnesses, examinations, tests, treatments, and outcomes. The medical record chronologically documents the care of the patient and is an important element contributing to high quality care. The medical record facilitates:

- the ability of the physician and other health care professionals to evaluate and plan the patient's immediate treatment, and to monitor his/her health care over time.
- communication and continuity of care among physicians and other health care professionals involved in the patient's care;
- accurate and timely claims review and payment;
- appropriate utilization review and quality of care evaluations; and
- collection of data that may be useful for research and education.

An appropriately documented medical record can reduce many of the "hassles" associated with claims processing and may serve as a legal document to verify the care provided, if necessary.

WHAT DO PAYERS WANT AND WHY?

Because payers have a contractual obligation to enrollees, they may require reasonable documentation that services are consistent with the insurance coverage provided. They may request information to validate:

- the site of service;
- the medical necessity and appropriateness of the diagnostic and/or therapeutic services provided; and/or
- that services provided have been accurately reported.

II. GENERAL PRINCIPLES OF MEDICAL RECORD DOCUMENTATION

The principles of documentation listed below are applicable to all types of medical and surgical services in all settings. For Evaluation and Management (E/M) services, the nature and amount of physician work and documentation varies by type of service, place of service and the patient's status. The general principles listed below may be modified to account for these variable circumstances in providing E/M services.

1. **The medical record should be complete and legible.**

2. **The documentation of each patient encounter should include:**

   - **reason for the encounter and relevant history, physical examination findings and prior diagnostic test results;**

   - **assessment, clinical impression or diagnosis;**

   - **plan for care; and**

   - **date and legible identity of the observer.**

3. **If not documented, the rationale for ordering diagnostic and other ancillary services should be easily inferred.**

4. **Past and present diagnoses should be accessible to the treating and/or consulting physician.**

5. **Appropriate health risk factors should be identified.**

6. **The patient's progress, response to and changes in treatment, and revision of diagnosis should be documented.**

7. **The CPT and ICD-9-CM codes reported on the health insurance claim form or billing statement should be supported by the documentation in the medical record.**

III. DOCUMENTATION OF E/M SERVICES

This publication provides definitions and documentation guidelines for the three key components of E/M services and for visits which consist predominately of counseling or coordination of care. The three *key* components--history, examination, and medical decision making--appear in the descriptors for office and other outpatient services, hospital observation services, hospital inpatient services, consultations, emergency department services, nursing facility services, domiciliary care services, and home services. While some of the text of CPT has been repeated in this publication, the reader should refer to CPT for the complete descriptors for E/M services and instructions for selecting a level of service. Documentation guidelines are identified by the symbol *•DG*.

The descriptors for the levels of E/M services recognize seven components which are used in defining the levels of E/M services. These components are:

- **history;**
- **examination;**
- **medical decision making;**
- **counseling;**
- **coordination of care;**
- **nature of presenting problem; and**
- **time.**

The first three of these components (i.e., history, examination and medical decision making) are the key components in selecting the level of E/M services. In the case of visits which consist predominantly of counseling or coordination of care, time is the key or controlling factor to qualify for a particular level of E/M service.

Because the level of E/M service is dependent on two or three key components, performance and documentation of one component (eg, examination) at the highest level does not necessarily mean that the encounter in its entirety qualifies for the highest level of E/M service.

These Documentation Guidelines for E/M services reflect the needs of the typical adult population. For certain groups of patients, the recorded information may vary slightly from that described here. Specifically, the medical records of infants, children, adolescents and pregnant women may have additional or modified information recorded in each history and examination area.

As an example, newborn records may include under history of the present illness (HPI) the details of mother's pregnancy and the infant's status at birth; social history will focus on family structure; family history will focus on congenital

anomalies and hereditary disorders in the family. In addition, the content of a pediatric examination will vary with the age and development of the child. Although not specifically defined in these documentation guidelines, these patient group variations on history and examination are appropriate.

A. DOCUMENTATION OF HISTORY

The levels of E/M services are based on four types of history (Problem Focused, Expanded Problem Focused, Detailed, and Comprehensive). Each type of history includes some or all of the following elements:

- **Chief complaint (CC);**
- **History of present illness (HPI);**
- **Review of systems (ROS); and**
- **Past, family and/or social history (PFSH).**

The extent of history of present illness, review of systems and past, family and/or social history that is obtained and documented is dependent upon clinical judgement and the nature of the presenting problem(s).

The chart below shows the progression of the elements required for each type of history. To qualify for a given type of history all three elements in the table must be met. (A chief complaint is indicated at all levels.)

History of Present Illness (HPI)	Review of Systems (ROS)	Past, Family, and/or Social History (PFSH)	Type of History
Brief	N/A	N/A	*Problem Focused*
Brief	Problem Pertinent	N/A	*Expanded Problem Focused*
Extended	Extended	Pertinent	*Detailed*
Extended	Complete	Complete	*Comprehensive*

●*DG: The CC, ROS and PFSH may be listed as separate elements of history, or they may be included in the description of the history of the present illness.*

●*DG: A ROS and/or a PFSH obtained during an earlier encounter does not need to be re-recorded if there is evidence that the physician reviewed and updated the previous information. This may occur when a physician updates his or her own record or in an institutional setting or group practice where many physicians use a common record. The review and update may be documented by:*

- *describing any new ROS and/or PFSH information or noting there has been no change in the information; and*
- *noting the date and location of the earlier ROS and/or PFSH.*

●*DG: The ROS and/or PFSH may be recorded by ancillary staff or on a form completed by the patient. To document that the physician reviewed the information, there must be a notation supplementing or confirming the information recorded by others.*

●*DG: If the physician is unable to obtain a history from the patient or other source, the record should describe the patient's condition or other circumstance which precludes obtaining a history.*

Definitions and specific documentation guidelines for each of the elements of history are listed below.

CHIEF COMPLAINT (CC)

The CC is a concise statement describing the symptom, problem, condition, diagnosis, physician recommended return, or other factor that is the reason for the encounter, usually stated in the patient's words.

●*DG: The medical record should clearly reflect the chief complaint.*

HISTORY OF PRESENT ILLNESS (HPI)

The HPI is a chronological description of the development of the patient's present illness from the first sign and/or symptom or from the previous encounter to the present. It includes the following elements:

- **location,**
- **quality,**
- **severity,**
- **duration,**
- **timing,**
- **context,**
- **modifying factors, and**
- **associated signs and symptoms.**

Brief **and** ***extended*** **HPIs are distinguished by the amount of detail needed to accurately characterize the clinical problem(s).**

A ***brief*** **HPI consists of one to three elements of the HPI.**

> ●***DG: The medical record should describe one to three elements of the present illness (HPI).***

An ***extended*** **HPI consists of at least four elements of the HPI or the status of at least three chronic or inactive conditions.**

> ●***DG: The medical record should describe at least four elements of the present illness (HPI), or the status of at least three chronic or inactive conditions.***

REVIEW OF SYSTEMS (ROS)

A ROS is an inventory of body systems obtained through a series of questions seeking to identify signs and/or symptoms which the patient may be experiencing or has experienced.

For purposes of ROS, the following systems are recognized:

- **Constitutional symptoms (e.g., fever, weight loss)**
- **Eyes**
- **Ears, Nose, Mouth, Throat**
- **Cardiovascular**
- **Respiratory**
- **Gastrointestinal**
- **Genitourinary**
- **Musculoskeletal**
- **Integumentary (skin and/or breast)**
- **Neurological**
- **Psychiatric**
- **Endocrine**
- **Hematologic/Lymphatic**
- **Allergic/Immunologic**

A *problem pertinent* ROS inquires about the system directly related to the problem(s) identified in the HPI.

> ***●DG: The patient's positive responses and pertinent negatives for the system related to the problem should be documented.***

An *extended* ROS inquires about the system directly related to the problem(s) identified in the HPI and a limited number of additional systems.

> ***●DG: The patient's positive responses and pertinent negatives for two to nine systems should be documented.***

A *complete* ROS inquires about the system(s) directly related to the problem(s) identified in the HPI *plus* all additional body systems.

●DG: At least ten organ systems must be reviewed. Those systems with positive or pertinent negative responses must be individually documented. For the remaining systems, a notation indicating all other systems are negative is permissible. In the absence of such a notation, at least ten systems must be individually documented.

PAST, FAMILY AND/OR SOCIAL HISTORY (PFSH)

The PFSH consists of a review of three areas:

- **past history (the patient's past experiences with illnesses, operations, injuries and treatments);**
- **family history (a review of medical events in the patient's family, including diseases which may be hereditary or place the patient at risk); and**
- **social history (an age appropriate review of past and current activities).**

For certain categories of E/M services that include only an interval history, it is not necessary to record information about the PFSH. Those categories are subsequent hospital care, follow-up inpatient consultations and subsequent nursing facility care.

A *pertinent* PFSH is a review of the history area(s) directly related to the problem(s) identified in the HPI.

> ***●DG: At least one specific item from any of the three history areas must be documented for a pertinent PFSH .***

A *complete* PFSH is of a review of two or all three of the PFSH history areas, depending on the category of the E/M service. A review of all three history areas is required for services that by their nature include a comprehensive assessment or reassessment of the patient. A review of two of the three history areas is sufficient for other services.

> ***●DG: At least one specific item from two of the three history areas must be documented for a complete PFSH for the following categories of E/M services: office or other outpatient services, established patient; emergency department; domiciliary care, established patient; and home care, established patient.***

> ***●DG: At least one specific item from each of the three history areas must be documented for a complete PFSH for the following categories of E/M services: office or other outpatient services, new patient; hospital observation services; hospital inpatient services, initial care; consultations; comprehensive nursing facility assessments; domiciliary care, new patient; and home care, new patient.***

B. DOCUMENTATION OF EXAMINATION

The levels of E/M services are based on four types of examination:

- ***Problem Focused*** **-- a limited examination of the affected body area or organ system.**

- ***Expanded Problem Focused*** **-- a limited examination of the affected body area or organ system and any ther symptomatic or related body area(s) or organ system(s).**

- ***Detailed*** **-- an extended examination of the affected body area(s) or organ system(s) and any other symptomatic or related body area(s) or organ system(s).**

- ***Comprehensive*** **-- a general multi-system examination, or complete examination of a single organ system and other symptomatic or related body area(s) or organ system(s).**

These types of examinations have been defined for general multi-system and the following single organ systems:

- **Cardiovascular**
- **Ears, Nose, Mouth and Throat**
- **Eyes**
- **Genitourinary (Female)**
- **Genitourinary (Male)**
- **Hematologic/Lymphatic/Immunologic**
- **Musculoskeletal**
- **Neurological**
- **Psychiatric**
- **Respiratory**
- **Skin**

A general multi-system examination or a single organ system examination may be performed by any physician regardless of specialty. The type (general multi-system or single organ system) and content of examination are selected by the examining physician and are based upon clinical judgement, the patient's history, and the nature of the presenting problem(s).

The content and documentation requirements for each type and level of examination are summarized below and described in detail in tables beginning on page 13. In the tables, organ systems and body areas recognized by CPT for purposes of describing examinations are shown in the left column. The content, or individual elements, of the examination pertaining to that body area or organ system are identified by bullets (•) in the right column.

Parenthetical examples, "(eg, ...)", have been used for clarification and to provide guidance regarding documentation. Documentation for each element must satisfy any numeric requirements (such as "Measurement of *any three of the following seven...*") included in the description of the element. Elements with multiple components but with no specific numeric requirement (such as "Examination of *liver* and *spleen*") require documentation of at least one component. It is possible for a given examination to be expanded beyond what is defined here. When that occurs, findings related to the additional systems and/or areas should be documented.

- ***DG: Specific abnormal and relevant negative findings of the examination of the affected or symptomatic body area(s) or organ system(s) should be documented. A notation of "abnormal" without elaboration is insufficient.***
- ***DG: Abnormal or unexpected findings of the examination of any asymptomatic body area(s) or organ system(s) should be described.***
- ***DG: A brief statement or notation indicating "negative" or "normal" is sufficient to document normal findings related to unaffected area(s) or asymptomatic organ system(s).***

GENERAL MULTI-SYSTEM EXAMINATIONS

General multi-system examinations are described in detail beginning on page 13. To qualify for a given level of multi-system examination, the following content and documentation requirements should be met:

- ***Problem Focused Examination*-should include performance and documentation of one to five elements identified by a bullet (•) in one or more organ system(s) or body area(s).**
- ***Expanded Problem Focused Examination*-should include performance and documentation of at least six elements identified by a bullet (•) in one or more organ system(s) or body area(s).**

- ***Detailed Examination*--should include at least six organ systems or body areas. For each system/area selected, performance and documentation of at least two elements identified by a bullet (•) is expected. Alternatively, a detailed examination may include performance and documentation of at least twelve elements identified by a bullet (•) in two or more organ systems or body areas.**

- ***Comprehensive Examination*--should include at least nine organ systems or body areas. For each system/area selected, all elements of the examination identified by a bullet (•) should be performed, unless specific directions limit the content of the examination. For each area/system, documentation of at least two elements identified by a bullet is expected.**

SINGLE ORGAN SYSTEM EXAMINATIONS

The single organ system examinations recognized by CPT are described in detail beginning on page 18. Variations among these examinations in the organ systems and body areas identified in the left columns and in the elements of the examinations described in the right columns reflect differing emphases among specialties. To qualify for a given level of single organ system examination, the following content and documentation requirements should be met:

- ***Problem Focused Examination*--should include performance and documentation of one to five elements identified by a bullet (•), whether in a box with a shaded or unshaded border.**

- ***Expanded Problem Focused Examination*--should include performance and documentation of at least six elements identified by a bullet (•), whether in a box with a shaded or unshaded border.**

- ***Detailed Examination*--examinations other than the eye and psychiatric examinations should include performance and documentation of at least twelve elements identified by a bullet (•), whether in box with a shaded or unshaded border.**

  Eye and psychiatric examinations should include the performance and documentation of at least nine elements identified by a bullet (•), whether in a box with a shaded or unshaded border.

- ***Comprehensive Examination*--should include performance of all elements identified by a bullet (•), whether in a shaded or unshaded box. Documentation of every element in each box with a shaded border and at least one element in each box with an unshaded border is expected.**

CONTENT AND DOCUMENTATION REQUIREMENTS

General Multi-System Examination

System/Body Area	Elements of Examination
Constitutional	• Measurement of **any three of the following seven** vital signs: 1) sitting or standing blood pressure, 2) supine blood pressure, 3) pulse rate and regularity, 4) respiration, 5) temperature, 6) height, 7) weight (May be measured and recorded by ancillary staff) • General appearance of patient (eg, development, nutrition, body habitus, deformities, attention to grooming)
Eyes	• Inspection of conjunctivae and lids • Examination of pupils and irises (eg, reaction to light and accommodation, size and symmetry) • Ophthalmoscopic examination of optic discs (eg, size, C/D ratio, appearance) and posterior segments (eg, vessel changes, exudates, hemorrhages)
Ears, Nose, Mouth and Throat	• External inspection of ears and nose (eg, overall appearance, scars, lesions, masses) • Otoscopic examination of external auditory canals and tympanic membranes • Assessment of hearing (eg, whispered voice, finger rub, tuning fork) • Inspection of nasal mucosa, septum and turbinates • Inspection of lips, teeth and gums • Examination of oropharynx: oral mucosa, salivary glands, hard and soft palates, tongue, tonsils and posterior pharynx
Neck	• Examination of neck (eg, masses, overall appearance, symmetry, tracheal position, crepitus) • Examination of thyroid (eg, enlargement, tenderness, mass)

System/Body Area	Elements of Examination
Respiratory	• Assessment of respiratory effort (eg, intercostal retractions, use of accessory muscles, diaphragmatic movement) • Percussion of chest (eg, dullness, flatness, hyperresonance) • Palpation of chest (eg, tactile fremitus) • Auscultation of lungs (eg, breath sounds, adventitious sounds, rubs)
Cardiovascular	• Palpation of heart (eg, location, size, thrills) • Auscultation of heart with notation of abnormal sounds and murmurs Examination of: • carotid arteries (eg, pulse amplitude, bruits) • abdominal aorta (eg, size, bruits) • femoral arteries (eg, pulse amplitude, bruits) • pedal pulses (eg, pulse amplitude) • extremities for edema and/or varicosities
Chest (Breasts)	• Inspection of breasts (eg, symmetry, nipple discharge) • Palpation of breasts and axillae (eg, masses or lumps, tenderness)
Gastrointestinal (Abdomen)	• Examination of abdomen with notation of presence of masses or tenderness • Examination of liver and spleen • Examination for presence or absence of hernia • Examination (when indicated) of anus, perineum and rectum, including sphincter tone, presence of hemorrhoids, rectal masses • Obtain stool sample for occult blood test when indicated

System/Body Area	Elements of Examination
Genitourinary	**MALE:** • Examination of the scrotal contents (eg, hydrocele, spermatocele, tenderness of cord, testicular mass) • Examination of the penis • Digital rectal examination of prostate gland (eg, size, symmetry, nodularity, tenderness) **FEMALE:** Pelvic examination (with or without specimen collection for smears and cultures), including • Examination of external genitalia (eg, general appearance, hair distribution, lesions) and vagina (eg, general appearance, estrogen effect, discharge, lesions, pelvic support, cystocele, rectocele) • Examination of urethra (eg, masses, tenderness, scarring) • Examination of bladder (eg, fullness, masses, tenderness) • Cervix (eg, general appearance, lesions, discharge) • Uterus (eg, size, contour, position, mobility, tenderness, consistency, descent or support) • Adnexa/parametria (eg, masses, tenderness, organomegaly, nodularity)
Lymphatic	Palpation of lymph nodes in **two or more** areas: • Neck • Axillae • Groin • Other

System/Body Area	Elements of Examination
Musculoskeletal	• Examination of gait and station • Inspection and/or palpation of digits and nails (eg, clubbing, cyanosis, inflammatory conditions, petechiae, ischemia, infections, nodes) Examination of joints, bones and muscles of **one or more of the following six** areas: 1) head and neck; 2) spine, ribs and pelvis; 3) right upper extremity; 4) left upper extremity; 5) right lower extremity; and 6) left lower extremity. The examination of a given area includes: • Inspection and/or palpation with notation of presence of any misalignment, asymmetry, crepitation, defects, tenderness, masses, effusions • Assessment of range of motion with notation of any pain, crepitation or contracture • Assessment of stability with notation of any dislocation (luxation), subluxation or laxity • Assessment of muscle strength and tone (eg, flaccid, cog wheel, spastic) with notation of any atrophy or abnormal movements
Skin	• Inspection of skin and subcutaneous tissue (eg, rashes, lesions, ulcers) • Palpation of skin and subcutaneous tissue (eg, induration, subcutaneous nodules, tightening)
Neurologic	• Test cranial nerves with notation of any deficits • Examination of deep tendon reflexes with notation of pathological reflexes (eg, Babinski) • Examination of sensation (eg, by touch, pin, vibration, proprioception)
Psychiatric	• Description of patient's judgment and insight Brief assessment of mental status including: • orientation to time, place and person • recent and remote memory • mood and affect (eg, depression, anxiety, agitation)

Content and Documentation Requirements

Level of Exam	Perform and Document:
Problem Focused	**One to five** elements identified by a bullet.
Expanded Problem Focused	**At least six** elements identified by a bullet.
Detailed	**At least two** elements identified by a bullet **from each of six areas/systems** OR **at least twelve** elements identified by a bullet **in two or more areas/systems**.
Comprehensive	Perform **all elements** identified by a bullet in **at least nine** organ systems or body areas and document **at least two** elements identified by a bullet **from each of nine areas/systems.**

Musculoskeletal Examination

System/Body Area	Elements of Examination
Constitutional	• Measurement of **any three of the following seven** vital signs: 1) sitting or standing blood pressure, 2) supine blood pressure, 3) pulse rate and regularity, 4) respiration, 5) temperature, 6) height, 7) weight (May be measured and recorded by ancillary staff) • General appearance of patient (eg, development, nutrition, body habitus, deformities, attention to grooming)
Head and Face	
Eyes	
Ears, Nose, Mouth and Throat	
Neck	
Respiratory	
Cardiovascular	• Examination of peripheral vascular system by observation (eg, swelling, varicosities) and palpation (eg, pulses, temperature, edema, tenderness)
Chest (Breasts)	
Gastrointestinal (Abdomen)	
Genitourinary	
Lymphatic	• Palpation of lymph nodes in neck, axillae, groin and/or other location

<table>
<tr><td>Musculoskeletal</td><td>• Examination of gait and station

Examination of joint(s), bone(s) and muscle(s)/ tendon(s) of four of the following six areas: 1) head and neck; 2) spine, ribs and pelvis; 3) right upper extremity; 4) left upper extremity; 5) right lower extremity; and 6) left lower extremity. The examination of a given area includes:

• Inspection, percussion and/or palpation with notation of any misalignment, asymmetry, crepitation, defects, tenderness, masses or effusions

• Assessment of range of motion with notation of any pain (eg, straight leg raising), crepitation or contracture

• Assessment of stability with notation of any dislocation (luxation), subluxation or laxity

• Assessment of muscle strength and tone (eg, flaccid, cog wheel, spastic) with notation of any atrophy or abnormal movements

NOTE: For the comprehensive level of examination, all four of the elements identified by a bullet must be performed and documented for each of four anatomic areas. For the three lower levels of examination, each element is counted separately for each body area. For example, assessing range of motion in two extremities constitutes two elements.</td></tr>
<tr><td>Extremities</td><td>[See musculoskeletal and skin]</td></tr>
<tr><td>Skin</td><td>• Inspection and/or palpation of skin and subcutaneous tissue (eg, scars, rashes, lesions, cafe-au-lait spots, ulcers) in four of the following six areas: 1) head and neck; 2) trunk; 3) right upper extremity; 4) left upper extremity; 5) right lower extremity; and 6) left lower extremity.

NOTE: For the comprehensive level, the examination of all four anatomic areas must be performed and documented. For the three lower levels of examination, each body area is counted separately. For example, inspection and/or palpation of the skin and subcutaneous tissue of two extremitites constitutes two elements.</td></tr>
</table>

Neurological/ Psychiatric	• Test coordination (eg, finger/nose, heel/ knee/shin, rapid alternating movements in the upper and lower extremities, evaluation of fine motor coordination in young children) • Examination of deep tendon reflexes and/or nerve stretch test with notation of pathological reflexes (eg, Babinski) • Examination of sensation (eg, by touch, pin, vibration, proprioception) Brief assessment of mental status including • Orientation to time, place and person • Mood and affect (eg, depression, anxiety, agitation)

Content and Documentation Requirements

Level of Exam	Perform and Document:
Problem Focused	**One to five** elements identified by a bullet.
Expanded Problem Focused	**At least six** elements identified by a bullet.
Detailed	**At least twelve** elements identified by a bullet.
Comprehensive	Perform **all** elements identified by a bullet; document every element in each box with a shaded border and at least one element in each box with an unshaded border.

Neurological Examination

System/Body Area	Elements of Examination
Constitutional	• Measurement of **any three of the following seven** vital signs: 1) sitting or standing blood pressure, 2) supine blood pressure, 3) pulse rate and regularity, 4) respiration, 5) temperature, 6) height, 7) weight (May be measured and recorded by ancillary staff) • General appearance of patient (eg, development, nutrition, body habitus, deformities, attention to grooming)
Head and Face	
Eyes	• Ophthalmoscopic examination of optic discs (eg, size, C/D ratio, appearance) and posterior segments (eg, vessel changes, exudates, hemorrhages)
Ears, Nose, Mouth and Throat	
Neck	
Respiratory	
Cardiovascular	• Examination of carotid arteries (eg, pulse amplitude, bruits) • Auscultation of heart with notation of abnormal sounds and murmurs • Examination of peripheral vascular system by observation (eg, swelling, varicosities) and palpation (eg, pulses, temperature, edema, tenderness)
Chest (Breasts)	
Gastrointestinal (Abdomen)	
Genitourinary	
Lymphatic	

Musculoskeleta l	• Examination of gait and station Assessment of motor function including: • Muscle strength in upper and lower extremities • Muscle tone in upper and lower extremities (eg, flaccid, cog wheel, spastic) with notation of any atrophy or abnormal movements (eg, fasciculation, tardive dyskinesia)
Extremities	[See musculoskeletal]
Skin	
Neurological	Evaluation of higher integrative functions including: • Orientation to time, place and person • Recent and remote memory • Attention span and concentration • Language (eg, naming objects, repeating phrases, spontaneous speech) • Fund of knowledge (eg, awareness of current events, past history, vocabulary) Test the following cranial nerves: • 2nd cranial nerve (eg, visual acuity, visual fields, fundi) • 3rd, 4th and 6th cranial nerves (eg, pupils, eye movements) • 5th cranial nerve (eg, facial sensation, corneal reflexes) • 7th cranial nerve (eg, facial symmetry, strength) • 8th cranial nerve (eg, hearing with tuning fork, whispered voice and/or finger rub) • 9th cranial nerve (eg, spontaneous or reflex palate movement) • 11th cranial nerve (eg, shoulder shrug strength) • 12th cranial nerve (eg, tongue protrusion) • Examination of sensation (eg, by touch, pin, vibration, proprioception) • Examination of deep tendon reflexes in upper and lower extremities with notation of pathological reflexes (eg, Babinski) • Test coordination (eg, finger/nose, heel/knee/shin, rapid alternating movements in the upper and lower extremities, evaluation of fine motor coordination in young children)
Psychiatric	

Content and Documentation Requirements

Level of Exam	Perform and Document:
Problem Focused	**One to five** elements identified by a bullet.
Expanded Problem Focused	**At least six** elements identified by a bullet.
Detailed	**At least twelve** elements identified by a bullet.
Comprehensive	Perform **all** elements identified by a bullet; document every element in each box with a shaded border and at least one element in each box with an unshaded border.

Psychiatric Examination

System/Body Area	Elements of Examination
Constitutional	• Measurement of **any three of the following seven** vital signs: 1) sitting or standing blood pressure, 2) supine blood pressure, 3) pulse rate and regularity, 4) respiration, 5) temperature, 6) height, 7) weight (May be measured and recorded by ancillary staff) • General appearance of patient (eg, development, nutrition, body habitus, deformities, attention to grooming)
Head and Face	
Eyes	
Ears, Nose, Mouth and Throat	
Neck	
Respiratory	
Cardiovascular	
Chest (Breasts)	
Gastrointestinal (Abdomen)	
Genitourinary	
Lymphatic	
Musculoskeletal	• Assessment of muscle strength and tone (eg, flaccid, cog wheel, spastic) with notation of any atrophy and abnormal movements • Examination of gait and station
Extremities	
Skin	
Neurological	

Psychiatric	• Description of speech including: rate; volume; articulation; coherence; and spontaneity with notation of abnormalities (eg, perseveration, paucity of language) • Description of thought processes including: rate of thoughts; content of thoughts (eg, logical vs. illogical, tangential); abstract reasoning; and computation • Description of associations (eg, loose, tangential, circumstantial, intact) • Description of abnormal or psychotic thoughts including: hallucinations; delusions; preoccupation with violence; homicidal or suicidal ideation; and obsessions • Description of the patient's judgment (eg, concerning everyday activities and social situations) and insight (eg, concerning psychiatric condition) Complete mental status examination including • Orientation to time, place and person • Recent and remote memory • Attention span and concentration • Language (eg, naming objects, repeating phrases) • Fund of knowledge (eg, awareness of current events, past history, vocabulary) • Mood and affect (eg, depression, anxiety, agitation, hypomania, lability)

Content and Documentation Requirements

Level of Exam	Perform and Document:
Problem Focused	**One to five** elements identified by a bullet.
Expanded Problem Focused	**At least six** elements identified by a bullet.
Detailed	**At least nine** elements identified by a bullet.
Comprehensive	Perform **all** elements identified by a bullet; document every element in each box with a shaded border and at least one element in each box with an unshaded border.

C. DOCUMENTATION OF THE COMPLEXITY OF MEDICAL DECISION MAKING

The levels of E/M services recognize four types of medical decision making (straight-forward, low complexity, moderate complexity and high complexity). Medical decision making refers to the complexity of establishing a diagnosis and/or selecting a management option as measured by:

- the number of possible diagnoses and/or the number of management options that must be considered;
- the amount and/or complexity of medical records, diagnostic tests, and/or other information that must be obtained, reviewed and analyzed; and
- the risk of significant complications, morbidity and/or mortality, as well as comorbidities, associated with the patient's presenting problem(s), the diagnostic procedure(s) and/or the possible management options.

The chart below shows the progression of the elements required for each level of medical decision making. To qualify for a given type of decision making, **two of the three elements in the table must be either met or exceeded.**

Number of diagnoses or management options	Amount and/or complexity of data to be reviewed	Risk of complications and/or morbidity or mortality	Type of decision making
Minimal	Minimal or None	Minimal	***Straightforward***
Limited	Limited	Low	***Low Complexity***
Multiple	Moderate	Moderate	***Moderate Complexity***
Extensive	Extensive	High	***High Complexity***

Each of the elements of medical decision making is described below.

NUMBER OF DIAGNOSES OR MANAGEMENT OPTIONS

The number of possible diagnoses and/or the number of management options that must be considered is based on the number and types of problems addressed during the encounter, the complexity of establishing a diagnosis and the management decisions that are made by the physician.

Generally, decision making with respect to a diagnosed problem is easier than that for an identified but undiagnosed problem. The number and type of diagnostic tests employed may be an indicator of the number of possible diagnoses. Problems which are improving or resolving are less complex than those which are worsening or failing to change as expected. The need to seek advice from others is another indicator of complexity of diagnostic or management problems.

•DG: *For each encounter, an assessment, clinical impression, or diagnosis should be documented. It may be explicitly stated or implied in documented decisions regarding management plans and/or further evaluation.*

- *For a presenting problem with an established diagnosis the record should reflect whether the problem is: a) improved, well controlled, resolving or resolved; or, b) inadequately controlled, worsening, or failing to change as expected.*
- *For a presenting problem without an established diagnosis, the assessment or clinical impression may be stated in the form of differential diagnoses or as a "possible", "probable", or "rule out" (R/O) diagnosis.*

•DG: *The initiation of, or changes in, treatment should be documented. Treatment includes a wide range of management options including patient instructions, nursing instructions, therapies, and medications.*

•DG: *If referrals are made, consultations requested or advice sought, the record should indicate to whom or where the referral or consultation is made or from whom the advice is requested.*

AMOUNT AND/OR COMPLEXITY OF DATA TO BE REVIEWED

The amount and complexity of data to be reviewed is based on the types of diagnostic testing ordered or reviewed. A decision to obtain and review old medical records and/or obtain history from sources other than the patient increases the amount and complexity of data to be reviewed.

Discussion of contradictory or unexpected test results with the physician who performed or interpreted the test is an indication of the complexity of data being reviewed. On occasion the physician who ordered a test may personally review the image, tracing or specimen to supplement information from the physician who prepared the test report or interpretation; this is another indication of the complexity of data being reviewed.

- **DG:** *If a diagnostic service (test or procedure) is ordered, planned, scheduled, or performed at the time of the E/M encounter, the type of service, eg, lab or x-ray, should be documented.*

- **DG:** *The review of lab, radiology and/or other diagnostic tests should be documented. A simple notation such as "WBC elevated" or "chest x-ray unremarkable" is acceptable. Alternatively, the review may be documented by initialing and dating the report containing the test results.*

- **DG:** *A decision to obtain old records or decision to obtain additional history from the family, caretaker or other source to supplement that obtained from the patient should be documented.*

- **DG:** *Relevant findings from the review of old records, and/or the receipt of additional history from the family, caretaker or other source to supplement that obtained from the patient should be documented. If there is no relevant information beyond that already obtained, that fact should be documented. A notation of "Old records reviewed" or "additional history obtained from family" without elaboration is insufficient.*

- **DG:** *The results of discussion of laboratory, radiology or other diagnostic tests with the physician who performed or interpreted the study should be documented.*

- **DG:** *The direct visualization and independent interpretation of an image, tracing or specimen previously or subsequently interpreted by another physician should be documented.*

RISK OF SIGNIFICANT COMPLICATIONS, MORBIDITY, AND/OR MORTALITY

The risk of significant complications, morbidity, and/or mortality is based on the risks associated with the presenting problem(s), the diagnostic procedure(s), and the possible management options.

- **DG:** *Comorbidities/underlying diseases or other factors that increase the complexity of medical decision making by increasing the risk of complications, morbidity, and/or mortality should be documented.*

- **DG:** *If a surgical or invasive diagnostic procedure is ordered, planned or scheduled at the time of the E/M encounter, the type of procedure, eg, laparoscopy, should be documented.*

- **DG:** *If a surgical or invasive diagnostic procedure is performed at the time of the E/M encounter, the specific procedure should be documented.*

- **DG:** *The referral for or decision to perform a surgical or invasive diagnostic procedure on an urgent basis should be documented or implied.*

The following table may be used to help determine whether the risk of significant complications, morbidity, and/or mortality is *minimal*, *low*, *moderate*, or *high*. Because the determination of risk is complex and not readily quantifiable, the table includes common clinical examples rather than absolute measures of risk. The assessment of risk of the presenting problem(s) is based on the risk related to the disease process anticipated between the present encounter and the next one. The assessment of risk of selecting diagnostic procedures and management options is based on the risk during and immediately following any procedures or treatment. **The highest level of risk in any one category (presenting problem(s), diagnostic procedure(s), or management options) determines the overall risk.**

Level of Risk	Presenting Problem(s)	Diagnostic Procedure(s) Ordered	Management Options Selected
Minimal	• One self-limited or minor problem, eg, cold, insect bite, tinea corporis	• Laboratory tests requiring venipuncture • Chest x-rays • EKG/EEG • Urinalysis • Ultrasound, eg, echocardiography • KOH prep	• Rest • Gargles • Elastic bandages • Superficial dressings
Low	• Two or more self-limited or minor problems • One stable chronic illness, eg, well controlled hypertension, non-insulin dependent diabetes, cataract, BPH • Acute uncomplicated illness or injury, eg, cystitis, allergic rhinitis, simple sprain	• Physiologic tests not under stress, eg, pulmonary function tests • Non-cardiovascular imaging studies with contrast, eg, barium enema • Superficial needle biopsies • Clinical laboratory tests requiring arterial puncture • Skin biopsies	• Over-the-counter drugs • Minor surgery with no identified risk factors • Physical therapy • Occupational therapy • IV fluids without additives
Moderate	• One or more chronic illnesses with mild exacerbation, progression, or side effects of treatment • Two or more stable chronic illnesses • Undiagnosed new problem with uncertain prognosis, eg, lump in breast • Acute illness with systemic symptoms, eg, pyelonephritis, pneumonitis, colitis • Acute complicated injury, eg, head injury with brief loss of consciousness	• Physiologic tests under stress, eg, cardiac stress test, fetal contraction stress test • Diagnostic endoscopies with no identified risk factors • Deep needle or incisional biopsy • Cardiovascular imaging studies with contrast and no identified risk factors, eg, arteriogram, cardiac catheterization • Obtain fluid from body cavity, eg lumbar puncture, thoracentesis, culdocentesis	• Minor surgery with identified risk factors • Elective major surgery (open, percutaneous or endoscopic) with no identified risk factors • Prescription drug management • Therapeutic nuclear medicine • IV fluids with additives • Closed treatment of fracture or dislocation without manipulation
High	• One or more chronic illnesses with severe exacerbation, progression, or side effects of treatment • Acute or chronic illnesses or injuries that pose a threat to life or bodily function, eg, multiple trauma, acute MI, pulmonary embolus, severe respiratory distress, progressive severe rheumatoid arthritis, psychiatric illness with potential threat to self or others, peritonitis, acute renal failure • An abrupt change in neurologic status, eg, seizure, TIA, weakness, sensory loss	• Cardiovascular imaging studies with contrast with identified risk factors • Cardiac electrophysiological tests • Diagnostic Endoscopies with identified risk factors • Discography	• Elective major surgery (open, percutaneous or endoscopic) with identified risk factors • Emergency major surgery (open, percutaneous or endoscopic) • Parenteral controlled substances • Drug therapy requiring intensive monitoring for toxicity • Decision not to resuscitate or to de-escalate care because of poor prognosis

D. DOCUMENTATION OF AN ENCOUNTER DOMINATED BY COUNSELING OR COORDINATION OF CARE

In the case where counseling and/or coordination of care dominates (more than 50%) of the physician/patient and/or family encounter (face-to-face time in the office or other or outpatient setting, floor/unit time in the hospital or nursing facility), time is considered the key or controlling factor to qualify for a particular level of E/M services.

> **•DG:** *If the physician elects to report the level of service based on counseling and/or coordination of care, the total length of time of the encounter (face-to-face or floor time, as appropriate) should be documented and the record should describe the counseling and/or activities to coordinate care.*

CODE COMPONENT	1995 REQUIREMENTS	1997 REQUIREMENTS	DRAFT GUIDELINES(JUNE 2000) THE GOOD NEWS – WHAT'S DIFFERENT
Hx - History of Present Illness	• Specific Requirements	• Specific Requirements	• Clearer requirements • Explicit recognition of medication monitoring
Hx – Review of Systems	• Specific body area or organ system requirements	• Specific body area or organ system requirements	• Less required • Clearer • Examples are provided
Hx – Past, Family, Social History	• Brief information required	• Brief information required	• No difference
Physical Exam	• Specifically referenced general multisystem exam • Description of single system exams inadequate • 4 levels • Requirements not clear	• General multi-system exam and 10 single system exams • 4 levels • Very prescriptive • Confusing shading & bullets format • Requirements often not relevant	• Physician *tailors* documentation to exam • Only 3 levels • Vignette examples • No Bullets • No Shading • Minimal counting • No irrelevant facts to record
Medical Decision Making	• 4 Levels • Laundry list of examples not reflective of clinical assessments & plans	• 4 Levels • Laundry list of examples not reflective • of clinical assessments & plans	• Only 3 levels • Physician Tailors documentation to assessment & plan of treatment • Vignette examples

APPENDIX - C

i. SAMPLE INITIAL EVALUATION

COMPREHENSIVE
MEDICAL HISTORY

INITIAL ASSESSMENT

COMPREHENSIVE/INITIAL EVALUATION

Date: ____________

I. A. Name ___ S.S. #_

First Middle Initial Last

B. Sex: M F C. Race D. Age_____ E. DOB ______

F. Address_ _State _Tel.

G. Occupation_ H. Employer

I. Nearest Relative's Name__ ____________ Tel. _

II. A. Referring Physician _ ____________

Name and Address

B. Family Physician ___ ____________

Name and Address

III. A. Describe the pain for which you are now seeking help in one sentence. (Example: "My back hurts.")

PAIN => Deep Right Hip, Down Thigh to Sometimes Slight Pain + Numbness Rt foot ARCH

IV. A. **H/O - PRESENT ILLNESS – PLEASE LIST ONLY RELEVANT PROBLEMS**

PROBLEM

1. ☐ Headaches Since: ____________
2. ☐ Neck Pain Since: ____________
3. ☐ Shoulder Pain R L Since: ____________
   (any part from arm to fingers) ____________
5. ☐ Thoracic Spine Pain Since: ____________
6. ☐ Chest Wall Pain Since: ____________
   (not heart related chest pain) ____________
7. ☑ Low Back Pain Since: 1998
8. ☑ Hip Pain (R) L Since: 1998
9. ☑ Lower Extremity Pain Since: 1998
   (any part from thigh to toes) (R) L ____________
10. ☐ Abdominal Wall Pain R L Since: ____________
11. ☐ Abdominal Pain Since: ____________
12. ☐ Groin Pain R L Since: ____________
13. ☐ Other________ Since: ____________

COMPREHENSIVE / INITIAL EVALUATION

PHYSICIAN - ——, M.D.

IDENTIFYING INFORMATION:

Name	:	John Do
Address	:	abc.
Telephone	:	XX X-XXX-XXXX
Date of Birth	:	x/xx/xxxx
Age (yrs.)	:	43
SS#	:	XXX-XX-XXXX
Referred by	:	Dr.—
Occupation	:	Firefighter
Employer	:	xxx
Location	:	ABC
Date of Evaluation	:	xx/xx/xxxx

INITIAL EVALUATION

☑ Paducah ☐ Marion

Name ______________________ Date ______

History Provided By: pt. Quality: good

History of Present Illness:

Mr. today c̄ c/o pain in (R, low back,) Rt. hip / buttock area that travels down back of Rt. leg into foot. at times Rt. foot goes numb. Denies any lower back pain. This seemed to have started 1998 without any accident or event. Began seeing chiropractor which seemed to help only temporarily. Then he went to Dr. who started on Relafen and sent to PT. Relafen helps quite a bit, but PT didn't seem to help much. Just basically dealt c̄ pain until May 2000 and then he saw Dr. (neurosurgeon) in Told him nothing surgically could be done and suggested for him to come to pain mgmt and cont. on Relafen.

Symptomatology: ☐ Location ☐ Quality ☐ Severity ☐ Duration ☐ Timing ☐ Context ☐ Modifying factors ☐ Associated signs & symptoms

1) INTERMITTENT THROBBING, CRAMPING PAIN ~~WITH~~ ON (R) SIDE OF LOW BACK PAIN AND (R) HIP WITH RADIATION TO (R) LOWER EXTREMITY ASSOCIATED WITH NUMBNESS AND TINGLING, SINCE 1998 WITH GRADUAL ONSET WITH NO SPECIFIC INCIDENT BUT WITH H/O OF HEAVY WORK WITH FAILURE TO RESPOND TO MEDICATIONS PT CHIROPRACTIC MANIPULATIONS AND EXERCISE UNTIL 9/2000, WITH BACK PAIN WORSE THAN LEG PAIN.

~~2) Rt KNEE PAIN~~

Systems	Multisystems	Single System	
		Musculoskeletal	Neurologic
Constitutional	Two elements	Two elements	Two elements
Musculoskeletal	Six elements	Five elements	Three elements
Neurological	Three elements	Two elements	Sixteen elements
Cardiovascular	Seven elements	One element (Peripheral)	Three elements
Chest / breasts	Two elements	----------	----------
Ears, nose, mouth and throat	Six elements	----------	----------
Eyes	Three elements	----------	One element (Ophthalmoscopy)
Genitourinary	Four elements - male Seven elements - female	----------	----------
Gastrointestinal	Five elements	----------	----------
Lymphatic	Four elements	One element	----------
Psychiatric	Four elements	Two elements	----------
Respiratory	Four elements	----------	----------
Skin	Two elements	One element	----------

HISTORY

Chief Complaint

''Pain - Deep right hip, down thigh to sometimes slight pain and numbness right foot arch.''

History of present illness

Mr. John Doe was a 43-year-old white male referred by Dr. — for evaluation and management of low back pain and lower extremity pain. He provided the history, he was a good historian. He complains of pain in his right lower back, hip/buttock area that travels down the back of his right leg into his foot. At this time, the right foot goes numb. He denies any lower back pain. This seemed to have started in 1998 without any accident or event. He began seeing a chiropractor, which seemed to help only temporarily. He then went to see Dr. —, who started him on Relafen and sent him to physical therapy. Relafen helps quite a bit, but physical therapy did not seem to help much. He just basically dealt with the pain until May 2000. At that time, he saw Dr. - in —. He told him nothing surgically could be done and suggested he go to pain management and continued on Relafen.

Symptomatology

Intermittent throbbing, cramping pain on the right side of low back and right hip with radiation to right lower extremity associated with numbness and tingling, since 1998 with gradual onset with no specific incident but with history of heavy work, with failure to respond to medications, physical therapy, chiropractic manipulations and exercise until September 2000, with back pain worse than leg pain.

B. **PRESENT PAIN HISTORY:** *(If your problem is headache only, without neck or face pain, please go to question IV D.)* For any other problem or headache with neck or face pain, complete this section.

1. PAIN RATIO (mark which item best describes the ratio between pain in your back/leg or neck/arm)

FOR BACK PAIN	FOR NECK PAIN
☐ Back pain only; no leg pain	☐ Neck pain only; no arm pain
☐ Back pain worse than leg pain	☐ Neck pain worse than arm pain
☐ Back pain and leg pain equal	☐ Neck pain and arm pain equal
☐ Leg pain worse than back pain	☐ Arm pain worse than neck pain
☑ Leg pain only; no back pain	☐ Arm pain only; no neck pain

2. Please mark which of these words best describe your pain. Put the mark on the line which gives the intensity of that particular quality of your pain. (only mark applicable ones - not all)

	Mild	Moderate	Severe	Unbearable	
1. Sharp	☐	☐	☑	☐	1.
2. Shooting	☐	☐	☑	☐	2.
3. Throbbing	☐	☐	☑	☐	3.
4. Cramping	☐	☐	☑	☐	4.
5. Stabbing	☐	☐	☐	☐	5.
6. Gnawing	☐	☐	☑	☑ Sometimes	6.
7. Hot - Burning	☐	☐	☐	☐	7.
8. Aching	☐	☐	☐	☐	8.
9. Heavy	☐	☐	☐	☐	9.
10. Tender	☐	☐	☐	☐	10.
11. Splitting	☐	☐	☐	☐	11.
12. Tiring - Exhausting	☐	☐	☐	☐	12.
13. Sickening	☐	☐	☐	☐	13.
14. Fearful	☐	☐	☐	☐	14.
15. Punishing - Cruel	☐	☐	☐	☐	15.

3. How much time during an average day (24 hour period) are you in pain?

☐ few hours ☐ less than 1/3rd of time ☑ almost 50% of time ☐ almost 2/3rds of time
☐ almost 24 hours ☐ anytime that I am not lying down ☐ pain is not present daily

4. Do you have any of the following related to pain: (only mark applicable ones - not all)

☑ 1. Numbness (Some) Rt. foot	☐ 4. Weakness
☑ 2. Tingling	NO — ☐ 5. Problems with Bowels maybe
☐ 3. Pins & Needles	☐ 6. Problems with Bladder

5. PAIN INTENSITY

On a scale of 1 to 10, with "0" representing no pain, "1" representing a nuisance which would not interfere with daily activities (i.e., toothache) while "10" would be the most severe pain imaginable (suicidal pain, having a baby or pain of a kidney stone), which number would describe your pain:

	Less Pain ← → More Pain
1. What is your pain like today?	0 - 1 - 2 - 3 - 4 - 5 - (6) - 7 - 8 - 9 - 10 -
2. What is your least pain?	0 - 1 - 2 - 3 - (4) - 5 - 6 - 7 - 8 - 9 - 10 -
3. What is your worst pain?	0 - 1 - 2 - 3 - 4 - 5 - 6 - 7 - 8 - (9) - 10 -
4. Overall average pain?	0 - 1 - 2 - 3 - 4 - 5 - 6 - (7) - 8 - 9 - 10 -

5. How many extremely bad days (horrible or excruciating pain) in a week do you experience? 3

Present Pain History

The present pain history includes the pain ratio when applicable, pain description utilizing McGill's short form questionnaire, average daily pain, associated problems with pain, pain intensity, various factors changing the pain, ability to perform activities of daily living, effect of pain on various types of activities, and the pain diagram which shows the location and distribution of pain along with intensity.

Pain Ratio

With regards to low back he described that: He experiences only leg pain without any back pain.

Pain description

The pain description is obtained utilizing the McGill Pain Questionnaire, which was developed by Melzack and Torgerson in 1971 to identify multi-dimensional aspects of the pain with 102 words, which was later modified by Melzack in 1987 to a short-form McGill Pain Questionnaire. The short-form McGill Pain questionnaire consists of 15 representative words from the sensory (N=11) and affective (N=4) categories of the standard, long-form McGill Pain Questionnaire. The short-form McGill Pain Questionnaire has been shown to correlate highly with the long-form McGill Pain Questionnaire. It was also studied in chronic pain of diverse etiology.

He described his pain on McGill's Pain Questionnaire utilizing the various descriptors with severity as well as character as follows:

He experiences severe sharp, shooting, throbbing, cramping, gnawing (sometimes), type(s) of pain.

Time spent in pain

He stated that he spends almost 50% of a day in pain.

Associated symptoms with pain

He described that he experiences the following associated symptoms with pain: some numbness of right foot, and tingling.

Pain intensity

In pain literature, the simplest, most widely used and most useful clinical method of measuring the severity of the pain is the measurement of the pain by visual analog scale. In general, the pain scale is accepted as a measurement of how bad the patient experiences or perceives the pain. On a scale of 0 to 10, ''0'' represents no pain, ''1'' represents a nuisance, which would not interfere with daily activities (i.e. toothache), while ''10'' would be the most severe pain imaginable (suicidal pain or pain experienced during a childbirth in a female or with kidney stone in a male).

He described his pain today as 6, his least pain as 4, his worst pain as 9, and his overall average pain as 7. In addition to this, he also stated that he generally experienced 3 extremely bad days per week where the pain is horrible or excruciating.

6. FACTORS CHANGING PAIN (Do any of the following make your pain change?)

		No Change	Somewhat Worse	A Lot Worse	Some Better	Complete Relief Pain Free	
1.	Sitting	☐	☐	☐	☑	☐ *Sometimes*	1.
2.	Standing	☐	☐	☒	☐	☐	2.
3.	Walking	☐	*Sometimes*	☒	☐	☐	3.
4.	Bending Forward	☐	☐	☐	☑	☐	4.
5.	Bending Backward	☐	☑	☐	☐	☐	5.
6.	Bending to Same Side	☒	☐	☐	☐	☐	6.
7.	Bending to Opposite Side	☐	☐	☐	☑	☐	7.
8.	Lying Down / Resting	☐	☑	☐	☑ *Sometimes*	☐	8.
9.	Driving	☐	☐	☐	☑	☐	9.
10.	Lifting	☑	☐	☐	☐	☐	10.
11.	Coughing / Sneezing	☑	☐	☐	☐	☐	11.
12.	Cold Weather	☑	☐	☐	☐	☐	12.
13.	Damp Weather	☑	☐	☐	☐	☐	13.
14.	Sexual Activity	☑	☐	☐	☐	☐	14.
15.	Overhead Activity	☑	☐	☐	☐	☐	15.

16. Other *until the last few Months, Sitting or Lying Down used to bring complete relief.* 16.

7. Are you able to perform any of the following without assistance?

1. Walk	☐ No	☑ Yes	4. Climb Stairs	☐ No	☑ Yes
2. Sit	☐ No	☑ Yes	5. Dress Self	☐ No	☑ Yes
3. Stand	☐ No	☑ Yes	6. Drive Car	☐ No	☑ Yes

8. EFFECT OF PAIN ON ACTIVITIES

(a) Please place a mark in the box which best describes the change in your condition now (after pain).

My desire to participate and actual participation in:	No Change	Decreased Some	Decreased Quite A Bit	Disappeared	Increased Somewhat	Increased Quite A Bit	
1. Personal Activities	☐	☑	☐	☐	☐	☐	1.
2. Household Cleaning, etc.	☐	☑	☐	☐	☐	☐	2.
3. Family Activities	☐	☑	☐	☐	☐	☐	3.
4. Recreation & Hobbies	☐	☑	☐	☐	☐	☐	4.
5. Sexual Relations	☑	☐	☐	☐	☐	☐	5.
6. Physical Exercise	☐	☑	☐	☐	☐	☐	6.
7. Watching TV	☐	☑	☐	☐	☐	☐	7.

(b) How often do you have to stop your activities and sit down or lie down to control your pain?

☐ Rarely - not daily ☐ Approximately once per day ☑ Several times per day

☐ I spend almost all day lying or sitting to control my pain

What aspect of your pain, or which pain, is the most bothersome to you and why? *when I'm Standing or Lying Down, it hurts - Sitting helps the Most. It seems to be draining my energy just dealing with it.*

Factors changing the pain

He stated that standing, walking factors make his pain significantly worse; where as bending backward, lying down/resting factors make his pain somewhat worse. In contrast, he also described that sitting, bending forward, bending to opposite side, driving, makes his pain somewhat better. He described that he experiences no changes in his pain pattern with overhead activity, bending to same side, lifting, coughing/sneezing, cold weather, damp weather, sexual activity.

Activities of daily living

He stated that generally he is capable of walking, sitting, standing, climbing stairs, dressing himself, and driving a car unassisted.

Effect of pain on activities

He stated that personal activities, household activities, family activities, recreation & hobbies, physical exercise, watching TV decreased somewhat. In addition, he stated that there is no change in sexual relation. He also stated that he had to stop his activities and sit down to or lie down to control his pain several times per day. He described that his most bothersome aspect with regards to his pain as: when he is standing or lying down, it hurts. Sitting helps the most. It seems to be draining his energy just dealing with it.

9. PAIN DIAGRAM (please mark the actual or exact location of pain):
Please read these instructions very carefully. We want you to indicate on the drawings on this page ACCURATELY where your pain is and how much pain you feel. Please read all instructions CAREFULLY.
   1. Mark on the drawing the spot where your pain usually is or starts. Mark this with an "X". If the pain starts at that spot (X) and travels to another part of your body, draw a line from the spot (X) where it starts to where it ends. If it is a whole area (example: whole arm, whole leg, etc.) that hurts, shade in that area.
   2. We also want to know how much pain you feel. Look at the list of words below, which most people agree describes intensity of pain. Each word has a number.

1 = MILD OR JUST FEELING OF DISCOMFORT
2 = MODERATE OR UNCOMFORTABLE
(3) = SEVERE OR DISTRESSING
4 = VERY SEVERE OR HORRIBLE
5 = EXCRUCIATING OR UNBEARABLE

Starts here, the longer I stand it moves on down the back of the leg to the instep.

REMEMBER TO:

SHOW WHERE YOUR PAIN USUALLY IS OR STARTS (X).

SHOW IF THE PAIN TRAVELS OR RADIATES.

SHOW IF THE PAIN IS EXTERNAL IN SKIN (E) OR DEEP IN MUSCLES OR BONES (I) OR BOTH (E & I).

SHOW OR RATE HOW MUCH PAIN YOU FEEL (1 - 5).

NOTES FOR STAFF ONLY (PLEASE DO NOT WRITE HERE):
Shows pain in (R) side of low back (R) hip and lower extremity. Internal - 3.

C. **SLEEP PATTERN**

1. Has your sleeping pattern changed due to pain? ☐ No ☒ Yes Having a hard time getting comfortable
2. Do you have a problem falling asleep? ☒ No ☐ Yes If yes, how many nights a week? ______
3. How many times do you wake up at night? 6 might be because of snoring maybe some type of sleep apnea How many nights a week? ______
4. When do you go to sleep? 10 P.M. 5. How many hours do you try to sleep each night? 7
6. How many hours do you actually sleep? 5
7. How do you feel when you wake up in the morning? tired
8. Do you sleep during the daytime? ☒ No ☐ Yes If yes, how long? ______

Pain diagram

Pain diagram provides the patient with the ability to describe both the type and nature of the pain. The diagram indicates the origin and ration of the pain, presence of sensitive areas or trigger points, and the severity of the pain ranging from 0 to 5, ''0'' being no pain and ''5'' being excruciating or unbearable pain.

On the pain diagram, he showed pain in right side of low back, right hip and lower extremity; internal and 3.

Sleep pattern

He stated that his sleep pattern has changed after the onset of the pain. He also stated that he has no problems falling asleep. He stated that he wakes up 6 times each night. He stated that, generally he goes to sleep around 10:00 p.m. In addition to this, he stated that he generally tries to sleep 7 hours each night. However, he actually sleeps only 5 hours. He stated that, when he wakes up in the morning, he feels tired. He stated that he does not sleep during the daytime.

V. PAST, FAMILY, AND SOCIAL HISTORY ☐ No problems in past

A. **PAST PAIN HISTORY (DO NOT describe present problem.)** (mark only applicable ones - not all)

1. ☐ Motor vehicle injury(ies) ______
2. ☑ Work related injury(ies) Knee injury, torn cartilege 1992 Rt Knee
3. ☑ Any other injury(ies) recent Knee Surgery 2000 July Rt Knee
4. ☐ Headache Hip Pain became more intense about this time frame
5. ☐ Pain in Neck ______
6. ☐ Pain in Upper Extremities ______
7. ☐ Pain in Upper Back ______
8. ☐ Pain in Mid-Back ______
9. ☐ Chest Wall Pain ______
10. ☐ Pain in Lower Back ______
11. ☐ Pain in Lower Extremities ______
12. ☐ Pain in Joints (example: shoulder, hip or knee) ______
13. ☐ Arthritis ______
14. ☐ Other ______

B. **EVALUATION AND TREATMENT HISTORY FOR PAIN**

1. Please list all doctors, chiropractors, therapists and emergency room doctors you have seen for your problem and when you first saw them.

PROVIDER SEEN	APPROX. # OF TIMES	DURING THE YEARS
		1999
		1998–2000
		2000

2. Total number of providers seen: 3

3. Which of the following tests have been performed? (mark only applicable ones - not all)

- ☑ a) Regular X-Rays of BACK
- ☐ b) CT Scan of ______
- ☐ c) Myelogram of ______
- ☑ d) MRI Scan of LOWER BACK
- ☐ e) Discogram of ______
- ☐ f) Bone Scan of ______
- ☐ g) Nerve Conduction of ______
- ☐ h) Other ______

PAST, FAMILY, SOCIAL HISTORY

Past history

He related torn cartilage, right knee from work related injury in 1992. He has history of right knee surgery in July 2000. However, there was no history of headache, pain in neck, pain in upper extremities, pain in upper back, pain in mid-back, chest wall pain, pain in back, pain in lower extremities, joints pain, arthritis.

Evaluation and treatment history for pain:

He was seen by 3 providers in the past these were:

Dr. -, - three occasions - 1999

Dr.- , - approximately 20 occasions - 1998-2000

Dr. - , - one occasion - 2000

In the past, he stated that he underwent regular X-rays of back, MRI scan of lower back.

4. Please list all operations you have **ever** had for the pain (not other surgeries).
PLEASE INCLUDE YEAR AND DOCTOR'S NAME
1. ____
2. ____
3. ____
4. ____
5. ____

5. Please describe other treatments, in sequence, since this problem started, with months / years.
1. ☑ Chiropractic Treatment off + on for 2 years
2. ☑ Physical Therapy 6 mons. 1999
3. ☐ Psychotherapy ____
4. ☐ Epidurals ____
5. ☐ Nerve Blocks ____
6. ☐ Cortisone Injections ____
7. ☐ Cortisone By Mouth ____
8. ☐ Other ____

6. a. What medicines are you now taking for pain, anxiety, etc., and how often for each? (do not list here medicines taken for medical problems)

	Medication	Dose	Frequency	Date Started	Time of Last Dose
i.	Relafin	(2) 500 mg tabs	twice a day	1999	Still taking
ii.	Serzone	150 mg	Bid		
iii.					
iv.					
v.					

How much relief do you obtain from drugs? Some More at the Beginning
Duration of relief: 4 h-8 hrs Side effects: ~~None~~

b. What other medicines (if any) and how long have you used them in the past?
~~Serzone 150 mg twice a Day (for Restlessness)~~
~~Allegra 60 mg twice Daily~~ Celebrex

C. i. **FAMILY PAIN HISTORY** ☐ No problems

Condition	Relationship	Condition	Relationship	Condition	Relationship
1. ☐ Migraine		7. ☑ Low Back Pain	mom	14. ☐ Lupus	
2. ☐ Headaches		8. ☐ Shoulder Pain		15. ☐ Multiple Sclerosis	
3. ☐ Neck Pain		9. ☐ Arm Pain		16. ☐ Epilepsy	
4. ☑ Upper Back Pain	Mom	10. ☐ Hip Pain		17. ☑ Depression	Aunt
5. ☐ Mid-Back Pain		11. ☐ Leg Pain		18. ☐ Schizophrenia	
6. ☐ Chest Wall Pain (not related to heart)		12. ☑ Arthritis	Mom, Grandmother	19. ☐ Alcoholism	
		13. ☐ Fibromyalgia		20. ☐	

ii. **FAMILY MEDICAL HISTORY** ☐ No problems

1. ☑ High Blood Pressure DAD
2. ☐ Heart Attack ____
3. ☐ Heart Disease ____
4. ☐ Diabetes ____
5. ☐ Bronchial Asthma ____
6. ☐ Bleeding Disorder ____
7. ☐ Hepatitis ____
8. ☑ Stroke - DAD

Past treatment History

He has history of chiropractic treatments off and on for two years. He also has attended physical therapy treatments for six months in 1999. However, he never underwent any psychotherapy, epidural/nerve blocks, cortisone injections or by mouth.

He stated that he is taking the following medications for management of his present problems. These include:

Relafen 500 mg. 2 tabs bid

Serzone 150 mg. bid

He stated that these medications provide some relief. He stated that he experienced no side effects with these medications. In addition to the above, he stated that he tried various other medications, which include Celebrex.

Family pain history

There was a history of upper back pain, low back pain, arthritis, depression, and high blood pressure and stroke in the family. However, there was no history of migraine, headaches, neck pain, mid-back pain, chest wall pain, shoulder pain, arm pain, hip pain, leg pain, fibromyalgia, lupus, multiple sclerosis, epilepsy, schizophrenia, alcoholism in the family.

D. **ENVIRONMENTAL INFORMATION**

1. List all the areas you have lived in (example: Paducah, KY):
2. Education: Highest grade completed ______
3. Marital status: [X] Married [ ] Separated [ ] Divorced [ ] Widowed [ ] Single How long? *2 yr.*
4. Do you live: [ ] Alone [X] with Spouse [ ] with Parents [ ] Other ______
5. Previous marriages: [ ] None [X] Yes If yes, how many? *1*
6. Number of children: Male *2* Female ______ Ages of children *13, 10*
7. If married, which of the below best describes your marriage?
   [X] Completely satisfactory [ ] Satisfactory [ ] Tolerable [ ] Intolerable [ ] No opinion
8. Has your pain problem changed your relationship with your spouse and family? [ ] No [X] Yes
   If yes, describe *Sometimes I'm not as Sports active & Sometimes I have to Sleep in another Bed to Keep from — I won't Keep my wife awake from my tossing & turning*
9. Excessive exposure at home to: [ ] None [ ] Fumes [ ] Dust [ ] Solvents [ ] Noise

E. **OCCUPATIONAL HISTORY:** [ ] Disabled since ______ [ ] Retired since ______ [ ] Homemaker
(If disabled, retired, over 65, or homemaker you may skip this section.)

1. Please list all previous occupations / jobs you have held in the last 10 years. (Attach separate sheet if necessary.) *Fire Fighter, Sales associate at JC Penney*
2. Please describe your current job (if unemployed, your very last job). *I sometimes Work in Hazardous Conditions with alot of Use of Upper & Lower Body functions*
   a. How long have you held this job? *15 yrs* 2. How many hours per week do your work? *56 AVE.*
   b. Does your work involve:
      Standing: [ ] No [X] Yes If yes, how long at a time? *4-5 Depends*
      Driving: [ ] No [ ] Yes If yes, how long at a time? ______
      Walking: [ ] No [X] Yes If yes, how long at a time? *Depends*
      Lifting: [ ] No [X] Yes If yes, how many lbs. more than 6-8 times per hour? ______
      If yes, how many lbs. less than 6 times per hour? ______
      Sitting: [ ] No [X] Yes If yes, how many hours per day? *4-5 Depends*
   c. Does your work involve vibration (i.e., machinery, driving, etc.)? [ ] No [X] Yes
      If yes, what is source of vibration? *Operating Rescue Equipment*
   d. Excessive exposure at work to: [X] Fumes [X] Dust [X] Solvents [X] Noise *depends on situation*
   e. Have you missed much work because of your current or previous illness, injury or pain?
      [X] No [ ] Yes When was the last day you worked "full duty"? ______
   f. If you are not working, are you currently receiving wage compensation? [ ] No [ ] Yes

F. **HABITS**

1. SMOKING: a. Do you smoke now? [X] No [ ] Yes Smoking since? ______
   How many cigarettes per day? ______ Cigars per day? ______ Pipe? ______
   b. Have you ever smoked? [ ] No [ ] Yes Explain ______
2. ALCOHOL: a. Do you drink alcohol? [X] No [ ] Yes If yes, how much? ______
   b. Have you ever had problems with alcohol? [ ] No [ ] Yes If yes, explain ______
3. CAFFEINATED DRINKS: Do you consume drinks with caffeine? [ ] No [X] Yes
   If yes, [X] Coffee [X] Tea [X] Iced Tea [X] Colas [ ] Other ______ No. of Cups Daily *8*
4. DRUGS: Do you use any street drugs? [X] No [ ] Yes If yes, explain ______

G. **HOBBIES:** List your hobbies: *Play Guitar & Sing*
Are you participating now? [ ] No [X] Yes If yes, describe: *Perform at Rathbones*

Social history

Environmental: He stated that he lived in —, — and —. He completed BS from — university. He stated that he has been married. He also stated that he lives with his wife. He stated that he was married one time in the past. He has 2 sons of ages 13 and 10 years. He stated that his marriage is completely satisfactory. He stated that his pain problems have changed his relationship with his wife and family members because sometimes he is not as sports active and sometimes he has to sleep in another bed so he does not keep his wife awake from him tossing and turning. He denied any excessive exposure due to fumes, dust, solvents or noise.

Occupational: He stated that, in the past he was employed as a fire fighter and sales associate at —. His present occupation is a fire fighter. He uses a lot of upper and lower body functions. He held this job for 15 years and working 56 hours per week on average In addition to this, he described that his work involves standing 4-5 hours at a time, walking, lifting,, and sitting for 4-5 hours per day. With regards to vibrations, he stated that his work involves vibration and source of the vibration is operating reserve equipment. He stated that he had excessive exposure to fumes, dust, solvents, and noise at work. He stated that he has not missed any work.

HABITS

Smoking

He does not smoke.

Alcohol

He does not drink alcohol and he never had a problem with alcohol.

Caffeinated Drinks

He drinks 8 cups of coffee, tea, iced tea and colas daily.

Drugs

He does not use any street drugs.

Hobbies

His hobbies are play guitar, and sing. He stated that he is able to participate in his hobbies.

VI. A. **MEDICAL HISTORY** (answer only applicable ones - do not mark all)

1. **Constitutional Symptoms** [x] No Problems
   - [x] Weight loss 20 lbs., during 1997
   - [ ] Weight gain 30 lbs., during 1999-2000
   - [ ] Recurrent fever
   - [ ] General weakness
   - [x] Fatigue
   - [ ] ______
2. **Skin** [x] No Problems
   - [ ] Dry skin
   - [ ] Recurrent rashes
   - [ ] Eczema
   - [ ] Itching
   - [ ] Changes in skin color
   - [ ] Changes in hair or nails
   - [ ] ______
3. **Hematologic / Lymphatic** [x] No Problems
   - [ ] Swollen glands
   - [ ] Low blood count (anemia)
   - [ ] Easy bruising
   - [ ] Easy bleeding
   - [ ] Slow to heal after cuts
   - [ ] h/o blood transfusions
   - [ ] Enlarged glands
   - [ ] Phlebitis
   - [ ] HIV positive
   - [ ] on blood thinners
   - [ ] ______
4. **Head / Face** [x] No Problems
   - [ ] Headaches
   - [ ] h/o head injury without residual problems
   - [ ] h/o head injury with residual problems of ______
   - [ ] Facial pain
   - [ ] TMJ R L
   - [ ] Tic douloureux R L ______
   - [ ] ______
5. **Eyes** [x] No Problems
   - [ ] Nearsighted
   - [ ] Farsighted
   - [ ] Wear glasses
   - [ ] Wear contact lenses
   - [ ] Cataracts at present time R L
   - [ ] Cataract surgery R L
   - [ ] Conjunctivitis R L
   - [ ] Glaucoma R L
   - [ ] Double vision R L
   - [ ] Blurred vision R L
   - [x] Reading Glasses
6. **Ear / Nose / Mouth**
   - i. **Ears** [x] No Problems
     - [ ] Hard of hearing R L
     - [ ] Hearing aids R L
     - [ ] Chronic ear discharge R L
     - [ ] Vertigo
     - [ ] Ringing in ears R L
     - [ ] ______
   - ii. **Nose / Sinuses** [ ] No Problems
     - [ ] Sinus discharge
     - [ ] Nasal discharge
     - [ ] Repeated nosebleeds
     - [ ] Deviated nasal septum
     - [ ] Chronic sinus problems
     - [ ] Chronic stuffy nose
     - [ ] Hay fever
     - [ ] Nasal polyps
     - [x] Sinus headaches SOMETIMES
   - iii. **Mouth / Throat** [x] No Problems
     - [ ] Teeth ___ Loose ___ None
     - [ ] Dentures ___ Full ___ Partial
     - [ ] Bleeding gums
     - [ ] Dry mouth
     - [ ] Sore throat
     - [ ] Hoarseness
     - [ ] Vocal cord polyps
     - [ ] Trouble swallowing
     - [ ] ______
7. **Chest / Breasts** [x] No Problems
   - [ ] Breast masses
   - [ ] Breast surgery
   - [ ] Chest surgery
   - [ ] ______
8. **Respiratory** [x] No Problems
   - [ ] Recurrent cough
   - [ ] Chronic bronchitis
   - [ ] Emphysema
   - [ ] COPD
   - [ ] Bronchial asthma
   - [ ] Tuberculosis
   - [ ] Wheezing
   - [ ] ______
9. **Cardiac / Peripheral - Vascular**
   - i. **Cardiac** [x] No Problems
     - [ ] Heart trouble
     - [ ] Swelling of feet
     - [ ] High blood pressure
     - [ ] Chest pain
     - [ ] Heart attack
     - [ ] Bypass surgery
     - [ ] Angioplasty
     - [ ] Mitral valve prolapse
     - [ ] Heart murmur

REVIEW OF SYSTEMS

Constitutional

There was a history of weight loss of 20 lbs. during 1997, and weight gain of 30 lbs from 1999-2000. He also described fatigue. However, there was no history of recurrent fever, general weakness.

Skin

There was no history of dry skin, recurrent rashes, eczema, itching, changes in hair, nails or skin color, etc.

Lymphatic/Hematological

There was no history of swollen glands, anemia, easy bruising, easy bleeding, difficulty to heal after cuts, blood transfusions, enlarged glands, phlebitis, HIV positive status, or being on blood thinners.

Head and Face

There was no history of any major abnormalities with the head and face.

Eyes

He wears reading glasses.

Ear/Nose/Mouth

Ear: No gross abnormalities were reported.

Nose/Sinuses: Mr. Doe reported sinus headaches sometimes.

Mouth and Throat: No abnormalities were reported.

Chest/Breasts

No gross abnormalities were reported.

Respiratory

He does not smoke. There was no history of major abnormalities reported with pulmonary system.

Cardiac/ Peripheral Vascular

Cardiac: There was no history of heart trouble, swelling of feet/ankles/leg, high blood pressure, chest pain/heart attack, bypass surgery/angioplasty, mitral valve prolapse, heart murmur, valvular surgery, heart failure, or shortness of breath with walking.

- [ ] Valvular surgery
- [ ] Heart failure
- [ ] Shortness of breath with walking
- [ ] ____________________

ii. Peripheral - Vascular [x] No Problems

- [ ] Poor circulation in arm R L
- [ ] Blood clots in arm R L
- [ ] Varicose veins R L
- [ ] Poor circulation in legs R L
- [ ] Blood clots in leg R L
- [ ] Vascular surgery R L
- [ ] ____________________

10. Hepatic - Biliary / Gastrointestinal / Abdominal

i. Hepatic - Biliary [x] No Problems

- [ ] Any liver disease
- [ ] h/o hepatitis Active_____ Inactive _____
- [ ] h/o jaundice due to liver disease
- [ ] h/o jaundice due to gallbladder disease
- [ ] Gallbladder problems
- [ ] ____________________

ii. Gastrointestinal [ ] No Problems

- [ ] Loss of appetite
- [ ] Abdominal pain
- [x] Problems with gas
- [ ] Heartburn
- [ ] Recurrent nausea
- [ ] Recurrent vomiting
- [ ] Recurrent diarrhea
- [x] Recurrent constipation
- [ ] Ulcer
- [ ] Hiatal hernia
- [ ] Regurgitation
- [ ] Reflux
- [ ] Indigestion
- [ ] h/o vomiting blood
- [ ] Blood in stools
- [ ] Loss of control of bowels
- [ ] ____________________

11. Urinary [ ] No Problems

- [x] Frequent urination
- [ ] Difficulty with urination
- [ ] Burning
- [ ] Inability to control
- [ ] Loss of control
- [ ] Blood in urine
- [x] Kidney stones once
- [ ] ____________________

12. Genital / Reproductive

Male [x] No Problems

- [ ] Discharge
- [ ] Pain in testicle(s) R L
- [ ] Lumps in testicle(s) R L
- [ ] Hydrocele R L
- [ ] Sexually transmitted disease(s)
- [ ] Sexual dysfunction
- [ ] ____________________

Female [ ] No Problems

- [ ] Menstruation regular____ irregular____
- [ ] LMP
- [ ] Post Menopausal Syndrome since ________
- [ ] Recurrent vaginal discharge
- [ ] No. of pregnancies ____ miscarriages____
- [ ] Cesarean sections 1 2 3 4
- [ ] Uterus removed
- [ ] Ovaries removed R L
- [ ] D & C (s)
- [ ] On hormones
- [ ] h/o cancer of uterus - ovary(ies)
- [ ] Sexual dysfunction
- [ ] Sexually transmitted disease(s)
- [ ] ____________________

13. Endocrine [x] No Problems

- [ ] Excessive thirst or urination
- [ ] Heat intolerance
- [ ] Cold intolerance
- [ ] Change in hat or glove size
- [ ] Thyroid trouble ___ underative ___overactive
- [ ] Sugar diabetes - since ________________
  Insulin dependent ________________
- [ ] Disease of pituitary gland
- [ ] Disease of adrenal gland
- [ ] ____________________

14. Musculoskeletal [ ] No Problems

- [ ] Muscle cramps
- [x] Stiff joints Knees
- [ ] Swelling of joints
- [ ] Generalized arthritis
- [ ] Rheumatoid arthritis
- [ ] Fibromyalgia syndrome
- [ ] Osteoporosis
- [ ] Neck pain
- [ ] Upper back pain
- [ ] Low back pain
- [ ] Heel spur(s) how many__________
- [ ] Gout
- [ ] Difficulty with walking
- [ ] Cold upper extremity(ies) R L
- [ ] Cold lower extremity(ies) R L
- [x] Pain in feet
- [ ] ____________________

15. Neurological / Psychiatric

i. Neurological [x] No Problems

- [ ] Frequent or recurrent headaches
- [ ] Fainting
- [ ] Blackouts
- [ ] Stroke
- [ ] Dizzy spells
- [ ] Gait difficulties
- [ ] Seizures
- [ ] Epilepsy
- [ ] Tremors
- [ ] Neuropathy
- [ ] Weakness
- [ ] Paralysis
- [ ] ____________________

Peripheral / Vascular: There was no history of varicose veins, poor circulation or blood clots in arms or legs. No vascular surgery was performed in the past.

Hepatic Biliary/ Gastro intestinal

Hepatic-Biliary: There was no history of liver disease, hepatitis, etc.

Gastro-intestinal: There was history of problems with gas.

Urinary

There was history of frequent urination.

Genital/Reproductive

No gross abnormalities were reported.

Endocrine

There was no history of thyroid problems, diabetes or hypoglycemia.

Musculoskeletal

He reported that there was history of stiff joints (knees), pain in feet. However, there was no history of muscle cramps, swelling of joint, generalized arthritis, rheumatoid arthritis, fibromyalgia syndrome, osteoporosis, neck pain, upper back pain, low back pain, heel spurs, gout, difficulty with walking, cold upper extremities, cold lower extremities,

Neurological / psychiatric

Neurological: Neurological history revealed no evidence of frequent or recurrent headaches, fainting/blackouts, stroke/ dizzy spells, gait difficulties, seizures/ epilepsy, tremors, neuropathy, weakness or paralysis.

ii. **Psychiatric** ☐ No Problems
☑ Problems with concentration
☐ Confusion
☐ Problems with thinking or thought process
☐ Problems with memory
☐ Depressed
☑ Anxious
☐ Shaky
☐ Agitated
☐ ______

16. **Other** ☑ No Problems
☐ Chicken Pox
☐ Rheumatic Fever
☐ Cancer
☐ Polio
☐ ______

17. i. **Allergies** ☐ No Problems
Drug Allergies ______
Food Allergies Maybe Milk
Environmental Allergies ______

ii. **Immunologic** ☐ No Problems
☐ Immunologic disorders______
☐ AIDS
☐ Lupus

B. Previous hospitalizations without surgery (include year and doctor's name)
1. ~~2000 Knee surgery~~, 1998 Kidney Surgery Stone: Dr.
2. ______
3. ______
4. ______
5. ______

C. Previous surgeries (include year and doctor's name - including surgeries listed on page 9)
1. YR 2000 Lt. Knee Surgery - Dr.
2. 1992 " " " " "
3. ______
4. ______
5. ______
6. ______

D. List all medications you currently take (prescription and nonprescription - including aspirin, Tylenol, etc. - including pain medications listed on page 9)

	Medication	Dose	Frequency	Date Started	Time of Last Dose
1.	Serzone	150 mg	2 times Daily	1999	Current
2.	Allegra	60 mg	2 times Daily	1995	"
3.	RellaFin	1000 mg	2 times Daily	1995	"
4.					
5.					
6.					
7.					
8.					

YOU ARE ALMOST DONE - GREAT JOB! PLEASE CONTINUE!

Psychiatric: He reported that he had problems with concentration, anxiety. However, there was no problem with confusion, thinking or thought process, memory, depression, shakiness, agitation.

Allergies / Immunologic

Allergies:

Drug(s): No known drug allergies.

Food(s): maybe milk.

Environmental: No known environmental allergies.

Immunologic: There was no history of any immunologic disorders.

Previous Hospitalizations

Kidney stone - Dr. - 1998

Previous Surgeries

Left knee surgery - Dr. - 2000

Left knee surgery - Dr. - 1992

Medications

Relafen 500 mg. 2 tabs bid

Serzone 150 mg. bid

Allegra 60 mg. bid

VII. PSYCHOLOGICAL HISTORY (Please answer as honestly as possible.)

This section asks some questions which may be repetitive and a few of the statements may seem unusual. Please do not be concerned, as these questions are included to describe people with many types of problems.

A. 1. Number of brothers and sisters: Older B_____ S_____ Younger B_____ S_____

2. Were you raised by: ☒ Mother & Father ☐ Mother ☐ Father ☐ Other ___________

3. Give a description of your father's personality: out going, Sense of Humor

4. Give a description of your mother's personality: out going, Serious Minded, Spiritual

5. Your childhood and home life while growing up were: (choose one)

☐ Happy ☒ Very Happy ☐ Neither Happy nor Unhappy ☐ Unhappy

B. **YOUR PAST / PRESENT EXPERIENCES**

1. Problems with memory	☐ No	☒ Yes Slight Short-Term
2. Flashbacks	☐ No	☐ Yes
3. Unusual experiences	☐ No	☐ Yes
4. Dizziness	☐ No	☐ Yes
5. Physical violence	☐ No	☐ Yes
6. Sexual abuse	☐ No	☐ Yes
7. Arrests	☐ No	☐ Yes
8. Jail sentences	☐ No	☐ Yes

C. **STRESS / ANXIETY**

Have you been tense, nervous or anxious?	☐ No	☒ Yes
1. Do you have excessive worry and anxiety about a number of events or activities?	☐ No	☒ Yes
2. Do you experience these worries and anxieties most of the time?	☐ No	☒ Yes
3. Do you find it difficult to control your worries?	☐ No	☒ Yes
4. Are your worries and anxieties associated with:		
a. Restlessness or feeling keyed up or on edge?	☐ No	☒ Yes
b. Being easily fatigued?	☒ No	☐ Yes
c. Having difficulty concentrating so that your mind goes blank?	☐ No	☒ Yes
d. Irritability or muscle tension?	☒ No	☐ Yes
e. Sleep disturbance (difficulty falling or staying asleep, or restless)?	☐ No	☒ Yes
5. Do you have panic attacks (intense fear of impending doom)?________	☒ No	☐ Yes
6. Do you have any phobias?________	☒ No	☐ Yes
7. Have you ever had a traumatic experience?________	☒ No	☐ Yes

D. **DEPRESSION**

1. Do you feel depressed (sad, empty)? ☐ No ☒ Mildly ☐ Moderately ☐ Significantly

2. Do you feel depressed most of each day?	☒ No	☐ Yes
3. Do you feel depressed nearly every day?	☐ No	☒ Yes
4. Does your family and/or friends think you are depressed?	☒ No	☐ Yes
5. Are you irritable (cranky, cross, grouchy) or restless and agitated?	☒ No	☐ Yes
6. Have you lost interest in all, or almost all, activities, most of the time?	☒ No	☐ Yes
7. Have you lost or gained a significant amount of weight over the past few months?	☐ No	☒ Yes
Is this due to change in appetite?	☐ No	☒ Yes
8. Do you have trouble getting to sleep or awaken frequently and ~~can't get back to sleep~~?	☐ No	☒ Yes
9. Do you sleep too much?	☒ No	☐ Yes
10. Do you feel sluggish and slow and you can't seem to get going?	☐ No	☒ Yes
Does this happen nearly every day?	☐ No	☒ Yes

PSYCHOSOCIAL EVALUATION

Proper evaluation of chronic pain often requires an appropriate psychological evaluation. Even though most clinicians who have experience in treating chronic pain, have developed skills to assess emotional or psychological parameters complicating pain problems, or psychological variables affecting the pain. It is well known that they are often unable to identify which of the variables are the most operative, or which psychological diagnoses are present. In fact, Waddell, et al showed that so called psychological impressions by physicians were hopelessly inaccurate when compared to appropriate psychological evaluation. Hence, it is assumed by the clinicians at — that besides producing physical limitations, chronic pain almost always causes some emotional disturbances and it is essential to explore the emotional aspects of the patient and the everyday effects of pain on the patient. He also underwent Pain Patient Profile (P3).

Validity

P3 was shown to be valid.

Developmental History

Mr. Doe was raised by his mother and father. He stated he comes from a family of 3. He described his father's personality and attitude towards him, past and present as, ''outgoing and sense of humor''. In addition, he also described his mother's personality and attitude towards him, past and present as, ''outgoing, serious minded and spiritual''. He described his childhood and home life while growing up as very happy.

Gross Psychological Pattern

In completing the questionnaire and interview, he provided the history that he has not experienced any significant problems with flashbacks, unusual experiences, dizziness, physical violence, sexual abuse, arrests, jail sentences. However, he stated that he experienced problems with memory.

11. Do you experience fatigue or loss of energy? ☐ No ☑ Yes
    Does this happen nearly every day? ☐ No ☑ Yes
12. Do you feel worthless ~~or guilty most of the time?~~ ☐ No ☑ Yes
13. Has your ability to think, concentrate and make decisions diminished? ☑ No ☐ Yes
14. Do you have thoughts of ending your own life (suicide)? ☑ No ☐ Yes
    If yes, do you have a plan? ☐ No ☐ Yes
15. Have you ever attempted suicide? ☑ No ☐ Yes
    If yes, how many times?________ When was the last attempt?________

E. **PREVIOUS PSYCHIATRIC HISTORY**

1. Have you ever had psychiatric / psychological treatment or evaluation? ☑ No ☐ Yes
   If yes, by whom and how many times?________
   Medication ________ ☐ No ☐ Yes
   Psychotherapy ________ ☐ No ☐ Yes
   Most recent treatment or visit on________

VIII. A. **LITIGATION**

i. You have or plan to have an attorney helping you? ☐ No ☐ Yes If yes, list name and address of attorney and how he / she is helping, etc.________

ii. Have you had any lawsuits in the past? Explain________

IX. **TREATMENT GOALS** Describe goals of your treatment.

- ☐ Return to work
- ☐ Be more active and functional
- ☐ Play with kids and grandkids
- ☐ Have sexual relations
- ☐ Participate in sports
- ☑ STAND, walk, lie Down without Pain

X. **CERTIFICATION**

I certify that I have answered truthfully all the questions, and have not knowingly withheld any information concerning any of the above problems, either past or present.

Your Signature ________ Witness ________

Date ________ Date ________

THANK YOU!

Signature of Reviewing Physician ________ Date ________

Stress and Anxiety

Patients with chronic pain are often tense, nervous, anxious, irritable, and angry. In addition, these feelings have significant effect on their family and friends, often producing marital strain secondary to tension, anxiety, and apprehension, either justified or not.

Pain management comprehensive questionnaire: Presented five questions, which include inquiries about excessive worry and anxiety, difficulty with controlling worries, features associated with anxieties such as restlessness, fatigue, difficulty with concentration, irritability, and sleep disturbances.

Using this global description, he stated that he has been tense, nervous, and anxious. Based on his individual item answers, he experiences substantial symptoms of stress and anxiety leading to the diagnosis of Generalized Anxiety Disorder.

Pain Patient Profile Anxiety evaluation: P3 anxiety scale consists of 12 items that assess inner turmoil, anger, worry, nervousness, restlessness, and emotional instability.

Anxiety T-Score on the evaluation was 41.

These scores represent **below-average** pain patient anxiety scores. Scores below the average pain patient score on anxiety score suggest adaptability, relaxation, self-confidence and security. He may be experiencing an appropriate level of concern about her pain, but remains generally optimistic and confident of improvement. Coping skills are generally intact and there is little suggestion of undue cognitive distress.

Depression

Chronic pain patients are often reluctant to use words such as depression, but they are generally free to discuss their frustration, anger, irritability, guilt, and fear. The literature has documented overwhelmingly that chronic pain patients suffer with insomnia, fatigue, lack of interest, poor concentration, and feelings of hopelessness which are features of depression, even if the patient does not admit to it directly.

Pain management comprehensive questionnaire: This psychosocial evaluation, specifically concentrating on depression, explores patients psychological status by questioning on 15 items, which include scope of depression, feelings of irritability and restlessness, lack of interest in activities, weight gain or weight loss, loss of appetite, sleep pattern, fatigue, lack of energy, guilt, inability to concentrate, thought(s) of suicide, or actual attempt(s) at suicide.

On global description he indicated that he feels mildly depressed by means of answering individual questions. He described that he feels depressed most of each day. Furthermore, he also reported a significant amount weight lost or gained over the past few months. He also reported having trouble getting to sleep or awakening frequently and having difficulty falling back to sleep. He reported that he feels sluggish and slow and can't seem to get going, and this occurs nearly every day. He experienced fatigue or loss of energy nearly every day as well. Additionally, he feels worthless and guilty most of time

Of the various aspects of depression evaluated using DSM-IV criteria, he presented clinically significant evidence of Major Depression.

PSYCHOSOCIAL EVALUATION

P3 ☐ No ☑ Yes MCMI III ☑ No ☐ Yes

I. PAIN PATIENT PROFILE (P3)

A. VALIDITY ☐ No ☑ Yes

B. DEPRESSION

	Patient's T-Score	
Below Average Pain Patient	(29 - 45)	35
Average Pain Patient	46 - 54	
Above Average Pain Patient	55 - 71	

C. ANXIETY

	Patient's T-Score	
Below Average Pain Patient	(29 - 45)	41
Average Pain Patient	46 - 55	
Above Average Pain Patient	56 - 71	

D. SOMATIZATION

	Patient's T-Score	
Below Average Pain Patient	(21 - 44)	32
Average Pain Patient	45 - 55	
Above Average Pain Patient	56 - 99	

II. MCMI III

A. VALIDITY ☐ No ☐ Yes

B. GROSS PSYCHOLOGICAL PROFILE

1. ☐ None
2. ☐ Mild
3. ☐ Mild to Moderate
4. ☐ Moderate
5. ☐ Moderately Severe
6. ☐ Severe

C. DEPRESSION

MCMI Dysthymic BR ________ Diagnosis: ☐ No ☐ Yes 300.40

Major Depression BR ________ Diagnosis: ☐ No ☐ Yes 296.3

D. ANXIETY

MCMI Anxiety BR ________ Diagnosis: ☐ No ☐ Yes 300.02

E. SOMATIZATION

MCMI Somatoform BR ________ Diagnosis: ☐ No ☐ Yes 300.81

F. OTHER PSYCHOLOGICAL PROBLEMS

☐ 1. None
☐ 2. Psychoactive substance abuse
☐ 3. Schizophrenia
☐ 4. Bipolar Disorder
☐ 5. Thought Disorder
☐ 6. Delusional Disorder
☐ 7. ________
☐ 8. ________

Pain Patient Profile Depression evaluation: The depression scale was constructed with 14 items that assess sleep, psychomotor activity, energy level, concentration and decision making, and feelings of helplessness, hopelessness, and low self-worth. The scale also samples behavioral manifestations of affective distress, including loss of interest, pleasure, or enjoyment in activities that were previously considered pleasurable.

Depression T-Score on the evaluation was 35.

This T-Score represents **below average** pain patient depression score. Lower scores on the depression scale suggest emotional stability, optimism, and self-confidence. Patients with low depression scores typically are not experiencing affective distress associated with pain or they are optimistic about their prospects for pain relief. Generally, these patients are capable of participating as active partners in treatment planning and implementation.

Pain Patient Profile Somatization evaluation: On P3 evaluation, somatization scale consists of 13 items, that assess concerns with physical health, bodily processes, muscle tension and spasms, somatic functioning, and physical abnormalities. In addition, the somatization scale measures the magnitude of patient's concern about pain.

Somatization T-Score on the evaluation was 32.

His T-score level places him in **below average** pain patient somatization group. Lower scores on the somatization scale reflect an absence of emotional threat and concentrated thought about pain and physical problems. Typically, the patient's coping skills are effective.

PREVIOUS PSYCHOLOGICAL/PSYCHIATRIC HISTORY

He stated that he had no previous psychological or psychiatric treatment or evaluation.

Litigation

He stated that he is not involved in any type of litigation at the present time for his pain. He denied that he ever had any litigation for any type of pain problems or injuries in the past.

Treatment Goal(s)

In this questionnaire, as well as personal interview, we offered the patient the option to describe goals of the treatment. On this evaluation, he described his goals of treatment as follows:

1. Stand, walk, lie down without pain

Certification

Mr. John R Doe certified that he answered all the questions truthfully about his pain problems, as well as health history and had not knowingly withheld any information concerning any of the above preceding problems, either past or present.

PHYSICAL EXAMINATION

FUNCTIONAL ASSESSMENT

1. PERCEIVED FUNCTION:

Sitting doesn't bother at a time | Driving doesn't bother at a time
Standing 10-15 min at a time | Walking 1 mile at a time
Balancing steady | Stooping doesn't bother
Lifting 50 lbs | Carrying 50-60 ft.
Kneeling hurts knees some | Squatting hurts knees some
Reaching - Straight doesn't bother | Overhead doesn't bother
Pushing / Pulling aggravates Rt. hip | Other ______

2. RANGE OF MOTION: ☐ **Arcon** ☐ **Cybex EDI** ☐ ______

Cervical ☐ Valid ☐ Invalid ______

Lumbar ☐ Valid ☐ Invalid ______

3. GRIP STRENGTH: Valid______ Invalid ______

4. LIFT CAPACITY: Static: Valid______ of 4 categories

PHYSICAL EVALUATION

1. INITIAL OBSERVATION:

i. Arrived: ☑ On time ☐ Late ☐ Early ______

ii. ☐ Accompanied by______ to center ☑ arrived alone to center

iii. ☐ Accompanied by______ to exam ☑ arrived to examination, alone

iv. Greeting manner: ☑ Pleasant ☐ Unpleasant ☐ Without any feeling ☐ ______

v. Any unusual or noteworthy initial behavior:

☑ None______ ☐ Nervous______ ☐ Overreacting______

vi. Tatoos: ☑ None ☐ 1 ☐ 2 ☐ 3 ☐ 4 ☐ 5 ☐ Numerous

vii. Reinforcement by spouse or other: ☐ Yes ☑ No By: ______

viii. Other ______

2. CONSTITUTIONAL: (Need at least 3) (Describe positive and negative)

i. Height 6'2" Weight 240#

ii. Pulse rate______mt ______reg ______irr ______reg irr

iii. Blood pressure______mm/hg ______supine ______sitting ______standing

iv. Respirations 16 /mt

v. Temperature______°F ______Oral ______Axillary

PHYSICAL EXAMINATION

FUNCTIONAL ASSESSMENT

Functional assessment included evaluation of the patient's perceived function, which was evaluated from his responses, which reflect perception of his abilities.

Perceived Functions:

Sitting	:	Does not bother
Standing	:	Ten to fifteen mintues
Walking	:	One mile
Driving	:	Does not bother
Balancing	:	Steady
Stooping	:	Does not bother
Lifting	:	Fifty pounds
Carrying	:	Fifty to sixty feet
Kneeling	:	Hurts knees some
Squatting	:	Hurts knee some
Reaching-straight	:	Does not bother
Reaching-overhead	:	Does not bother
Pulling/pushing	:	Aggravates right hip

3. GENERAL APPEARANCE: (Describe positive and negative)

☐ WNL

i. Development ✓ Well developed ______ Poorly developed
ii. Nutrition ✓ Well nourished ______ Undernourished
iii. Build ______ normal ______ thin ✓ overweight
______ somewhat obese ______ obese
iv. Body habitus ✓ independent ______ walked with a cane
______ walked with walker ______ wheelchair bound ______ bedridden
v. Deformities ✓ no physical disabilities ______ disabilities
vi. Grooming ✓ well groomed ______ poorly groomed ______ casual

4. SKIN: (Describe positive and negative)

☑ WNL

	Scars	Rashes	Lesions	Ulcers	Café-au-lait spots
Head	___	___	___	___	___
Face	___	___	___	___	___
Neck	___	___	___	___	___
Thoracic Spine	___	___	___	___	___
Chest	___	___	___	___	___
Lumbar Spine	___	___	___	___	___
Abdomen	___	___	___	___	___
Upper Extremity (Right)	___	___	___	___	___
Upper Extremity (Left)	___	___	___	___	___
Lower Extremity (Right)	___	___	___	___	___
Lower Extremity (Left)	___	___	___	___	___

5. HEMATOLOGIC / LYMPHATIC: (Describe positive and negative)

☑ WNL

______ Anemic ______ Cyanosis

Enlarged lymph nodes:

______ Neck R - L ______ Supraclavicular R - L
______ Axilla R - L ______ Groin R - L
______ Popliteal R - L ______ Other ______________

6. EYES: ☐ WNL

☑ Wearing glasses ☐ Wearing contacts
☐ Erythema R - L ☐ Sty R - L ☐ Chalazion R - L
☐ Conjunctivitis ☐ Ectropion R - L ☐ Ptosis R - L
☐ Proptosis R - L ☐ Nystagmus R - L ☐ Strabismus R - L
☐ Swelling R - L ☐ Abnormal pupillary reaction ☐ ______________

Ophthalmology ☐ WNL ______________________

PHYSICAL EVALUATION

Observation

He arrived on time. He arrived alone to center. He presented to the examination room alone. His greeting manner was pleasant. There was no unusual or noteworthy initial behavior. There were no tattoos present. There was no reinforcement noted during history talking or evaluation.

Constitutional

His height was 6 ft. 2 inches. His weight was 240 lbs. His respiratory rate was 16 per minute.

General appearance

Development: He was well developed.

Nutrition: He was well nourished.

Build: He was overweight.

Body Habitus: He was independent.

Deformities: There were no physical disabilities noted.

Grooming: He was well groomed.

Skin

Examination of the skin showed no evidence of scars, rashes, lesions, ulcers, or café-au-lait spots either in the head, trunk, neck, upper or lower extremities.

Hematologic/Lymphatic

Examination was grossly within normal limits with no evidence of anemia, cyanosis, or enlarged lymph nodes either in the neck, groin, axilla, or any other regions.

Eyes

He was wearing glasses.

7. EARS, NOSE, MOUTH & THROAT: ☑ ALL WNL

i. Ears: ☐ WNL

_________Lesions R - L _________Discharge R - L _________Hard of Hearing R - L

ii. Nose / Sinuses: ☐ WNL

_________Lesions _________Discharge _________Sinus Tenderness R - L

iii. Mouth & Throat: ☐ WNL

________No teeth ________Missing teeth ________Partials ↑ ↓ ________Dentures ↑ ↓

________Full dentures ________Gingivitis

________Pallor____________________ ________Cyanosis____________________

8. CHEST: ☑ WNL Breasts ☐ Deferred

________Scars Midline R - L ________Tenderness Midline R - L

________Masses R - L ____________________

9. RESPIRATORY: ☑ WNL

________Shortness of breath ________Intercostal retraction ________Visible respiratory effort

________Dullness ________Flatness ________Hyper resonance ________Rubs R - L

________Prolonged expiration R - L ________Wheezing R - L ________Rales R - L ________Ronchi R - L

10. CARDIOVASCULAR / PERIPHERAL VASCULAR:

i. Cardiovascular: ☑ WNL

________Abnormal PMI ________Tachycardia ________Bradycardia ________Abnormal carotid pulses

________Irregular cardiac rhythm ________Murmur: Grade_______ Type_______

ii. Peripheral Vascular: (Describe positive and negative)

☑ WNL

	UE	LE		UE	LE
Varicosities	R - L	R - L	Swelling	R - L	R - L
Abnormal Pulses	R - L	R - L	Edema	R - L	R - L
Temperature Change	R - L	R - L	Tenderness	R - L	R - L

11. GASTROINTESTINAL (ABDOMINAL): ☑ WNL

________Tenderness ________Masses ________Rigidity

________Enlarged liver ________Palpable spleen ________Incisional hernia

________Inguinal hernia R - L ________Abnormal bowel sounds ____________________

12. GENITOURINARY:

Male: ☐ WNL ☑ Deferred

________Hydrocele R - L ________Spermatocele R - L ________Tenderness of cord R - L

________Testicular mass R - L ________Penile warts Prostate ______enlarged ______tender

________Nodular ________Asymmetric ____________________

Female: ☐ WNL ☐ Deferred

________lesions ________masses ________discharge

________cystocele ________rectocele

Ears, Nose, Mouth, and Throat

Ears: Gross examination of the ears was without any major abnormalities with any obvious lesions, or ear discharge.

Nose/Sinuses: Examination of the nose was within normal limits with no evidence of lesions, or discharge.

Mouth and Throat: There were no gross abnormalities reported.

Chest/Breasts

Examination of the chest was grossly within normal limits with no scars or any other major abnormalities.

Respiratory

Examination of the respiratory system showed that there was no shortness of breath, prolonged respiration, wheezing, rales, or rhonchi.

Cardiovascular

Heart: Cardiovascular examination showed normal heart rhythm with no evidence of murmurs or gallop.

Peripheral: Examination of the peripheral vascular system showed no evidence of swelling or varicosities, temperature abnormalities, edema, or tenderness. Pulses were grossly within normal limits.

Gastrointestinal (Abdomen): Examination of the gastrointestinal system and abdomen revealed no evidence of masses, unusual tenderness, enlarged liver, rigidity, or palpable spleen.

Genitourinary: Genitourinary examination was deferred.

13. PSYCHIATRIC: (Describe positive and negative)

[✓] WNL			
Lack of orientation to	______time	______place	______person
Abnormal mood and affect	______depressed	______anxious	
Shaky	______agitated	______irritated	
Lack of memory	______recent	______remote	
______Lack of concentration	______Lack of attention span		
Language difficulty	______naming objects	______repeating phrases	______speech
Lack of knowledge	______current events	______past history	

14. MUSCULOSKELETAL (NEUROLOGICAL):

i. Dominance: [✓] Right handed [ ] Left handed [ ] ______________________

ii. Posture:

i. Cervical Lordosis ______________		[✓] Normal	[ ] Increased	[ ] Decreased
ii. Lumbar Lordosis ______________		[✓] Normal	[ ] Increased	[ ] Decreased
iii. Kyphosis ______________	[ ] None	[✓] Mild	[ ] Moderate	[ ] Severe
iv. Scoliosis ______________	[ ] None	[✓] Mild	[ ] Moderate	[ ] Severe

iii. Gait:

i. Straight Line ______________	[✓] Normal	[ ] Limp	[ ] Unable
ii. On Heels ______________	[✓] Normal	[ ] Limp	[ ] Unable
iii. On Toes ______________	[✓] Normal	[ ] Limp	[ ] Unable

iv. Coordination: [✓] WNL

Abnormal:
______________finger / nose
______________heel / knee / shin
______________rapid alternating movements in upper extremities
______________rapid alternating movements in lower extremities

v. Head / Face / Neck: [✓] WNL

Abnormal:

Head: ______lesions R - L ______masses R - L ______effusions R - L
______crepitus R - L ______asymmetry ______defects R - L ______tenderness R - L

Face: ______lesions R - L ______masses R - L ______effusions R - L
______crepitus R - L ______asymmetry ______defects R - L ______tenderness R - L
______TMJ tenderness R - L ______Enlarged salivary glands R - L
______Supraorbital tenderness R - L ______Supratrochlear tenderness R - L
______Auriculotemporal tenderness R - L ______ ______________________

Neck: ______lesions R - L ______masses R - L ______effusions R - L
______crepitus R - L ______asymmetry ______defects R - L
______thyromegaly ______jugular distension R - L

Physical Evaluation Continued....

Psychiatric: Gross psychiatric evaluation showed orientation to time, place, and person with normal mood and effect with no history of lack of memory, concentration, attention span, language difficulties or knowledge.

MUSCULOSKELETAL/NEUROLOGICAL EXAMINATION

Dominance: He was right handed.

Posture: His posture showed normal cervical lordosis, normal lumbar lordosis, mild kyphosis, and mild scoliosis.

Gait: His gait pattern evaluation showed that he was able to walk in a straight line, as well as on his heels, and toes without any problems.

Coordination: Evaluation of his coordination with fingers/nose, heel/knee/shin, rapid alternating movements in upper extremities, and rapid alternating movements in lower extremities was grossly within normal limits.

HEAD/FACE/NECK:

Head: Examination of head revealed no evidence of lesions, masses, crepitus, asymmetry, defects, tenderness, or effusions.

Face: Examination of face showed no evidence of lesions, masses, crepitation, asymmetry defects, tenderness, effusions, sinus tenderness, TMJ tenderness, or enlarged salivary glands.

Neck: Examination of neck showed no evidence of lesions, masses, crepitus, asymmetry, defects, tenderness, effusions, enlarged salivary glands, thyromegaly, tracheal deviation, or jugular distention.

vi. Cranial Nerves: [✓] WNL

Testing of Cranial Nerves (Abnormals)

_____2nd (visual acuity) ________________ R ☐ ____________ L ☐ ____________

_____3rd, 4th & 6th (pupils) ________________ R ☐ ____________ L ☐ ____________

_____5th (facial sensation) ________________ R ☐ ____________ L ☐ ____________

_____7th (facial symmetry, strength) ________ R ☐ ____________ L ☐ ____________

_____8th (hearing w/ tuning fork) __________ R ☐ ____________ L ☐ ____________

_____9th (palate movement) ________________ R ☐ ____________ L ☐ ____________

_____11th (shoulder shrug strength) ________ R ☐ ____________ L ☐ ____________

_____12th (tongue protrusion) ______________ R ☐ ____________ L ☐ ____________

vii. Cervical Spine: [✓] WNL

A. Inspection: i. [✓] WNL

scar(s) ____anteriorly in neck _____posteriorly in neck _____shoulder R - L _____arm R - L

____forearm R - L _____hand R - L _____finger(s) R - L

B. Inspection / Palpation: i. [✓] WNL

_____masses M - R - L _____lesions M - R - L _____effusion R - L _____defect R - L

_____contracture R - L _____dislocation R - L _____subluxation R - L _____laxity R - L

_____fasciculations R - L _____discoloration R - L _____amputation R - L

_____crepitus M - R - L _____swelling M - R - L

Palpation: ii.

ii. [✓] WNL	RIGHT			MIDLINE / SPINOUS PROCESS TENDERNESS	LEFT		
	Tenderness	Spasm	Trigger Points	Levels -	Tenderness	Spasm	Trigger Points
Superficial							
Non-Anatomic				Severity			
Paravertebral				0 1 2 3			
Suboccipital w/o HA							
Suboccipital w/ HA							
Periauricular w/o HA							
Periauricular w/ HA							
Upper Trapezius							
Shoulder							
AC Joint							
Arm							
Elbow							
Forearm							
Wrist							
Fingers							

Cranial Nerves:

Cranial nerve examination from 2 to 12 was grossly within normal limits bilaterally.

Cervical Spine:

Inspection - There was no evidence of scars on anterior or posterior aspect of the neck, shoulders, arms, forearm, hand, or fingers. Inspection revealed no masses, lesions, effusions, defects, contractures, dislocations, subluxation, laxity, fasciculations, discoloration, or amputation.

Palpation - Palpation was carried out in the cervical spine posteriorly as well as anteriorly, in the suboccipital region, upper trapezius, both shoulders, suprascapular muscles, and both upper extremities for the presence of tenderness superficial, organic, and non-organic; paravertebral muscle spasm, tightness in the muscles, and trigger points.

Palpation revealed no masses, lesions, effusions, defects, contractures, crepitus, swelling, dislocations, subluxation, laxity, or fasciculations. Palpation of the cervical spine was within normal limits.

C. Cervical Range of Motion: ☑ WNL

	Reduced	Normal	Increased	Pain				Better	
				None	Mild	Moderate	Severe	Some Relief	Complete Relief
Flexion									
Extension									
Right lateral rotation									
Right lateral flexion									
Left lateral rotation									
Left lateral flexion									

	RIGHT	LEFT	Focal Deficits
D. Shoulders (ROM):	(N) ↓ ↑	(N) ↓ ↑	
Impingement:	+ (–)	+ (–)	
E. Elbow:	✓	✓	
F. Wrist:	✓	✓	
G. Hand:	✓	✓	
H. Fingers:	✓	✓	
I. Motor Examination:			
Motor Strength in extremities	✓	✓	______
Grip Strength	✓	✓	______
Wasting	✓	✓	
Tone	✓	✓	
J. Sensory Examination:	✓	✓	______
K. Reflexes:			
Biceps (C5, C6)	1	1	
Triceps (C6, C7)	1	1	
Brachioradialis (C5, C6)	1	1	
L. Other Signs:			
Adsons'	+ (–)	+ (–)	
Tinel's	+ (–)	+ (–)	
Phalen's	+ (–)	+ (–)	

M. Non-Physiological Signs:

i. Tenderness ______ + (–)

ii. Distraction ______ + (–)

iii. Simulation ______ + (–)

iv. Regional ______ + (–)

v. Overreaction ______ + (–)

Positive in ______ out of 5 categories

Range of Motion - On examination of range of motion of cervical spine, as well as upper extremities was grossly within normal limits. Range of motion of the both shoulders was normal with no evidence of impingement. Range of motion of all other joints was grossly within normal limits.

Motor Examination - On examination for motor strength of upper extremities was grossly within normal limits.

Wasting - There was no wasting noted.

Grip Strength - The grip strength evaluation by manual testing was shown to be normal

Sensory evaluation - There was no sensory dysfunction noted in either upper extremity.

Reflexes - Deep tendon reflex evaluation showed the following:

		Right	Left
1.	Biceps	1	1
2.	Triceps	1	1
3.	Brachioradialis	1	1

Other neurological tests:

Phalen's Test	Negative	Negative
Tinel's Test	Negative	Negative
Adson's Test	Negative	Negative

Non-physiological signs - Non-physiological signs for cervical spine, which were derived from Waddell's non-physiological signs for low back pain were utilized with four categories with the following responses.

i.	Non-specific tenderness (Superficial/non-anatomic)	Negative
ii.	Presence of distraction	Negative
iii.	Regional (motor/sensory)	Negative
iv.	Simulation	Negative
v.	Overreaction	Negative

viii. Thoracic Spine / Ribs: ☑ WNL

A. Inspection: i. ☑ WNL ____________________

Scar(s) ____ thoracic spine M R L

B. Inspection / Palpation: ii. ☑ WNL

_____masses M - R - L _____lesions M - R - L _____effusion R - L _____defect R - L

_____contracture R - L _____dislocation R - L _____subluxation R - L _____laxity R - L

_____fasciculations R - L _____discoloration R - L _____amputation R - L

_____crepitus M - R - L _____swelling M - R - L

ii. ☑ WNL	RIGHT			MIDLINE / SPINOUS PROCESS TENDERNESS	LEFT		
	Tenderness	Spasm	Trigger Points	Levels -	Tenderness	Spasm	Trigger Points
Superficial				Severity			
Non-Anatomic				0 1 2 3			
Paravertebral							
Upper Trapezius							
Suprascapular							
Supraspinatus							
Infraspinatus							
Middle Trapezius							
Chest Wall							

ix. Lumbar Spine / Pelvis: ☐ WNL

A. Inspection: i. ☑ WNL

Scar(s) _____lumbar spine _____hip(s) R - L _____thigh(s) R - L

_____knee(s) R - L _____leg(s) R - L _____ankle(s) R - L

_____feet R - L ____________ ____________

B. Inspection / Palpation: ii. ☑ WNL

_____masses M - R - L _____lesions M - R - L _____effusion R - L _____defect R - L

_____contracture R - L _____dislocation R - L _____subluxation R - L _____laxity R - L

_____fasciculations R - L _____discoloration R - L _____amputation R - L

_____crepitus M - R - L _____swelling M - R - L

Thoracic Spine

Inspection - There was no evidence of scars on thoracic spine or chest wall. Inspection revealed no masses, lesions, effusions, defects, contracture(s), dislocation, subluxation, laxity, or fasciculations.

Palpation - Palpation revealed no masses, lesions, effusions, defects, contractures, crepitus, swelling, dislocations, subluxation, laxity, or fasciculations. Palpation of the thoracic spine was within normal limits.

Lumbar Spine

Inspection - There was no evidence of scars on lumbar spine, hips, thighs, knees, legs, ankles or feet. Inspection revealed no masses, lesions, effusions, defects, contracture(s), discoloration, swelling, varicose veins, subluxation, laxity, or fasciculations.

Palpation - Palpation was carried out in lower back, hips, knees, and ankles for the presence of tenderness, paravertebral muscle spasm, and tenderness in muscle groups as well as for the presence of trigger points.

Palpation revealed no masses, lesions, effusions, defects, contractures, crepitus, swelling, varicose veins, subluxation, laxity, or fasciculations.

ii. ☐ WNL	RIGHT			MIDLINE / SPINOUS PROCESS TENDERNESS	LEFT		
	Tenderness	Spasm	Trigger Points	Levels - L5, S1	Tenderness	Spasm	Trigger Points
Superficial	0			Severity	0		
Non-Anatomic	0			0 (1) 2 3	0		
Paravertebral	2	0	0		↓		
Sciatic Notch	2				↓		
SI Joint	2				↓		
Ilio-Lumbar	0				↓		
Glut Max	↓				↓		
Glut Med	↓				↓		
Groin	↓				↓		
Ischial Tuberosities	↓				↓		
Hips	↓				↓		
Knees	↓				↓		
Ankles	↓				↓		
Foot	↓				↓		
Toes	↓				↓		
Other	✓				✓		

C. Lumbar Range of Motion: ☐ WNL

	Reduced	Normal	Increased	Pain				Better	
				None	Mild	Moderate	Severe	Some Better	Complete Relief
Flexion		✓		✓					
Deflexion				✓					
Extension	20°					✓			
Right lateral rotation		✓		✓					
Right lateral flexion		✓		✓					
Left lateral rotation		✓		✓					
Left lateral flexion		✓		✓					

		RIGHT	LEFT
D.	Hip:	(N) ↓ ↑	(N) ↓ ↑
	Patrick-Fabere's Test:	+ (−)	+ (−)
E.	Knee:	✓	✓
F.	Ankle:	✓	✓
G.	Foot:	✓	✓
H.	Toes:	✓	✓

There was no superficial or nonanatomic tenderness. There was mild midline/spinous process tenderness from L5, S1. There was moderate paravertebral tenderness L5, S1 on the right side without paravertebral spasm or trigger points. There was moderate tenderness noted in sciatic notch region on the right side. There was SI joint tenderness noted, which was moderate on the right side. However, there was no ilio-lumbar, glut max, glut med, groin or ischial tuberosities, hips, knees, ankle, or foot toe tenderness noted.

Range of motion - On manual examination range of motion of lumbar spine, as well as lower extremities was grossly within normal limits.

On manual examination, range of motion of the both hips was normal with negative Patrick-Fabere's Test.

Examination of all other joints was grossly within normal limits.

	RIGHT	LEFT	Focal Deficits
I. Motor Examination:			
Strength	✓	✓	___
Wasting	✓	✓	
Tone	✓	✓	
J. Sensory Examination:	✓	✓	___
K. Reflexes:			
Quadriceps Femoralis (L3, L4)	1	1	
Achilles (L5, S1)	1	1	
Superficial	✓	✓	
L. Straight Leg Raising			
Sitting	70	90	
Supine			
Active	___	___	
Passive	70	90	
Back Pain	(+) −	+ (−)	
Sciatic Tension Signs	+ (−)	+ (−)	

M. Waddell's Non-Physiological signs:

i. Tenderness	+	(−)
ii. Simulation	+	(−)
iii. Distraction	+	(−)
iv. Regional	+	(−)
v. Overreaction	+	(−)

Positive in 0 out of 5 categories

x. Fibromyalgia Screen ☑ Negative ☐ Positive

Bilateral Tenderness present in following:

Suboccipital ___ Lateral Epicondylec(s) ___

Cervical C4 - 6 ___ Greater Trochanters ___

Second Costochondral Junction ___ Knee Medial (Fat Pad) ___

Trapezius ___ Gluteus Maximus ___

Supraspinatus ___

Other: ___

Motor strength - On manual examination for motor strength was normal with no focal neurological deficits noted.

Sensory -Sensory examination was within normal limits.

Reflexes - i. Deep tendon reflex evaluation was as follows:

	RIGHT	LEFT
Quadriceps Femoralis	1	1
Achilles	1	1

ii. Superficial reflexes were shown to be within normal limits.

Straight leg raising - Straight leg raising evaluation showed the following:

	RIGHT	LEFT
Sitting	70°	90°
Supine - Passive	70°	90°
Response to SLR:		
Back pain	Positive	Negative
Sciatic Tension	Negative	Negative

Non-physiological signs – Non-physiological signs of lumbar spine evaluation were described by Waddell, et al. Originally these included five with non-specific tenderness, simulation, distraction, regional disturbances, and over-reaction. Subsequently, over-reaction was removed from the non-physiological signs. The remaining four categories were evaluated:

1.	Non-specific tenderness (Superficial/non-anatomic)	Negative
2.	Simulation (Axial loading/rotation)	Negative
3.	Distraction (Range of motion/SLR)	Negative
4.	Regional Disturbances (Motor/sensory)	Negative
5.	Overreaction	Negative

Fibromyalgia Screen - Evaluation for fibromyalgia syndrome utilizing Fibromyalgia Screen developed by American Rheumatological Society was shown to be negative.

SYMPTOM MAGNIFICATION

. **Lack of Strategy to Control Symptoms** ☐ Yes ☑ No ☐ N/A

. **Lack of Control over Environment** ☐ Yes ☑ No ☐ N/A

. **OVERT PAIN BEHAVIOR:**

i. PAIN BEHAVIOR (Keefe and Block, Behavioral Theory, 1982)

(1) Guarding	☐ Yes	☑ No	(5) Sighing	☐ Yes	☑ No
(2) Bracing	☐ Yes	☑ No	(6) Pacing	☐ Yes	☑ No
(3) Rubbing	☐ Yes	☑ No	(7) Shifting	☐ Yes	☑ No
(4) Grimacing	☐ Yes	☑ No	(8) Other	☐ Yes	☐ No

Positive (> 2 signs) ______ Negative (< 2 signs) ✓ NA ______

ii. MCGILL'S PAIN QUESTIONNAIRE Positive ______ Negative ✓

iii. PAIN RATING Positive ______ Negative ✓

iv. PAIN DIAGRAM Positive ______ Negative ✓

SUMMARY OF CATEGORY

Positive (> 2 categories) ______ Negative (≤ 2 categories) ✓ NA ______

. LACK OF OBJECTIVE FINDINGS

i. No paravertebral muscle spasm	☑ Yes	☐ No	☐ N/A	______
ii. No motor weakness	☑ Yes	☐ No	☐ N/A	______
iii. No sensory deficit	☑ Yes	☐ No	☐ N/A	______
iv. No alteration of reflexes	☑ Yes	☐ No	☐ N/A	______
v. No positive nerve tension signs	☑ Yes	☐ No	☐ N/A	______
vi. No evidence of trigger points	☑ Yes	☐ No	☐ N/A	______

SUMMARY OF CATEGORY

Positive (all yes) ✓ Negative (at least 1 No) ______ NA ______

. LACK OF LABORATORY EVIDENCE

i. Radiological - (No abnormalities) ☐ Yes ☑ No ☐ NA

ii. Electrodiagnostic - (No abnormalities) ☐ Yes ☐ No ☑ NA

SUMMARY OF CATEGORY

Positive (all yes) ______ Negative (at least 1 No) ✓ NA ______

. CERVICAL SYMPTOMS OF ABNORMAL ILLNESS BEHAVIOR

i. Pain	☐ Anatomic distribution	☐ Whole arm pain
ii. Numbness	☐ Dermatomal	☐ Whole arm numbness
iii. Weakness	☐ Myotomal	☐ Whole arm giving way
iv. Time Pattern	☐ Varies with time and activity	☐ Never free of pain
v. Response to Treatment	☐ Variable benefit	☐ Intolerance of treatments ☐ Emergency admission(s) to hospital

Positive (> 3 symptoms) ☐ ______ Negative (< 2 symptoms) ☐ ______ NA ✓

EVALUATION OF SYMPTOM MAGNIFICATION

As per the description by Matheson in 1981, the definition of symptom magnification has evolved into the following, ''symptom magnification is a conscious or unconscious, self destructive, socially reinforced behavior response pattern consisting of reports or displays of symptoms which function to control the life or circumstances of the sufferer.'' Symptom magnification syndrome does not constitute a psychiatric diagnosis, or a diagnosis of malingering, and it is a treatable condition. Even though symptom magnification, non-physiological behavior, positive Waddell's Signs, somatization disorder, functional overlay, psychological overlay, psychological pain and partial malingering all share some features, signs, effects and conclusions, symptom magnification syndrome is considered as a separate entity.

1. Lack of strategy to control symptoms.		**NO**
2. Lack of control over Environment.		**NO**
3. Overt Pain Behavior.		**NO**
a. Pain Behavior	No	
Guarding	No	
Bracing	No	
Rubbing	No	
Grimacing	No	
Sighing	No	
Pacing	No	
Shifting	No	
b. McGill's Pain Questionnaire	No	
Negative with normal symptomatology		
c. Pain Rating	No	
Negative - Normal pain rating description		
d. Pain Diagram	No	
Negative - Anatomical distribution		

SUMMARY - Mr. Doe was positive in 0 out of 4 subcategories tested. Hence, he was negative in this category for symptom magnification.

4. Lack of Objective findings.		**YES**
a. No paravertebral muscle spasm.	Yes	
b. No motor weakness.	Yes	
c. No sensory deficit.	Yes	
d. No alteration of reflexes.	Yes	
e. Negative nerve tension signs.	Yes	
f. No evidence trigger points.	Yes	

SUMMARY - Mr. Doe was positive in 6 out of 6 subcategories tested. Hence, he was positive in this category for symptom magnification.

5. Lack of Laboratory evidence.		**NO**
a. Radiological	No	
b. Electrodiagnostic	NA	

SUMMARY - Mr. Doe was positive in 0 out of 1 subcategory tested. Hence, he was negative in this category for symptom magnification.

6. Symptoms of Abnormal Illness Behavior - Cervical		**NA**
a. Pain - Lack of anatomic distribution.	Na	
b. Numbness - Lack of dermatomal pattern.	Na	
c. Weakness - Lack of myotomal pattern.	Na	
d. Time pattern - Lack of variability.	Na	
e. Response to treatment - Lack of benefit.	Na	

7. CERVICAL SIGNS OF ABNORMAL ILLNESS BEHAVIOR

i.	Tenderness	☑ Anatomic distribution	☐ Non-anatomic
ii.	Distraction	☑ No change or limited	☐ Improves with distraction
iii.	Simulation	☑ No neck pain	☐ Neck pain
iv.	Regional	☑ Anatomical	☐ Non-anatomical
v.	Overreaction	☑ None or Minimal	☐ Present

Positive (> 3 signs) ☐ ________ Negative (< 3 signs) ☑ ________ NA ________

8. WADDELL'S SYMPTOMS OF ABNORMAL ILLNESS BEHAVIOR (LUMBAR)

		Normal Illness Behavior	Abnormal Illness Behavior
i.	Pain	☑ Anatomic distribution	☐ Whole leg pain
			☐ Tailbone pain
ii.	Numbness	☑ Dermatomal	☐ Whole leg numbness
iii.	Weakness	☑ Myotomal	☐ Whole leg giving way
iv.	Time Pattern	☑ Varies with time and activity	☐ Never free of pain
v.	Response to Treatment	☑ Variable benefit	☐ Intolerance of treatments
			☐ Emergency admission(s) to hospital

Positive (≥ 3 symptoms) ☐ ________ Negative (< 3 symptoms) ☑ ________ NA ________

9. WADDELL'S SIGNS OF ABNORMAL ILLNESS BEHAVIOR (LUMBAR)

i.	Tenderness	☑ Anatomic distribution	☐ Non-anatomic
ii.	Simulation	☑ No lumbar pain	☐ Lumbar pain
iii.	Distraction	☑ Limited	☐ Improves with distraction
iv.	Regional	☑ Anatomical	☐ Non-anatomical
v.	Overreaction	☑ None or minimal	☐ Present

Positive (≥ 3 signs) ☐ ________ Negative (< 3 signs) ☑ ________ NA ________

10. LACK OF MAXIMUM VOLUNTARY EFFORT

		YES	NO	NA
i.	COV's > 14 - hand grip	☐	☐	☑
ii.	COV's > 14 - static strength	☐	☐	☑
iii.	Invalid range of motion - inclinometry	☐	☐	☑

Positive (> 2 or > 50%) ________ Negative (< 2 or < 50%) ________ NA ✓ ________

11. LACK OF COOPERATION

		YES	NO	NA
i.	In completing questionnaire	☐	☑	☐
ii.	With psychological evaluation	☐	☑	☐
iii.	With physical evaluation	☐	☑	☐

Positive ________ Negative ✓ ________ NA ________

12. SOMATOFORM IMPLICATIONS

		YES	NO	NA
i.	MCMI - Somatization	☐	☐	☑
ii.	P3 - Somatization	☐	☑	☐

Positive ________ Negative ✓ ________ NA ________

Diagnosis

☐ Positive ≥ ________ ☐ Borderline ≥ ________ ☐ Negative < ________

7. Signs of Abnormal Illness Behavior - Cervical **NO**

a.	Tenderness - Lack of anatomic distribution.	No
b.	Distraction - Improves with distraction	No
c.	Simulation - Neck pain	No
d.	Regional - Non-anatomical	No
e.	Overreaction	No

SUMMARY - Mr. Doe was positive in 0 out of 5 subcategories tested. Hence, he was negative in this category for symptom magnification.

8. Waddell's Symptoms of Abnormal Illness Behavior - Lumbar **NO**

a.	Pain - Lack of anatomic distribution.	No
b.	Numbness - Lack of dermatomal pattern.	No
c.	Weakness - Lack of myotomal pattern.	No
d.	Time pattern - Lack of variability.	No
e.	Response to treatment - Lack of benefit.	No

SUMMARY - Mr. Doe was positive in 0 out of 5 subcategories tested. Hence, he was negative in this category for symptom magnification.

9. Waddell's Signs of Abnormal Illness Behavior - Lumbar **NO**

a.	Tenderness - Lack of anatomic distribution.	No
b.	Distraction - Improves with distraction	No
c.	Simulation - Lumbar pain	No
d.	Regional - Non-anatomical	No
e.	Overreaction	No

SUMMARY - Mr. Doe was positive in 0 out of 5 subcategories tested. Hence, he was negative in this category for symptom magnification.

10. Lack of Maximum Voluntary Effort. **NA**

a.	COV's > 14 - hand grip	NA
b.	COV's > 14 - Static strength	NA
c.	Invalid range of motion - inclinometer	NA

11. Lack of Cooperation. **NO**

a.	Lock of cooperation in completing questionnaire.	No
b.	Lack of cooperation with psychological evaluation.	No
c.	Lack of cooperation with physical evaluation	No

SUMMARY - Mr. Doe was positive in 0 out of 3 subcategories tested. Hence, he was negative in this category for symptom magnification

12. Somatoform Implication **NO**

a.	MCMI - Somatization	NA
b.	P3 - Somatization	No

SYMPTOM MAGNIFICATION SUMMARY - Mr. Doe was positive in 1 out of 10 categories tested. Hence, there was no significant evidence of symptom magnification.

MEDICAL DECISION MAKING

i. REVIEW OF INVESTIGATIONS ☑ Yes ☐ None available ☐ Requested ☐ Dictated

ii. REVIEW OF RECORDS ☑ Yes ☐ None available ☐ Requested ☑ Dictated

iii. IMPRESSION

PHYSICAL ☑ Dictated ☐ See coding section

MEDICAL ☐ Dictated ☐ See coding section NONE

PSYCHOLOGICAL ☐ Dictated ☐ See coding section

☑ Depression ☐ General Anxiety Disorder ☐ Somatization Disorder

☐

iv. PLAN

Investigations ☑ None ordered ☐ Ordered

a. Drugs

1. ☐ None
2. ☑ To continue SERZONE, [illegible] ROLAGEN
3. ☐ Will start
4. ☐ Will wean off
5. ☐

MEDICAL DECISION MAKING

Review of Investigations

12/20/99 – Lumbar spine – Old epiphyseal wedging of the lower thoracic upper lumbar bodies. Narrowing of the L5-S1 interspace with some facet degenerative change. There is in fact some grade I anterolisthesis of L5 on S1 and I suspect that the defect at the lamina of L5 is post surgical in nature.

12/20/99 – Right hip – Negative right hip.

2/21/00 – MRI/Lumbar spine – Some bulging of the L3-4 and 4-5 discs particularly in the inferior foramina on the left side at L3-4 and 4-5. Grade I spondylolisthesis of L5 on S1 which I believe is associated with bilateral pars defects at L5. Associated disc bulge related to the spondylolisthesis and a component of some central herniation probably present at the L5-S1 level. There is disc material bulging into the foramina bilaterally at L5-S1 associated with the listhesis .

Review of Records

His records from XX were reviewed. These indicated that Dr.—, Assistant Professor of Neurosurgery, felt that Mr. Doe had low back pain with a radicular component without evidence of obvious nerve root or other thecal sac compression. He also stated that in view of the bilateral pars fractures, however he thought it would be useful to obtain plain films with flexion and extension which were performed.

He was also diagnosed with anxiety disorder by Dr. —

Impression

1. Lumbar facet joint arthropathy
2. Lumbar disc displacement
3. Acquired spondylolisthesis
4. Sacroiliitis
5. Traumatic arthritis of both knees
6. Depression
7. No evidence of symptom magnification

Plan

At this time, I explained my impressions about his pain and associated problems, various modalities of treatments, his options, complications, prognosis, and duration of treatment.

Investigations: No investigations were ordered at the present time.

Drugs

At this time it was decided that we will continue the previous drug therapy of Serzone and Relafen.

b. Physical therapy

1. ☐ None due to lack of response or significant progress in past ______
2. ☐ None due to increased pain with physical therapy in past ______
3. ☐ None due to patient's refusal to undergo physical therapy ______
4. ☐ None due to the condition which is not amenable to physical therapy / rehab ______
5. ☐ Will continue at ______
6. ☑ Will start at PPT & Psy
7. ☐ Will consider later ______
8. ☐ Will manage with home exercise program ______
9. ☐ ______

c. Psychotherapy

1. ☐ None due to lack of major psychological problems ______
2. ☐ None due to patient's refusal to undergo psychological intervention ______
3. ☐ Will continue ______
4. ☐ Will start at ______
5. ☑ Will consider later ______
6. ☐ ______

d. Injections

1. ☐ None due to ______
2. ☐ Will consider later ______
3. ☑ Will start with: ☑ C / T / L Facet Blocks ☐ C / T / L Discography
   ☐ C / T / L / S Selective Epidural ☐ C / T / Lum / Caudal Epidural
   ☐ C / T / L Symp Block ☐ ______
4. ☑ Follow if necessary with: ☑ Facet Blocks ☑ Epidurals ☐ Hyertonic ☑ RFTN
   ☐ Endoscopy ☐ Cryo ☐ IDET ☐ ______
5. ☐ ______

v. **DURATION OF TREATMENT** 1. ☐ No Rx 2. ☐ 2 - 4 weeks 3. ☐ 4 - 6 weeks 4. ☐ 6 - 8 weeks 5. ☑ 9 - 12 weeks

______

vi. **PROGNOSIS** 1. ☐ Very good 2. ☑ Good 3. ☐ Good to fair 4. ☐ Fair
5. ☐ Fair to poor 6. ☐ Poor

vii. **DISCUSSION** ✓ ______

______

viii. **DISCHARGE / DISPOSITION** ✓ ______

______

SIGNATURE OF PHYSICIAN **DATE** ______

Physical therapy

Following the appropriate discussions about physical therapy, rehabilitation exercises and its influence in improving functional status it was decided that we will start physical therapy at —.

Psychotherapy

After the discussions with regards to the benefits of psychological intervention, behavioral modification and necessity of both interventions in improving pain management, it was decided that we will consider at a later date.

Neural Blockade

Following the appropriate discussions including complications, benefits, advantages and disadvantages it was decided that initially we will proceed with: Lumbar facet blocks.

Following this injection therapy, we will make a diagnostic impression of the problem. If she obtains good pain relief following this injection therapy there is no necessity for any further treatment, however, if pain returns we will consider other options in injection therapy.

At this time, we also discussed about other options to follow the initial injection therapy, which will include facet blocks, epidurals and Radiofrequency thermoneurolysis.

Course of Treatment

Following the appropriate discussions, including complications, benefits, advantages, disadvantages, it was decided that initial duration of treatment would be 9-12 weeks with further follow-up along with maintenance therapy as required based on the progress and improvement.

Prognosis

Following the review of available information, physical as well as psychological status, diagnostic impressions, therapeutic options available, and his understanding of the treatment modalities including complications, advantages and disadvantages. His prognosis is considered to be good.

However this prognosis may change on the response or lack thereof based on further evaluation, and management.

Discussion

At this time, once again we discussed about various issues involved in his management including my impressions, his perceptions, treatment options available and development of realistic goals in management. Once again, it was emphasized that pain relief is desirable, however, it may not be achievable in all cases, even though it is a goal one can hope for and it is achieved in only a small number of patients. Thus it was emphasized on understanding the process of chronic pain development, its management, limitations and frustrations off its management, thus necessity of developing practical goals which should include to increase the functional capacity with reduction in pain and quality of life. It was also emphasized that it is extremely important to modify pain behavior with positive attitude and relaxation techniques, also avoid pain generating activities with modifications of activity as much as possible and finally eliminate drug dependency, however, even if the drugs are continued, they will be administered in a controlled fashion and he should follow the narcotic contract.

Discharge/Disposition

Following the above discussions, discharged was carried out with the following prescriptions: Relafen 500 mg. x 2, bid. He will return on November 20, 2000.

____

, M.D.

CONDENSED EVALUATION

Date: ____________________

I. A. Name ___ S.S. #_
First Middle Initial Last
B. Sex: __ M __ F C. Race D. Age______ E. DOB __________
F. Address_ _State _Tel.
G. Occupation_ H. Employer
I. Nearest Relative's Name__ ____________________ Tel. _

II. A. Referring Physician _ ____________________
Name and Address
B. Family Physician ___ ____________________
Name and Address

III. A. Describe the pain for which you are now seeking help in one sentence. (Example: "My back hurts.")
PAIN => Deep Right Hip, Down Thigh to Sometimes Slight Pain + Numbness Rt foot ARCH

IV. A. **H/O - PRESENT ILLNESS – PLEASE LIST ONLY RELEVANT PROBLEMS**

PROBLEM

1. ☐ Headaches Since: ____________________
2. ☐ Neck Pain Since: ____________________
3. ☐ Shoulder Pain R L Since: ____________________
(any part from arm to fingers) ____________________
5. ☐ Thoracic Spine Pain Since: ____________________
6. ☐ Chest Wall Pain Since: ____________________
(not heart related chest pain) ____________________
7. ☑ Low Back Pain Since: 1998
8. ☑ Hip Pain (R) L Since: 1998
9. ☑ Lower Extremity Pain Since: 1998
(any part from thigh to toes) (R) L ____________________
10. ☐ Abdominal Wall Pain R L Since: ____________________
11. ☐ Abdominal Pain Since: ____________________
12. ☐ Groin Pain R L Since: ____________________
13. ☐ Other__________ Since: ____________________

INITIAL EVALUATION

PHYSICIAN -XYZ M.D.

IDENTIFYING INFORMATION:

Name	:	John Deo
Address	:	abc.
Telephone	:	XX X-XXX-XXXX
Date of Birth	:	xx/xx/xxxx
Age (yrs.)	:	43
SS#	:	XXX-XX-XXXX
Referred by	:	Dr.—
Occupation	:	Firefighter
Employer	:	xxx
Location	:	ABC
Date of Evaluation	:	xx/xx/xxxx

INITIAL EVALUATION

☑ Paducah ☐ Marion

Name ____ Date ____

History Provided By: pt. Quality: good

History of Present Illness: R, low back,

Mr. today c̄ c/o pain in Rt. hip/buttock area that travels down back of Rt. leg into foot. at times Rt. foot goes numb. Denies any lower back pain. This seemed to have started 1998 without any accident or event. Began seeing chiropractor which seemed to help only temporarily. Then he went to Dr. who started on Relafen and sent to PT. Relafen helps quite a bit, but PT didn't seem to help much. Just basically dealt c̄ pain until May 2000 and then he saw Dr. (neurosurgeon) in . Told him nothing surgically could be done and suggested for him to come to pain mgmt and cont. on Relafen.

Symptomatology: ☐ Location ☐ Quality ☐ Severity ☐ Duration ☐ Timing ☐ Context ☐ Modifying factors ☐ Associated signs & symptoms

1) INTERMITTENT THROBBING, CRAMPING PAIN ~~WITH~~ ON (R) SIDE OF LOW BACK PAIN AND (R) HIP WITH RADIATION TO (R) LOWER EXTREMITY ASSOCIATED WITH NUMBNESS AND TINGLING, SINCE 1998 WITH GRADUAL ONSET WITH NO SPECIFIC INCIDENT BUT WITH H/O OF HEAVY WORK WITH FAILURE TO RESPOND TO MEDICATIONS PT CHIROPRACTIC MANIPULATIONS AND EXERCISE UNTIL 9/2000, WITH BACK PAIN WORSE THAN LEG PAIN.

2) ~~Bit Kidd [illegible]~~

Systems	Multisystems	Single System: Musculoskeletal	Single System: Neurologic
Constitutional	Two elements	Two elements	Two elements
Musculoskeletal	Six elements	Five elements	Three elements
Neurological	Three elements	Two elements	Sixteen elements
Cardiovascular	Seven elements	One element (Peripheral)	Three elements
Chest / breasts	Two elements	----------	----------
Ears, nose, mouth and throat	Six elements	----------	----------
Eyes	Three elements	----------	One element (Ophthalmoscopy)
Genitourinary	Four elements - male Seven elements - female	----------	----------
Gastrointestinal	Five elements	----------	----------
Lymphatic	Four elements	One element	----------
Psychiatric	Four elements	Two elements	----------
Respiratory	Four elements	----------	----------
Skin	Two elements	One element	----------

HISTORY

Chief Complaint

''Pain - Deep right hip, down thigh to sometimes slight pain and numbness right foot arch.''

History of present illness

Intermittent throbbing, cramping pain on the right side of low back and right hip with radiation to right lower extremity associated with numbness and tingling, since 1998 with gradual onset with no specific incident but with history of heavy work, with failure to respond to medications, physical therapy, chiropractic manipulations and exercise until September 2000, with back pain worse than leg pain.

V. PAST, FAMILY, AND SOCIAL HISTORY ☐ No problems in past

A. **PAST PAIN HISTORY (DO NOT describe present problem.)** (mark only applicable ones - not all)

1. ☐ Motor vehicle injury(ies)
2. ☑ Work related injury(ies) Knee injury, torn cartilage 1992 Rt Knee
3. ☑ Any other injury(ies) recent Knee Surgery 2000 Daly Rt Knee
4. ☐ Headache Hip Pain became more intense about this time frame
5. ☐ Pain in Neck
6. ☐ Pain in Upper Extremities
7. ☐ Pain in Upper Back
8. ☐ Pain in Mid-Back
9. ☐ Chest Wall Pain
10. ☐ Pain in Lower Back
11. ☐ Pain in Lower Extremities
12. ☐ Pain in Joints (example: shoulder, hip or knee)
13. ☐ Arthritis
14. ☐ Other

B. **EVALUATION AND TREATMENT HISTORY FOR PAIN**

1. Please list all doctors, chiropractors, therapists and emergency room doctors you have seen for your problem and when you first saw them.

PROVIDER SEEN	APPROX. # OF TIMES	DURING THE YEARS
		1999
		1998 – 2000
		2000

2. Total number of providers seen: 3
3. Which of the following tests have been performed? (mark only applicable ones - not all)
   - ☑ a) Regular X-Rays of Back
   - ☐ b) CT Scan of
   - ☐ c) Myelogram of
   - ☑ d) MRI Scan of Lower Back
   - ☐ e) Discogram of
   - ☐ f) Bone Scan of
   - ☐ g) Nerve Conduction of

4. Please list all operations you have **ever** had for the pain (not other surgeries).
   PLEASE INCLUDE YEAR AND DOCTOR'S NAME
   1.
   2.
   3.
   4.
   5.
5. Please describe other treatments, in sequence, since this problem started, with months / years.
   1. ☑ Chiropractic Treatment off & on for 2 years
   2. ☑ Physical Therapy 6 mons. 1999
   3. ☐ Psychotherapy
   4. ☐ Epidurals
   5. ☐ Nerve Blocks
   6. ☐ Cortisone Injections
   7. ☐ Cortisone By Mouth
   8. ☐ Other
6. a. What medicines are you now taking for pain, anxiety, etc., and how often for each? (do not list here medicines taken for medical problems)

	Medication	Dose	Frequency	Date Started	Time of Last Dose
i.	Relafin	(2) 500 MG TABS	twice a Day	1999	Still taking
ii.	Serzone	150 mg	Bid		
iii.					
iv.					
v.					

How much relief do you obtain from drugs? Some More at the Beginning

Duration of relief: 4 h-8 hrs side effects:

b. What other medicines (if any) and how long have you used them in the past?
~~Serzone 150 mg twice a Day (for Restlessness)~~
~~Allegra 60 mg twice Daily~~ Celebrex

C. i. **FAMILY PAIN HISTORY** ☐ No problems

Condition	Relationship	Condition	Relationship	Condition	Relationship
1. ☐ Migraine		7. ☑ Low Back Pain	mom	14. ☐ Lupus	
2. ☐ Headaches		8. ☐ Shoulder Pain		15. ☐ Multiple Sclerosis	
3. ☐ Neck Pain		9. ☐ Arm Pain		16. ☐ Epilepsy	
4. ☑ Upper Back Pain	Mom	10. ☐ Hip Pain		17. ☑ Depression	Aunt
5. ☐ Mid-Back Pain		11. ☐ Leg Pain		18. ☐ Schizophrenia	
6. ☐ Chest Wall Pain (not related to heart)		12. ☑ Arthritis	Mom, Grandmother	19. ☐ Alcoholism	
		13. ☐ Fibromyalgia		20. ☐	

ii. **FAMILY MEDICAL HISTORY** ☐ No problems

1. ☑ High Blood Pressure DAD	5. ☐ Bronchial Asthma
2. ☐ Heart Attack	6. ☐ Bleeding Disorder
3. ☐ Heart Disease	7. ☐ Hepatitis
4. ☐ Diabetes	8. ☑ Stroke – DAD

PAST, FAMILY, SOCIAL HISTORY

Past history

He related torn cartilage, right knee from work related injury in 1992. He has history of right knee surgery in July 2000. However, there was no history of headache, pain in neck, pain in upper extremities, pain in upper back, pain in mid-back, chest wall pain, pain in back, pain in lower extremities, joints pain, arthritis.

Evaluation and treatment history for pain

He was seen by 3 providers in the past these were:

Dr. x - three occasions - 1999

Dr. xx, - approximately 20 occasions - 1998-2000

Dr. xxx, - one occasion - 2000

In the past, he stated that he underwent regular X-rays of back, MRI scan of lower back.

He has history of chiropractic treatments off and on for two years. He also has attended physical therapy treatments for six months in 1999. However, he never underwent any psychotherapy, epidural/nerve blocks, cortisone injections or by mouth.

He stated that he is taking the following medications for management of his present problems. These include:

Relafen 500 mg. 2 tabs bid

Serzone 150 mg. bid

He stated that these medications provide some relief. He stated that he experienced no side effects with these medications. In addition to the above, he stated that he tried various other medications, which include Celebrex.

Family history

There was a history of upper back pain, low back pain, arthritis, depression, and high blood pressure and stroke in the family. However, there was no history of migraine, headaches, neck pain, mid-back pain, chest wall pain, shoulder pain, arm pain, hip pain, leg pain, fibromyalgia, lupus, multiple sclerosis, epilepsy, schizophrenia, alcoholism in the family.

D. **ENVIRONMENTAL INFORMATION**

1. List all the areas you have lived in
2. Education: Highest grade completed Bachelor of Science
3. Marital status: ☒ Married ☐ Separated ☐ Divorced ☐ Widowed ☐ Single How long? 1 yr.
4. Do you live: ☐ Alone ☒ with Spouse ☐ with Parents ☐ Other
5. Previous marriages: ☐ None ☒ Yes If yes, how many? 1
6. Number of children: Male 2 Female ____ Ages of children 13, 10
7. If married, which of the below best describes your marriage?
   ☒ Completely satisfactory ☐ Satisfactory ☐ Tolerable ☐ Intolerable ☐ No opinion
8. Has your pain problem changed your relationship with your spouse and family? ☐ No ☒ Yes
   If yes, describe Sometime I'm not as Sports active & Sometimes I have to Sleep in another Bed to ~~Keep~~ So I Won't Keep my wife awake from my tossing & turn
9. Excessive exposure at home to: ☐ None ☐ Fumes ☐ Dust ☐ Solvents ☐ Noise

E. **OCCUPATIONAL HISTORY:** ☐ Disabled since ____ ☐ Retired since ____ ☐ Homemaker

(If disabled, retired, over 65, or homemaker you may skip this section.)

1. Please list all previous occupations / jobs you have held in the last 10 years. (Attach separate sheet if necessary.) Fire Fighter, Sales associate at J C Penney
2. Please describe your current job (if unemployed, your very last job). I sometime Work in Hazardous Conditions with alot of Use of Uppers & Lower Body functions
   a. How long have you held this job? 15 yrs 2. How many hours per week do your work? 56 AVE.
   b. Does your work involve:
      - Standing: ☐ No ☒ Yes If yes, how long at a time? 4-5 Depends
      - Driving: ☐ No ☐ Yes If yes, how long at a time?
      - Walking: ☐ No ☒ Yes If yes, how long at a time? Depends
      - Lifting: ☐ No ☒ Yes If yes, how many lbs. more than 6-8 times per hour?
        If yes, how many lbs. less than 6 times per hour?
      - Sitting: ☐ No ☒ Yes If yes, how many hours per day? 4-5 Depends
   c. Does your work involve vibration (i.e., machinery, driving, etc.)? ☐ No ☒ Yes
      If yes, what is source of vibration? Operating Rescue Equipment
   d. Excessive exposure at work to: ☒ Fumes ☒ Dust ☒ Solvents ☒ Noise Depend on situation
   e. Have you missed much work because of your current or previous illness, injury or pain?
      ☒ No ☐ Yes When was the last day you worked "full duty"?
   f. If you are not working, are you currently receiving wage compensation? ☐ No ☐ Yes

F. **HABITS**

1. SMOKING: a. Do you smoke now? ☒ No ☐ Yes Smoking since?
   How many cigarettes per day?____ Cigars per day?____ Pipe? ____
   b. Have you ever smoked? ☐ No ☐ Yes Explain
2. ALCOHOL: a. Do you drink alcohol? ☒ No ☐ Yes If yes, how much?
   b. Have you ever had problems with alcohol? ☐ No ☐ Yes If yes, explain
3. CAFFEINATED DRINKS: Do you consume drinks with caffeine? ☐ No ☒ Yes
   If yes, ☒ Coffee ☒ Tea ☒ Iced Tea ☒ Colas ☐ Other ____ No. of Cups Daily 8
4. DRUGS: Do you use any street drugs? ☒ No ☐ Yes If yes, explain

G. **HOBBIES:** List your hobbies: Play Guitar & Sing

Are you participating now? ☐ No ☒ Yes If yes, describe: Perform at Restkomes

Social history

Environmental: He stated that he lived in Xyz. He completed BS from Murray State university. He stated that he has been married. He also stated that he lives with his wife. He stated that he was married one time in the past. He has 2 sons of ages 13 and 10 years. He stated that his marriage is completely satisfactory. He stated that his pain problems have changed his relationship with his wife and family members because sometimes he is not as sports active and sometimes he has to sleep in another bed so he does not keep his wife awake from him tossing and turning. He denied any excessive exposure due to fumes, dust, solvents or noise.

Occupational: He stated that, in the past he was employed as a fire fighter and sales associate at J. C. Penney's. His present occupation is a fire fighter. He uses a lot of upper and lower body functions. He held this job for 15 years and working 56 hours per week on average In addition to this, he described that his work involves standing 4-5 hours at a time, walking, lifting,, and sitting for 4-5 hours per day. With regards to vibrations, he stated that his work involves vibration and source of the vibration is operating reserve equipment. He stated that he had excessive exposure to fumes, dust, solvents, and noise at work. He stated that he has not missed any work.

Habits

Smoking: He does not smoke.

Alcohol: He does not drink alcohol and he never had a problem with alcohol.

Caffeinated Drinks: He drinks 8 cups of coffee, tea, iced tea and colas daily.

Drugs: He does not use any street drugs.

Hobbies: His hobbies are play guitar, and sing. He stated that he is able to participate in his hobbies.

VI. A. **MEDICAL HISTORY** (answer only applicable ones - do not mark all)

1. Constitutional Symptoms ☑ No Problems
- ☑ Weight loss _20_ lbs., during _1997_
- ☐ Weight gain _30_ lbs., during _1999-2000_
- ☐ Recurrent fever
- ☐ General weakness
- ☑ Fatigue
- ☐ ____

2. Skin ☑ No Problems
- ☐ Dry skin
- ☐ Recurrent rashes
- ☐ Eczema
- ☐ Itching
- ☐ Changes in skin color
- ☐ Changes in hair or nails
- ☐ ____

3. Hematologic / Lymphatic ☑ No Problems
- ☐ Swollen glands
- ☐ Low blood count (anemia)
- ☐ Easy bruising
- ☐ Easy bleeding
- ☐ Slow to heal after cuts
- ☐ h/o blood transfusions
- ☐ Enlarged glands
- ☐ Phlebitis
- ☐ HIV positive
- ☐ on blood thinners
- ☐ ____

4. Head / Face ☑ No Problems
- ☐ Headaches
- ☐ h/o head injury without residual problems
- ☐ h/o head injury with residual problems of ____
- ☐ Facial pain
- ☐ TMJ R L
- ☐ Tic douloureux R L ____
- ☐ ____

5. Eyes ☑ No Problems
- ☐ Nearsighted
- ☐ Farsighted
- ☐ Wear glasses
- ☐ Wear contact lenses
- ☐ Cataracts at present time R L
- ☐ Cataract surgery R L
- ☐ Conjunctivitis R L
- ☐ Glaucoma R L
- ☐ Double vision R L
- ☐ Blurred vision R L
- ☑ _Reading Glasses_

6. Ear / Nose / Mouth

i. Ears ☑ No Problems
- ☐ Hard of hearing R L
- ☐ Hearing aids R L
- ☐ Chronic ear discharge R L
- ☐ Vertigo
- ☐ Ringing in ears R L
- ☐ ____

ii. Nose / Sinuses ☐ No Problems
- ☐ Sinus discharge
- ☐ Nasal discharge
- ☐ Repeated nosebleeds
- ☐ Deviated nasal septum
- ☐ Chronic sinus problems
- ☐ Chronic stuffy nose
- ☐ Hay fever
- ☐ Nasal polyps
- ☑ _Sinus headaches Sometimes_

iii. Mouth / Throat ☑ No Problems
- ☐ Teeth ___ Loose ___ None
- ☐ Dentures ___ Full ___ Partial
- ☐ Bleeding gums
- ☐ Dry mouth
- ☐ Sore throat
- ☐ Hoarseness
- ☐ Vocal cord polyps
- ☐ Trouble swallowing
- ☐ ____

7. Chest / Breasts ☑ No Problems
- ☐ Breast masses
- ☐ Breast surgery
- ☐ Chest surgery
- ☐ ____

8. Respiratory ☑ No Problems
- ☐ Recurrent cough
- ☐ Chronic bronchitis
- ☐ Emphysema
- ☐ COPD
- ☐ Bronchial asthma
- ☐ Tuberculosis
- ☐ Wheezing
- ☐ ____

9. Cardiac / Peripheral - Vascular

i. Cardiac ☑ No Problems
- ☐ Heart trouble
- ☐ Swelling of feet
- ☐ High blood pressure
- ☐ Chest pain
- ☐ Heart attack
- ☐ Bypass surgery
- ☐ Angioplasty
- ☐ Mitral valve prolapse
- ☐ Heart murmur

REVIEW OF SYSTEMS

Constitutional

There was a history of weight loss of 20 lbs. during 1997, and weight gain of 30 lbs from 1999-2000. He also described fatigue. However, there was no history of recurrent fever, general weakness.

Skin

There was no history of dry skin, recurrent rashes, eczema, itching, changes in hair, nails or skin color, etc.

Lymphatic/Hematological

There was no history of swollen glands, anemia, easy bruising, easy bleeding, difficulty to heal after cuts, blood transfusions, enlarged glands, phlebitis, HIV positive status, or being on blood thinners.

Head and Face

There was no history of any major abnormalities with the head and face.

Eyes

He wears reading glasses.

Ear/Nose/Mouth

Ear: No gross abnormalities were reported.

Nose/Sinuses: Mr. Doe reported sinus headaches sometimes.

Mouth and Throat: No abnormalities were reported.

Chest/Breasts

No gross abnormalities were reported.

Respiratory

He does not smoke. There was no history of major abnormalities reported with pulmonary system.

Cardiac/ Peripheral Vascular

Cardiac: There was no history of heart trouble, swelling of feet/ankles/leg, high blood pressure, chest pain/heart attack, bypass surgery/angioplasty, mitral valve prolapse, heart murmur, valvular surgery, heart failure, or shortness of breath with walking.

Peripheral / Vascular: There was no history of varicose veins, poor circulation or blood clots in arms or legs. No vascular surgery was performed in the past.

- [ ] Valvular surgery
- [ ] Heart failure
- [ ] Shortness of breath with walking
- [ ] ______________

ii. Peripheral - Vascular [x] No Problems
- [ ] Poor circulation in arm R L
- [ ] Blood clots in arm R L
- [ ] Varicose veins R L
- [ ] Poor circulation in legs R L
- [ ] Blood clots in leg R L
- [ ] Vascular surgery R L
- [ ] ______________

10. Hepatic - Biliary / Gastrointestinal / Abdominal

i. Hepatic - Biliary [x] No Problems
- [ ] Any liver disease
- [ ] h/o hepatitis Active_____ Inactive _____
- [ ] h/o jaundice due to liver disease
- [ ] h/o jaundice due to gallbladder disease
- [ ] Gallbladder problems
- [ ] ______________

ii. Gastrointestinal [ ] No Problems
- [ ] Loss of appetite
- [ ] Abdominal pain
- [x] Problems with gas
- [ ] Heartburn
- [ ] Recurrent nausea
- [ ] Recurrent vomiting
- [ ] Recurrent diarrhea
- [x] Recurrent constipation
- [ ] Ulcer
- [ ] Hiatal hernia
- [ ] Regurgitation
- [ ] Reflux
- [ ] Indigestion
- [ ] h/o vomiting blood
- [ ] Blood in stools
- [ ] Loss of control of bowels
- [ ] ______________

11. Urinary [ ] No Problems
- [x] Frequent urination
- [ ] Difficulty with urination
- [ ] Burning
- [ ] Inability to control
- [ ] Loss of control
- [ ] Blood in urine
- [x] ~~Kidney stones~~ once
- [ ] ______________

12. Genital / Reproductive

Male [x] No Problems
- [ ] Discharge
- [ ] Pain in testicle(s) R L
- [ ] Lumps in testicle(s) R L
- [ ] Hydrocele R L
- [ ] Sexually transmitted disease(s)
- [ ] Sexual dysfunction
- [ ] ______________

Female [ ] No Problems
- [ ] Menstruation regular____ irregular____
- [ ] LMP
- [ ] Post Menopausal Syndrome since ________
- [ ] Recurrent vaginal discharge
- [ ] No. of pregnancies ____ miscarriages____
- [ ] Cesarean sections 1 2 3 4
- [ ] Uterus removed
- [ ] Ovaries removed R L
- [ ] D & C (s)
- [ ] On hormones
- [ ] h/o cancer of uterus - ovary(ies)
- [ ] Sexual dysfunction
- [ ] Sexually transmitted disease(s)
- [ ] ______________

13. Endocrine [x] No Problems
- [ ] Excessive thirst or urination
- [ ] Heat intolerance
- [ ] Cold intolerance
- [ ] Change in hat or glove size
- [ ] Thyroid trouble ___ underative ___overactive
- [ ] Sugar diabetes - since ______________
  Insulin dependent ______________
- [ ] Disease of pituitary gland
- [ ] Disease of adrenal gland
- [ ] ______________

14. Musculoskeletal [ ] No Problems
- [ ] Muscle cramps
- [x] Stiff joints Knees
- [ ] Swelling of joints
- [ ] Generalized arthritis
- [ ] Rheumatoid arthritis
- [ ] Fibromyalgia syndrome
- [ ] Osteoporosis
- [ ] Neck pain
- [ ] Upper back pain
- [ ] Low back pain
- [ ] Heel spur(s) how many__________
- [ ] Gout
- [ ] Difficulty with walking
- [ ] Cold upper extremity(ies) R L
- [ ] Cold lower extremity(ies) R L
- [x] Pain in feet
- [ ] ______________

15. Neurological / Psychiatric

i. Neurological [x] No Problems
- [ ] Frequent or recurrent headaches
- [ ] Fainting
- [ ] Blackouts
- [ ] Stroke
- [ ] Dizzy spells
- [ ] Gait difficulties
- [ ] Seizures
- [ ] Epilepsy
- [ ] Tremors
- [ ] Neuropathy
- [ ] Weakness
- [ ] Paralysis
- [ ] ______________

Hepatic Biliary/ Gastro intestinal

Hepatic-Biliary: There was no history of liver disease, hepatitis, etc.

Gastro-intestinal: There was history of problems with gas.

Urinary

There was history of frequent urination.

Genital/Reproductive

No gross abnormalities were reported.

Endocrine

There was no history of thyroid problems, diabetes or hypoglycemia.

Musculoskeletal

He reported that there was history of stiff joints (knees), pain in feet. However, there was no history of muscle cramps, swelling of joint, generalized arthritis, rheumatoid arthritis, fibromyalgia syndrome, osteoporosis, neck pain, upper back pain, low back pain, heel spurs, gout, difficulty with walking, cold upper extremities, cold lower extremities,

Neurological / psychiatric

Neurological: Neurological history revealed no evidence of frequent or recurrent headaches, fainting/blackouts, stroke/ dizzy spells, gait difficulties, seizures/ epilepsy, tremors, neuropathy, weakness or paralysis.

Psychiatric: He reported that he had problems with concentration, anxiety. However, there was no problem with confusion, thinking or thought process, memory, depression, shakiness, agitation.

ii. **Psychiatric** ☐ No Problems
☑ Problems with concentration
☐ Confusion
☐ Problems with thinking or thought process
☐ Problems with memory
☐ Depressed
☑ Anxious
☐ Shaky
☐ Agitated
☐ ____________

16. **Other** ☑ No Problems
☐ Chicken Pox
☐ Rheumatic Fever
☐ Cancer
☐ Polio
☐ ____________

17. i. **Allergies** ☐ No Problems
Drug Allergies ____________

Food Allergies Maybe Milk

Environmental Allergies ____________

ii. **Immunologic** ☐ No Problems
☐ Immunologic disorders____________
☐ AIDS
☐ Lupus

B. Previous hospitalizations without surgery (include year and doctor's name)
1. ~~2000 Knee surgery~~, 1998 ~~Kidney Surgery~~
2.
3.
4.
5.

C. Previous surgeries (include year and doctor's name - including surgeries listed on page 9)
1. YR. 2000 Lt. Knee Surgery –
2. 1992 " " " " " "
3.
4.
5.
6.

D. List all medications you currently take (prescription and nonprescription - including aspirin, Tylenol, etc. - including pain medications listed on page 9)

	Medication	Dose	Frequency	Date Started	Time of Last Dose
1.	Serzone	150 mg	2 times Daily	1999	Current
2.	Allegra	60 mg	2 times Daily	1999	"
3.	RellaFin	1000 mg	2 times Daily	1999	"
4.					
5.					
6.					
7.					
8.					

YOU ARE ALMOST DONE - GREAT JOB! PLEASE CONTINUE!

Allergies / Immunologic

Allergies:

Drug(s): No known drug allergies.

Food(s): maybe milk.

Environmental: No known environmental allergies.

Immunologic: There was no history of any immunologic disorders.

Previous Hospitalizations

Kidney stone - Dr. - 1998

Previous Surgeries

Left knee surgery - Dr. - 2000

Left knee surgery - Dr. - 1992

Medications

Relafen 500 mg. 2 tabs bid

Serzone 150 mg. bid

Allegra 60 mg. bid

VII. PSYCHOLOGICAL HISTORY (Please answer as honestly as possible.)

This section asks some questions which may be repetitive and a few of the statements may seem unusual. Please do not be concerned, as these questions are included to describe people with many types of problems.

A. 1. Number of brothers and sisters: Older B_____ S_____ Younger B_____ S_____

2. Were you raised by: ☒ Mother & Father ☐ Mother ☐ Father ☐ Other _____________

3. Give a description of your father's personality: out going, Sense of Humor

4. Give a description of your mother's personality: out going, Serious Minded, Spiritual

5. Your childhood and home life while growing up were: (choose one)

☐ Happy ☒ Very Happy ☐ Neither Happy nor Unhappy ☐ Unhappy

B. **YOUR PAST / PRESENT EXPERIENCES**

1. Problems with memory	☐ No	☒ Yes Slight Short-Term
2. Flashbacks	☐ No	☐ Yes
3. Unusual experiences	☐ No	☐ Yes
4. Dizziness	☐ No	☐ Yes
5. Physical violence	☐ No	☐ Yes
6. Sexual abuse	☐ No	☐ Yes
7. Arrests	☐ No	☐ Yes
8. Jail sentences	☐ No	☐ Yes

C. **STRESS / ANXIETY**

Have you been tense, nervous or anxious?	☐ No	☒ Yes
1. Do you have excessive worry and anxiety about a number of events or activities?	☐ No	☒ Yes
2. Do you experience these worries and anxieties most of the time?	☐ No	☒ Yes
3. Do you find it difficult to control your worries?	☐ No	☒ Yes
4. Are your worries and anxieties associated with:		
a. Restlessness or feeling keyed up or on edge?	☐ No	☒ Yes
b. Being easily fatigued?	☒ No	☐ Yes
c. Having difficulty concentrating so that your mind goes blank?	☐ No	☒ Yes
d. Irritability or muscle tension?	☒ No	☐ Yes
e. Sleep disturbance (difficulty falling or staying asleep, or restless)?	☐ No	☒ Yes
5. Do you have panic attacks (intense fear of impending doom)?_______________	☒ No	☐ Yes
6. Do you have any phobias?_______________	☒ No	☐ Yes
7. Have you ever had a traumatic experience?_______________	☒ No	☐ Yes

D. **DEPRESSION**

1. Do you feel depressed (sad, empty)? ☐ No ☒ Mildly ☐ Moderately ☐ Significantly

2. Do you feel depressed most of each day?	☒ No	☐ Yes
3. Do you feel depressed nearly every day?	☐ No	☒ Yes
4. Does your family and/or friends think you are depressed?	☒ No	☐ Yes
5. Are you irritable (cranky, cross, grouchy) or restless and agitated?	☒ No	☐ Yes
6. Have you lost interest in all, or almost all, activities, most of the time?	☒ No	☐ Yes
7. Have you lost or gained a significant amount of weight over the past few months?	☐ No	☒ Yes
Is this due to change in appetite?	☐ No	☒ Yes
8. Do you have trouble getting to sleep or awaken frequently and ~~can't get back to sleep~~?	☐ No	☒ Yes
9. Do you sleep too much?	☒ No	☐ Yes
10. Do you feel sluggish and slow and you can't seem to get going?	☐ No	☒ Yes
Does this happen nearly every day?	☐ No	☒ Yes

PSYCHOSOCIAL EVALUATION

Proper evaluation of chronic pain often requires an appropriate psychological evaluation. Even though most clinicians who have experience in treating chronic pain, have developed skills to assess emotional or psychological parameters complicating pain problems, or psychological variables affecting the pain. It is well known that they are often unable to identify which of the variables are the most operative, or which psychological diagnoses are present. In fact, Waddell, et al showed that so called psychological impressions by physicians were hopelessly inaccurate when compared to appropriate psychological evaluation. Hence, it is assumed by the clinicians at — that besides producing physical limitations, chronic pain almost always causes some emotional disturbances and it is essential to explore the emotional aspects of the patient and the everyday effects of pain on the patient. He also underwent Pain Patient Profile (P3).

Validity

P3 was shown to be valid.

Developmental History

Mr. Doe was raised by his mother and father. He stated he comes from a family of 3. He described his father's personality and attitude towards him, past and present as, ''outgoing and sense of humor''. In addition, he also described his mother's personality and attitude towards him, past and present as, ''outgoing, serious minded and spiritual''. He described his childhood and home life while growing up as very happy.

Gross Psychological Pattern

In completing the questionnaire and interview, he provided the history that he has not experienced any significant problems with flashbacks, unusual experiences, dizziness, physical violence, sexual abuse, arrests, jail sentences. However, he stated that he experienced problems with memory.

Stress and Anxiety

Patients with chronic pain are often tense, nervous, anxious, irritable, and angry. In addition, these feelings have significant effect on their family and friends, often producing marital strain secondary to tension, anxiety, and apprehension, either justified or not.

Pain management comprehensive questionnaire: Presented five questions, which include inquiries about excessive worry and anxiety, difficulty with controlling worries, features associated with anxieties such as restlessness, fatigue, difficulty with concentration, irritability, and sleep disturbances.

Using this global description, he stated that he has been tense, nervous, and anxious. Based on his individual item answers, he experiences substantial symptoms of stress and anxiety leading to the diagnosis of Generalized Anxiety Disorder.

Pain Patient Profile Anxiety evaluation: P3 anxiety scale consists of 12 items that assess inner turmoil, anger, worry, nervousness, restlessness, and emotional instability.

Anxiety T-Score on the evaluation was 41.

These scores represent **below-average** pain patient anxiety scores. Scores below the average pain patient score on anxiety score suggest adaptability, relaxation, self-confidence and security. He may be experiencing an appropriate level of concern about her pain, but remains generally optimistic and confident of improvement. Coping skills are generally intact and there is little suggestion of undue cognitive distress.

Depression

Chronic pain patients are often reluctant to use words such as depression, but they are generally free to discuss their frustration, anger, irritability, guilt, and fear. The literature has documented overwhelmingly that chronic pain patients suffer with insomnia, fatigue, lack of interest, poor concentration, and feelings of hopelessness which are features of depression, even if the patient does not admit to it directly.

PSYCHOSOCIAL EVALUATION

P3 ☐ No ☑ Yes MCMI III ☑ No ☐ Yes

I. PAIN PATIENT PROFILE (P3)

A. VALIDITY ☐ No ☑ Yes

B. DEPRESSION — Patient's T-Score

Below Average Pain Patient	(29 - 45)	35
Average Pain Patient	46 - 54	
Above Average Pain Patient	55 - 71	

C. ANXIETY — Patient's T-Score

Below Average Pain Patient	(29 - 45)	41
Average Pain Patient	46 - 55	
Above Average Pain Patient	56 - 71	

D. SOMATIZATION — Patient's T-Score

Below Average Pain Patient	(21 - 44)	32
Average Pain Patient	45 - 55	
Above Average Pain Patient	56 - 99	

II. MCMI III

A. VALIDITY ☐ No ☐ Yes

B. GROSS PSYCHOLOGICAL PROFILE
1. ☐ None
2. ☐ Mild
3. ☐ Mild to Moderate
4. ☐ Moderate
5. ☐ Moderately Severe
6. ☐ Severe

C. DEPRESSION

MCMI Dysthymic BR ________ Diagnosis: ☐ No ☐ Yes 300.40

Major Depression BR ________ Diagnosis: ☐ No ☐ Yes 296.3

D. ANXIETY

MCMI Anxiety BR ________ Diagnosis: ☐ No ☐ Yes 300.02

E. SOMATIZATION

MCMI Somatoform BR ________ Diagnosis: ☐ No ☐ Yes 300.81

F. OTHER PSYCHOLOGICAL PROBLEMS

☐ 1. None
☐ 2. Psychoactive substance abuse
☐ 3. Schizophrenia
☐ 4. Bipolar Disorder
☐ 5. Thought Disorder
☐ 6. Delusional Disorder
☐ 7. ________
☐ 8. ________

Pain management comprehensive questionnaire: This psychosocial evaluation, specifically concentrating on depression, explores patients psychological status by questioning on 15 items, which include scope of depression, feelings of irritability and restlessness, lack of interest in activities, weight gain or weight loss, loss of appetite, sleep pattern, fatigue, lack of energy, guilt, inability to concentrate, thought(s) of suicide, or actual attempt(s) at suicide.

On global description he indicated that he feels mildly depressed by means of answering individual questions. He described that he feels depressed most of each day. Furthermore, he also reported a significant amount weight lost or gained over the past few months. He also reported having trouble getting to sleep or awakening frequently and having difficulty falling back to sleep. He reported that he feels sluggish and slow and can't seem to get going, and this occurs nearly every day. He experienced fatigue or loss of energy nearly every day as well. Additionally, he feels worthless and guilty most of time

Of the various aspects of depression evaluated using DSM-IV criteria, he presented clinically significant evidence of Major Depression.

Pain Patient Profile Depression evaluation: The depression scale was constructed with 14 items that assess sleep, psychomotor activity, energy level, concentration and decision making, and feelings of helplessness, hopelessness, and low self-worth. The scale also samples behavioral manifestations of affective distress, including loss of interest, pleasure, or enjoyment in activities that were previously considered pleasurable.

Depression T-Score on the evaluation was 35.

This T-Score represents **below average** pain patient depression score. Lower scores on the depression scale suggest emotional stability, optimism, and self-confidence. Patients with low depression scores typically are not experiencing affective distress associated with pain or they are optimistic about their prospects for pain relief. Generally, these patients are capable of participating as active partners in treatment planning and implementation.

Pain Patient Profile Somatization evaluation: On P3 evaluation, somatization scale consists of 13 items, that assess concerns with physical health, bodily processes, muscle tension and spasms, somatic functioning, and physical abnormalities. In addition, the somatization scale measures the magnitude of patient's concern about pain.

Somatization T-Score on the evaluation was 32.

His T-score level places him in **below average** pain patient somatization group. Lower scores on the somatization scale reflect an absence of emotional threat and concentrated thought about pain and physical problems. Typically, the patient's coping skills are effective.

11. Do you experience fatigue or loss of energy? ☐ No ☑ Yes
    Does this happen nearly every day? ☐ No ☑ Yes
12. Do you feel worthless ~~or guilty most of the time?~~ ☐ No ☑ Yes
13. Has your ability to think, concentrate and make decisions diminished? ☑ No ☐ Yes
14. Do you have thoughts of ending your own life (suicide)? ☑ No ☐ Yes
    If yes, do you have a plan? ☐ No ☐ Yes
15. Have you ever attempted suicide? ☑ No ☐ Yes
    If yes, how many times?______ When was the last attempt?______

E. **PREVIOUS PSYCHIATRIC HISTORY**

1. Have you ever had psychiatric / psychological treatment or evaluation? ☑ No ☐ Yes
   If yes, by whom and how many times?______
   Medication ______ ☐ No ☐ Yes
   Psychotherapy ______ ☐ No ☐ Yes
   Most recent treatment or visit on______

VIII. A. **LITIGATION**

i. You have or plan to have an attorney helping you? ☐ No ☐ Yes If yes, list name and address of attorney and how he / she is helping, etc.______

ii. Have you had any lawsuits in the past? Explain______

IX. TREATMENT GOALS Describe goals of your treatment.

☐ Return to work ☐ Have sexual relations
☐ Be more active and functional ☐ Participate in sports
☐ Play with kids and grandkids ☑ *Stand, walk, lie Down without Pain*

X. CERTIFICATION

I certify that I have answered truthfully all the questions, and have not knowingly withheld any information concerning any of the above problems, either past or present.

Your Signature Witness

Date Date

THANK YOU!

Signature of Reviewing Physician Date

PREVIOUS PSYCHOLOGICAL/PSYCHIATRIC HISTORY

He stated that he had no previous psychological or psychiatric treatment or evaluation.

Litigation

He stated that he is not involved in any type of litigation at the present time for his pain. He denied that he ever had any litigation for any type of pain problems or injuries in the past.

Treatment Goals

In this questionnaire, as well as personal interview, we offered the patient the option to describe goals of the treatment. On this evaluation, he described his goals of treatment as follows:

1. Stand, walk, lie down without pain

Certification

Mr. John R Doe certified that he answered all the questions truthfully about his pain problems, as well as health history and had not knowingly withheld any information concerning any of the above preceding problems, either past or present.

PHYSICAL EVALUATION

1. INITIAL OBSERVATION:
   - i. Arrived: [x] On time [ ] Late [ ] Early ____________
   - ii. [ ] Accompanied by ____________ to center [x] arrived alone to center
   - iii. [ ] Accompanied by ____________ to exam [x] arrived to examination, alone
   - iv. Greeting manner: [x] Pleasant [ ] Unpleasant [ ] Without any feeling [ ] ____________
   - v. Any unusual or noteworthy initial behavior:
     [x] None ________ [ ] Nervous ________ [ ] Overreacting ________
   - vi. Tatoos: [x] None [ ] 1 [ ] 2 [ ] 3 [ ] 4 [ ] 5 [ ] Numerous
   - vii. Reinforcement by spouse or other: [ ] Yes [x] No By: ____________
   - viii. Other ____________

2. CONSTITUTIONAL: (Need at least 3) (Describe positive and negative)
   - i. Height 6'2" Weight 240#
   - ii. Pulse rate ________ mt ________ reg ________ irr ________ reg irr
   - iii. Blood pressure ________ mm/hg ________ supine ________ sitting ________ standing
   - iv. Respirations 16 /mt
   - v. Temperature ________ °F ________ Oral ________ Axillary

3. GENERAL APPEARANCE: (Describe positive and negative)
   [ ] WNL
   - i. Development ✓ Well developed ____ Poorly developed
   - ii. Nutrition ✓ Well nourished ____ Undernourished
   - iii. Build ____ normal ____ thin ✓ overweight
     ____ somewhat obese ____ obese
   - iv. Body habitus ✓ independent ____ walked with a cane
     ____ walked with walker ____ wheelchair bound ____ bedridden
   - v. Deformities ✓ no physical disabilities ____ disabilities
   - vi. Grooming ✓ well groomed ____ poorly groomed ____ casual

4. SKIN: (Describe positive and negative)
   [x] WNL

	Scars	Rashes	Lesions	Ulcers	Café-au-lait spots
Head					
Face					
Neck					
Thoracic Spine					
Chest					
Lumbar Spine					
Abdomen					
Upper Extremity (Right)					
Upper Extremity (Left)					
Lower Extremity (Right)					
Lower Extremity (Left)					

5. HEMATOLOGIC / LYMPHATIC: (Describe positive and negative)
   [x] WNL
   ____ Anemic ____ Cyanosis
   Enlarged lymph nodes:
   ____ Neck R - L ____ Supraclavicular R - L
   ____ Axilla R - L ____ Groin R - L
   ____ Popliteal R - L ____ Other ____________

6. EYES: [ ] WNL
   [x] Wearing glasses [ ] Wearing contacts
   [ ] Erythema R - L [ ] Sty R - L [ ] Chalazion R - L
   [ ] Conjunctivitis [ ] Ectropion R - L [ ] Ptosis R - L
   [ ] Proptosis R - L [ ] Nystagmus R - L [ ] Strabismus R - L
   [ ] Swelling R - L [ ] Abnormal pupillary reaction [ ] ________
   Ophthalmology [ ] WNL ____________

7. EARS, NOSE, MOUTH & THROAT: [x] ALL WNL
   - i. Ears: [ ] WNL
     ____ Lesions R - L ____ Discharge R - L ____ Hard of Hearing R - L
   - ii. Nose / Sinuses: [ ] WNL
     ____ Lesions ____ Discharge ____ Sinus Tenderness R - L
   - iii. Mouth & Throat: [ ] WNL
     ____ No teeth ____ Missing teeth ____ Partials ↑ ↓ ____ Dentures ↑ ↓
     ____ Full dentures ____ Gingivitis
     ____ Pallor ____________ ____ Cyanosis ____________

8. CHEST: [x] WNL Breasts [ ] Deferred
   ____ Scars Midline R - L ____ Tenderness Midline R - L
   ____ Masses R - L ____________

9. RESPIRATORY: [x] WNL
   ____ Shortness of breath ____ Intercostal retraction ____ Visible respiratory effort
   ____ Dullness ____ Flatness ____ Hyper resonance ____ Rubs R - L
   ____ Prolonged expiration R - L ____ Wheezing R - L ____ Rales R - L ____ Ronchi R - L

10. CARDIOVASCULAR / PERIPHERAL VASCULAR:
    - i. Cardiovascular: [x] WNL
      ____ Abnormal PMI ____ Tachycardia ____ Bradycardia ____ Abnormal carotid pulses
      ____ Irregular cardiac rhythm ____ Murmur: Grade ____ Type ____
    - ii. Peripheral Vascular: (Describe positive and negative)
      [x] WNL

	UE	LE		UE	LE
Varicosities	R - L	R - L	Swelling	R - L	R - L
Abnormal Pulses	R - L	R - L	Edema	R - L	R - L
Temperature Change	R - L	R - L	Tenderness	R - L	R - L

11. GASTROINTESTINAL (ABDOMINAL): [x] WNL
    ____ Tenderness ____ Masses ____ Rigidity
    ____ Enlarged liver ____ Palpable spleen ____ Incisional hernia
    ____ Inguinal hernia R - L ____ Abnormal bowel sounds ____________

12. GENITOURINARY:
    Male: [ ] WNL [x] Deferred
    ____ Hydrocele R - L ____ Spermatocele R - L ____ Tenderness of cord R - L
    ____ Testicular mass R - L ____ Penile warts Prostate ____ enlarged ____ tender
    ____ Nodular ____ Asymmetric ____________
    Female: [ ] WNL [ ] Deferred
    ____ lesions ____ masses ____ discharge
    ____ cystocele ____ rectocele

13. PSYCHIATRIC: (Describe positive and negative)
    [x] WNL
    Lack of orientation to ____ time ____ place ____ person
    Abnormal mood and affect ____ depressed ____ anxious
    Shaky ____ agitated ____ irritated
    Lack of memory ____ recent ____ remote
    ____ Lack of concentration ____ Lack of attention span
    Language difficulty ____ naming objects ____ repeating phrases ____ speech
    Lack of knowledge ____ current events ____ past history

PHYSICAL EVALUATION

Constitutional: His height was 6 ft. 2 inches. His weight was 240 lbs. His respiratory rate was 16 per minute.

General appearance

Development: He was well developed.

Nutrition: He was well nourished.

Build: He was overweight.

Body Habitus: He was independent.

Deformities: There were no physical disabilities noted.

Grooming: He was well groomed.

Skin: Examination of the skin showed no evidence of scars, rashes, lesions, ulcers, or café-au-lait spots either in the head, trunk, neck, upper or lower extremities.

Hematologic/Lymphatic: Examination was grossly within normal limits with no evidence of anemia, cyanosis, or enlarged lymph nodes either in the neck, groin, axilla, or any other regions.

Cardiovascular: Heart: - Cardiovascular examination showed normal heart rhythm with no evidence of murmurs or gallop.

Peripheral: Examination of the peripheral vascular system showed no evidence of swelling or varicosities, temperature abnormalities, edema, or tenderness. Pulses were grossly within normal limits.

Psychiatric: Gross psychiatric evaluation showed orientation to time, place, and person with normal mood and effect with no history of lack of memory, concentration, attention span, language difficulties or knowledge.

13. PSYCHIATRIC: (Describe positive and negative)

[✓] WNL

Lack of orientation to ______time ______place ______person

Abnormal mood and affect ______depressed ______anxious

Shaky ______agitated ______irritated

Lack of memory ______recent ______remote

______Lack of concentration ______Lack of attention span

Language difficulty ______naming objects ______repeating phrases ______speech

Lack of knowledge ______current events ______past history

14. MUSCULOSKELETAL (NEUROLOGICAL):

i. Dominance: [✓] Right handed [ ] Left handed [ ] ____________

ii. Posture:

i. Cervical Lordosis ______		[✓] Normal	[ ] Increased	[ ] Decreased
ii. Lumbar Lordosis ______		[✓] Normal	[ ] Increased	[ ] Decreased
iii. Kyphosis ______	[ ] None	[✓] Mild	[ ] Moderate	[ ] Severe
iv. Scoliosis ______	[ ] None	[✓] Mild	[ ] Moderate	[ ] Severe

iii. Gait:

i. Straight Line ______	[✓] Normal	[ ] Limp	[ ] Unable
ii. On Heels ______	[✓] Normal	[ ] Limp	[ ] Unable
iii. On Toes ______	[✓] Normal	[ ] Limp	[ ] Unable

iv. Coordination: [✓] WNL

Abnormal: ______finger / nose

______heel / knee / shin

______rapid alternating movements in upper extremities

______rapid alternating movements in lower extremities

v. Head / Face / Neck: [✓] WNL

Abnormal:

Head: ______lesions R - L ______masses R - L ______effusions R - L

______crepitus R - L ______asymmetry ______defects R - L ______tenderness R - L

Face: ______lesions R - L ______masses R - L ______effusions R - L

______crepitus R - L ______asymmetry ______defects R - L ______tenderness R - L

______TMJ tenderness R - L ______Enlarged salivary glands R - L

______Supraorbital tenderness R - L ______Supratrochlear tenderness R - L

______Auriculotemporal tenderness R - L ______ ____________

Neck: ______lesions R - L ______masses R - L ______effusions R - L

______crepitus R - L ______asymmetry ______defects R - L

______thyromegaly ______jugular distension R - L

MUSCULOSKELETAL/NEUROLOGICAL EXAMINATION

Dominance: He was right handed.

Posture: His posture showed normal cervical lordosis, normal lumbar lordosis, mild kyphosis, and mild scoliosis.

Gait: His gait pattern evaluation showed that he was able to walk in a straight line, as well as on his heels, and toes without any problems.

Coordination: Evaluation of his coordination with fingers/nose, heel/knee/shin, rapid alternating movements in upper extremities, and rapid alternating movements in lower extremities was grossly within normal limits.

Head/Face/Neck

Head: Examination of head revealed no evidence of lesions, masses, crepitus, asymmetry, defects, tenderness, or effusions.

Face: Examination of face showed no evidence of lesions, masses, crepitation, asymmetry defects, tenderness, effusions, sinus tenderness, TMJ tenderness, or enlarged salivary glands.

Neck: Examination of neck showed no evidence of lesions, masses, crepitus, asymmetry, defects, tenderness, effusions, enlarged salivary glands, thyromegaly, tracheal deviation, or jugular distention.

vi. Cranial Nerves: ☐ WNL

Testing of Cranial Nerves (Abnormals)

_____2nd (visual acuity) ______ R ☐ ______ L ☐ ______
_____3rd, 4th & 6th (pupils) ______ R ☐ ______ L ☐ ______
_____5th (facial sensation) ______ R ☐ ______ L ☐ ______
_____7th (facial symmetry, strength) ______ R ☐ ______ L ☐ ______
_____8th (hearing w/ tuning fork) ______ R ☐ ______ L ☐ ______
_____9th (palate movement) ______ R ☐ ______ L ☐ ______
_____11th (shoulder shrug strength) ______ R ☐ ______ L ☐ ______
_____12th (tongue protrusion) ______ R ☐ ______ L ☐ ______

vii. Cervical Spine: ☐ WNL

A. Inspection: i. ☐ WNL

scar(s) _____anteriorly in neck _____posteriorly in neck _____shoulder R - L _____arm R - L
_____forearm R - L _____hand R - L _____finger(s) R - L

B. Inspection / Palpation: i. ☐ WNL

_____masses M - R - L _____lesions M - R - L _____effusion R - L _____defect R - L
_____contracture R - L _____dislocation R - L _____subluxation R - L _____laxity R - L
_____fasciculations R - L _____discoloration R - L _____amputation R - L
_____crepitus M - R - L _____swelling M - R - L

Palpation: ii.

ii. ☐ WNL	RIGHT			MIDLINE / SPINOUS PROCESS TENDERNESS	LEFT		
	Tenderness	Spasm	Trigger Points	Levels -	Tenderness	Spasm	Trigger Points
Superficial							
Non-Anatomic				Severity			
Paravertebral				0 1 2 3			
Suboccipital w/o HA							
Suboccipital w/ HA							
Periauricular w/o HA							
Periauricular w/ HA							
Upper Trapezius							
Shoulder							
AC Joint							
Arm							
Elbow							
Forearm							
Wrist							
Fingers							

C. Cervical Range of Motion: ☐ WNL

	Reduced	Normal	Increased	Pain				Better	
				None	Mild	Moderate	Severe	Some Relief	Complete Relief
Flexion									
Extension									
Right lateral rotation									
Right lateral flexion									
Left lateral rotation									
Left lateral flexion									

		RIGHT	LEFT	
D.	Shoulders (ROM):	N ↓ ↑	N ↓ ↑	
	Impingement:	+ –	+ –	
E.	Elbow:			
F.	Wrist:			
G.	Hand:			
H.	Fingers:			
I.	Motor Examination:			Focal Deficits
	Motor Strength in extremities			
	Grip Strength			
	Wasting			
	Tone			
J.	Sensory Examination:			
K.	Reflexes:			
	Biceps (C5, C6)			
	Triceps (C6, C7)			
	Brachioradialis (C5, C6)			
L.	Other Signs:			
	Adsons'	+ –	+ –	
	Tinel's	+ –	+ –	
	Phalen's	+ –	+ –	

M. Non-Physiological Signs:

i. Tenderness ______ + –
ii. Distraction ______ + –
iii. Simulation ______ + –
iv. Regional ______ + –
v. Overreaction ______ + –

Positive in ______ out of 5 categories

Cranial Nerves

Cranial nerve examination from 2 to 12 was grossly within normal limits bilaterally.

Cervical Spine

Inspection - There was no evidence of scars on anterior or posterior aspect of the neck, shoulders, arms, forearm, hand, or fingers. Inspection revealed no masses, lesions, effusions, defects, contractures, dislocations, subluxation, laxity, fasciculations, discoloration, or amputation.

Palpation - Palpation was carried out in the cervical spine posteriorly as well as anteriorly, in the suboccipital region, upper trapezius, both shoulders, suprascapular muscles, and both upper extremities for the presence of tenderness superficial, organic, and non-organic; paravertebral muscle spasm, tightness in the muscles, and trigger points.

Palpation revealed no masses, lesions, effusions, defects, contractures, crepitus, swelling, dislocations, subluxation, laxity, or fasciculations. Palpation of the cervical spine was within normal limits.

Range of Motion - On examination of range of motion of cervical spine, as well as upper extremities was grossly within normal limits. Range of motion of the both shoulders was normal with no evidence of impingement. Range of motion of all other joints was grossly within normal limits.

Motor Examination - On examination for motor strength of upper extremities was grossly within normal limits.

Wasting - There was no wasting noted.

Grip Strength - The grip strength evaluation by manual testing was shown to be normal

Sensory evaluation - There was no sensory dysfunction noted in either upper extremity.

Reflexes - Deep tendon reflex evaluation showed the following:

		Right	**Left**
1.	Biceps	1	1
2.	Triceps	1	1
3.	Brachioradialis	1	1

Other neurological tests

Phalen's Test	Negative	Negative
Tinel's Test	Negative	Negative
Adson's Test	Negative	Negative

viii. Thoracic Spine / Ribs: ☑ WNL

A. Inspection: i. ☑ WNL

Scar(s) ____ thoracic spine M R L

B. Inspection / Palpation: ii. ☑ WNL

_____masses M - R - L _____lesions M - R - L _____effusion R - L _____defect R - L
_____contracture R - L _____dislocation R - L _____subluxation R - L _____laxity R - L
_____fasciculations R - L _____discoloration R - L _____amputation R - L
_____crepitus M - R - L _____swelling M - R - L

ii. ☑ WNL	RIGHT			MIDLINE / SPINOUS PROCESS TENDERNESS	LEFT		
	Tenderness	Spasm	Trigger Points	Levels -	Tenderness	Spasm	Trigger Points
Superficial				Severity			
Non-Anatomic				0 1 2 3			
Paravertebral							
Upper Trapezius							
Suprascapular							
Supraspinatus							
Infraspinatus							
Middle Trapezius							
Chest Wall							

ix. Lumbar Spine / Pelvis: ☐ WNL

A. Inspection: i. ☑ WNL

Scar(s) _____lumbar spine _____hip(s) R - L _____thigh(s) R - L
_____knee(s) R - L _____leg(s) R - L _____ankle(s) R - L
_____feet R - L

B. Inspection / Palpation: ii. ☑ WNL

_____masses M - R - L _____lesions M - R - L _____effusion R - L _____defect R - L
_____contracture R - L _____dislocation R - L _____subluxation R - L _____laxity R - L
_____fasciculations R - L _____discoloration R - L _____amputation R - L
_____crepitus M - R - L _____swelling M - R - L

ii. ☐ WNL	RIGHT			MIDLINE / SPINOUS PROCESS TENDERNESS	LEFT		
	Tenderness	Spasm	Trigger Points	Levels - L5,S1	Tenderness	Spasm	Trigger Points
Superficial	0			Severity	0		
Non-Anatomic	0			0 (1) 2 3	0		
Paravertebral	2	0	0				
Sciatic Notch	2						
SI Joint	2						
Ilio-Lumbar	0						
Glut Max							
Glut Med							
Groin							
Ischial Tuberosities							
Hips							
Knees							
Ankles							
Foot							
Toes							
Other	✓				✓		

C. Lumbar Range of Motion: ☐ WNL

	Reduced	Normal	Increased	Pain				Better	
				None	Mild	Moderate	Severe	Some Better	Complete Relief
Flexion		✓		✓					
Deflexion				✓					
Extension	20/					✓			
Right lateral rotation		✓		✓					
Right lateral flexion		✓		✓					
Left lateral rotation		✓		✓					
Left lateral flexion		✓		✓					

	RIGHT	LEFT
D. Hip:	(N) ↓ ↑	(N) ↓ ↑
Patrick-Fabere's Test:	+ (−)	+ (−)
E. Knee:	✓	✓
F. Ankle:	✓	✓
G. Foot:	✓	✓
H. Toes:	✓	✓

THORACIC SPINE

Inspection - There was no evidence of scars on thoracic spine or chest wall. Inspection revealed no masses, lesions, effusions, defects, contracture(s), dislocation, subluxation, laxity, or fasciculations.

Palpation - Palpation revealed no masses, lesions, effusions, defects, contractures, crepitus, swelling, dislocations, subluxation, laxity, or fasciculations. Palpation of the thoracic spine was within normal limits.

LUMBAR SPINE

Inspection -There was no evidence of scars on lumbar spine, hips, thighs, knees, legs, ankles or feet. Inspection revealed no masses, lesions, effusions, defects, contracture(s), discoloration, swelling, varicose veins, subluxation, laxity, or fasciculations.

Palpation - Palpation was carried out in lower back, hips, knees, and ankles for the presence of tenderness, paravertebral muscle spasm, and tenderness in muscle groups as well as for the presence of trigger points.

Palpation revealed no masses, lesions, effusions, defects, contractures, crepitus, swelling, varicose veins, subluxation, laxity, or fasciculations. There was no superficial or nonanatomic tenderness. There was mild midline/spinous process tenderness from L5, S1. There was moderate paravertebral tenderness L5, S1 on the right side without paravertebral spasm or trigger points. There was moderate tenderness noted in sciatic notch region on the right side. There was SI joint tenderness noted, which was moderate on the right side. However, there was no iIio-lumbar, glut max, glut med, groin or ischial tuberosities, hips, knees, ankle, or foot toe tenderness noted.

Range of motion - On manual examination range of motion of lumbar spine, as well as lower extremities was grossly within normal limits.

On manual examination, range of motion of the both hips was normal with negative Patrick-Fabere's Test.

Examination of all other joints was grossly within normal limits.

	RIGHT	LEFT	Focal Deficits
I. Motor Examination:			
Strength	✓	✓	___
Wasting	✓	✓	
Tone	✓	✓	
J. Sensory Examination:	✓	✓	___
K. Reflexes:			
Quadriceps Femoralis (L3, L4)	1	1	
Achilles (L5, S1)	1	1	
Superficial	✓	✓	
L. Straight Leg Raising			
Sitting	70	90	
Supine			
Active	___	___	
Passive	70	90	
Back Pain	(+) –	+ (–)	
Sciatic Tension Signs	+ (–)	+ (–)	

M. Waddell's Non-Physiological signs:

i. Tenderness ______ + ______ (–)

ii. Simulation ______ + ______ (–)

iii. Distraction ______ + ______ (–)

iv. Regional ______ + ______ (–)

v. Overreaction ______ + ______ (–)

Positive in 0 out of 5 categories

x. Fibromyalgia Screen ☑ **Negative** ☐ **Positive**

Bilateral Tenderness present in following:

Suboccipital ______ Lateral Epicondylec(s) ______

Cervical C4 - 6 ______ Greater Trochanters ______

Second Costochondral Junction ______ Knee Medial (Fat Pad) ______

Trapezius ______ Gluteus Maximus ______

Supraspinatus ______

Other: ______

Motor strength - Examination of motor strength was within normal limits.

Sensory -Sensory examination was within normal limits.

Reflexes - i. Deep tendon reflex evaluation was as follows:

	RIGHT	LEFT
Quadriceps Femoralis	1	1
Achilles	1	1

ii. Superficial reflexes were shown to be within normal limits.

Straight leg raising - Straight leg raising evaluation showed the following:

	RIGHT	LEFT
Sitting	70°	90°
Supine - Passive	70°	90°
Response to SLR:		
Back pain	Positive	Negative
Sciatic Tension	Negative	Negative

MEDICAL DECISION MAKING

i. **REVIEW OF INVESTIGATIONS** ☑ Yes ☐ None available ☐ Requested ☐ Dictated

ii. **REVIEW OF RECORDS** ☑ Yes ☐ None available ☐ Requested ☑ Dictated

iii. **IMPRESSION**

PHYSICAL ☑ Dictated ☐ See coding section

MEDICAL ☐ Dictated ☐ See coding section NONE

PSYCHOLOGICAL ☐ Dictated ☐ See coding section

☑ Depression ☐ General Anxiety Disorder ☐ Somatization Disorder

☐

iv. **PLAN**

Investigations ☑ None ordered ☐ Ordered

a. Drugs

1. ☐ None
2. ☑ To continue SERZONE, CELEBREX, RELAFEN
3. ☐ Will start
4. ☐ Will wean off
5. ☐

MEDICAL DECISION MAKING

Review of Investigations

12/20/99 – Lumbar spine – Old epiphyseal wedging of the lower thoracic upper lumbar bodies. Narrowing of the L5-S1 interspace with some facet degenerative change. There is in fact some grade I anterolisthesis of L5 on S1 and I suspect that the defect at the lamina of L5 is post surgical in nature.

12/20/99 – Right hip – Negative right hip.

2/21/00 – MRI/Lumbar spine – Some bulging of the L3-4 and 4-5 discs particularly in the inferior foramina on the left side at L3-4 and 4-5. Grade I spondylolisthesis of L5 on S1 which I believe is associated with bilateral pars defects at L5. Associated disc bulge related to the spondylolisthesis and a component of some central herniation probably present at the L5-S1 level. There is disc material bulging into the foramina bilaterally at L5-S1 associated with the listhesis

Review of Records

His records from Vanderbilt University were reviewed. These indicated that Dr. dd, Assistant Professor of Neurosurgery, felt that Dr. ss had low back pain with a radicular component without evidence of obvious nerve root or other thecal sac compression. He also stated that in view of the bilateral pars fractures, however he thought it would be useful to obtain plain films with flexion and extension which were performed.

He was also diagnosed with anxiety disorder by Dr. xx.

Impression

1. Lumbar facet joint arthropathy
2. Lumbar disc displacement
3. Acquired spondylolisthesis
4. Sacroiliitis
5. Traumatic arthritis of both knees
6. Depression

Plan

At this time, I explained my impressions about his pain and associated problems, various modalities of treatments, his options, complications, prognosis, and duration of treatment.

Investigations: No investigations were ordered at the present time.

Drugs: At this time it was decided that we will continue the previous drug therapy of Serzone and Relafen.

b. Physical therapy

1. [ ] None due to lack of response or significant progress in past ______
2. [ ] None due to increased pain with physical therapy in past ______
3. [ ] None due to patient's refusal to undergo physical therapy ______
4. [ ] None due to the condition which is not amenable to physical therapy / rehab ______
5. [ ] Will continue at ______
6. [x] Will start at PPT & Psy
7. [ ] Will consider later ______
8. [ ] Will manage with home exercise program ______
9. [ ] ______

c. Psychotherapy

1. [ ] None due to lack of major psychological problems ______
2. [ ] None due to patient's refusal to undergo psychological intervention ______
3. [ ] Will continue ______
4. [ ] Will start at ______
5. [x] Will consider later ______
6. [ ] ______

d. Injections

1. [ ] None due to ______
2. [ ] Will consider later ______
3. [x] Will start with: [x] C / T / L Facet Blocks [ ] C / T / L Discography [ ] C / T / L / S Selective Epidural [ ] C / T / Lum / Caudal Epidural [ ] C / T / L Symp Block [ ] ______
4. [x] Follow if necessary with: [x] Facet Blocks [x] Epidurals [ ] Hyertonic [x] RFTN [ ] Endoscopy [ ] Cryo [ ] IDET [ ] ______
5. [ ] ______

v. **DURATION OF TREATMENT** 1. [ ] No Rx 2. [ ] 2 - 4 weeks 3. [ ] 4 - 6 weeks 4. [ ] 6 - 8 weeks 5. [x] 9 - 12 weeks

______

vi. **PROGNOSIS** 1. [ ] Very good 2. [x] Good 3. [ ] Good to fair 4. [ ] Fair 5. [ ] Fair to poor 6. [ ] Poor

vii. **DISCUSSION** ✓ ______

______

viii. **DISCHARGE / DISPOSITION** ✓ ______

______

SIGNATURE OF PHYSICIAN ______ **DATE** ______

Physical therapy: Following the appropriate discussions about physical therapy, rehabilitation exercises and its influence in improving functional status it was decided that we will start physical therapy at Paducah Physical Therapy and Psychology.

Psychotherapy: After the discussions with regards to the benefits of psychological intervention, behavioral modification and necessity of both interventions in improving pain management, it was decided that we will consider at a later date.

Neural Blockade: Following the appropriate discussions including complications, benefits, advantages and disadvantages it was decided that initially we will proceed with: Lumbar facet blocks.

Following this injection therapy, we will make a diagnostic impression of the problem. If she obtains good pain relief following this injection therapy there is no necessity for any further treatment, however, if pain returns we will consider other options in injection therapy.

At this time, we also discussed about other options to follow the initial injection therapy, which will include facet blocks, epidurals and Radiofrequency thermoneurolysis.

Course of Treatment

Following the appropriate discussions, including complications, benefits, advantages, disadvantages, it was decided that initial duration of treatment would be 9-12 weeks with further follow-up along with maintenance therapy as required based on the progress and improvement.

Prognosis

Following the review of available information, physical as well as psychological status, diagnostic impressions, therapeutic options available, and his understanding of the treatment modalities including complications, advantages and disadvantages. His prognosis is considered to be good.

However this prognosis may change on the response or lack thereof based on further evaluation, and management.

Discussion

At this time, once again we discussed about various issues involved in his management including my impressions, his perceptions, treatment options available and development of realistic goals in management. Once again, it was emphasized that pain relief is desirable, however, it may not be achievable in all cases, even though it is a goal one can hope for and it is achieved in only a small number of patients. Thus it was emphasized on understanding the process of chronic pain development, its management, limitations and frustrations off its management, thus necessity of developing practical goals which should include to increase the functional capacity with reduction in pain and quality of life. It was also emphasized that it is extremely important to modify pain behavior with positive attitude and relaxation techniques, also avoid pain generating activities with modifications of activity as much as possible and finally eliminate drug dependency, however, even if the drugs are continued, they will be administered in a controlled fashion and he should follow the narcotic contract.

Discharge/Disposition

Following the above discussions, discharged was carried out with the following prescriptions: Relafen 500 mg. x 2, bid. He will return on November 20, 2000.

____

, M.D.

APPENDIX - C

ii. SAMPLE OFFICE FOLLOW-UPS

Name: ____________

Date: ____________ SS#: ____

Sex: ____ Age: ____

Physician: ____________

CHIEF STATEMENT: "HURTING AGAIN"

HISTORY OF PRESENT ILLNESS: ____________

PAIN STATUS:

1. ☑ >75% Relief for 2wks
2. ☑ >50% Relief for 2wks
3. ☐ <50% Relief for ____
4. ☐ No Relief ____

SIDE EFFECTS OF TREATMENT ☑ NONE

	Initial	Last Appt	0	1	2	3	4	5	6	7	8	9	10
Average Pain						✓							
General Health										✓			
Mental Health										✓			
Physical Function									✓				
Social Function									✓				
Vitality									✓				

MEDICATION USE: ☐ None ☒ Same ____ ☑ Decreased ____ ☐ Increased ____

PHYSICAL EXAM: ____________

Signature of Physician ____________

DATE: 3/12/01
NAME: abc
DATE OF BIRTH: 9/2/60
SS#: xxx-xx-xxxx

HISTORY

Chief complaint (statement): "Hurting again."

History of Present Illness: Mr. abc returns for a follow up visit. He states that following the last visit, he did great for about 2 weeks and after that his pain started returning, but he still did very well for another 2 weeks. He has been taking a lot less medication. He's extremely pleased with his overall progress. He wants to undergo another injection therapy. However, he didn't bring a driver.

Symptomatology: Intermittent axial pain in low back with no significant radiation, with numbness in lateral aspect of right calf and pain in right foot in front with radiation to toes, since 1998 which started following a lifting injury, with gradual increase in intensity which failed to respond to physical therapy, chiropractic and medication therapy until 12/2000.

Pain Status: Experienced more than 75% relief for 2 weeks.

Experienced more than 50% relief for 2 weeks.

Side Effects of Treatment: None rendered.

Medication Usage: Same.

OVERALL HEALTH ASSESSMENT

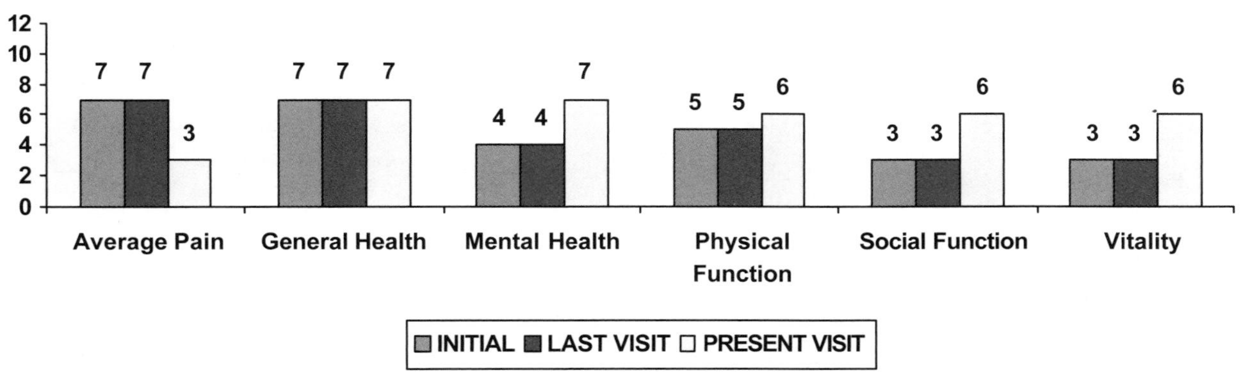

PAST, FAMILY AND SOCIAL HISTORY

Reviewed on 2/15/01 with no interval changes.

REVIEW OF SYSTEMS

Reviewed on 2/15/01 with no interval changes.

Allergies: None

Previous Surgeries:
Pneumonia - 1982

PHYSICAL EXAMINATION

Constitutional: His height was 6 ft. 1 inch. His weight was 209 lbs.
General appearance: He was well developed and well nourished. His build was normal. He was independent. There were no physical disabilities noted. He was casually dressed.
Skin: Examination of the skin showed no evidence of scars, rashes, lesions, ulcers, or café-au-lait spots either in the head, trunk, neck, upper or lower extremities.
Respiratory: Examination of the respiratory system showed that there was no shortness of breath, prolonged respiration, wheezing, rales, or rhonchi.
Psychiatric: Gross psychiatric evaluation showed orientation to time, place, and person with normal mood and effect with no history of lack of memory, concentration, attention span, language difficulties or knowledge.

Musculoskeletal/Neurological Examination

Dominance: He was right handed.
Posture: His posture showed normal cervical lordosis, normal lumbar lordosis, mild kyphosis, and mild scoliosis.
Gait: His gait pattern evaluation showed that he was able to walk in a straight line, as well as on his heels, and toes without any problems.
Cervical Spine: There was no evidence of scars on the anterior or posterior aspect of the neck, shoulders, arms, forearm, hand, or fingers. Palpation of the cervical spine was within normal limits. Range of motion of both shoulders was normal with no evidence of impingement. The deep tendon reflexes evaluation showed for Biceps 1 on the right side and 1 on the left side, Triceps 1 on the right side and 1 on the left side, and Brachioradialis 1 on the right side and 1 on the left side.
Thoracic Spine: There was no evidence of scars on the thoracic spine or chest wall. Palpation of the thoracic spine was within normal limits.
Lumbar Spine: There was no evidence of scars on the lumbar spine, hips, thighs, knees, legs, ankles or feet. There was no superficial or nonanatomic tenderness. There was mild midline/spinous process tenderness L5, S1. There was moderate tenderness noted in right foot. Range of motion lumbar spine was grossly within normal limits. Extension was reduced 20% with moderate pain. Range of motion of the both hips was normal with negative Patrick-Fabere's Test. Sensory examination was reduced at SI on the right with no focal neurological deficits. Straight leg raising in supine position was 90° on the right side and 90° on the left side. Sciatic tension signs were negative on both sides. The deep tendon reflexes were as follows: Quadriceps Femoralis 1 on the right side, and 1 on the left side, Achilles 1 on the right side, and 1 on the left side. Superficial reflexes were shown to be within normal limits.

Review of Investigations:

9/29/89 – Lumbar spine – Mild hypertrophic spurring at L4 and L5. Transition vertebra at the lumbosacral junction.
9/29/89 – Lumbar CT – There is some central bulging at L5-S1. No other abnormality is seen.
9/16/99 – MRI/Lumbar – Stable lumbar MRI, with a moderate sized central HNP seen at L5-S1, there is probably actually some decrease in size of the herniated disc material, though slight. Other degenerative changes are present including facet overgrowth at L4-5 and L5-S1. Mild right-sided neuroforaminal narrowing at L5-S1 is noted and also appears stable. Broad-based disc bulge is noted at L4-5. One new finding is a small Schmorl's node at the inferior endplate of L4, of questionable clinical significance.
8/9/00 – MRI/Lumbar – Stable lumbar MRI with no change in appearance of size of the small central disc herniation at L5-S1. Other degenerative findings remain stable, include Schmorl's nodes within the inferior endplates of L5 and L4. Mild to right sided neuroforaminal narrowing is again noted at L5-S1 and is stable.

Medication:
1. Lortab 7.5 mg, tid
2. Ibuprofen, prn
3. Depakote 250 mg, IV po bid

Impression:
1. Lumbar disc displacement
2. Temporal epilepsy - stable

Plan and Discussion: At this time, once again we discussed about various aspects of his pain management. Once again I explained to him that we will increase the duration between the injections. After this treatment it will be 2 months before he will be returning. He understands this. Meanwhile, today it was decided that we will discharge him.

Discharge / Disposition: He was discharged in satisfactory condition to return in 10 days for further follow up. At this time, he was provided with a prescription for Lortab 7.5 mg, po t.i.d. for 25 tablets with no refills.

____
MD

SAMPLE OFFICE FOLLOW UP WITHOUT PROCEDURES

DATE: 3/21/01
NAME: xyz
DATE OF BIRTH: 11/12/57
SS#: XXX-XX-XXXX

HISTORY

Chief complaint (statement): "Headaches are coming back."

History of Present Illness: Ms. xyz returns for a follow up visit. She states that overall, she did great. She had very few headaches but she feels like that was because of her problems. She started eating chocolate, etc, not following any rules. She went to the hospital one time and got Stadol Nasal Spray. She is using this only like once in 2 weeks or so. She is also not taking much medication. She has decreased usage of narcotics, etc. Overall, she is pretty happy with her progress. Following the discussions, it was decided that we will continue her on the pain medication since she is already decreasing the dosage. She understands this.

Symptomatology:
1. Intermittent throbbing headaches associated with occasional nausea and vomiting without aura, since 1972 with worsening in 1967, with gradual increase in intensity, especially after spine injury since 1994.
2. Intermittent neck pain with headaches and shoulder pain, without numbness or weakness since 1994, which started following a fall with gradual increase and non-responsive to medical management.

Pain Status: Experienced more than 50% relief with medication.

Side Effects of Treatment: No side effects were experienced.

Medication Usage: Decreased.

PAST, FAMILY AND SOCIAL HISTORY

Was reviewed on 12-6-00 with no interval changes noted.

REVIEW OF SYSTEMS

Was reviewed on 12-6-00 with no interval changes noted.
Allergies: DHE, Ergotamine and Levbid.
Previous Surgeries:
1. TIA - France - 1963

PHYSICAL EXAMINATION

Constitutional: Her height was 5 ft. 5 inches. Her weight was 170 lbs. Her blood pressure was 112/84 mm/Hg. Her respiratory rate was 16 per minute. Her pulse rate was 68 beats per minute. Her temperature was 96° F.
General appearance: She was well developed and well nourished. Her build was normal. She was independent. There were no physical disabilities noted. She was well groomed.
Skin: Examination of the skin showed no evidence of scars, rashes, lesions, ulcers, or café-au-lait spots either in the head, trunk, neck, upper or lower extremities.
Chest/Breasts: Examination of the breasts was deferred.
Respiratory: Examination of the respiratory system showed that there was no shortness of breath, prolonged respiration, wheezing, rales, or rhonchi.
Peripheral: Examination of the peripheral vascular system showed evidence of varicosities in the lower extremities.
Psychiatric: Gross psychiatric evaluation showed orientation to time, place, and person with normal mood and effect with no history of lack of memory, concentration, attention span, language difficulties or knowledge.

Musculoskeletal/Neurological Examination

Dominance: She was right handed.

Posture: Her posture showed normal cervical lordosis, normal lumbar lordosis, mild kyphosis, and mild scoliosis.

Gait: Her gait pattern evaluation showed that she was able to walk in a straight line, as well as on her heels, and toes without any problems.

Coordination: Evaluation of her coordination with fingers/nose, heel/knee/shin, rapid alternating movements in upper extremities, and rapid alternating movements in lower extremities was grossly within normal limits.

Head/Face/Neck:

Head: Examination of the head revealed no evidence of lesions, masses, crepitus, asymmetry, defects, tenderness, or effusions.

Face: Face was also examined for lesions, masses, crepitus, asymmetry, defects, tenderness, effusions, sinus tenderness, TMJ tenderness, or enlarged salivary glands, following was found abnormal bilateral auriculotemporal tenderness.

Neck: Examination of the neck showed no evidence of lesions, masses, crepitus, asymmetry, defects, tenderness, effusions, enlarged salivary glands, thyromegaly, tracheal deviation, or jugular distention.

Cranial Nerves: Cranial nerve examination from 2 to 12 was grossly within normal limits bilaterally.

Cervical Spine: There was no evidence of scars on the anterior or posterior aspect of the neck, shoulders, arms, forearm, hand, or fingers. There was no superficial or nonanatomic tenderness. There was no midline or spinous process tenderness. There was moderate paravertebral tenderness from C2-C4 bilaterally without paravertebral spasm or trigger points. There was moderate suboccipital tenderness bilaterally without elicitation of a headache. There was moderate upper trapezius tenderness bilaterally. Range of motion of the cervical spine was reduced 10% in all directions with mild pain. Range of motion of both shoulders was normal with no evidence of impingement. The deep tendon reflexes evaluation showed for Biceps absent on the right side and absent on the left side, Triceps absent on the right side, and absent on the left side, and Brachioradialis absent on the right side, and absent on the left side.

Thoracic Spine: There was no evidence of scars on the thoracic spine or chest wall. There was moderate tenderness noted in infraspinatus region on the right side.

Lumbar Spine: There was no evidence of scars on the lumbar spine, hips, thighs, knees, legs, ankles or feet. Palpation of lumbar spine was within the normal limits. On manual examination range of motion lumbar was showed normal. Range of motion of the both hips was normal with negative Patrick-Fabere's Test. Straight leg raising in supine position was 90° on the right side and 90° on the left side. Sciatic tension signs were negative on both sides. The deep tendon reflexes were as follows: Quadriceps Femoralis absent on the right side, and absent on the left side, Achilles absent on the right side, and absent on the right side. Superficial reflexes were shown to be within normal limits.

Review of Investigations: 11/21/00 – MRI of the head – Normal MR of the brain
11/21/00 – MR of the cervical spine – Minimal C3/4 and C4/5 and mild C5/6 and C6/7 disc degenerative changes.

Medication:

1. Alprazolam, tid
2. Allegra, 180 mg qd
3. Nasonex, 2 qd
4. Lortab, 7.5 mg tid
5. Neurontin, 100 mg hs bid
6. Elavil, 10 mg q hs
7. Effexor XR, 150 mg qd

Impression:

1. Cervical facet joint arthropathy.
2. Cervical intervertebral disc disease
3. Non-intractable migraine w/o aura
4. Auriculotemporal neuritis
5. Chronic sinusitis - stable
6. Bilateral varicose veins - stable
7. Irritable bowel syndrome - stable
8. Fibrocystic breast disease - stable
9. Depression - stable
10. Generalized Anxiety Disorder - stable

PLAN AND DISCUSSION

At this time, we discussed about various aspects of her pain management. Following the discussions, understanding all of the associated complications and benefits, it was decided that we would continue her on conservative management.

DISCHARGE / DISPOSITION

She was discharged in satisfactory condition to return in 3 months for further follow up. At this time, she was provided with a prescription for Neurontin, 100 mg po bid for 75 with 2 refills, Elavil, 10 mg po q hs for 40 tablets with 2 refills and Effexor XR, 150 mg po once daily for 40 tablets with one refill.

____
, MD

APPENDIX - C

iii. INTERVENTIONAL PROCEDURE DOCUMENTATION IN ASC AND HOPD

SAMPLE

HISTORY AND PHYSICAL

Name:	John Doe
Sex:	Male
Date of Birth:	xx/xx/xx
Age (yrs.):	43
SS#:	xxx-xx-xxxx
Date:	11/20/00

HISTORY

Chief Complaint: "Still hurting."

History of present illness: Intermittent throbbing, cramping pain on the right side of low back and right hip with radiation to right lower extremity associated with numbness and tingling, since 1998 with gradual onset with no specific incident but with history of heavy work, with failure to respond to medications, physical therapy, chiropractic manipulations and exercise until September 2000, with back pain worse than leg pain..

Past history: He related torn cartilage, right knee from work related injury in 1992. He has history of right knee surgery in July 2000. However, there was no history of headache, pain in neck, pain in upper extremities, pain in upper back, pain in mid-back, chest wall pain, pain in back, pain in lower extremities, joints pain, arthritis.

Evaluation and treatment history for pain:
He was seen by 3 providers in the past these were:
Dr. - three occasions - 1999
Dr. , - approximately 20 occasions - 1998-2000
Dr. , - one occasion - 2000.
He has history of chiropractic treatments off and on for two years. He also has attended physical therapy treatments for six months in 1999.
In the past, he stated that he underwent regular X-rays of back, MRI scan of lower back.

REVIEW OF SYSTEMS

Constitutional: There was a history of weight loss of 20 lbs. during 1997, and weight gain of 30 lbs from 1999-2000. He also described fatigue. However, there was no history of recurrent fever, general weakness.
Respiratory: He does not smoke. There was no history of major abnormalities reported with pulmonary system.
Gastro-intestinal: There was history of problems with gas.
Urinary: There was history of frequent urination.
Musculoskeletal: He reported that there was history of stiff joints (knees), pain in feet.
Neurological: Neurological history revealed no evidence of frequent or recurrent headaches, fainting/blackouts, stroke/ dizzy spells, gait difficulties, seizures/ epilepsy, tremors, neuropathy, weakness or paralysis.
Psychiatric: He reported that he had problems with concentration, anxiety.
Other systems : All other systems were grossly within the normal limits.
Allergies:
Drug(s): No known drug allergies.
Food(s): maybe milk.
Environmental: No known environmental allergies.
Smoking: He does not smoke.
Anticoagulants: None
Previous Hospitalizations: Kidney stone - Dr. - 1998
Previous Surgeries: Left knee surgery - 2000, Left knee surgery - 1992
Medications: Relafen 500 mg. 2 tabs bid, Serzone 150 mg. bid , Allegra 60 mg. bid

PHYSICAL EVALUATION

Constitutional: His height was 6 ft. 2 inches. His weight was 240 lbs.
General appearance: He was well developed and well nourished. He was overweight. He was independent. There were no physical disabilities noted. He was well groomed.
Skin: Examination of the skin showed no evidence of scars, rashes, lesions, ulcers, or café-au-lait spots either in the head, trunk, neck, upper or lower extremities.
Respiratory: Examination of the respiratory system showed that there was no shortness of breath, prolonged respiration, wheezing, rales, or rhonchi.
Psychiatric: Gross psychiatric evaluation showed orientation to time, place, and person with normal mood and effect with no history of lack of memory, concentration, attention span, language difficulties or knowledge.

Musculoskeletal/Neurological Examination
Dominance: He was right handed.
Posture: His posture showed normal cervical lordosis, normal lumbar lordosis, mild kyphosis, and mild scoliosis.
Gait: His gait pattern evaluation showed that he was able to walk in a straight line, as well as on his heels, and toes without any problems.
Cervical Spine: There was no evidence of scars. Palpation of the cervical spine was within normal limits. On examination of range of motion of cervical spine, as well as upper extremities was grossly within normal limits. Range of motion of the both shoulders was normal with no evidence of impingement. Range of motion of all other joints was grossly within normal limits. On examination of motor strength of upper extremities was grossly within normal limits. There was no wasting noted. There was no sensory dysfunction noted in either upper extremity. The deep tendon reflexes evaluation showed for Biceps 1 on right side and 1 on left side, Triceps 1 on right side, and 1 on left side, and Brachioradialis 1 on right side, and 1 on left side.
Thoracic Spine: Examination the thoracic spine was grossly within normal limits.
Lumbar Spine: There was no evidence of scars on lumbar spine. There was no superficial or nonanatomic tenderness. There was mild midline/spinous process tenderness from L5, S1. There was moderate paravertebral tenderness L5, S1 on the right side without paravertebral spasm or trigger points. There was moderate tenderness noted in sciatic notch region on the right side. There was SI joint tenderness noted, which was moderate on the right side. On manual examination of range of motion of lumbar spine, as well as lower extremities was grossly within normal limits. Range of motion of the both hips was normal with negative Patrick-Fabere's Test. Examination of all other joints was grossly within normal limits. Examination of motor strength of lower extremities was grossly within normal limits. Sensory examination was within normal limits. Straight leg raising in supine position was 70° on the right side and 90° on the left side. Sciatic tension signs were negative on both sides. The deep tendon reflexes were as follows: Quadriceps Femoralis 1 on right side, and 1 on left side, Achilles 1 on right side, and 1 on left side. Superficial reflexes were shown to be within normal limits.

Review of Investigations:
12/20/99 – Lumbar spine – Old epiphyseal wedging of the lower thoracic upper lumbar bodies. Narrowing of the L5-S1 interspace with some facet degenerative change. There is in fact some grade I anterolisthesis of L5 on S1 and I suspect that the defect at the lamina of L5 is post surgical in nature.
12/20/99 – Right hip – Negative right hip.
2/21/00 – MRI/Lumbar spine – Some bulging of the L3-4 and 4-5 discs particularly in the inferior foramina on the left side at L3-4 and 4-5. Grade I spondylolisthesis of L5 on S1 which I believe is associated with bilateral pars defects at L5. Associated disc bulge related to the spondylolisthesis and a component of some central herniation probably present at the L5-S1 level. There is disc material bulging into the foramina bilaterally at L5-S1 associated with the listhesis

Impression:
Lumbar facet joint arthropathy
Lumbar disc displacement
Acquired spondylolisthesis
Sacroiliitis
Traumatic arthritis of both knees
Depression
No evidence of symptom magnification

PROCEDURE(S)
Right lumbar facet joint nerve blocks L3/4 - L5/S1
Probable right SI joint injection
Probable right selective epidural with local anesthetic and steroids L5, S1

____
Signature

SAMPLE PROCEDURAL FOLLOW UP

Name: ____________________

Date: ____________ SS#: ____________

Sex: ____________ Age: ____________

Physician: ____________________

CHIEF STATEMENT: STILL HURTING

HISTORY OF PRESENT ILLNESS: ____________________

PAIN STATUS:

1. ☐ **>75% Relief for** ____________
2. ☐ **>50% Relief for** ____________
3. ☐ **<50% Relief for** ____________
4. ☐ **No Relief** ____________

SIDE EFFECTS OF TREATMENT ☑ **NONE** [illegible]

	Initial	Last Appt	0	1	2	3	4	5	6	7	8	9	10
Average Pain	7									✓			
General Health	7									✓			
Mental Health	7							✓		✓			
Physical Function	4						✓						
Social Function	3					✓							
Vitality	4						✓						

MEDICATION USE: ☐ **None** ☑ **Same** ____________ ☐ **Decreased** ____________ ☐ **Increased** ____________

PHYSICAL EXAM: ____________________

DATE: 11/20/2000

NAME: John Doe

DATE OF BIRTH: xx / xx / xxxx

SS#: 111-11-1111

CHIEF STATEMENT: "Still hurting."

OVERALL HEALTH ASSESSMENT:

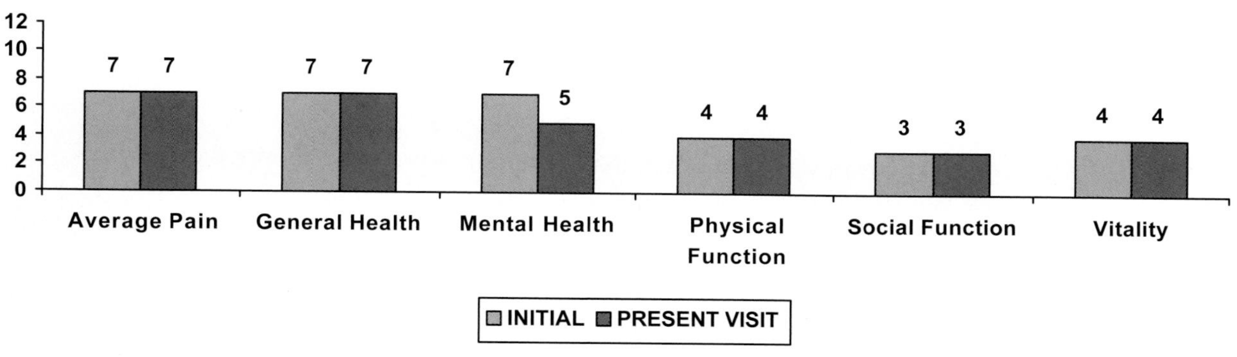

HISTORY OF PRESENT ILLNESS: Mr. John Doe returns for a follow up visit. Following the last visit, he states that nothing has changed. He's still hurting. Today he's here for further evaluation and management with injection therapy. He is still looking forward to this. Once again we went over the process we go through with diagnostic blocks. He understood and wanted to undergo injection therapy.

SIDE EFFECTS OF TREATMENT: None rendered.

MEDICATION USAGE: Same.

PHYSICAL EXAMINATION: This was completed as per Ambulatory Surgery Center format.

PLAN AND DISCUSSION: Once again we discussed about various aspects of his pain management. Following the discussions, understanding all the associated complications and benefits, it was decided that we will proceed with injection therapy. He understood and agreed with this.

PROCEDURE (S): He was transferred to the holding area where appropriate preparation was carried out. Subsequently, in the operating room, he was treated with right lumbar facet joint nerve blocks from L3/4 - L5/S1 utilizing 1 cc of Xylocaine 2% preservative free mixed with 1 cc of Sarapin and 4 mg of DepoMedrol without any problems.

Following this, he reported 100% pain relief, with previous moments which were painful.

DISCHARGE / DISPOSITION: He was discharged in satisfactory condition to return in 1 month for further follow up. At this time, he was provided with a prescription for Relafen, 500 mg, 2 tablets po t.i.d. for 120 with no refills.

____

Signature

Name: ____________________

Date: __________ SS#: __________

Sex: __________ Age: __________

Physician: ____________________

PERIOPERATIVE ORDERS

1. Please admit to Ambulatory Surgery Center.
2. Please obtain informed consent for the surgery.
3. Please check initial admitting vital signs.
4. Please start intravenous infusion with LR / D5LR / NS as needed.
5. Please monitor vital signs appropriately, intraoperatively and postoperatively.
6. Please position appropriately for the procedure.
7. Please administer intravenously as follows and as needed, for sedation and pain control
   - [x] Versed in increments of 1 to 2 mg to a maximum of 10 mg
   - [x] Fentanyl in increments of 1 to 2 ml to a maximum of 10 ml
   - [ ] Demerol in increments of 12.5 mg to a maximum of 100 mg
   - [ ] ____________________
   - [ ] ____________________
8. Please administer the following as needed
   - [ ] Zofran 4 to 6 mg intravenously for nausea and vomiting
   - [ ] Phenergan 12.5 mg to 25 mg intravenously for nausea and vomiting
   - [ ] Ephedrine 10 mg intravenous push for systolic pressure < 110
   - [ ] Atropine 0.4 mg intravenous push for bradycardia < 40 per minute
   - [ ] Mazicon 0.1 - 0.4 mg intravenous push need for reversal of sedation
   - [ ] Narcan 0.1 - 0.4 mg intravenous push as needed for reversal of sedation
   - [ ] Oxygen by ventimask or nasal cannula, if required
   - [ ] Benadryl 25 mg to 50 mg intravenously for itching or rash
   - [ ] Ancef 1 gm to 2 gm intravenously
   - [ ] ____________________
9. Discontinue IV prior to discharge.
10. Please check all injection sites for bleeding, swelling, etc.
11. Discharge when ready with appropriate orders and instructions.
12. ____________________
13. ____________________
14. ____________________
15. ____________________

Name: ______
Date: ______ SS#: ______
Sex: ______ Age: ______
Physician: ______

ARRIVAL: ☑ Ambulatory ☐ Wheelchair Time ____

Informants: ☑ Self ☐ Family ☐ Other

PAST MEDICAL HISTORY ☑ None

- ☐ Diabetes
- ☐ Hypertension
- ☐ Kidney Disease
- ☐ Pulmonary Disease
- ☐ Arthritis
- ☐ Migraine Headache
- ☐ Other______
- ☐ Cardio-Vasc Disease
- ☐ Psych Disorder
- ☐ Seizure Disorders
- ☐ Substance Abuse
- ☐ CVA
- ☐ Last Menstrual Period

PREOPERATIVE Surgical Checklist

- ☑ ALLERGIES NKA
- ☑ History and Physical on chart and reviewed
- ☑ Surgical permit signed
- ☑ Verification of Procedure
- ☑ Surgeon ☑ Procedure ☑ Side
- ☐ Pre-op Test Results on Chart
- ☑ None Ordered ☐ Checked

Test Done Results

- ☐ Diabetic: Fingerstick Glucose ______
- ☐ NPO Since: ______
- ☑ V/S: B/P 139/79 T 99° P 68 R 22
- ☐ Voided
- ☐ Dentures/Partial Plates Removed
- ☐ Contact Lenses/Glasses Removed
- ☐ Jewelry: ☐ Removed ☐ Secured
- ☐ Misc.: Hairpins, Nail Polish Removed
- ☑ Side Rails Up
- ☑ Pre-operative teaching completed
- ☑ Voices understanding

Home Meds: ☑ None ☐ Unsure of Name/Dose

To surgery holding @ 1000

NURSING ASSESSMENT

Pre-op Psychosocial Status

☑ Alert ☑ Oriented x 3 ☐ Confused
☐ Age Appropriate ☐ Relaxed ☐ Anxious
☐ NN

Pre-Op Skin Condition

☑ Skin intact	Open Areas	☑ No	☐ Yes
☐ Fragile Skin	Rash	☑ No	☐ Yes
	Bruises	☑ No	☐ Yes

- ☐ Communication Impairment ______
- ☐ Special Considerations ______

Shave/Skin prep ______ ☑ N/A

IV Site (R) hand Size 22

Started by CS

IV Fluids

- ☑ 0.9% N/S 1000cc
- ☐ D5W
- ☐ ______

IV Site #2 ______
Size ______
Started By ______

PRE-PROCEDURE MEDICATIONS ADMINISTERED

NURSES NOTES

1. I authorize the performance upon Myself

   the following operation(s) and/or procedure(s)

   Right lumbar facet joint nerve blocks L3/4 - L5/S1

   Probable right SI joint injections

   Probable right selective epidural with local

   anesthetic et steroids L5, S1

   to be performed by Dr. _

2. I consent to the performance of the operation(s) / procedure(s) in addition to or different from those not contemplated - whether or not arising from presently unforeseen conditions, which the above named doctor may consider necessary and/or advisable in the course of the operation(s) / procedure(s) including but not limited to arthrotomy.

3. I consent to endoscopic surgery of the joint(s) if it is deemed to be necessary by the doctor. This means surgical removal of all or part of either or both menisci, removal of loose or foreign bodies, removal of ligamentous stumps, biopsy, shaving of all joint surfaces, and/or release of appropriate structure to permit proper anatomical realignment within the joint, all of this to be accomplished with standard arthroscopic equipment.

4. I consent to the administration of such medications, anesthetics, and use of x-ray equipment as may be considered necessary or advised by the physician.

5. The nature and purpose of the operation(s) / procedure(s), possible alternative methods of treatments, the risks involved, the possible consequences, and the possibility of complications have been explained to me by a physician.

6. Specifically, with pain management procedure(s), along with: possible alternative methods, treatments, including option of no treatment, the risk involved which include, but not limited to: numbness, weakness, reaction to local anesthetics, steroids and/or other medications, dural puncture with subsequent complications, pneumothorax, hematoma formation, urinary retention, muscle spasm, and increase in pain following injection therapy, injection into the blood vessels or around spinal cord with complications, and infection were explained to me in laymen's language by a physician.

Page 1 of 2

AUTHORIZATION AND CONSENT FOR INVASIVE / OPERATIVE PROCEDURES
Continued from Page 1

7. The possible consequences (failure of procedure to be effective and increase in level of pain, and the possibility of complications as shown under Sections 5 and 6), have been explained to me in a layman's language by a physician.

8. I understand and acknowledge that no guarantee or assurance has been given by anyone as to the results that may be obtained.

9. I consent to the photographing or televising of the procedures to be performed, including appropriate portions of my body, and inclusion or publication of results of evaluations, treatment, progress, complications, and outcome provided my identity is not revealed.

10. For the purpose of advancing medical education, I consent to the admittance of observers to the operating room.

11. I consent to the screening for H.I.V. and/or Hepatitis B and/or other applicable lab work in the event that a health care worker / employee is exposed to my blood or body fluids.

12. I consent to the disposal by Ambulatory Surgery Center (Pain Management Center of Paducah) authorities of any tissue or body parts which it may be necessary to remove.

13. I hereby warrant that I have not been legally adjudged as incompetent. I further certify that I am fully able to understand and weigh the benefits versus the risks of the above listed procedure(s).

14. I warrant that I willfully consent to the operation(s) and/or procedure(s) and am under no duress by the above named physician, the center or staff to consent to the above listed procedure(s).

15. I further acknowledge that all the appropriate blanks were filled in prior to my signing of this document.

The authorization and consent for operation(s), anesthetics, and other invasive procedure(s) and acknowledgement of receipt of the information is valid until revoked by me in writing. I also explicitly consent that my ability to revoke this consent is not valid once the operation(s), anesthetics, or other procedure(s) has/have been started or completed.

Signature of Patient or Person authorized ______________ Signature of Representative of the Center ______________

______________ Date / Time ______________ Date / Time

OPERATING ROOM RECORD (LOCAL)

Name:

Date: SS#:

Sex: Age:

Physician:

Surgeon:

Circulator: CBaker Asst.: VHicks

Anesthesia: Local w/Sedation ☑ Local ☐

Premedication: None ☑ Room #: OR3

Patient in OR From 1020 To 1030

Time of Operation From 1021 To 1028

Monitoring: EKG ☑ Pulse Oximetry ☑

BP ☑ Automatic ☑ Manual ☐

Diagnosis: Lumbar facet arthropathy

Operative Procedure(s): Right lumbar facet joint nerve blocks L3/4–L5/S1

Drug / Route		Time / Amount	Time / Amount	Time / Amount	Time / Amount	TOTAL
Versed	IVP SLOW	1023 3mg				3mg
Fentanyl	IVP SLOW	1022 1cc				1cc

TIME	HR	BP	O_2SAT	RESP	EKG
1020	62	124/60	97	16	SR
1025	64	130/61	94	16	SR

Intravenous Fluids/Infusions:

Cathlon - # 22 / Site (R) hand

NS-500 ML ☐ 1000 ML ☑

Position: Supine ☐ Sitting ☐ Prone ☑

Lateral R ☐ L ☐ Padding ☑

Skin Prep: MD ☑ RN ☐ TECH ☐ LPN ☐

Betadine ☐ Alcohol ☑ Duraprep ☐ Other ☐

Radiography: Time: 19 Seconds

Radiographer: KCash

Contrast ☐ ML

Drugs For Blocks: Depo-Medrol ✓ MG.

Celestone MG.

Xylocaine ☑ Marcaine ☐ Sarapin ☑

2%

Transferred to: RR ☑

Via: Stretcher ☑

Remarks:

Signature of Circulator: R.N.

Signature of Surgeon:

POST SURGICAL RECORD

Name:
Date: SS#:
Sex: Age:
Physician:

Anesthesiologist ______ Time Received 1030
Anesthetist ______ PACU Nurse ______
Surgeon ______ Allergies NKA
Procedure See OR record
______ SR ↑ x 2 ☑ yes ☐ no

Intravenous Infusion		
IV Site (R) hand		
Solution NS	Amount given	INF Added
Pre PACU IV Fluids	150 cc	
PACU	100 cc	
TOTAL	250 cc	
IV d'cd @ 1050 Site Clean		

Time	Medication	IV Patent	Dose/Route	Nurse

Anesthetic: ☐ Gen ☑ Local ☐ Regional: Type ______ ☐ MAC ☐ Other ______

Airway: ☑ None ☐ LMA ☐ ET ☐ NT ☐ Oral ☐ Trach | Time Discont. | O_2 ☐ Yes ☑ No via ☐ Mask ☐ Can | Time Discont.

Breath Sounds: ☐ Clear ☐ Diminished ☐ Rhonchi/Rales

Dressing Site ______ ☐ Dry & Intact ☐ ______
Drains: ☐ N/A ☑ ______ ☐ Extremity Elevated
Skin: ☑ Warm ☑ Dry ☐ Cool ☐ Diaphoretic ☐ Warm Touch ___On ___Off

Score System ASSESSMENT		ADM.	DIS.
ACTIVITY			
Moves 4 Extremities	2	2	2
Moves 2 Extremities	1		
Move None	0		
RESPIRATIONS			
Deep Breathes & Coughs	2	2	2
Limited Respirations	1		
No Spontaneous Resp.	0		
V/S			
B/P Within 20% Pre Op.	2	2	2
B/P Within 20-50% Pre Op.	1		
50% Deviation B/P	0		
CONSCIOUSNESS			
Fully Alert	2	2	2
Arousable to Name	1		
No Response To Voice	0		
COLOR			
Normal - Pink	2	2	2
Pale, Dusky	1		
Cyanotic	1		
CIRCULATION			
Finger/toe circ., Movement, Sensation Intact	2	2	2
Blanched, Numb Finger/Toe	1		
Pale, Cyanotic, Absent Pulses	0		
		12	12

Vital Signs

Times	1030	1040	1050
V BP Λ 200–10 scale; • P; ° RR			
SaO_2	94	94	95
EKG	SR	SR	SR
Drsg. Dry			
Skin Temp.			

Transfer to room 1050
☐ W/C ☑ Ambulatory ☐ Stretcher
☐ Carried

Discharge Summary:

Alert/active	☑ Y	☐ N
Voided	☐ Y	☐ N
Vitals stable	☑ Y	☐ N
Drsg/Op Site Dry	☑ Y	☐ N
Tolerating liquids	☐ Y	☐ N
Minimal nausea	☐ Y	☐ N
Pain controlled	☐ Y	☐ N
See NN	☐	

Patient Instructions:
☐ Instructed per physician
☑ Discharge instructions given with understanding voiced
☐ Post-op exercises reviewed ☐ N/A
☑ Appointment
☑ Prescription
☑ Notification of physician if indicated
Accompanied by wife · 554-0063
Discharged/Transferred ☑ Home ☐ W/C
☐ Carried ☑ Ambulatory ☐ Ambul./Van

Nurse Signature ______ (RN) LPN
Time out 1100
Discharge Order by ______ MD

NURSE NOTES

______

Name:

Date: SS#:

Sex: Age:

Physician:

IMPORTANT INSTRUCTIONS FOLLOWING PAIN MANAGEMENT PROCEDURES (INJECTIONS, NERVE BLOCKS, EPIDURALS, AND OTHER PROCEDURES)

WHY?

You were given a number of medications during the procedure. These sometimes include sedatives, narcotics, local anesthetics, steroids, and other medications. Any of these drugs or procedure itself, sometimes can cause side effects, including drowsiness, temporary numbness, weakness and soreness.

WHAT SHOULD I DO?

1. Rest for a few hours and use assistance if needed.
2. Resume activity as tolerated, but do not overdo.
3. Resume regular diet.

MY RESTRICTIONS:

1. Do not drive or operate machinery for at least 12 hours.
2. Do not make important decisions for 12-24 hours after treatment.
3. Walk with assistance as long as numbness, weakness, or drowsiness is present.

NOTIFY US:

1. Excessive or abnormal bleeding / persistent chills or fever over 100°F.
2. If there is a major change in pain pattern or level.

EMERGENCY:

1. In case of emergency, call (270) 554-8373.
2. If unable to reach physician, report to the nearest emergency room and request them to inform physician at Pain Management Center.

FEW OTHER THINGS:

1. Take your usual medication.
2. Apply ice massage as instructed; may use heat if ice is intolerable.
3. If IV site becomes painful, place warm towels on the site for 20 min. 2-3 times / day.

FOLLOW-UP:

Call us and let us know your progress if you don't answer our follow-up call. If you have any further questions ask us. Feel free.

Thank you,
Staff of Ambulatory Surgery Center

I certify that I understand the follow-up instructions and I have received a copy thereof:

Signature Patient / Responsible Adult Date Nurse's Signature

OPERATIVE REPORT

FACILITY:	—— -
DATE OF SERVICE:	11/20/00
PATIENT'S NAME:	XYZ
PATIENT'S S.S.#:	xxx-xx-xxxx
SURGEON:	—, M.D.
CIRCULATOR:	— , RN — , CST
RADIOGRAPHER	—, RT
ANESTHESIA:	Local with sedation

Diagnosis:

1. Lumbar facet joint arthropathy

Procedure(s) Performed:

1. Right lumbar facet joint nerve blocks, L3/4 – L5/S

INDICATIONS AND MEDICAL NECESSITY:

1. Intermittent throbbing and cramping low back pain on the right side with radiation in to right lower extremity secondary to lumbar facet joint arthropathy, lumbar disc displacement, acquired spondylolisthesis and sacroiliitis.

2. Pain in both knee joints secondary to traumatic arthritis.

3. Psychological problems with depression.

4. No evidence of significant medical problems or symptom magnification.

5. Physical deconditioning syndrome with inability to function close to near normal lifestyle and to carry on with normal activities with continuing deterioration of physical and functional status secondary to multiple problems as described above.

6. Failure of various modalities of treatments in the past including medication, chiropractic treatments and physical therapy.

7. Surgical candidacy only with fusion.

8. No evidence of major intraspinal obstruction.

DESCRIPTION OF PROCEDURE(S)

Preoperative:

Following the initial discussions and after addressing all of the concerns, he desires to undergo the procedure. Hence, with appropriate preparation, that is wearing a Center's gown and shoe covers, he was escorted to the preoperative holding area by a nurse. Following this, appropriate preoperative evaluation, which included checking of the medical status, allergies, consent, and mental status. Following this, with understanding he signed an appropriate consent. Subsequently, it was decided that we will place an intravenous infusion. This was carried out. Subsequent to this, appropriate return of the blood was noted. Hence, this was connected to intravenous tubing which was connected to 1000 cc of normal saline, 0.9%, and was taped into place. At this time, appropriate infusion was observed with no evidence of infiltration. Following this, once again, his vital signs were recorded and he was ready to be transported to the operating room.

Intraoperative:

He was received in the operating room on the stretcher in satisfactory condition. Subsequently, he was explained about prone position and the procedure along with utilization of imaging intensifier. He understands this. Hence, he was positioned in prone position with his assistance with pillows under him in a comfortable position. Following this, appropriate monitors were applied. These included automatic blood pressure cuff, pulse oximetry and electrocardiogram. At this time, he was slowly sedated.

Following the above, it was decided to proceed with right multiple lumbar facet joint nerve blocks. Hence, once again in absolute sterile fashion, local anesthetic infiltration was carried out at multiple levels and a #22, 3.5 inch spinal needle was placed into the skin and was advanced slowly into the subcutaneous tissue approximately one-half inch or so. Initially, the first block was performed at L3/4 level focusing on the right side. The position of the needle was confirmed by intermittent fluoroscopy. Under fluoroscopic visualization, the needle was advanced to the base of the transverse process of L3/4. Subsequently, the needle was slowly walked down the superior articular process and the transverse process. At this time, aspiration was negative and there was no irritation of the nerve root. Hence, a small volume of local anesthetic was injected along the tract of the medial branch at two locations. Following this, the needle was removed and appropriate pressure was applied. At this time, attention was focused on L4/5 level on the right side. At this time once again, the needle was advanced under intermittent fluoroscopy to the base of the transverse process. Following this, the needle was walked down the superior articular process and the transverse process. At this time, once again aspiration was negative. There was no nerve root irritation. Hence, a small volume of local anesthetic was injected at this level. Following this, the needle was removed and appropriate pressure was applied.

At this time, attention was focused on L5/S1 level on the right side. Hence, the needle was slowly advanced, once again under fluoroscopic visualization, to the base of the superior articular process in the sacrum. At this time once again, aspiration was negative. There was no nerve root irritation noted. Once again, injection was repeated into the dorsal ramus at this level at two locations.

For this procedure, a total of 1 cc of Xylocaine 2% preservative free with 1 cc of Sarapin and 4 mg of DepoMedrol was used without any problems.

Following the above injections, he was observed to be in satisfactory condition. Hence, he was turned into the supine position. At this time, once again, his IV was observed for any signs of infiltration, etc. None were observed. Hence, he was transferred to recovery room in supine position without any problems.

Postoperative:

In the recovery room, once again, he was closely monitored for any potential complications and side effects. No such complications or side effects were noted. Following the appropriate completion of the infusion and ambulation, his IV was discontinued. At this time, once again, there were no signs of infiltration, irritation, etc.

Disposition and Discharge:

He was discharged in satisfactory condition with written and oral instructions. His site was observed to be clear. He was ambulating. He was also instructed to call me or report to the emergency room in case he developed any problems

____

Name:

Date: SS#:

Sex: Age:

Physician:

Postoperative Follow-up

Complications

1. Bleeding No ☑ Yes ☐
2. Swelling No ☑ Yes ☐
3. Pain No ☑ Yes ☐
4. Fever No ☑ Yes ☐
5. Muscle spasms No ☑ Yes ☐
6. Soreness No ☑ Yes ☐
7. Numbness No ☑ Yes ☐
8. Weakness No ☑ Yes ☐
9. Dizziness No ☑ Yes ☐
10. Nausea / Vomiting No ☑ Yes ☐
11. Voiding difficulty No ☑ Yes ☐
12. Other

Pain Relief

Excellent - (76 - 100%) ☑ 2-3 days

Fair - (26 - 50%) ☐

Good - (51 - 75%) ☐

Poor - (0 - 25%) ☐

Ratings: 1 - Poor 2 - Fair 3 - Average 4 - Good 5 - Excellent

(CIRCLE ONE)

Service / Satisfaction

1. Were instructions prior to procedure and prior to discharge adequate? 1 2 3 (4) 5
2. Did you feel as though the nurses were concerned with your welfare? 1 2 3 (4) 5
3. Was your recovery time and care in Ambulatory Surgery adequate? 1 2 3 (4) 5
4. What information would have been beneficial to you prior to procedure? None ☑
5. Is there anything we can do to better serve you or your family? No ☑
6. Further comments: Relafen working 50-70%, shots increased to 90%

Action

None ☐

Phone: ☑ Left Message 11/22/00 1005 VD No Answer:

Mailed Postcard: ☐

Signature of Interviewer

Date: Time:

ASC-05

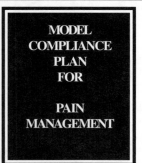

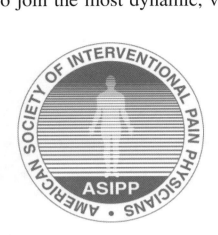

American Society of Interventional Pain Physicians

Since 1998

2831 Lone Oak Road
Paducah, Kentucky 42003
(270) 554-9412, fax: (270) 554-8987
www.asipp.org

The Voice of Interventional Pain Medicine

Professional Membership Application

Please type or print

1. **Name** ____
   Last First MI

   Organization ____________________
   Address: ____________________
   City: __________ **State:** ______ **Zip:** ________
   Phone: __________ **Fax:** __________
   Email: ____________________

   Home Address: ____________________
   City: __________ **State:** ____ **Zip** ________
   Phone: __________ **Fax:** __________
   Email: ____________________
   Preferred Mailing Address: Organization Home

2. **Personal Data: (for statistical purposes only)** Date of Birth ______ / ______ / ______ Male Female
3. **Medical Degree:** MD DO other____________________(specify)

   Residency in Specialty of ____________________ Accredited Pain Management Fellowship Yes No
4. **I am currently certified by the following board(s)**

   American Board of Anesthesiology
   American Board of PMR
   American Board of Psychiatry and Neurology
   ABA Subspecialty in Pain Management
   Other ABMS Primary Board(s)____________________
   AMA Member
5. What percentage of your clinical practice is in the field of Interventional Pain Management: 0% 1 – 49% 50 – 100%
6. Primary professional practice setting (please check all that apply): Ambulatory surgery Hospital Office practice
7. I hereby make application for

   ◆ Active Membership – Must be a physician specializing in Pain Management, Spinal Injections or Neural Blockade.

Life Membership dues	$ 5,000.00 or $500.00 each month for 1 year
Annual Membership dues	$ 200.00
Fellows and Residents	$ 100.00
Additional contribution	$ 100.00 $250.00 $500.00 $1000.00 Other __________
Total - Dues and/or contributions	$ __________

   ◆ Associate Membership – Non-Pain Management Physicians, Scientists, Nurses, Physician Assistants, Nurse Practitioners, Administrators, Pharmacists, Physical Therapists and Psychologists, etc. (associated with active practice of Pain Management)

   Annual Associate Membership dues $ 100.00
8. State Society Information

   I am a member of ____________________ State Association(s)

   I am interested in joining ____________________ State Association(s)

   I am not interested in joining or working with the State Association(s)
9. **METHOD OF PAYMENT**

   Check #__________(Payable to ASIPP)

   Bill my: Mastercard Visa Discover American Express

   Credit Card # ____________________ Exp. Date __________

   Authorized Signature ____________________ (Required on all credit card orders)
10. Signature of Applicant ____________________ Sponsoring Member: ____________________

    (Not Required - For Statistical Purposes Only)

FOR OFFICE USE ONLY

ASIPP Order Form

For your convenience, please photocopy this form

Phone: (270) 554-9412
Fax: (270) 554-8987

Mail to: American Society of Interventional Pain Physicians
2831 Lone Oak Road
Paducah, Kentucky 42003

See our on-line ordering form at www.asipp.org

Description	Product Code	Quantity	Unit Price Member	Unit Price Non-Member	Total
Model Compliance Plan	MCP		$250.00	$450.00	
Subscription to Pain Physician Journal and News- One Year	SUB-1		Free	$100.00	
Pain Management Policy & Procedure Manual - Hard Copy	PM-HC		$400.00	$600.00	
Pain Management Policy & Procedure Manual - Computer Disk	PM-CD		$400.00	$600.00	
Pain Management Policy & Procedure Manual - Both Hard Copy & Computer Disk	PM-B		$500.00	$700.00	
Ambulatory Surgery Policy & Procedure Manual - Hard Copy	ASC-HC		$400.00	$600.00	
Ambulatory Surgery Policy & Procedure Manual - Computer Disk	ASC-CD		$400.00	$600.00	
Ambulatory Surgery Policy & Procedure Manual - Both Hard Copy & Computer Disk	ASC-B		$500.00	$700.00	
Membership Dues (Fill out Membership Application Form)	Fellow or Resident $100.00		Associate $100.00	Active $200.00	
Back Issues Pain Physician Journal Per Issue (Postage Included)	BIPP-J		$25.00	$40.00	
2001 "Real" New Millennial Guidelines Issue of Pain Physician	BIPP-JG		$25.00	$40.00	
ASIPP Guidelines on CD-ROM	AG-CD		$20.00	$40.00	
Back Issues Pain Physician News (Newsletter) Per Issue	BIPP-N		$10.00	$20.00	
Pain Management Evaluation Report ®	PMER®		$2,000	$2,500	
Interventional Pain Medicine: Documentation, Coding, & Billing: Book	DCB- Book		$275.00	$300.00	
Interventional Pain Medicine: Documentation, Coding, & Billing : Book - 4 copies	DCB-B-4		$1000.00	$1100.00	
Low Back Pain: Diagnosis and Treatment an Interventional Approach : Book	LBP- Book		$150.00	$200.00	
Low Back Pain: Diagnosis and Treatment an Interventional Approach: Book and CD	LBP- BCD		$175.00	$225.00	
		Subtotal			
		KY Residents add 6% Sales Tax			
		Postage & Handling*			
		Grand Total			

Bill my: ☐ Master Card ☐ Visa
☐ Discover ☐ American Express

____
Acct. #

Month Year
☐☐ ☐☐
Expiration Date

____
Signature
(required on all credit card orders)

Please Make Checks Payable to ASIPP

For Policy and Procedure Manuals (Hard Copy), you will receive the entire two (2) volume set together with instructions

* Add: $20.00 shipping and handling for each policy and procedure manual & $10.00 for each model compliance program
Add: $15.00 shipping and handling for one book, $25.00 for four copies
Add: $5.00 shipping and handling for each computer disk order

Ship to:

Name: ______________________________

Street Address ______________________________

City ______________ State ______________ Zip __________

Daytime Phone:

Area Code __________ Number ____________